The Hydraulics Trainer Volume 1

Basic Principles and Components of Fluid Technology

Instruction and Information
on the
Basic Principles and Components of Fluid Technology

Authors
H. Exner • R. Freitag • Dr.-Ing. H. Geis • R. Lang • J. Oppolzer
P. Schwab • E. Sumpf
U. Ostendorff
Hydromatik GmbH, Ulm
M. Reik
HYDAC GmbH, Sulzbach

Editor
Rudi A. Lang
Mannesmann Rexroth GmbH

Issued by Mannesmann Rexroth GmbH
Postfach 340

W-8770 Lohr a. Main

Telefon (0 93 52) 18-10 30
Telefax (0 93 52) 18-10 40
Telex 6 89 418-20

Printed by Schleunungdruck GmbH
Eltertstr. 27

W-8772 Marktheidenfeld

Lithography MainTeam Chemiegraphische GmbH
Goldbacherstraße 14

W-8750 Aschaffenburg

Photographs and Diagrams Brueninghaus Hydraulik GmbH, Horb
Hydromatik GmbH, Ulm
HYDAC GmbH, Sulzbach
Mannesmann Rexroth GmbH, Lohr

Issue RE 00301/1978 (1st issue, 1978)
RE 00290/10.91 (2nd issue, 1991)

ISBN 3-8023-0266-4

Preface

Hydraulics is a relatively new technology used in power transmission, which may be adapted to market requirements.

The use of hydraulic drives, as well as hydraulic open loop and closed loop control systems has gained in importance in the field of automation. Nowadays, it is unusual to find an automatic production procedure which does not use hydraulic components.

However, in spite of the wide range of applications, there are still many more to be found. Hence, manufacturers are expanding their experience by referring to literature and attending training courses.

This manual *Basic Principles and Components of Hydraulics* (from the series *The Hydraulics Trainer)* should aid you in gaining knowledge of hydraulics systems. It is not only intended to be used as a training text, but also as an aid to the hydraulics system operator.

This trainer deals with the basic principles and functions of hydraulic components. Relationships between functions are clarified by means of numerous tables, illustrations and diagrams. This manual is therefore an invaluable reference aid for everyday work.

This manual is the result of collective work by a group of authors, to whom we are most grateful. We would also like to thank Mr Rudi A. Lang, who acted as project manager and editor. In addition, Mr Herbert Wittholz must be thanked for his careful proofreading of the chapter on basic principles and also for his many useful comments.

Mannesmann Rexroth GmbH
Lohr a. Main

Contents

Chapter 1

Basic Principles

Rudi A. Lang

Chapter 2

Symbols to DIN ISO 1219

Rudi A. Lang

Chapter 3

Hydraulic Fluids

Eberhard Sumpf

Chapter 4

Hydaulic Pumps

Rudhard Freitag

Chapter 5

Hydraulic Motors

Rudhard Freitag

Chapter 6

Axial Piston Units

Udo Ostendorff

Chapter 7

Hydraulic Cylinders

Paul Schwab

Chapter 8

Rotary actuators

Paul Schwab

Chapter 9

Accumulators and Accumulator Applications

Martin Reik

Chapter 10

Non Return Valves

Dr. Harald Geis, Johann Oppolzer

Chapter 11

Directional Valves

Dr. Harald Geis, Johann Oppolzer

Chapter 12

Pressure Control Valves

Dr. Harald Geis, Hans Oppolzer

Chapter 13

Flow Control Valves

Dr. Harald Geis, Johann Oppolzer

Chapter 14

Filters and Filtration Technology

Martin Reik

Chapter 15

Accessories

Martin Reik

Chapter 16

Connections

Herbert Exner

Chapter 17

Small hydraulic power units

Herbert Exner

Appendix

Chapter 1

Basic Principles

Rudi A. Lang

1. Introduction

As this chapter describes basic principles, certain terms from Physics must also be mentioned. It must be noted that even though Physics used to be thought of as a completely separate subject to Chemistry, it is now realised that there is no clear dividing line between the two subjects. Chemistry also determines processes which occur in life. A link between the two subjects is the effect of electrical or electronic actions.

Processes mentioned may very slightly from recent common hydraulics practice, however we hope that what we describe is acceptable. Deviations from practice will be mentioned in footnotes. Physical processes in all technical fields will be described uniformly, due to the way we describe the processes.

1.1 Fluid power

This field was until recently described as "oil hydraulics and pneumatics". This was not only corrected in DIN, but the industry has also adopted the subject designation of "fluid power". When the title "oil hydraulics" appeared many years ago, mineral oil manufacturers became interested in it, as this subject would probably deal with the problems in pipelines, since hydraulics was supposed to be the science of fluid flow laws.

In fact, this subject area deals with the transfer of energy and, when the fluid is stationary, with the transfer of pressure. However, in the transfer of pressure, for example, at the same time as a hydraulic cylinder or motor operates, the pump may generate a flow, and hence the flow laws need to be considered as well. Because of this, the term "hydraulics" has been retained in fluid power to describe the hydraulic characteristic, as opposed to the "mechanical" or "pneumatic" characteristics. However, wherever possible, a phrase such as "some hydraulics is built into the system" should be avoided.

Care should be taken that the mechanical characteristics of a pressure fluid, (i.e the ability to transfer pressure) are made use of in fluid power systems. This is not only true for the hydraulics in fluid power, but also for pneumatics. The term fluid includes liquid, steam or gases, i.e. air is also a fluid when considered as a mixture of gases. As fluid power is concerned with the mechanical characteristics of fluids, we use the term hydro-mechanics when we are dealing with liquids and aero-mechanics when we are dealing with air.

1.2 Hydro-mechanics

In "hydraulic" fluid power the laws of hydro-mechanics are used. Pressure, or energy, or signals in the form of pressure are transferred, and the laws of hydro-statics (mechanics of still fluids) and of hydro-kinetics [1)] (mechanics of moving fluids) apply.

1.2.1 Hydro-statics

The term hydro-static pressure is common in Physics. It is the pressure which acts on the base of an open container filled with fluid, and which is dependent on the height of the head of liquid inside the container. A hydraulic paradox occurs here, which is that the shape of the container is irrelevant, and only the height of the head of liquid determines the pressure. Hence, this also means that the pressure at the bottom of the container is higher than at the top of the container. This fact is well-known, if you consider the pressure of water deep down in the open sea. The behaviour is the same in a "sea of air".

In statics, care must be taken that the forces are balanced. This is also true for analogue forces in hydro-statics. At the base of a container, at the bottom of the sea, or at a particular height in the place to be measured, the pressure present does not create any changes in the existing relationships.

If the fluid is enclosed in a closed container, as for example, in a hydraulic cylinder in fluid power, and if much higher pressures are needed than exist due to gravity at a certain height in a fluid, then these pressures are created via appropriate technical measures, e.g. by a hydraulic pump. Fluid is pumped into the closed container at a pressure produced by the hydraulic pump, and this

[1)] This field is still widely known as "hydro-dynamics".In reference english books, it used only to be called hydro-kinetics, but recently, especially from American sources, hydro-dynamics has been used instead. Here is however recommended that hydro-dynamics be used to cover both hydro-statics and hydro-kinetics, as stated in DIN 13317. In this standard, dynamics covers both statics and kinetics, as dynamics deals in general with forces, and not only with the forces which are generated from kinetic energy.

pressure exerts itself equally on all sides of the container. This fact may be made use of, by making the base of the container movable. The base then moves,when pressure is applied, and providing that the hydraulic pump continues to supply fluid under pressure, a head of liquid is moved.

If the hydraulic cylinder (also under pressure) is at rest, e.g. in clamping hydraulics the forces are in equilibrium. This effect may be described as hydro-static. However, if the piston in the cylinder is moved by a supply of flow under pressure, then not only is the pressure produced from potential energy effective, but a boost pressure is also effective which is created by the kinetic energy. This pressure must be and is taken into account in fluid power systems. The relationships in this process or system may not really be described wholly as hydro-static, but the hydro-static relationships predominate.

Systems of this type, where hydro-static relationships are predominant and the transfer of pressure is most important, operate at relatively high pressures and low flow velocities in order to keep the influence of hydro-kinetics[1] as low as possible.

1.2.2 Hydro-kinetics

Systems in which the kinetic energy of moving fluids is used to transfer power are not usually considered to be part of fluid power, even though there is no physical reason for them not to be included. These often so-called "hydro-dynamic drives" are the ones which as already mentioned should really be called "hydro-kinetic drives". In this type of drive, as in fluid power the laws of hydro-statics must be considered as well as those of hydro-kinetics, but in this case the laws of hydro-kinetics are the predominant ones.

Considering the fact that both types of energy are active in "hydro-dynamic drives" they must also both be active in systems where hydro-statics is predominant. Hence these systems are also "hydro-dynamic" systems, and so to form sub-groups of hydro-statics and hydro-dynamics would be incorrect.

The still so-called "hydro-dynamic drives" operate according to their designation with high flow velocities and relatively small pressures.

1.3 Types of energy transfer (choice)

	Hydraulics [2]	Pneumatics [3]	Electrics	Mechanics
Energy source (Drive)	Electric motor Combustion engine Accumulator	Electric motor Combustion engine Pressure tank	Power supply Battery	Electric motor Combustion engine Weight force Tension force (spring)
Energy transfer elements	Pipes and hoses	Pipes and hoses	Electrical cable, magnetic field	Mechancal parts Levers, shafts, etc.
Energy carriers	Fluids	Air	Electrons	Rigid and elastic objects
Force density (Power density)	Large, high pressures, large forces, small flow	Relatively small, low pressures	Small, with respect to power weight Electric motor with hydraulic motor 1 : 10	Large, selection and distribution of required flow is often not as good as in hydraulics
Smooth control (acceleration, deceleration)	Very good via pressure and flow	Good via pressure and flow	Good to very good electrical open loop and closed loop control	Good
Types of movement ≙ of outputs	Linear and rotary movements via hydraulic cylinders and hydraulic motors easily attainable	Linear and rotary movements via pneumatic cylinders and pneumatic motors easily attainable	Primarily rotary movement, linear movement: solenoid → small forces → short strokes, poss. linear motor	Linear and rotary movements

Table 1: *Features of types of energy transfer*

[1] see footnote on page 23
[2] as part of fluid power, even though hydraulics deals with far more than just fluid power.
[3] as part of fluid power, even though pneunatics deals with far more than just fluid power.

1.4 Quantities, symbols, units

(see DIN 1301 part 1 and DIN 1304 part 1)

Quantity	Symbol	SI unit	Dimension	Conversion to other accepatable units	Relationship
Length Distance	l s	Metre	m	1 m = 100 cm = 1000 mm	
Area	A	Metre squared	m^2	$1\ m^2 = 10\,000\ cm^2 = 1\,000\,000\ mm^2$ $= 10^6\ mm^2$	$A = l \cdot l$
Volume	V	Metre cubed	m^3	$1\ m^3 = 1000\ dm^3$ $1\ dm^3 = 1\ L$	$V = A \cdot h$
Time	t	Seconds	s	$1\ s = \frac{1}{60}\ min$	
Velocity	v	Metre per second	$\frac{m}{s}$	$1\frac{m}{s} = \frac{60\ m}{min}$	$v = \frac{s}{t}$
Acceleration	a	Metre per second squared	$\frac{m}{s^2}$	Acceleration due to gravity (rounded off) $g = 9{,}81\ \frac{m}{s^2}$	$a = \frac{s}{t^2}$
Flow	q_V, Q	Metre cubed per second	$\frac{m^3}{s}$	Litre per minute $\frac{L}{min}$ $1\frac{m^3}{s} = 60\,000\frac{L}{min}$	$Q = \frac{V}{t}$ $Q = v \cdot A$
Speed	n	Revolutions per second Revolutions per minute	$\frac{1}{s}$ $\frac{1}{min}$ (rpm)	$\frac{1}{s} = \frac{60}{min}$	$n = \frac{1}{t}$
Mass	m	Kilogram	kg	1 kg = 1000 g	$m = V \cdot \rho$
Density	ρ	Kilogram per metre cubed	$\frac{kg}{m^3}$	Kilogram per decimetre cubed $\frac{kg}{dm^3}$ $1\frac{kg}{m^3} = 0{,}001\frac{kg}{dm^3}$	$\rho = \frac{m}{V}$
Force	F	Newton	N	$1\ N = 1\frac{kg \cdot m}{s^2}$	$F = m \cdot a$ $F_G = m \cdot g$
Pressure	p	Newton per metre squared Pascal	$\frac{N}{m^2}$ Pa	$1\frac{N}{m^2} = 1\ Pa = 0{,}00\,001\ bar$ $1\ bar = 10\frac{N}{cm^2} = 10^5\frac{N}{m^2}$ $10^{-5}\ bar = 1\ Pa$	$p = \frac{F}{A}$
Work	W	Joule	J	1 J = 1 Ws = 1 Nm $1\ kWh = 3{,}6\ MJ = 3{,}6 \cdot 10^6\ WS$	
Power	P	Watt	W	$1\ W = 1\frac{J}{s} = 1\frac{Nm}{s}$	$P = Q \cdot p$
Temperature Temperature in Celsius	T, Θ t, ϑ	Kelvin	K	Celsius °C	$0\ °C \triangleq 273\ K$ $0\ K \triangleq -273\ °C$

Table 2: *Quantities, symbols and units*

The following analogies are relevant for linear movements (hydraulic cylinders) and rotations (hydraulic motors):

Hydraulic cylinders			**Hydraulic motor**		
Parameter	Symbol	SI unit	Parameter	Symbol	SI unit
Distance	s	m	Angle	α	rad
			Frequency of rotation (Speed)	f	$\frac{1}{s}$
Velocity	v	$\frac{m}{s}$	Angular velocity	ω	$\omega = \frac{\alpha}{t}$ $\frac{rad}{s}$
Acceleration	a	$\frac{m}{s^2}$	Angular acceleration	φ	$\varphi = \frac{\omega}{t}$ $\frac{rad}{s^2}$
Force	F	N	Torque	T	$T = \frac{V_g \bullet \Delta p \bullet \eta_{mh}}{20 \bullet \pi}$ Nm
Power	P	W	Power	P	$P = T \bullet \omega$ $\frac{Nm}{s}$
Mass	m	kg	Moment of inertia	J	kgm^2

Table 3: *Analogies*

2. Physics Terms

2.1 Mass, Force, Pressure

2.1.1 Mass *m*

A weight force is created by a mass on the ground due to gravity.

2.1.2 Force *F*

According to Newton's law:

Force = mass • acceleration
$F = m \bullet a.$

If the general acceleration a is replaced by the acceleration due to gravity g (g = 9.81 m/s^2), the following is obtained:

Weight force = mass • acceleration due to gravity
$F = m \bullet g.$

For a mass of 1 kg, this results in a weight force of
$F = 1\ kg \bullet 9.81\ m/s^2 = 9.81\ kg\ m/s^2$.

The SI unit for force is the Newton

$$1\ N = \frac{kg\ m}{s^2}.$$

A mass of 1 kg creates a force of 9.81 N on the ground.

In practice, it is generally adequate to use 10 N or 1 daN instead of 9.81 N for a weight force of 1 kg.

2.1.3 Pressure *p*

In descriptions of processes involving fluids, pressure is one of the most important quantities.

If a force acts perpendicularly to a surface and acts on the whole surface, then the force F divided by the area of the surface A is the pressure p

$$p = \frac{F}{A}.$$

The derived SI unit for pressure is the Pascal

$$\frac{1\ N}{m^2} = 1\ \text{Pascal (1 Pa)}.$$

In practice, it is more common to use the bar unit

$$1\ bar = 10^5\ Pa.$$

In fluid power, pressure is indicated by p. If positive or negative is not indicated, p is taken as pressure above atmospheric (gauge) pressure (*Diagram 1*).

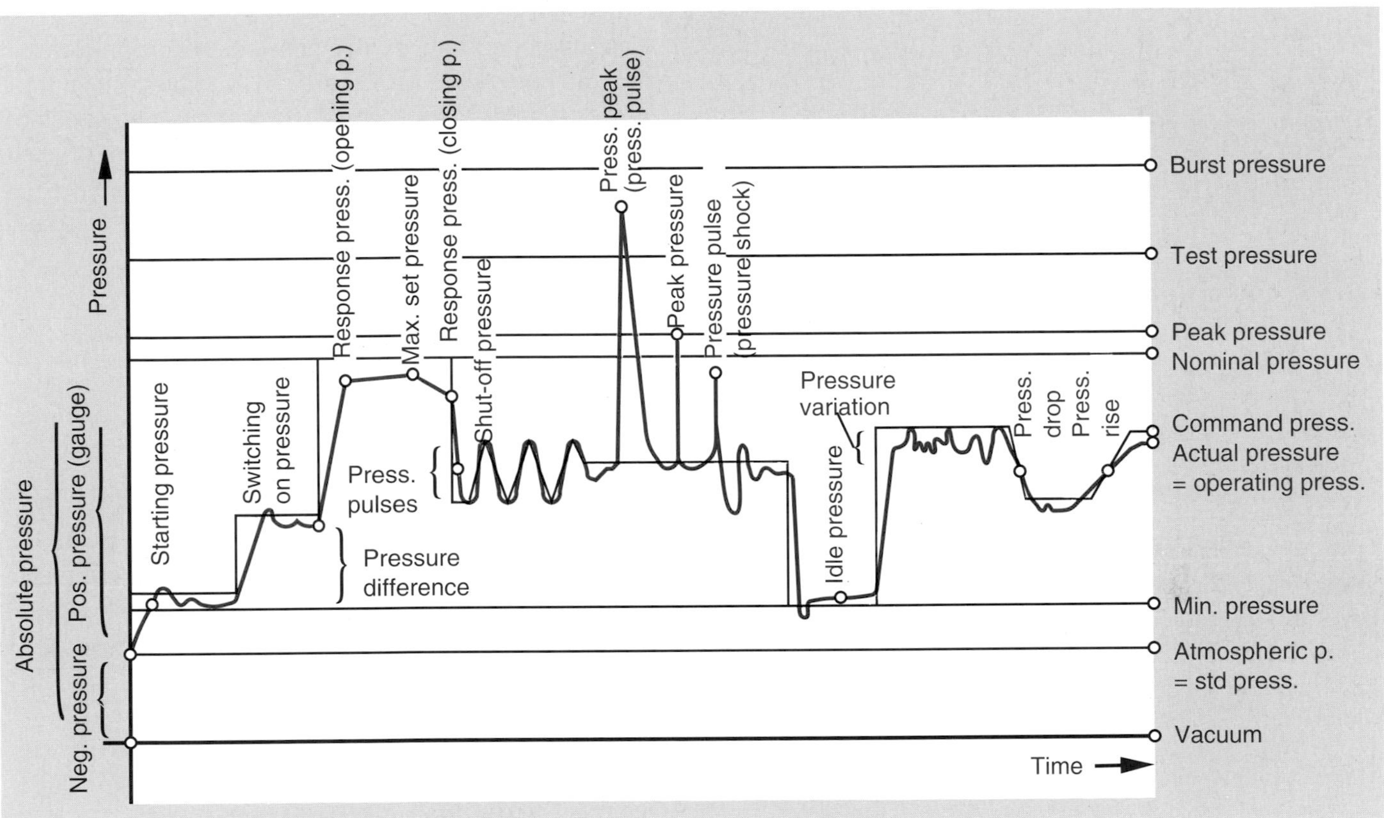

Diagram 1: *Pressures to DIN 24312*

2.2 Work, Energy, Power

2.2.1 Work

If an object is moved by a force F over a certain distance s, the force has then done work W.

Work is a product of distance covered s and the force F which acts in the direction of the displacement

$$W = F \bullet s.$$

The SI unit for work is the Joule

$$1\text{ J} = 1\text{ Nm} = 1\text{ Ws}.$$

2.2.2 Energy

If an object is capable of work, it has "stored work".

This type of "stored work" is known as energy.

Work and energy hence have the same unit.

Depending on the type of "stored work", there are two types of energy:

- Potential energy (energy due to position, E_p) and
- Kinetic energy (energy due to movement, E_k).

2.2.2.1 Potential energy

An object may sink to a particular level due to its high initial position and it hence carries out work.

The amount of work stored is dependent on the weight force $m \bullet g$ of the object and on the height h

$$E_p = (m \bullet g) \bullet h.$$

2.2.2.2 Kinetic energy

If a moving object meets an object at rest, the moving object performs work on the body at rest (e.g. deformation work).

The work stored is contained in the movement of the object in this case.

The amount of energy is dependent on the mass *m* and the velocity *v* of the object

$$E_k = \frac{(m \cdot v^2)}{2} .$$

2.2.3 Power

Power is given by work divided by time

$$P = \frac{W}{t} .$$

The SI unit for power is the Watt

$$1\text{W} = 1 \frac{\text{J}}{\text{s}} .$$

2.3 Velocity, acceleration

2.3.1 Velocity

Velocity *v* is the distance *s* divided by time *t* taken to cover this distance

$$v = \frac{s}{t} .$$

The SI unit for velocity is the metre per second.

2.3.2 Acceleration

If an object does not move at constant velocity, it experiences an acceleration *a*.

The change in velocity may be positive (increase in velocity/acceleration) or negative (decrease in acceleration/deceleration).

The linear acceleration *a* is given by velocity *v* divided by time *t*

$$a = \frac{v}{t} .$$

The SI unit for acceleration (deceleration) is metre per second squared.

2.4 Hydro- mechanics

Hydro-mechanics deals with physical characteristics and behaviour of fluids in stationary (hydro-statics) and moving (hydro-kinetics [1)]) states.

The difference between liquids and solid particles is that the particles in liquids are easily moved within the mass of liquids. Hence, liquids do not assume a specific shape, but instead, they assume the form of the container surrounding them.

In comparison with gases, liquids are not as compressible.

2.4.1 Hydro-statics

The laws of hydro-statics strictly apply only to an ideal liquid, which is considered to be without mass, without friction and incompressible.

With these relationships, it is possible to deduce the behaviour of ideal, that is, loss-free circuits. However, losses of one form or another do appear in all components in fluid systems. In components, which operate according to the throttling principle, the losses which arise are indeed a pre-requisite for them to function.

2.4.2 Pressure

If pressure is applied, as shown in *Fig. 1*, on surfaces of the same area ($A_1 = A_2 = A_3$), the forces which are produced are the same size ($F_1 = F_2 = F_3$).

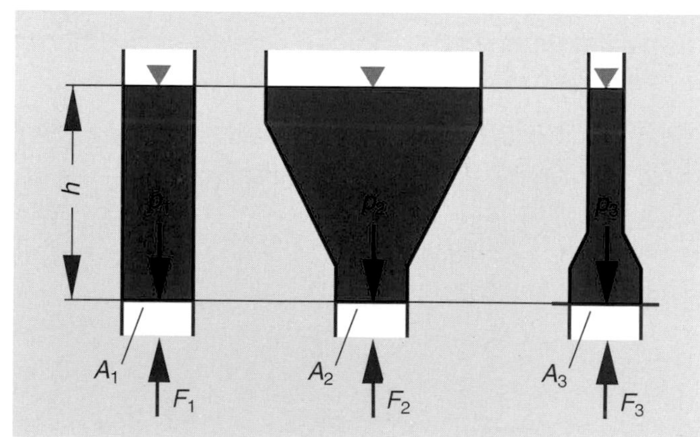

Fig. 1: *The hydro-static paradox*

[1)] see footnote[1)] on page 23

2.4.2.1 Pressure due to external forces

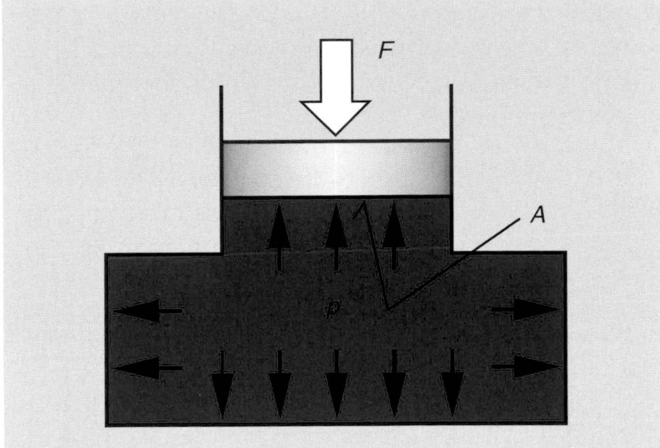

Fig. 2: *Pascal's law*

The basic principle in hydro-statics is Pascal's law:

"The effect of a force acting on a stationary liquid spreads in all directions within the liquid. The amount of pressure in the liquid is equal to the weight force, with respect to the area being acted upon. The pressure always acts at right angles to the limiting surfaces of the container."

In addition, the pressure acts equally on all sides. Neglecting pressure due to gravity, pressure is equal at all points (*Fig. 2*).

Because of the pressures used in modern hydraulic circuits, the pressure due to gravity may usually be neglected.

Example: 10 m water column ≈ 1 bar.

2.4.2.2 Force Transmission

As pressure acts equally in all directions, the shape of the container is irrelevant.

The following example (*Fig. 3*) will demonstrate how the hydro-static pressure may be used.

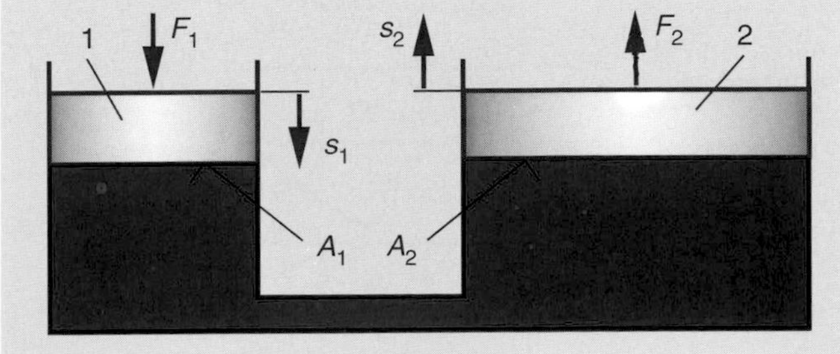

Fig. 3: *Example of force transmission*

When force F_1 acts on area A_1, a pressure is produced of

$$p = \frac{F_1}{A_1}.$$

Pressure p acts at every point in the system, which includes surface A_2. The attainable force F_2 (equivalent to a load to be lifted) is given by

$$F_2 = p \bullet A_2.$$

Hence

$$\frac{F_1}{A_1} = \frac{F_2}{A_2}$$

or

$$\frac{F_2}{F_1} = \frac{A_2}{A_1}.$$

The forces are in the same ratio as the areas.

Pressure p in such a system always depends on the size of the force F and the effective area A. This means, that the pressure keeps increasing, until it can overcome the resistance to the liquid movement.

If it is possible, by means of force F_1 and area A_1, to reach the pressure required to overcome load F_2 (via area A_2), the load F_2 may be lifted. (Frictional losses may be neglected.)

The displacements s_1 and s_2 of the pistons vary in inverse proportion to the areas

$$\frac{s_1}{s_2} = \frac{A_2}{A_1}.$$

The work done by the force piston (1) W_1 is equal to the work done by the load piston (2) W_2

$$W_1 = F_1 \bullet s_1,$$

$$W_2 = F_2 \bullet s_2.$$

2.4.2.3 Pressure transmission

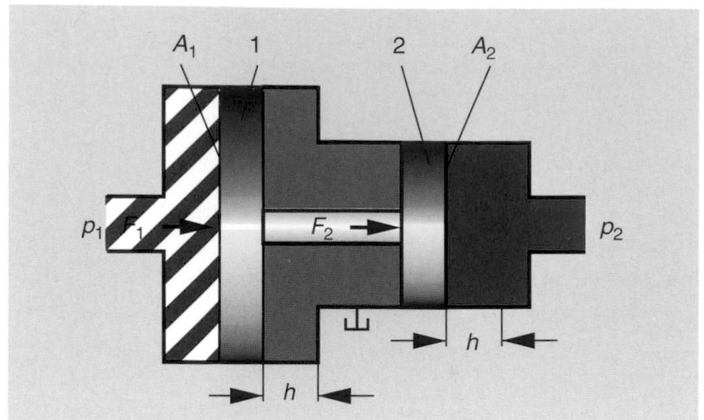

Fig. 4: *Pressure transmission*

Two pistons of different sizes (*Fig. 4: 1 and 2*) are fixed together by means of a rod. If area A_1 is pressurised with pressure p_1, a force F_1 is produced at piston (1). Force F_1 is transferred via the rod to area A_2 of piston (2) and hence pressure p_2 is obtained there.

Ignoring losses due to friction:

$$F_1 = F_2 \quad \text{and} \quad p_1 \bullet A_1 = p_2 \bullet A_2 .$$

Hence $p_1 \bullet A_1 = F_1$ and $p_2 \bullet A_2 = F_2$

or

$$\frac{p_1}{p_2} = \frac{A_2}{A_1} .$$

In pressure transfer the pressures vary in inverse proportion to the areas.

2.4.3 Hydro-kinetics

Hydro-kinetics[1)] is concerned with the liquid flow laws and the effective forces which result. Hydro-kinetics may also be used to partially explain the types of losses which occur in hydro-statics.

If the frictional forces at limiting surfaces of objects and liquids are ignored and those between the individual liquid layers are also ignored, it may be assumed that the flow is free or ideal.

The important results and conformity to the natural laws for ideal flows may be adequately described and are dealt with in the following sections.

[1)] see footnote[1)] on page 23

2.4.3.1 Flow Law

If liquid flows through a pipe of varying diameters, at any particular time the same volume flows at all points. This means, that the velocity of liquid flow must increase at a narrow point (*Fig. 5*).

Flow Q is given by the volume of fluid V divided by time t

$$Q = V/t .$$

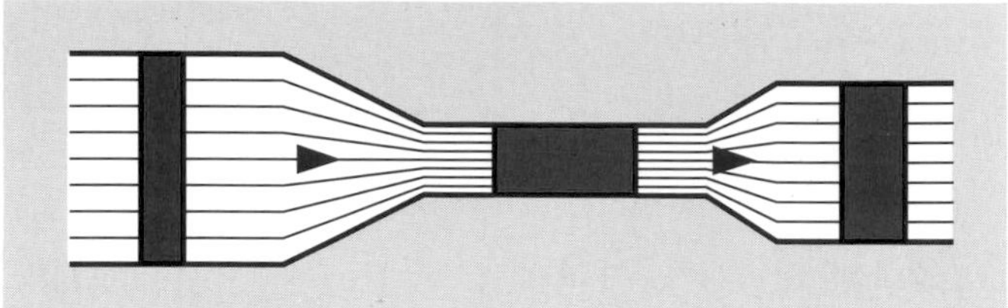

Fig. 5: *Flow*

Liquid volume V is itself given by area A times length s (*Fig. 6a*)

$$V = A \bullet s .$$

If $A \bullet s$ is substituted for V (*Fig. 6b*), Q is then given by

$$Q = \frac{A \bullet s}{t} .$$

Distance s divided by time t is velocity v

$$v = \frac{s}{t} .$$

Flow Q hence equals the cross-sectional area of the pipe A multiplied by the velocity of the liquid v (*Fig. 6c*)

$$Q = A \bullet v .$$

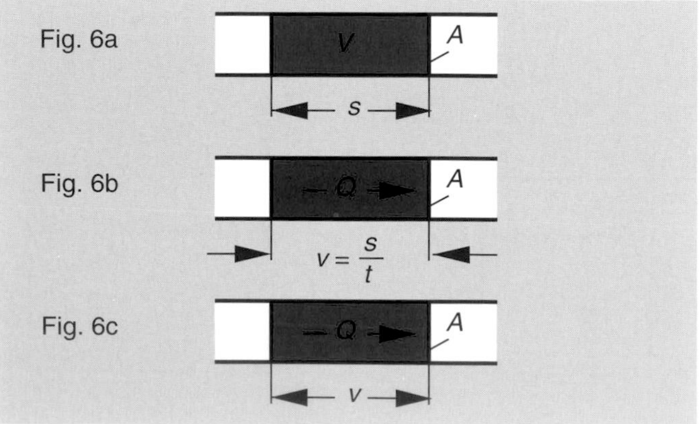

Fig. 6: *Flow*

The same flow Q in L/min occurs at any point in the pipe. If a pipe has cross-sectional areas A_1 and A_2, corresponding velocities must occur at the cross-sections (*Fig. 7*)

$$Q_1 = Q_2,$$
$$Q_1 = A_1 \cdot v_1,$$
$$Q_2 = A_2 \cdot v_2.$$

Hence the continuity equation is produced

$$A_1 \cdot v_1 = A_2 \cdot v_2.$$

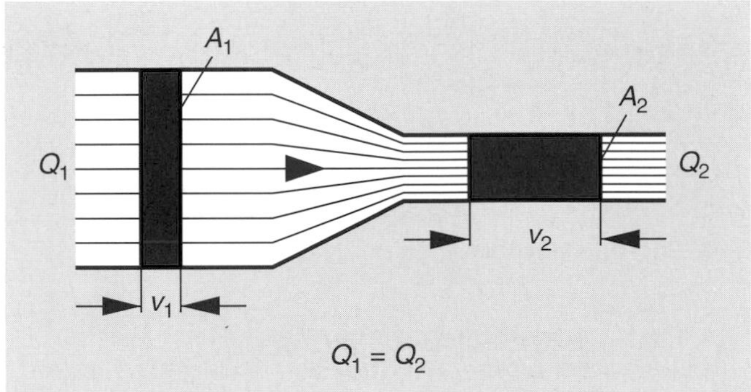

Fig. 7: *Velocity of flow*

2.4.3.2 Law of conservation of energy

The law of conservation of energy, with respect to a flowing fluid, states that the total energy of a flow of liquid does not change, as long as energy is not supplied from the outside or drained to the outside.

Neglecting the types of energy which do not change during flow, the total energy is made up of:

- Potential energy
  → positional energy, dependent on the height of head of liquid and on static pressure

and

- Kinetic energy
  → movement energy, dependent on the velocity of flow and on back pressure.

Hence Bernoulli's equation is produced

$$g \cdot h + \frac{p}{\rho} + \frac{v^2}{2} = \text{constant.}$$

With respect to pressure energy, this means

$$p_{tot} = p_{st} + \rho \cdot g \cdot h + \frac{\rho}{2} \cdot v^2$$

whereby

p_{st} = static pressure,
$\rho \cdot g \cdot h$ = pressure due to height of head of liquid,
$(\rho/2) \cdot v^2$ = back pressure.

Let's now consider both the continuity equation and the Bernoulli equation. The following may be deduced:

If the velocity increases as the cross-section decreases, movement energy increases. As the total energy remains constant, potential energy and/or pressure must become smaller as the cross-section decreases.

There is no measurable change in potential energy. However, the static pressure changes, dependent upon the back pressure, i.e. dependent on the velocity of flow. (*Fig. 8*: The height of the head of liquid is a measure of the pressure present at each head.)

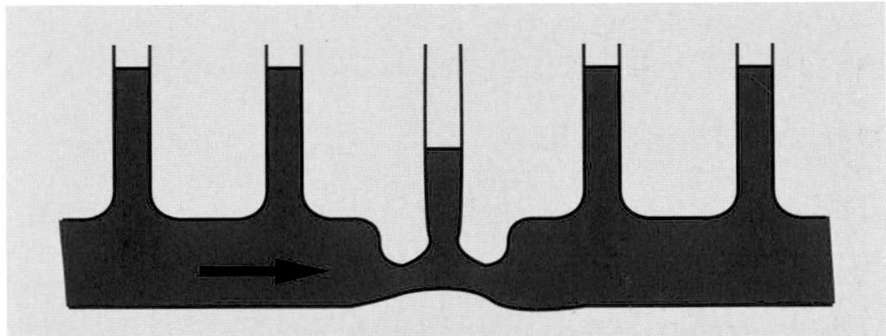

Fig. 8: *Dependence of columns of liquid on pressure*

It is mainly the static pressure which is of importance in "hydro-static systems", as the height of head of liquid and velocity of flow are usually too small.

2.4.3.3 Friction and pressure losses

So far in looking at conformity to natural laws for liquid flow, we have assumed that there is no friction between liquid layers as they move against each other and also that there is no friction as liquids move against an object.

However, hydraulic energy cannot be transferred through pipes without losses. Friction occurs at the pipe surface and within the liquid, which generates heat. Hence hydraulic energy is transformed to heat. The loss created in this way in hydraulic energy actually means that a pressure loss occurs within the hydraulic circuit.

The pressure loss - differential pressure - is indicated by Δp (*Fig. 9*). The larger the friction between the liquid layers (internal friction), the larger the viscosity (tenacity) of the liquid becomes.

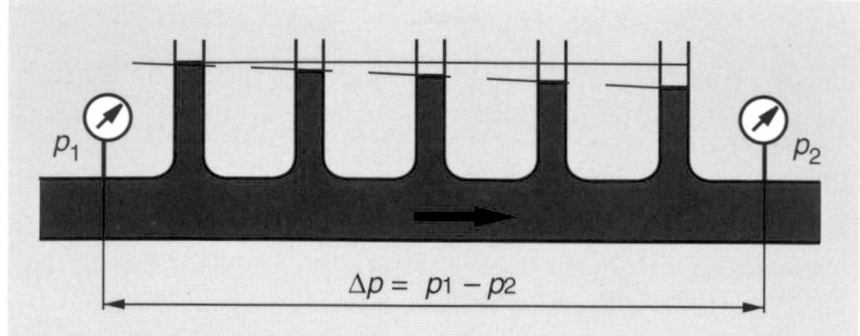

Fig. 9: *Viscosity*

Frictional losses are mainly dependent upon:

- Length of pipe,
- Cross-sectional area of pipe,
- Roughness of pipe surface,
- Number of pipe bends,
- Velocity of flow and
- Viscosity of the liquid.

2.4.3.4 Types of flow

The type of flow is also an important factor when considering energy loss within a hydraulic circuit.

There are two different types of flow:

- Laminar flow and
- Turbulent flow.

Up to a certain velocity, liquids move along pipes in layers (laminar). The inner-most liquid layer travels at the highest speed. The outer-most liquid layer at the pipe surface does not move (*Fig. 10*). If the velocity of flow is increased, at the critical velocity the type of flow changes and becomes whirling (turbulent, *Fig. 11*).

Hence the flow resistance increases and thus the hydraulic losses increase. Therefore turbulent flow is not usually desirable.

The critical velocity is not a fixed quantity. It is dependent on the viscosity of a liquid and on the cross-sectional area through which flow occurs. The critical velocity may be calculated and should not be exceeded in hydraulic circuits.

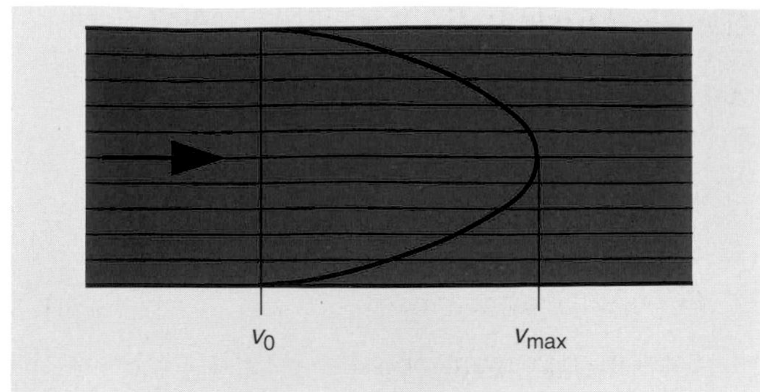

Fig. 10: *Laminar flow*

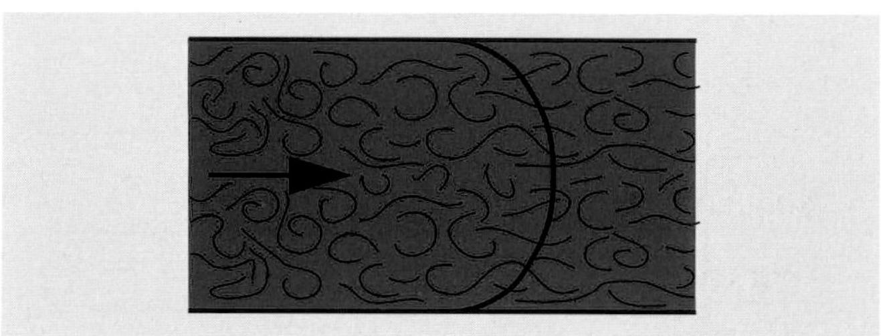

Fig. 11: *Turbulent flow*

2.4.3.4.1 Reynold's number *Re*

The type of flow may be roughly determined using Reynold's number

$$Re = \frac{v \cdot d_h}{\nu}$$

whereby

v = velocity of flow in m/s,

d_h = hydraulic diameter in m, with circular cross-sections equal to the pipe internal diameter, and otherwise calculated as $d_h = 4 \cdot A/U$,

A = cross-sectional area,

U = circumference,

ν = kinetic viscosity in m^2/s and

Re_{crit} ≈ 2300.

This value only applies for round, technically smooth, straight pipes.

At Re_{crit} the type of flow changes from laminar to turbulent and vice versa.

Laminar flow occurs for $Re < Re_{crit}$, and turbulent flow occurs for $Re > Re_{crit}$.

3. Hydraulic circuits

3.1 Important characteristics of hydraulic circuits

- Transfer of large forces (torques) at relatively small volumes.
- Operation may commence from rest under full load.
- Smooth adjustment (open loop or closed loop control) of the following is easily achieved:
  - speed
  - torque
  - force
- Simple protection against over-loading.
- Suitable for both quick and very slow controlled sequences of movements.
- Storage of energy with gases.
- Simple central drive system is available.
- Decentralised transformation of hydraulic into mechanical energy is possible.

3.2 Design of a hydraulic circuit

Mechanical energy is converted to hydraulic energy in hydraulic circuits. This energy is then transferred as hydraulic energy, processed either in an open loop or closed loop circuit, and then converted back to mechanical energy.

3.2.1 Energy conversion

Hydraulic pumps are primarily used to convert energy and next hydraulic cylinders and motors do so.

3.2.2 Control of energy

Hydraulic energy and its associated transfer of power exist in a hydraulic circuit in the form of pressure and flow. In this form, their size and direction of action are effected by variable displacement pumps and open loop and closed loop control valves.

3.2.3 Transport of energy

The pressure fluid, which is fed through pipes, hoses and bores within a manifold, transports the energy or only transfers the pressure.

3.2.4 Further information

In order to store and take care of the pressure fluid, a series of additional devices are necessary, such as tank, filter, cooler, heating element and measurement and testing devices.

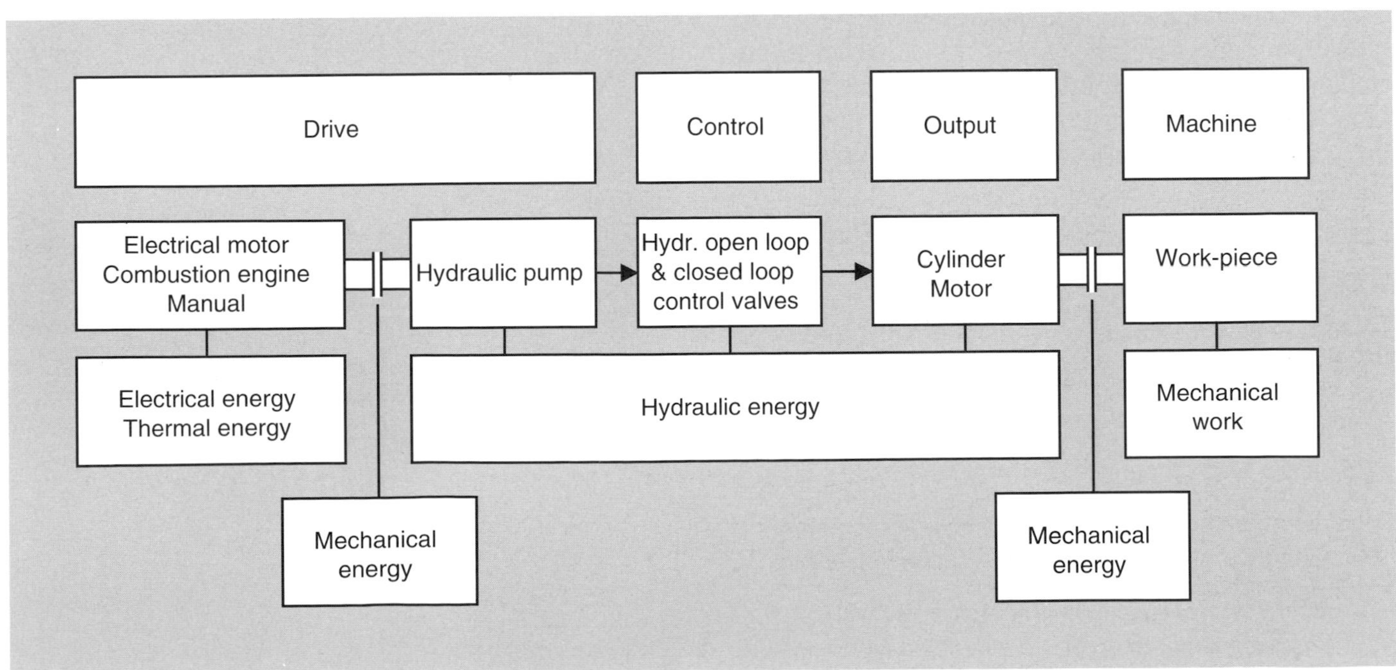

Fig. 12: *Transfer of energy in a hydraulic circuit*

3.3 Design of a simple hydraulic circuit

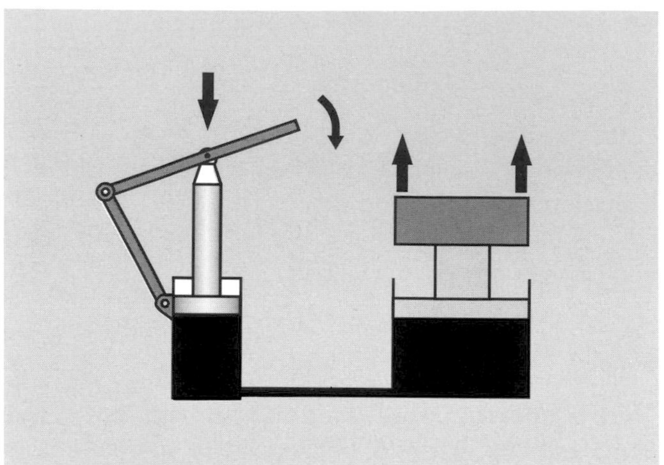

Fig. 13: *Principle of a hydraulic circuit*

The piston of a hand pump is loaded with a force (*Fig. 13*). This force divided by the piston area results in the attainable pressure ($p = F/A$).

The more the piston is pressed on, i.e. the greater the force on the piston is, the higher the pressure rises. However, the pressure only rises until, with respect to the cylinder area, it is in a position to overcome the load ($F=p \cdot A$).

If the load remains constant, pressure does not increase any further. Consequently, it acts according to the resistance, which is opposed to the flow of the liquid.

The load can therefore be moved, if the necessary pressure can be built up. The speed, at which the load moves, is dependent on the flow which is fed to the cylinder. With reference to *Fig. 13*, this means that the faster the piston of the hand pump is lowered, the more liquid per unit time is supplied to the cylinder, and the faster the load will lift.

In the illustrations shown in *Figs. 14 to 19*, this principle (*Fig. 13*) is extended to further devices, which

- control the direction of movement of the cylinder (directional valve),
- effect the speed of the cylinder (flow control valve),
- limit the load of the cylinder (pressure relief valve),
- prevent the system at rest from being completely drained via the hydraulic pump (check valve) and
- supply the hydraulic circuit continuously with pressure liquid (via an electric motor driven hydraulic pump)

In the following sections, a simple circuit will be designed and illustrated via sectional diagrams and symbols to DIN ISO 1219.

3.3.1 Step 1 (*Figs. 14 and 15*)

Hydraulic pump (1) is driven by a motor (electric motor or combustion engine). It sucks fluid from tank (2) and pushes it into the lines of the hydraulic circuit through various hydraulic devices up to the hydraulic cylinder (5). As long as there is no resistance to flow, the fluid is merely pushed further.

Cylinder (5) at the end of the line represents a resistance to flow. Pressure therefore increases until it is in a position to overcome this resistance, i.e. until the piston in the cylinder (5) moves. The direction of movement of the piston in the cylinder (5) is controlled via directional valve (6).

At rest, the hydraulic circuit is prevented from being drained via the hydraulic pump (1) by check valve (3).

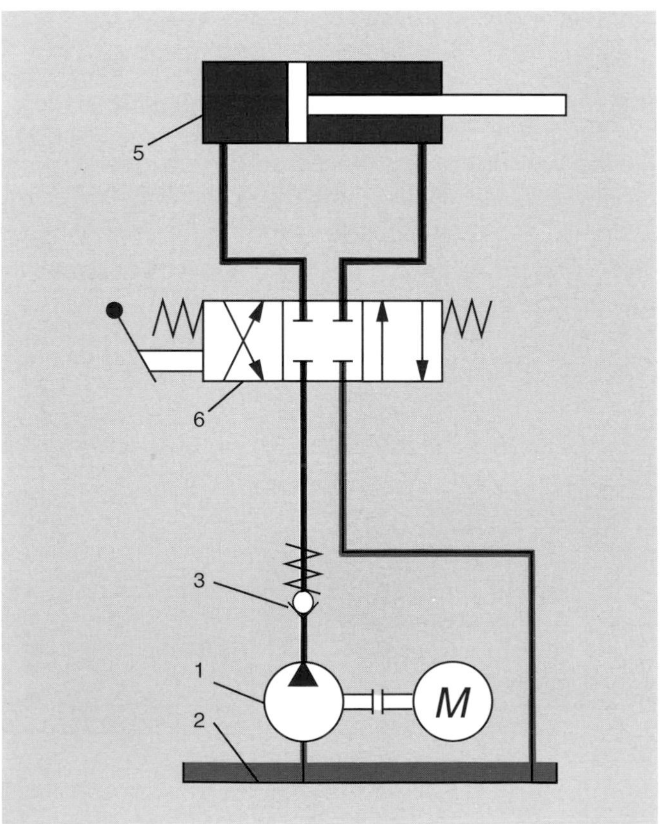

Fig. 14

Basic Principles

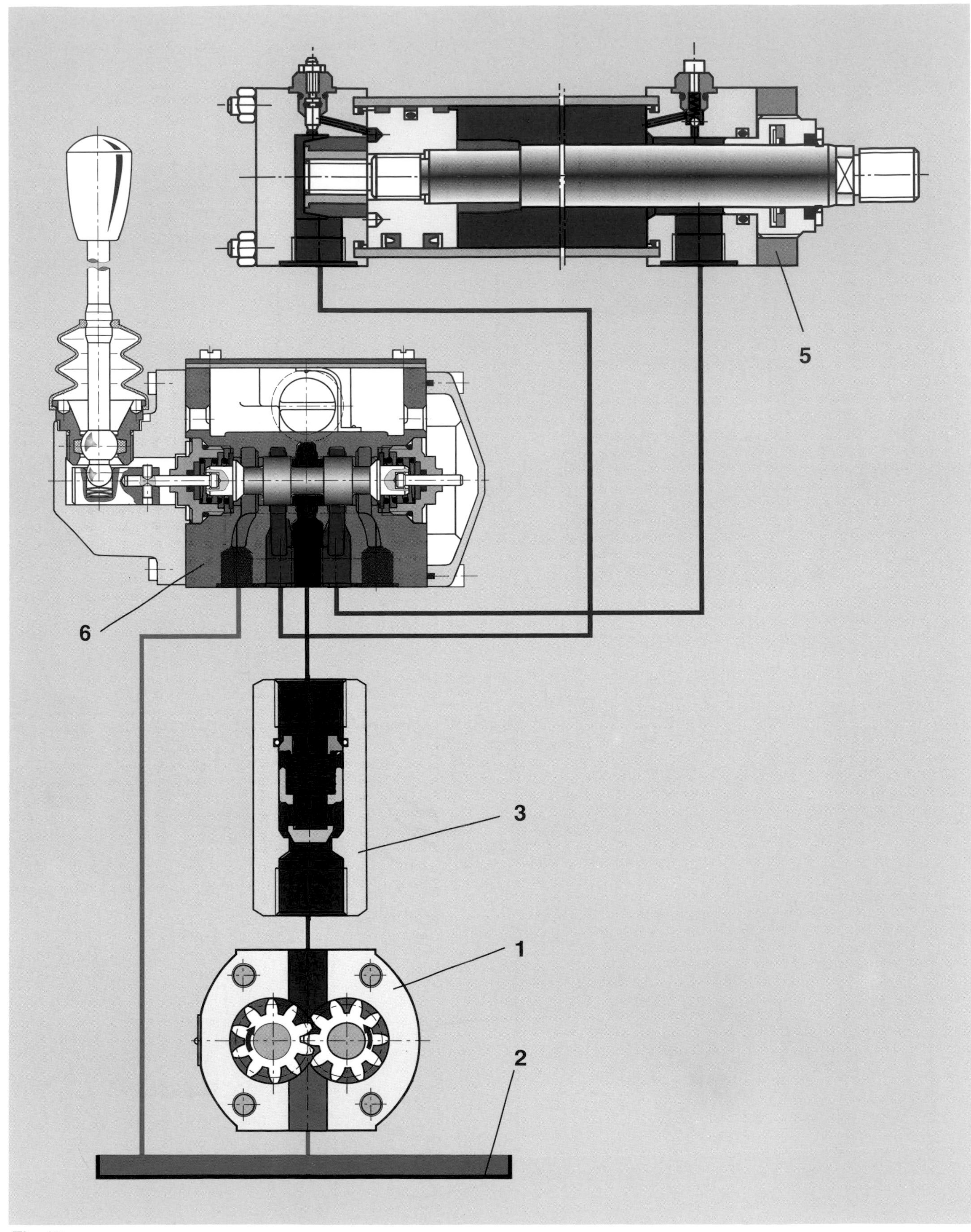

Fig. 15

3.3.2 Step 2 (*Figs. 16 and 17*)

So that the hydraulic circuit is protected from excess pressures and hence from overloading, the maximum pressure must be limited.

This is achieved using a pressure relief valve (4).

A spring as mechanical force, presses a poppet onto the seat of the valve. Pressure in the line acts on the surface of the seat. In accordance with the equation, $F = p \cdot A$, the poppet is lifted from its seat when the force from pressure • area exceeds the spring force. Pressure now no longer rises. The flow still delivered by the hydraulic pump (1) flows via pressure relief valve (4) directly back to the tank.

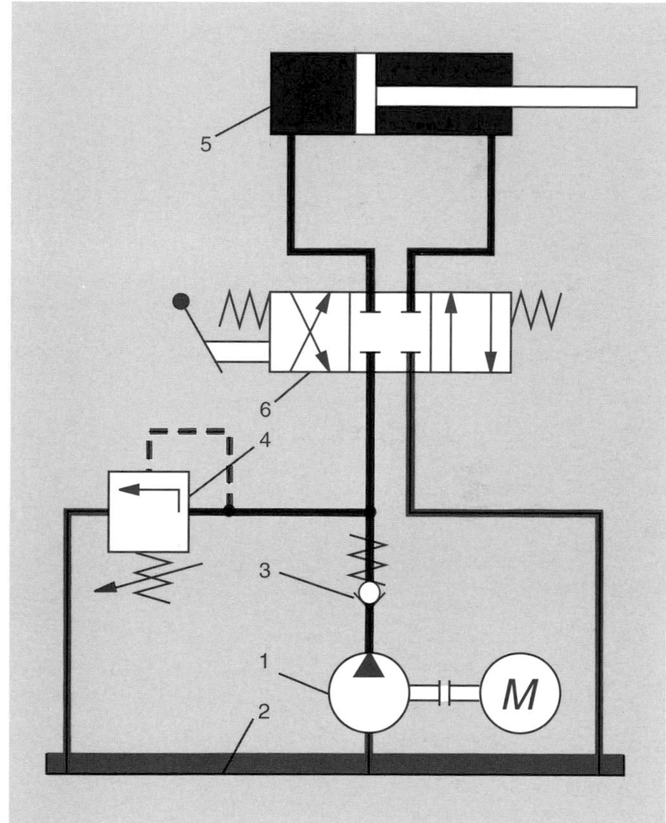

Fig. 16

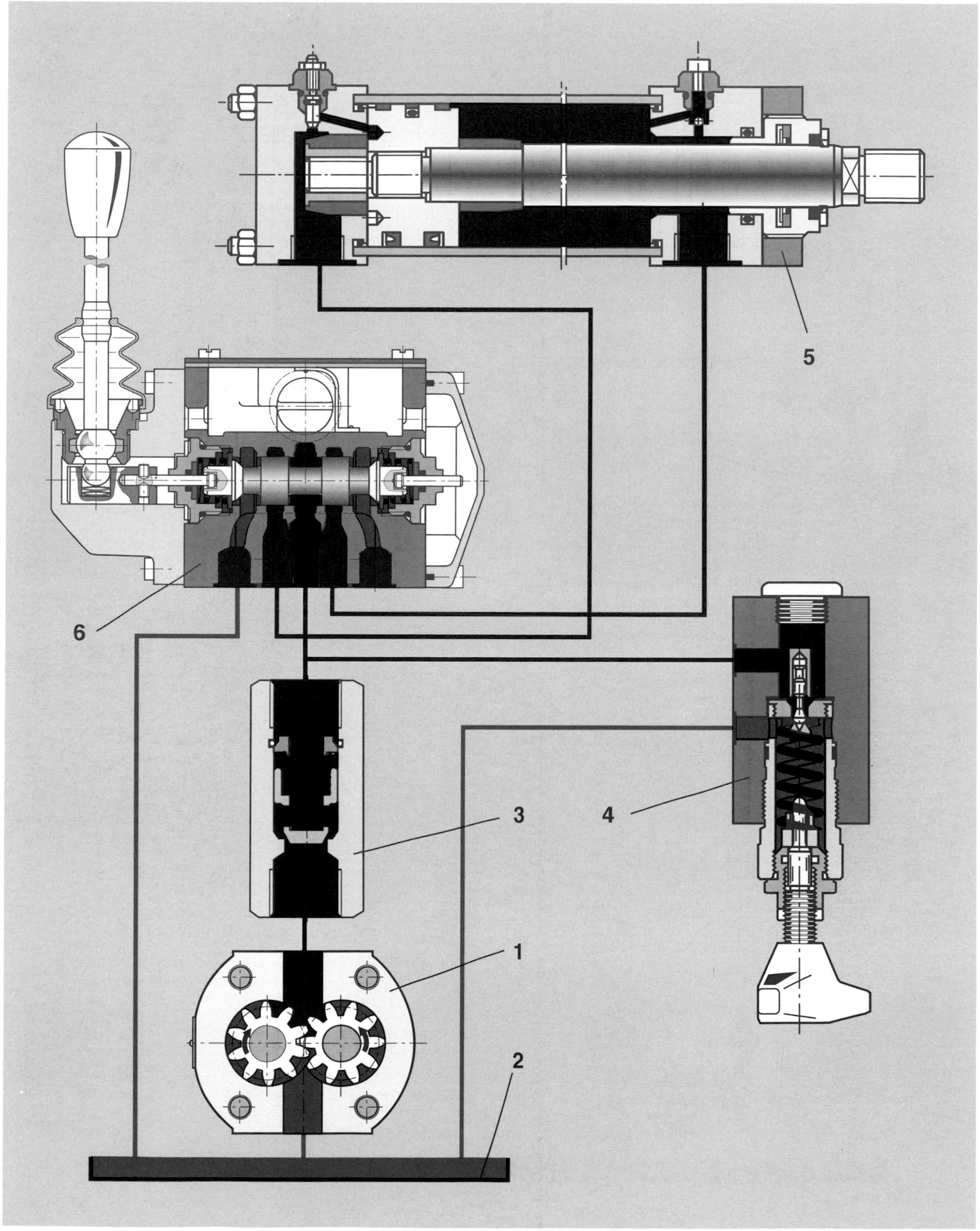

Fig. 17

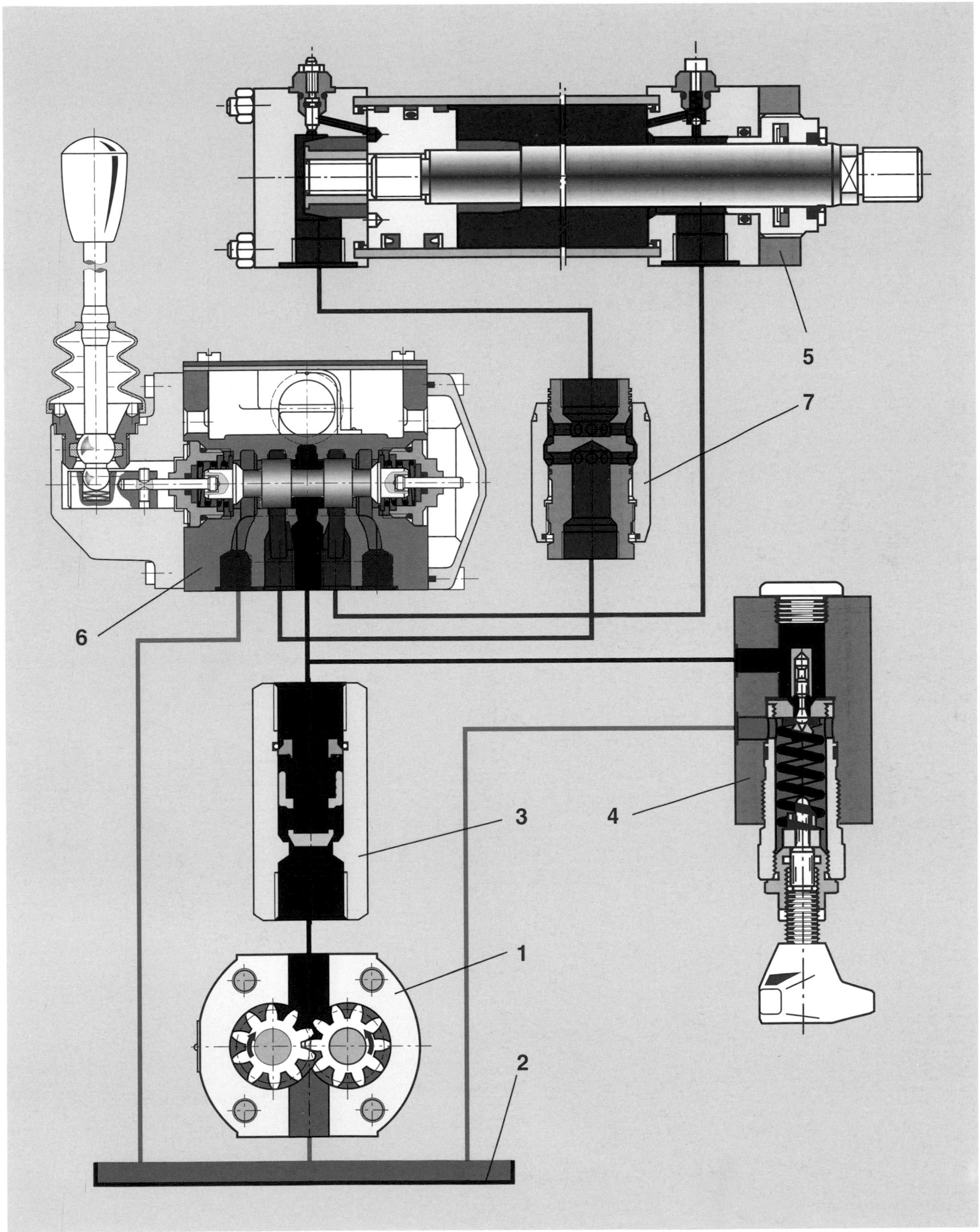

Fig. 18

Basic Principles

3.3.3 Step 3 (*Figs. 18 and 19*)

In order to change the speed of movement of the piston in the hydraulic cylinder (5), the amount of flow to the cylinder must be controlled. This may be achieved, using a flow control valve (7).

The cross-sectional area of a pipe may be changed, using a flow control valve. If the area is decreased, less liquid per unit time reaches cylinder (5). The piston in cylinder (5) hence moves slower. The excess liquid, which is now delivered by pump (1), is drained to tank (2) via pressure relief valve (4).

The following pressures occur in a hydraulic circuit:

- pressure set at pressure relief valve (4) acts between hydraulic pump (1) and flow control valve (7)

  and

- pressure dependent on load acts between flow control valve (7) and cylinder (5).

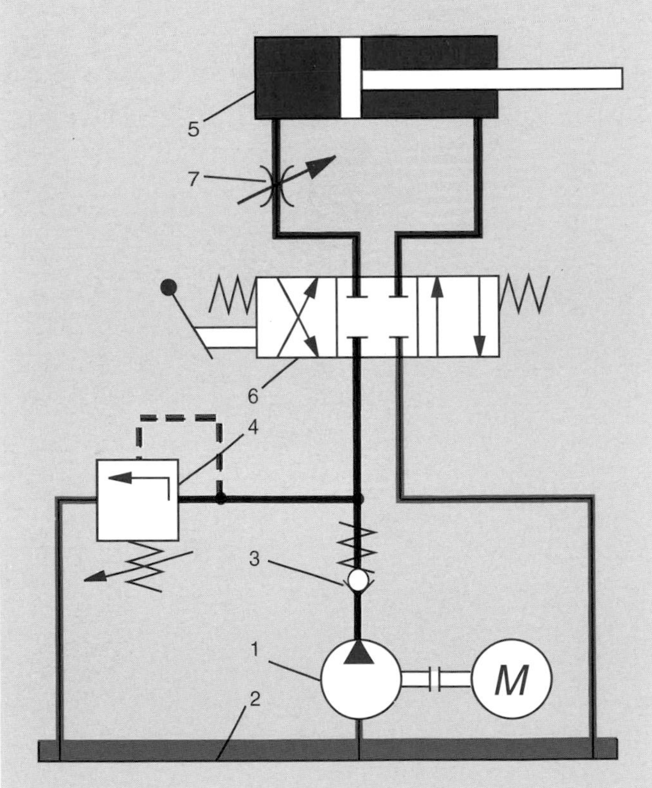

Fig. 19

Notes

Chapter 2

Symbols to DIN ISO 1219

Rudi A. Lang

Symbols for hydraulic systems are for functional interpretation and comprise one or more basic symbols and in geneneral one or more function symbols. Symbols are neither dimensioned nor specified for any particular position.

The following list is incomplete. It is designed as an aid for creating symbols.

Name/ description/examples	Symbol
Basic symbols	
Lines	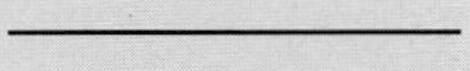
Continuous Main line, electrical line	
Dashed Control line, drain line, transition position	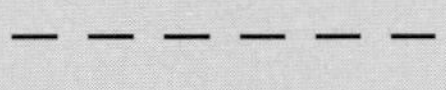
Chain dotted To group two or more components in a sub-assembly.	
Double Mechanical connection (shaft, lever, piston rod)	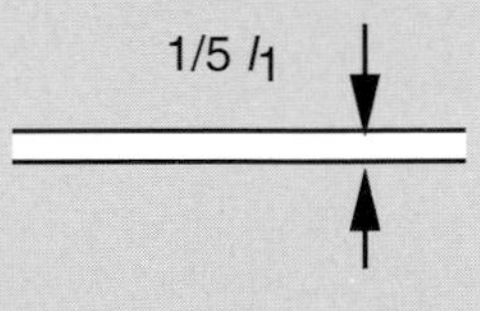 1/5 l_1
Circle Energy trånsfer unit	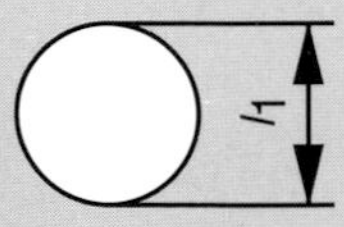 l_1
Measuring device	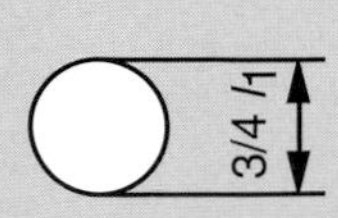 3/4 l_1
Check valves, rotary connection, mechanical pivots, Rollers (always with centre point)	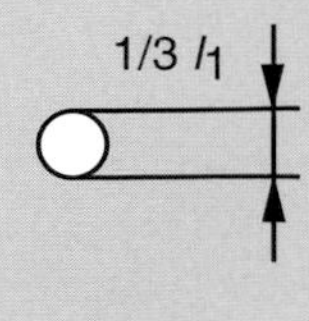 1/3 l_1

Name/ description, examples	Symbol
Semi-circle Motor or pump with limited angle of rotation (Rotary actuator)	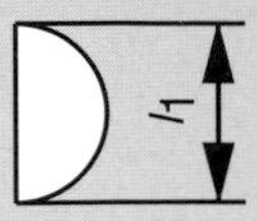 l_1
Square Connections perpendicular to sides. Control elements Drive unit (except for E motor)	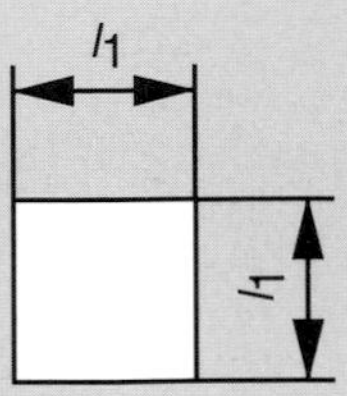 l_1, l_1
Connections to corners of preparation devices (filters, separators, lubricating devices, heat exchangers)	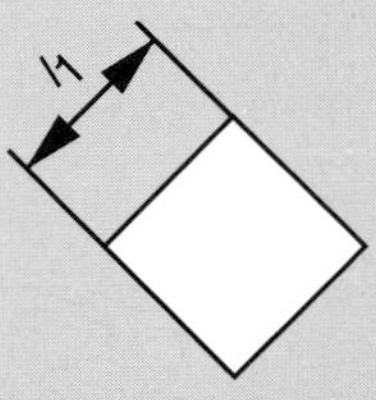 l_1
Damping in positioning elements, accumulator weight	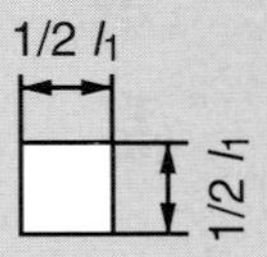 1/2 l_1, 1/2 l_1
Rectangle Cylinders, valves	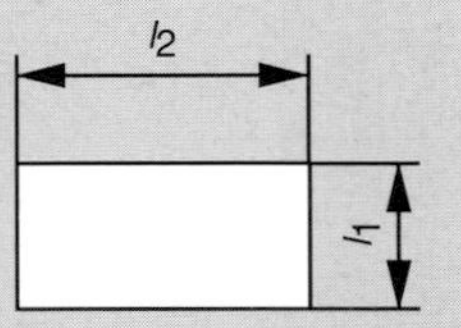 l_2, l_1
Piston in cylinder	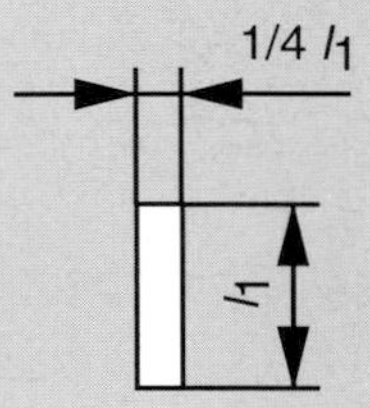 1/4 l_1, l_1
Adjustment element	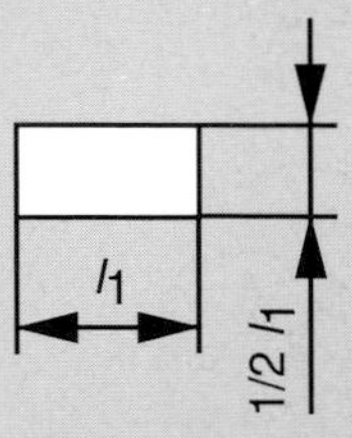 l_1, 1/2 l_1
Offsets for connecting lines	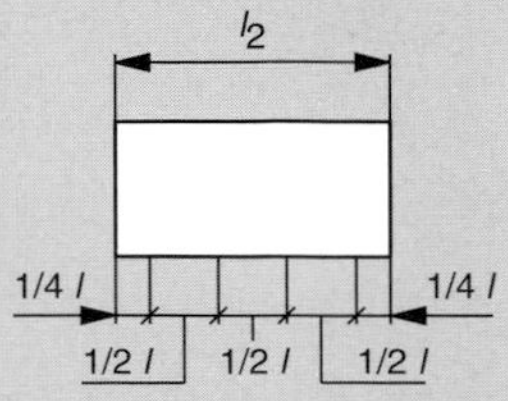 l_2, 1/4 l, 1/4 l, 1/2 l, 1/2 l, 1/2 l

Name/ description, examples	Symbol
Open rectangle Tank	l_3 ; 1/2 l_1
Oval Pressure tank Accumulator Gas bottle	2 l_1 ; l_1
Function symbols *Triangle* Shows direction of flow and operating medium	
Filled, hydraulic	
Open, pneumatic	
Arrows Straight Linear movement, path and direction of flow through a valve, direction of heat flow	≈ 30° ; 0,3 l
Curved Rotational movement, direction of rotation viewed on shaft end	90°
Diagonal arrow Adjustability in pumps, motors, springs, solenoids	
Electrical	
Closed path or connection	
Linear electrical positioning elements acting in opposition	

Name/ description, examples	Symbol
Temperature display or control	
Drive unit	M
Spring	
Throttle	
Seat of check valve	90°
Flow lines Connection	0,2 l_1
Cross-over	
Flexible line	
Connections Breather connection (continuous)	
Limited with respect to time Open / closed	
Quick release coupling without mechanically opening check valves	
With mechanically opening check valves	
Rotary coupling with 1 through channel	
Rod, linear movement	
Shaft, rotational movement	
Detent, maintains specified position	

Name/ description, examples	Symbol
Operational modes General symbol	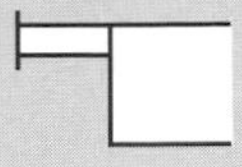
Push button	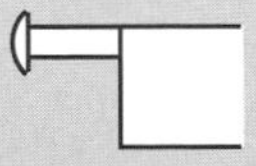
Pull-out knob	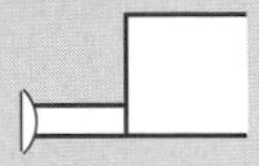
Push button/pull-out knob	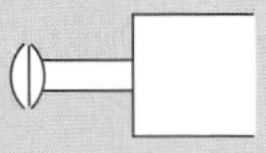
Lever	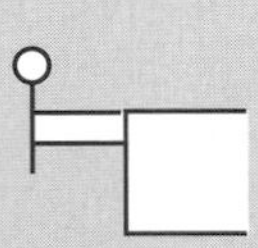
Pedal, 1 direction of operation	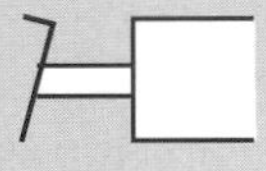
Pedal, 2 directions of operation	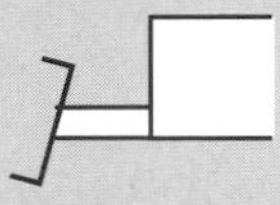
Push rod	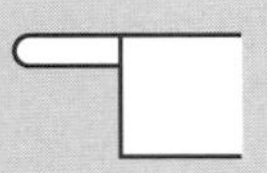
Push rod with stroke limitation	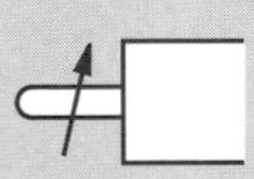
Spring	
Roller shaft	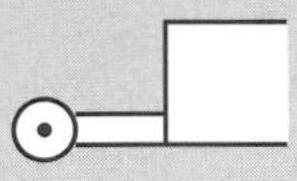
Roller lever	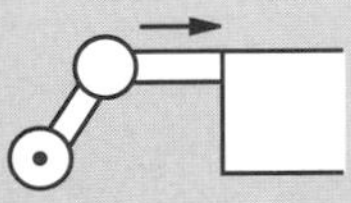
Electrical, 1 winding	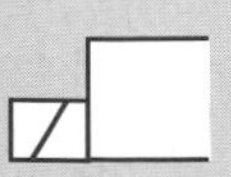
Electrical, 2 windings which act in opposition to each other	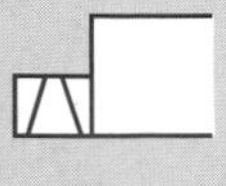
Electrical, 2 windings which act in opposition to each other and which may be steplessly adjusted	
2 parallel acting operators	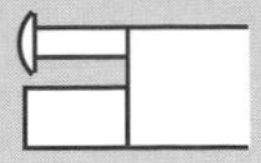

Name/ description, examples	Symbol
Operation by means of pressurisation or pressure relief Directly acts on positioning element	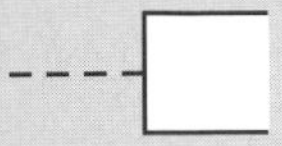
By means of opposed control areas of different sizes	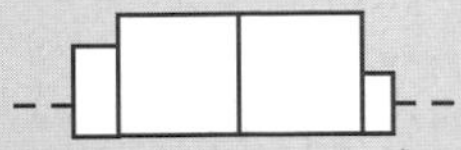
Internal control channel	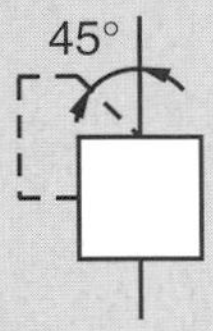 45°
External control channel	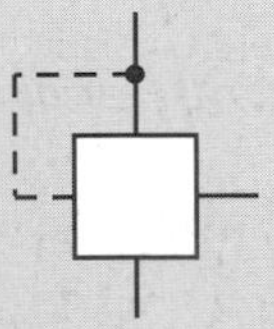
Pneumatic/hydraulic operation	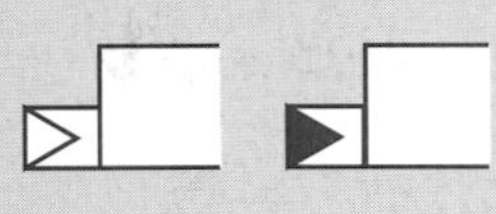
2 stage hydraulic operation	
2 stage electro-hydraulic operation, external pilot oil supply	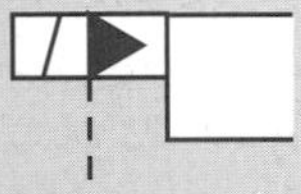
2 stage pneumatic-hydraulic operation, external pilot oil return	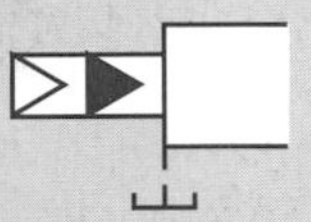
2 stage electro-hydraulic operation, spring centering of mid-position, external pilot oil feed and return	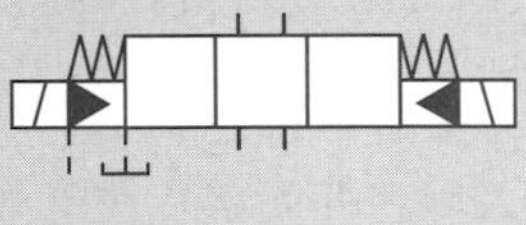
2 stage electro-hydraulic operation, pressure centering of mid-position, external pilot oil feed and return	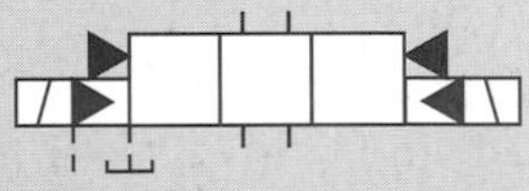
External feedback of actual position of positioning element	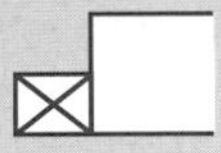
Internal feedback of actual position of positioning element	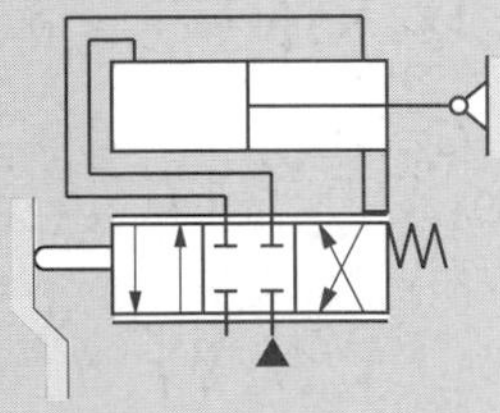

Name/ description, examples	Symbol
Energy sources Hydraulic	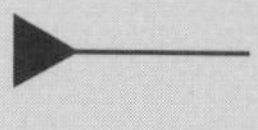
Pneumatic	
Electrical motor	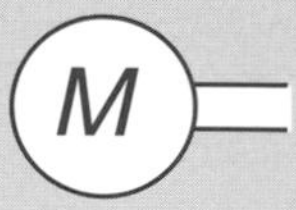 M
Drive unit, except for electrical motor	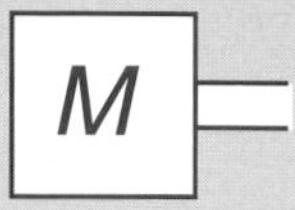 M
Energy transfer and storage *Hydraulic pumps and motors*	
Fixed displacement pump, general	
Fixed displacement pump, 1 direction of flow, 1 direction of rotation	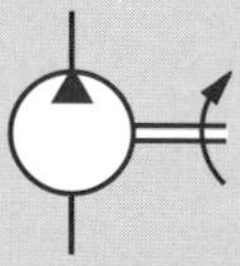
Variable displacement pump, 2 directions of flow, 1 direction of rotation, Case drain port	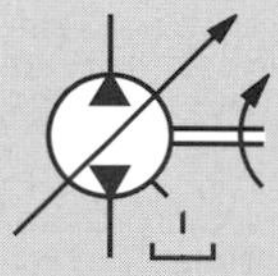
Fixed displacement motor, 2 directions of flow, 2 directions of rotation	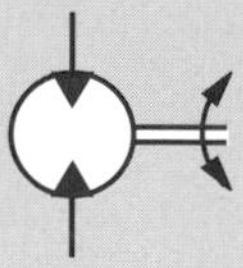
Fixed displacement pump/motor, 1 direction of flow, 1 direction of rotation	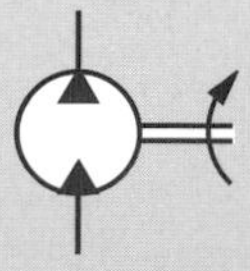
Variable displacement pump/motor, manual adjustment 2 directions of flow, 2 directions of rotation, Case drain port	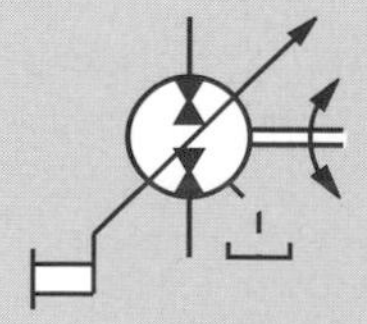
Hydraulic rotary actuator	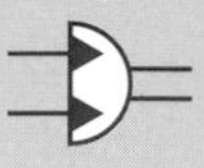

Name/ description, examples	Symbol
Hydraulic compact drive	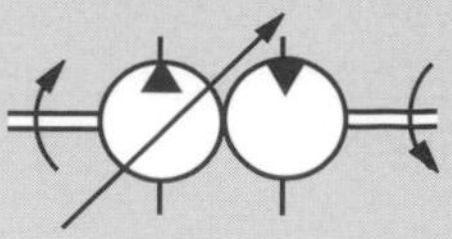
Variable displacement pump with pressure compensator, 1 direction of flow, 1 direction of rotation, Case drain port	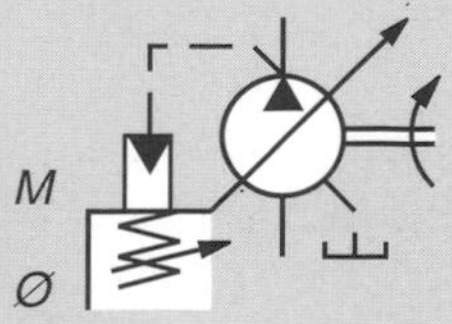 M Ø
Variable displacement pump/motor with pressure compensator, 2 directions of flow, 2 directions of rotation, Case drain port	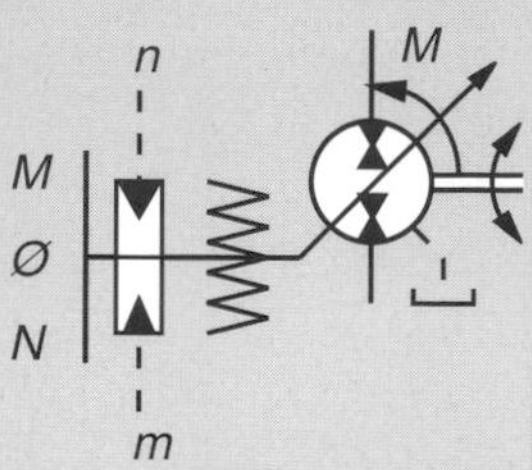 n M M Ø N m
Hydraulic cylinders Single acting hydraulic cylinder, return stroke via pressurisation, full bore connected to tank	
Double acting single rod hydraulic cylinder, adjustable damping at both ends of stroke	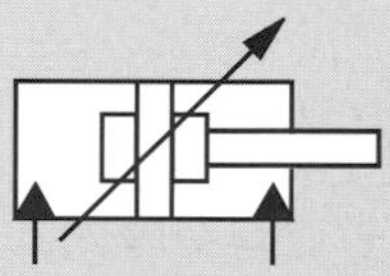
Telescopic hydraulic cylinder, single acting	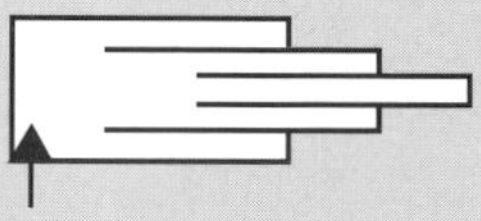
Telescopic hydraulic cylinder, double acting	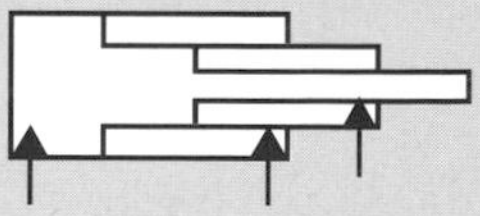
Accumulators Without initial pressure	
With initial gas pressure	

Name/ description, examples	Symbol
Gas bottle in upright position only	
Open and closed loop control of energy *Directional valves* Two position valve with 1 cross-over point	
Two position valve with stepless control of spool position	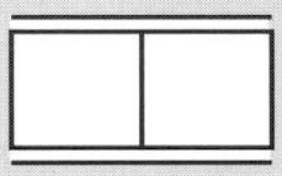
Three position valve with stepless control of spool position	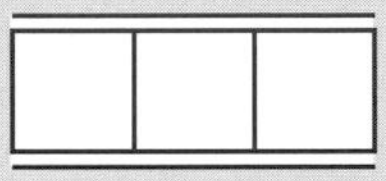
Two position valve, 2 ports, normally closed, 2 directions of flow	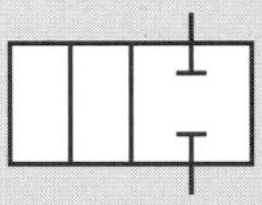
Two position valve, 2 ports, normally open, 2 directions of flow	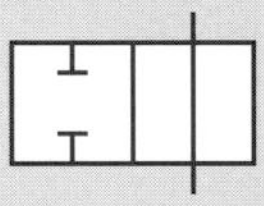
Two position valve, 3 ports, normally open, 2 directions of flow	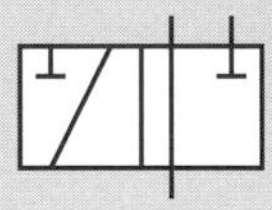
2/2 way directional valve, 2 ports, 2 spool positions	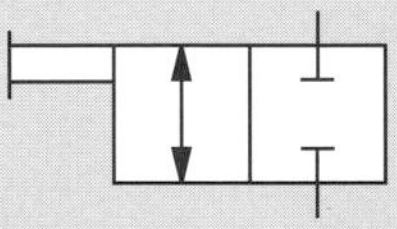
3/2 way directional valve, 3 ports, 2 spool positions, 1 cross-over point, solenoid operation, spring offset	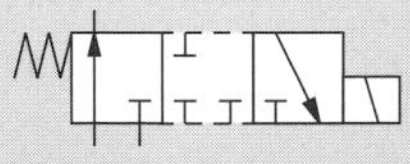
5/2 way directional valve, 5 ports, 2 spool positions, pressure operated in both dir-ections	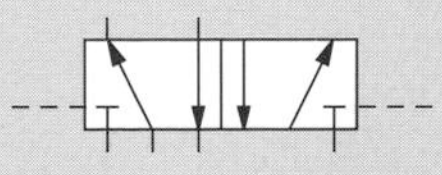

Name/ description, examples	Symbol
4/3 way directional valve, (detailed diagram) electro-hydraulically operated, 4 ports, 3 spool positions, spring centered mid-position, emergency stop operation, external pilot oil return	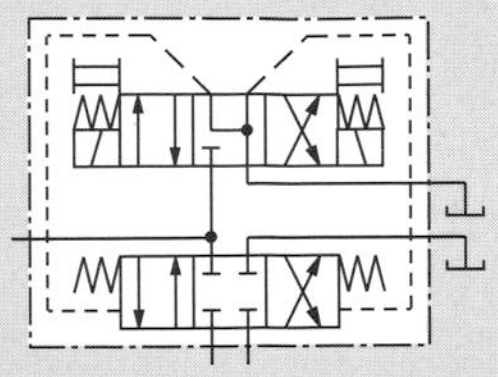
(simplified diagram)	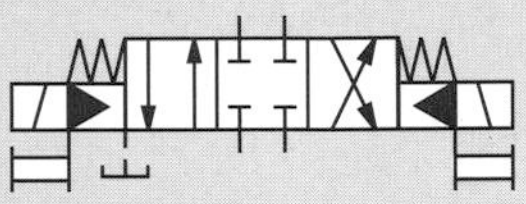
4/3 way directional valve, (detailed diagram) electro-hydraulically operated, 4 ports, 3 spool positions, pressure centered mid-posi-tion, emergency stop operation, external pilot oil return	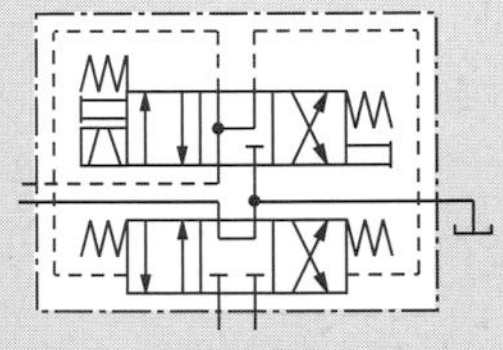
(simplified diagram)	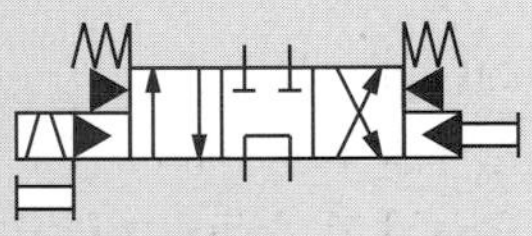
Continuously variable (modulating valves) Modulating valve, negative overlap	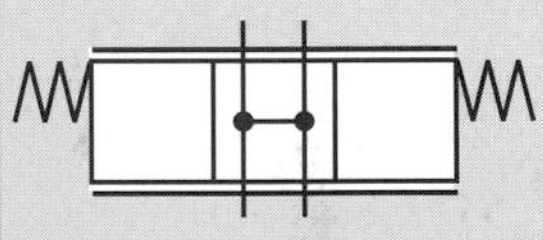
Modulating valve, positive overlap	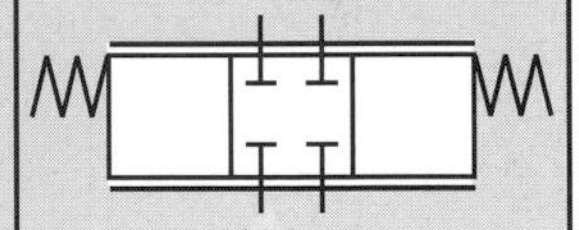
4/3 way servo valve (typical example)	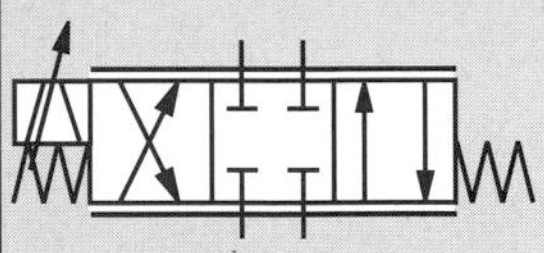
Check valves/ isolating valves Check valve, without spring loading	
Check valve, spring loaded	
Check valve, pilot operated, without spring pre-load	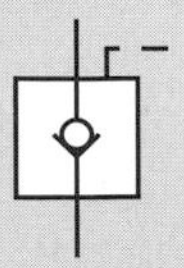

Name/ description, examples	Symbol
Check valve, pilot operated, with spring pre-load	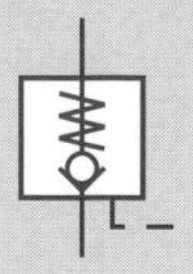
Shuttle valve	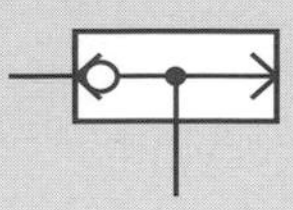
Air bleed valve	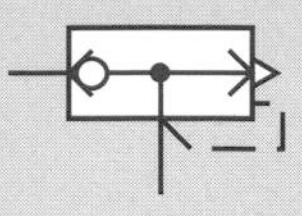
Pressure control valves Pressure relief valve, direct operated, internal pilot oil feed	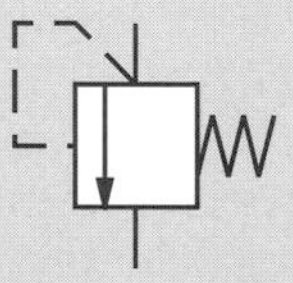
Pressure relief valve, direct operated, external pilot oil feed	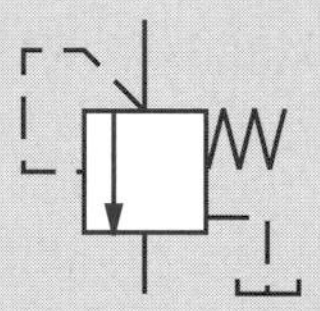
Pressure relief valve, pilot operated, internal pilot oil feed and return	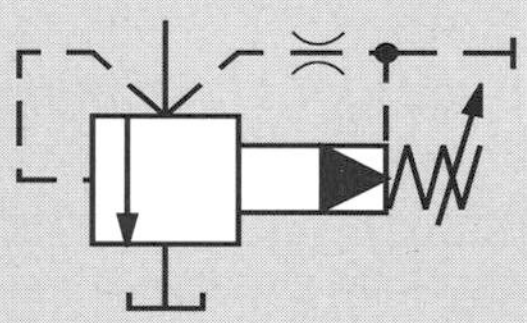
Pressure relief valve, pilot operated, electrically operated relief, internal pilot oil feed, external pilot oil return	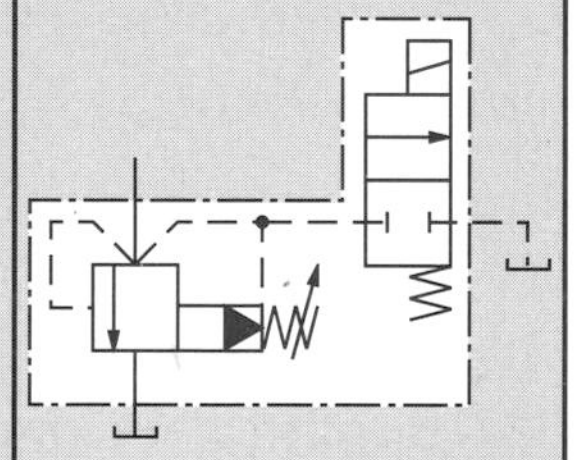
2 way pressure reducing valve, direct operated, internal pilot oil feed	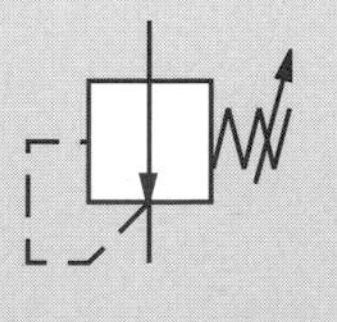
2 way pressure reducing valve, pilot operated, internal pilot oil feed, external pilot oil return	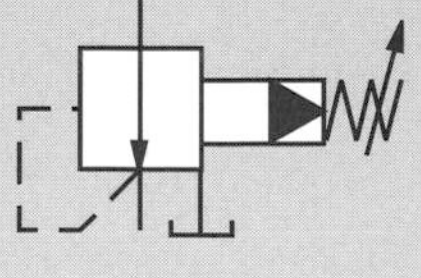
3 way pressure reducing valve, direct operated, internal pilot oil feed	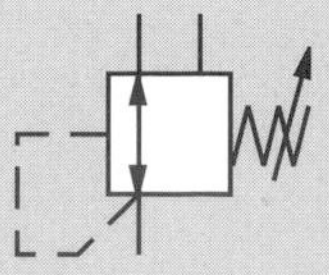

Name/ description, examples	Symbol
Flow control valves Throttle valve, adjustable	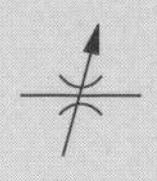
Shut-off valve	
Deceleration valve	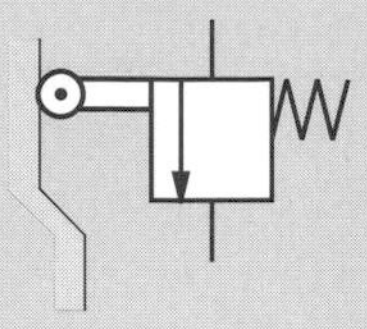
Throttle/check valve	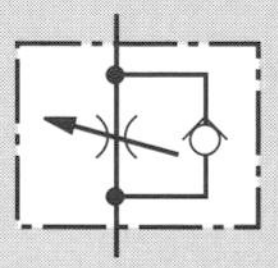
2 way flow control valve, pressure compensated	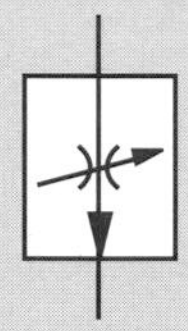
2 way flow control valve, pressure and temperature compensated	
3 way flow control valve, pressure and temperature compensated	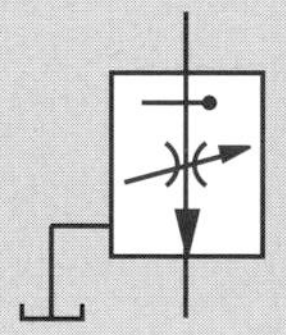
Flow divider	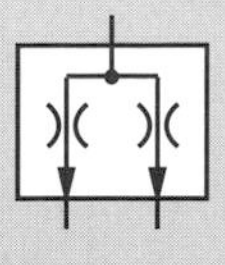
2 way cartridge valves (logic elements) Directional valve, leakage free, differing effective areas	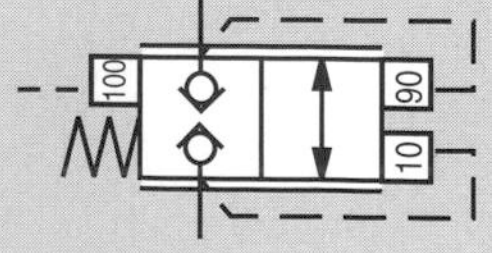 100 90 10
Flow control valve	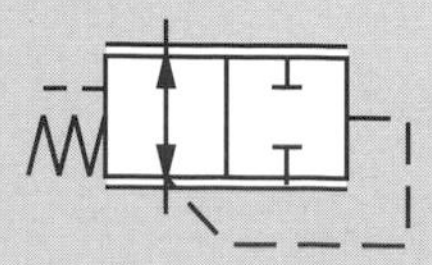

Name/ description, examples	Symbol
Directional valve, leakage free in one direction, identical effective areas	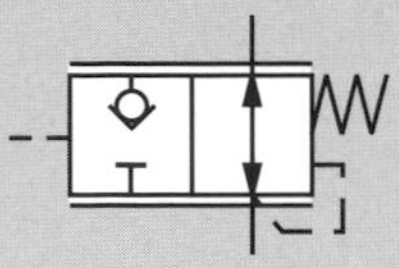
Fluid storage and preparation Ventilated tank	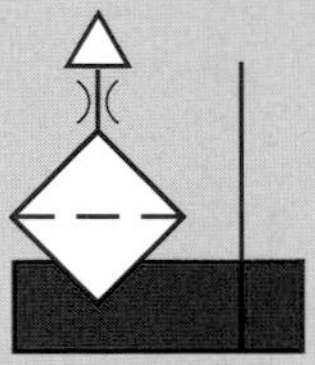
Pressure tank	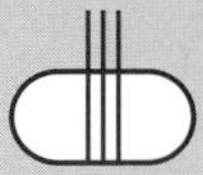
Filter	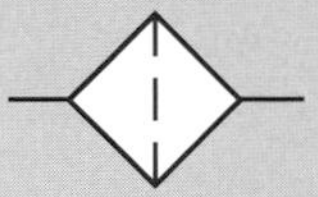
Filter with clogging indicator	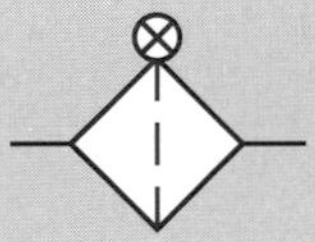
Separator	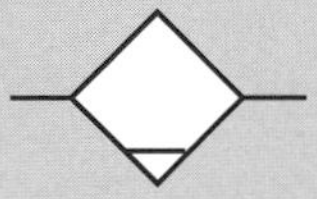
Filter with separator	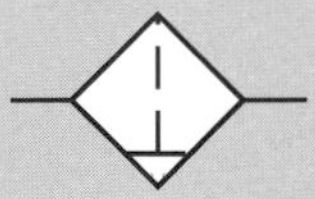
Preparation unit comprising: filter, separator, pressure reducing valve, pressure gauge and lubricator	
Cooler	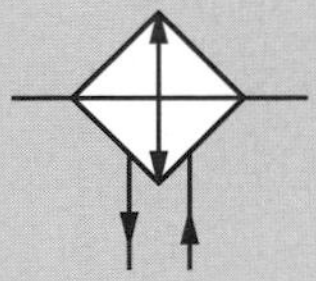
Heater	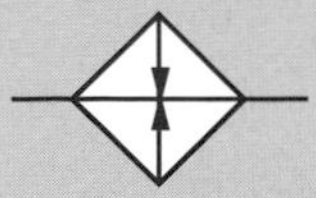
Temperature control	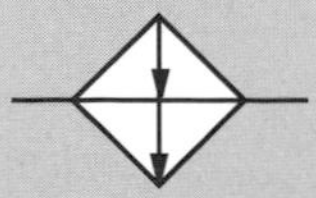

Name/ description, examples	Symbol
Measuring devices and indicators Pressure indicator, general	
Pressure gauge	
Differential pressure gauge	
Fluid level measuring device	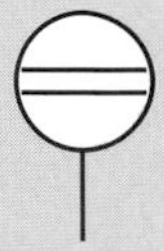
Thermometer	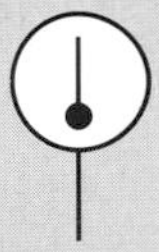
Flow indicator	
Flowmeter	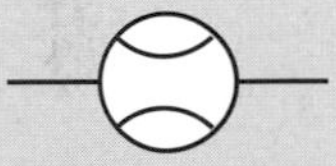
Tachometer	
Torque meter	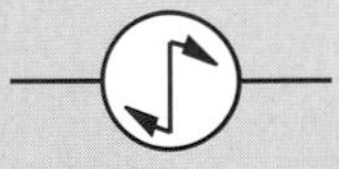
Hydro-electric pressure switch	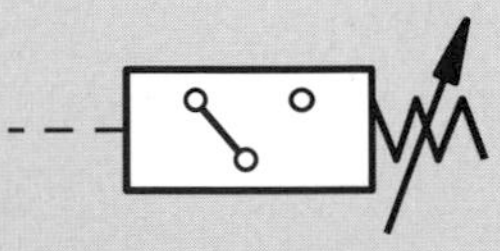
Limit switch	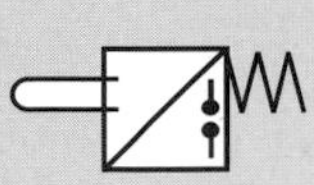

Notes

Chapter 3

Hydraulic Fluids

Eberhard Sumpf

1 Introduction

The main function of a hydraulic fluid in a hydraulic system is to transfer forces and movements.

Further tasks and characteristics are required of the hydraulic fluid, due to the diverse range of applications and installations of hydraulic drives.

As a fluid does not exist, which is equally suitable for all areas of application, the special features of applications must be taken into account, when selecting a fluid. Only if this is done, is it possible to achieve relatively interference free and economic operation.

Application	Suitable fluids *)	Max. operating pressure	Ambient temperature	Place of installation
Vehicle construction	1 • 2 • 3	250 bar	–40 to + 60 °C	inside & outside
Mobile machines	1 • 2 • 3	315 bar	–40 to + 60 °C	inside & outside
Special vehicles	1 • 2 • 3 • 4	250 bar	–40 to + 60 °C	inside & outside
Agriculture and forestry machines	1 • 2 • 3	250 bar	–40 to + 50 °C	inside & outside
Ship building	1 • 2 • 3	315 bar	–60 to + 60 °C	inside & outside
Aircraft	1 • 2 • 5	210 (280) bar	–65 to +60 °C	inside & outside
Conveyors	1 • 2 • 3 • 4	315 bar	–40 to + 60 °C	inside & outside
Machine tools	1 • 2	200 bar	18 to 40 °C	inside
Presses	1 • 2 • 3	630 bar	18 to 40 °C	mainly inside
Ironworks, rolling mills, foundaries	1 • 2 • 4	315 bar	10 to 150 °C	inside
Steelworks, water hydraulics	1 • 2 • 3	220 bar	–40 to + 60 °C	inside & outside
Power stations	1 • 2 • 3 • 4	250 bar	–10 to +60 °C	mainly inside
Theatres	1 • 2 • 3 • 4	160 bar	18 to 30 °C	mainly inside
Simulation and testing devices	1 • 2 • 3 • 4	1000 bar	18 to 150 °C	mainly inside
Mining	1 • 2 • 3 • 4	1000 bar	up to 60 °C	outside & underground
Special applications	2 • 3 • 4 • 5	250 (630) bar	–65 to 150 °C	inside & outside

*) 1= mineral oil; 2= synthetic hydraulic fluids; 3= eccologically acceptable fluids; 4= water, HFA, HFB; 5= special fluids

Table 1: *Hydraulic drive applications and the fluids which are suitable for them*

2 Fluid requirements

2.1 Lubrication and anti-wear characteristics

The fluid must be capable of covering all moving parts with a tenacious lubricating film. The lubricating film may be destroyed, as a result of high pressures, insufficient oil delivery, low viscosity and either slow or very fast sliding movements. This would result in wear due to fretting (standard clearance tolerance e.g. in directional valves is 8 to 10 µm).

As well as wear due to fretting, there is also wear due to fatigue, abrasion and corrosion.

- Wear due to abrasion occurs between parts, which slide across each other, when contaminated (with solid particles e.g. metal dust, slag, sand, etc.) unfiltered or insufficiently filtered fluids are used. The foreign particles carried along may also cause abrasion in the devices at high fluid velocities.
- The metallic structure of components may change due to cavitation and this can result in wear due to fatigue. Wear may be magnified due to contamination of the fluid with water at the bearings in the pump.

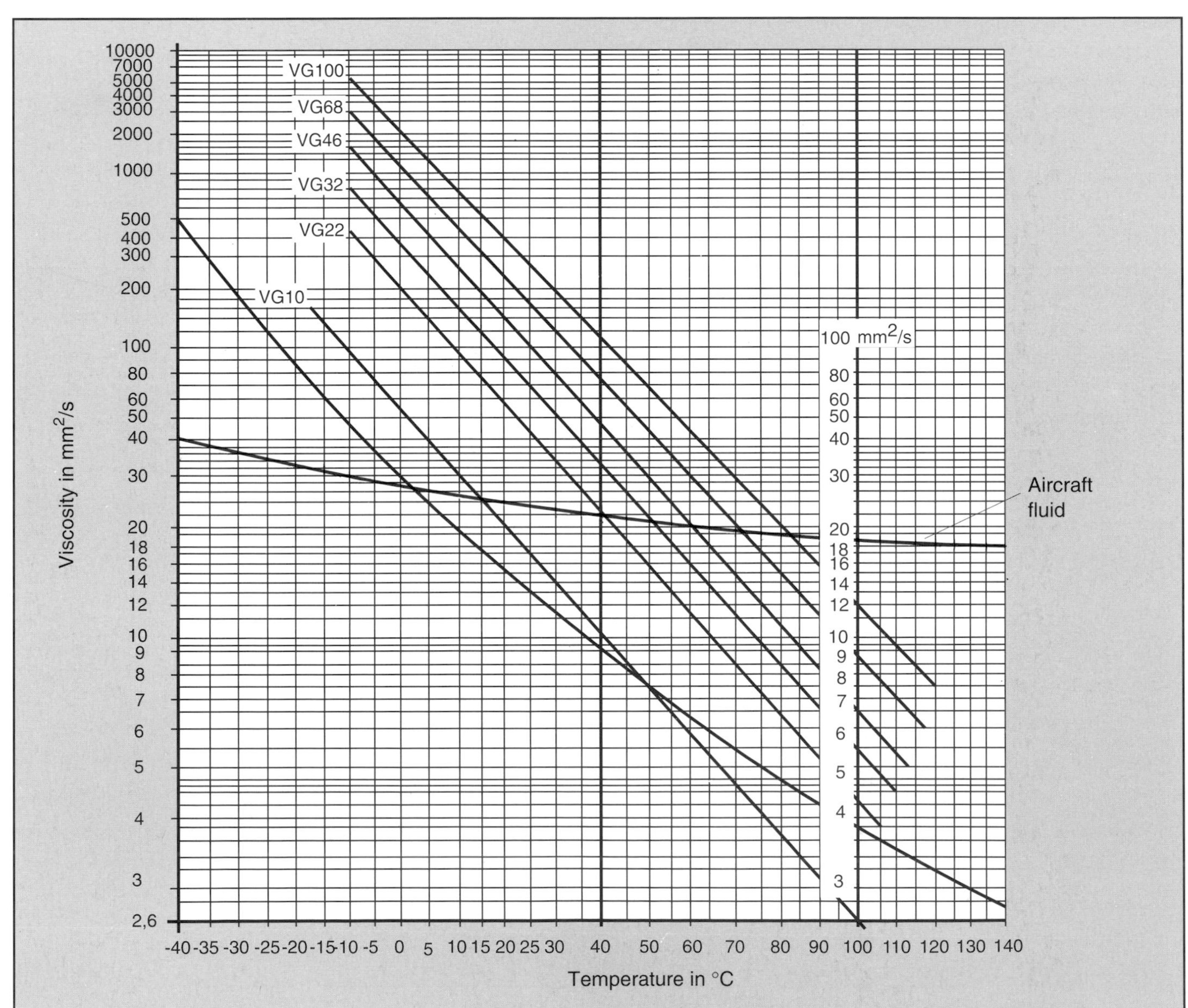

Diagram 1: *Viscosity/temperature diagram*

- Wear due to corrosion occurs as a result of long idle times in the hydraulic system and due to unsuitable fluids being used. Rust is formed due to the effect of damp on the sliding surfaces, and this results in an increase in the wear in devices.

2.2 Viscosity

Viscosity is the name given to the characteristic of a fluid, where a fluid exerts a resistance to the laminar movement of two neighbouring fluid layers against each other (see DIN 51 550).

The most important parameter when selecting a fluid is the viscosity. It is not a measure of the quality of a fluid, but instead provides information on the behaviour of a fluid at a particular reference temperature. In order to be able to take application limits into account when selecting hydraulic components, it is important to take note of the minimum and maximum permissible viscosities given in the documentation from a hydraulic component manufacturer.

2.3 Viscosity index

Fluids must not become very much "thicker" or "thinner" when the temperature varies, even over a wide temperature range, as otherwise the flows at throttling points change (change in velocity of the actuator). Determination of the viscosity index is to DIN ISO 2909. The best viscosity index for a fluid is indicated by the flattest curve in a viscosity-temperature diagram.

Fluids with a high viscosity index are primarily required in applications, where large changes in temperature occur, for example, in mobile machines and in road and air transport.

2.4 Behaviour of viscosity with respect to pressure

The viscosity of fluids changes as pressure increases. This characteristic must be taken into account when planning hydraulic systems which use pressures of more than 200 bar. By approximately 400 bar, the viscosity has already been doubled.

2.5 Compatibility with different materials

A fluid must be fully compatible with other materials used in hydraulic systems, such as those used for bearings, seals, paints, etc. Where, the fluid leaks out from the hydraulic system and comes into contact with other system parts, such as electrical lines, mechanical components, etc., the fluid must also be compatible with these parts.

2.6 Stability against shearing

Fluids become mechanically loaded, when they reach control lands and on the opening and closing of valve seats. The fluid flow is then "sheared". This process effects the service life of a fluid.

If a fluid contains viscosity index enhancers, the sensitivity to shearing increases. Under normal loads on shearing via valves and pumps, the viscosity temporarily drops, but then reverts back to normal. If the shear load is increased too much due to the shear rigidity of the viscosity index enhancers present, then these enhancers will be partly damaged and the original viscosity no longer reached. This results in a permanent drop in viscosity.

2.7 Stability against thermal loads

The temperature of a fluid may increase during system operation (if possible not above 80°C). When the system is idle, the temperature is reduced again. This repetitive process has an effect on the service life of the fluid. Hence in many systems, the operating temperature of the fluid is kept constant by using heat exchangers (heating and cooling system).

The advantage of this is that a stable operating curve for viscosity and a longe service life for the fluid are produced. The disadvantages of this are higher purchasing and operating costs (flow for heat and water/air for cooling).

2.8 Stability against oxidation

The ageing process in mineral oils is influenced by oxygen, heat, light and catalysis. A mineral oil with a better ageing characteristic, has oxidation inhibitors in it, which prevent oxygen from being quickly absorbed. Increased absorption of oxygen would in addition lead to an increase in the corrosion of components.

Copper, lead, bronze, brass and steel have a particularly high catalytic effect and may influence the age of a fluid.

These materials are found in hydraulic components.

2.9 Low compressibility

The dissolved air carried along in the fluid determines how much the fluid column is compressed. This characteristic influences the accuracy of hydraulic drives. In open loop and closed loop control processes, compressibility influences response times. If large volumes trapped under pressure are quickly opened, decompression shocks occur in the system. Fluid compressibility is defined by a factor, which is dependent on the fluid and increases with increases in temperature and decreases with increases in pressure.

A compressibility factor of 0.7 to 0.8 % per 100 bar based on theoretical calculations may be used as a reference value for mineral oil. A factor of 0.45 % per 100 bar may be used for water.

Compressibility increases considerably, when undissolved air (air bubbles) is transported in the fluid. The undissolved air may no longer be separated from the fluid, hence considerably increasing the compressibility factor, if a tank of the wrong size or construction is used or if the wrong pipes are used. These mistakes also result in noise, jolting movements and a large rise in temperature in the hydraulic system (in addition see the diesel effect).

The diesel effect is the spontaneous combustion of a air-gas mixture. Mineral oil contains may small air bubbles. If mineral oil is pressurised very quickly, i.e. compressed, the air bubbles become so hot, that a spontaneous combustion may occur. Hence, at specific points a large increase in temperature and pressure occurs, which may damage the seals on the hydraulic components. In addition, the age of the fluid will be reduced.

2.10 Little expansion due to temperature

If the temperature of the fluid increases due to atmospheric pressure, the volume of the fluid increases. If a large quantity of fluid is to be used in a system, the operating temperature of the system must be taken into account.

Example:

The volume of mineral oil increases by 0.7 % per 10 °C increase in temperature.

2.11 Little formation of foam

Rising air bubbles may form foam on the surface in a tank.The formation of foam may be minimised by correctly arranging the return lines in the tank and by proper construction of the tank, e.g. by installing baffles. Mineral oils contain chemical additives, which reduce foam. The tendency for a fluid to form foam increases with age, contamination and condensation.

If the pump sucks foaming oil, this may severely damage the system and result in the pump failing within a short time.

2.12 Low intake of air and good release of air

Fluids should be able to absorb and transport as little air as possible, but able to release any air carried along as quickly as possible. Chemical additives have a positive effect on these requirements.

The release of air or degree of separation of air is determined in accordance with DIN 51 381. The time in minutes which it takes for the air bubbles to separate in mineral oil up to 0.2 % volume is measured. The degree of separation of air worsens as the temperature of the fluid increases.

2.13 High boiling point and low steam pressure

The higher the boiling point of the fluid used, the higher the maximum operating temperature of the system may be.

2.14 High density

The density of a fluid is the ratio of its mass to its volume. The density should be as high as possible, so that greater power may be transferred with the same volume of fluid. This characteristic is of less importance in hydro-static drives, than it is hydro-dynamic drives. The density of mineral oil is between 0.86 and 0.9 g/cm^3.

Density is used to convert the viscosity-density ratio (kinematic viscosity) to viscosity (dynamic viscosity) or vice versa.

In practice, the reference temperature for density is 15°C.

2.15 Good thermal conductivity

Heat created in pumps, valves, motors, cylinders and pipes should be transported by the fluid to tank. The heat returned to the tank is partly removed to the outside through the walls of the tank. If the radiation surfaces are not sufficient, additional heat exchangers (coolers) must be included in the design of the system, so that the system and fluid does not overheat.

2.16 Good di-electric (non-conducting) characteristics

If possible the fluid should not be able to transfer electrical energy (e.g. in short circuits, cable breaks, etc.) Solenoid armatures are usually covered by fluid which removes any heat created and damps the stepping of the armature.

2.17 Non-hygroscopic

In systems, which operate on mineral oil, care must be taken that the mineral oil remains free of water, as otherwise damage may occur which could lead to the system failing. Water may enter via cylinder and shaft seals, via badly sealed water coolers or via condensed moisture on the tank walls. In addition, the new fluid which is filled into the tank may already contain water (condensation). If the content of water is greater than 0.2 % of the total volume, the fluid must be changed. Water and fluid may be separated whilst a system is being operated, by using separators and centrifuges (primarily in large systems).

In systems which operate outside (high humidity and rain) a dehumidifiermay be connected behind the air filter to dry the required air (dependent on shuttle volume).

As water has a higher specific weight , water contained in the fluid may collect at the bottom of the tank during idle times (mineral oil and water do not undergo any chemical interaction and hence may be separated again).

If a oil level indicator is fixed to the tank, the water may be easily recognised. If the oil drain valve is carefully opened at the tank, water comes out first. In larger systems, water warning devices are often installed at the deepest point of the tank. When a certain level of water is reached , this sets off an electrical warning signal. A determination of the degree of separation of water in a particular time interval has not been possible in practice.

2.18 Fire-resistant - does not burn

Hydraulic systems are also installed in hot conditions; in manufacturing plants which may operate at very high temperatures (steel making) or where naked flames occur (furnaces & heating devices). In order to reduce the risks involved when pipes and/or hoses burst, the fluid used for such applications has a high flash point and is fire-resistant.

2.19 Non-toxic as a fluid, as vapour and after decomposition

In order to avoid fluids being a danger to health or the environment, the reference notes in fluid manufacturers' documents must be taken into consideration.

2.20 Good protection against corrosion

Manufacturers of pumps, valves, motors and cylinders test these devices using mineral oil, as the mineral oil protects the devices from corrosion. The ability of mineral oil to protect against corrosion is achieved by adding chemicals, which form a water-resistant film on metal surfaces and which neutralise corrosive decomposition products of ageing mineral oil.

Once the hydraulic components have been tested, mineral oil left in the components is returned to tank.The mineral oil film on the components protects them from corrosion until commissioning takes place. If components are stored for longer periods, special measures need to be carried out to protect the components from corrosion (e.g. by using preservative oil).

2.21 No formation of sticky substances

During long idle periods of the hydraulic system, during operation, during warming up and cooling down, and due to the ageing of a fluid, the fluid must not form any substances which could lead to "sticking" of moving parts in hydraulic components.

2.22 Good filtration capability

During operation in hydraulic systems fluid is continuously filtered in feed or return lines or in both directions, in order to filter wear particles from the fluid. The fluid and its viscosity effect the size of filter and filter mesh material required.

As viscosity increases, back pressure (Δp) increases. Hence a larger filter needs to be included in the design. If aggressive fluids are used, special material is required for the filter mesh.

The active substances in the fluid must not be allowed to settle in the filters. If fine filters with pore sizes of 5µm or less are used in systems, fluids must be tested to find out their suitability for these conditions.

2.23 Compatible and exchangeable with other fluids

Due to rebuilding or moving of production lines, changed environmental conditions or new laws, it may be necessary to change a fluid. In these cases, fluid and component manufacturers must be consulted as to the suitability of fluid and components installed into the hydraulic system to the new conditions for installation.

In addition, all hydraulic devices, seals and hoses must be completely removed and the old fluid completely removed from them. If a comprehensive procedure is not carried out in such cases, this may lead to a complete malfunction of the hydraulic system.

2.24 Formation of silt

The fluid and its additives should not decompose leading to a formation of silt (sticking effects) during the complete period of use.

2.25 User-friendly servicing

Fluids which (for example) must be first stirred and mixed after a long idle time before they can be used, require much effort in servicing. Fluids which have additives which rapidly lose their characteristics or evaporate, must be regularly chemically and/or physically inspected.

It should be possible to inspect a fluid by means of a simple process. In limiting cases, fluid and filter manufacturers can analyse samples and decide whether a fluid may remain or needs to be changed.

2.26 Eccolocically acceptable

The best way of looking after the environment when using hydraulic systems is by comprehensively carrying out the planning, design, assembly, operation and servicing of the system.

Using eccologically acceptable fluids is no substitute for the above.

Eccologically acceptable fluids should fulfil the following requirements:

- Good bio-degradability
- Easy to remove
- Non-toxic to fish
- Non-toxic to bacteria
- No danger to water
- No danger to food
- No danger to fodder
- No skin or mucus irritations due to the fluid in any of its three states (solid, liquid or gas)
- No smell or at least a pleasant one.

As yet neither legal guide-lines nor standards exist which define the characteristic "environmentally compatible" (or better "environmentally friendly").

2.27 Cost and availability

Fluids should basically be used which are good value and which have become widely used. This is especially important for applications of hydraulic systems in fields which have not yet been industrialised.

It is difficult to give a complete appraisal of eccologically acceptable fluids as information is scattered and rarely in a consistent form. The selection of a fluid with respect to economic considerations can only occur, having carefully considered the operating cost and future costs. Hence it is important to find out about the physical and chemical characteristics of a fluid, so that errors may be avoided in new designs, exchanging of parts or repairs.

3. Summary of common fluids

Hydraulic oil based on mineral oil	WEC	Fire-resistant fluids	WEC	Environmentally-friendly fluids	WEC	Special fluids	WEC
DIN 51524, part 1 Hydraulic oil HL Hydraulic fluid based on mineral oil with active additives to increase protection against corrosion and stability against ageing.	2	Clear water HFA types (95/5) HFA-E (emulsion) HFA-M (micro-emulsion) HFA-S (solution)	0 3 3 0-1	Base fluid Plant oil (HTG) (Trigliceride) Polyglycol (HPG) Synthetic ester (HE)	 0-1 0-1 0-1	Synthetic oil (e.g. Poly-α olefin and glycol) Aircraft fluid Fluids compatible with rolling oil etc.	
DIN 51524, part 2 Hydraulic oil HLP As hydraulic oil HL, but with addtional active additives for reducing wear due to etching in mixed friction region.	2	HFA-V (thickened) 80% H_2O + 20% concentration HFB (water-in-oil emulsion) 40% H_2O + 60% mineral oil	~1 3				
DIN 51524, part 2 Hydraulic oil HLP-D As hydraulic oil HLP, but with additional active dispersant and detergent additives. In contrast to HLP oils no requirements exist for degrees of separation of air and water.	3	HFC (water glycol) 40% H_2O + 60% glycol HFD-R (Phosphate ester) HFD-U (other combination) (in general poly-ester)	0-1 1-(2) ~1				
DIN 51524, part 1 Hydraulic oil HLP As hydraulic oil HLP, but with additional active additives for improving the viscosity/temperature behaviour.	2						

Table 2: *Hydraulic fluids and their danger to water class (WGK)*

WEN Water endangerment no.	0 to 1,9	2 to 3,9	4 to 5,9	> 6
WEC Water endangerment class	0	1	2	3
Note	In general no danger to water	A little dangerous to water	Danger to water	Very dangerous to water

Table 3

4. Example of selection of suitable hydraulic components

A hangar crane system may comprise a hydrostatic transmission drive and a hydraulic winch. The crane should be able to move around in the hangar and also able to move outside to load lorries. The ambient temperature must be chosen as a limit for Winter (-10°C) and as a limit for Summer (+ 40 °C).

From an available supply of fluids, the fluid with code ISO VG 32 is to be used. The pump flow was calculated as approx. 110 L/min at 1450 rpm and the presumed operating pressure is to be 150 bar.

The minimum and maximum viscosities for the fluid may be deduced from the V-T diagram.

Once these values have been set, suitable pumps, valves and actuators (hydraulic motors and hydraulic cylinders) may be selected in accordance with technical data.

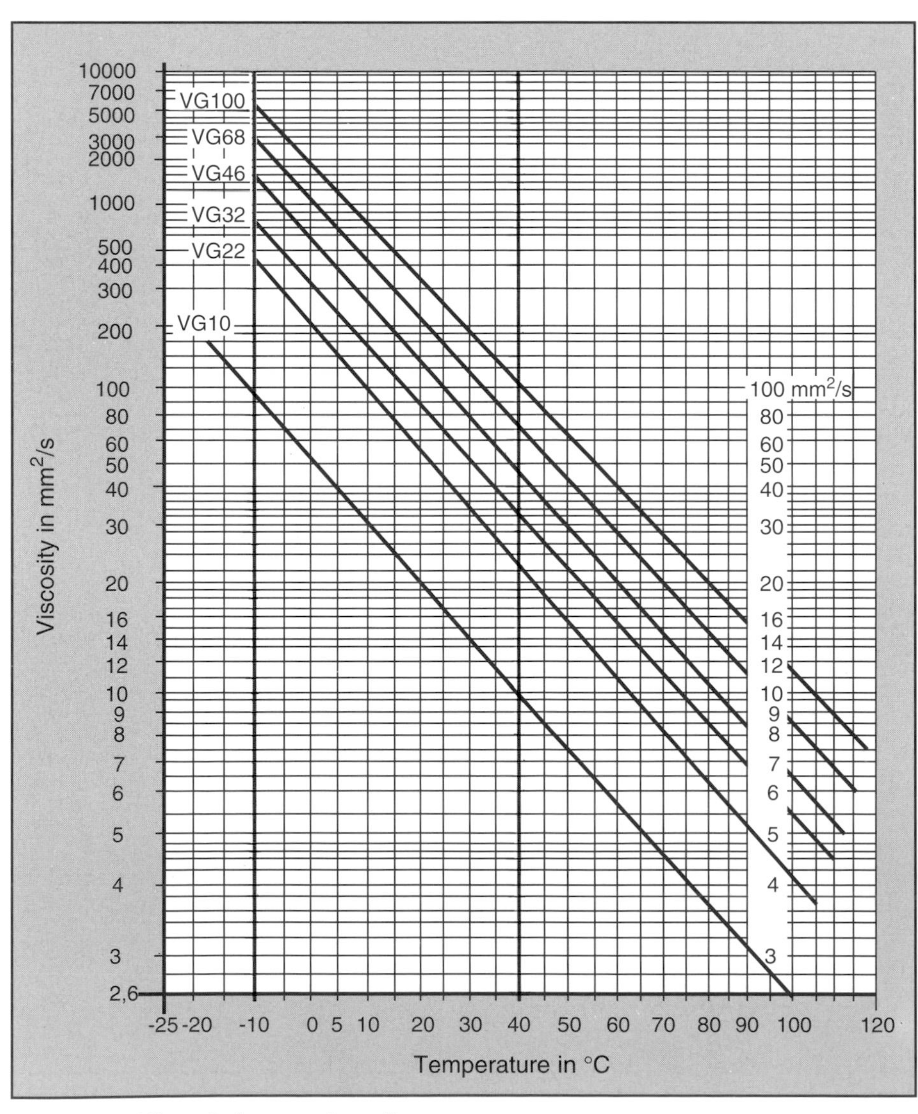

Diagram 2: *Viscosity/temperature diagram*

4.1 Fluid temperature and viscosity ranges of required hydraulic components

The following parameters have been taken from the component catalogue "RE 00 101" from Mannesmann Rexroth.

Gear pump G4 (Fixed displacement pump)
Fluid temperature range -15 to 80°C
Viscosity range 10 to 300 mm^2/s

Vane pump V2 (Fixed displacement pump)
Fluid temperature range -10 to 70°C
Viscosity range 16 to 160 mm^2/s

Vane pump V4 (Variable displacement pump)
Fluid temperature range -10 to 70°C
Viscosity range 16 to 160 mm^2/s
(at op. temperature and zero stroke pressure < 63 bar)
Viscosity range 25 to 160 mm^2/s
(at op. temperature and zero stroke pressure > 63 bar)

Isolating valve S
Fluid temperature range -30 to 80°C
Viscosity range 2.8 to 380 mm^2/s

Directional valve WE
Fluid temperature range -30 to 80°C
Viscosity range 2.8 to 500 mm^2/s

Directional valve WEH
Fluid temperature range -30 to 80°C
Viscosity range 2.8 to 500 mm^2/s

Pressure relief valve DBD
Fluid temperature range -30 to 80°C
Viscosity range 10 to 800 mm^2/s

4.2 Evaluation

On the basis of the hydraulic pump parameters it is clear that either a gear or axial piston pump may be used. Vane pumps are not suitable for this application, as the viscosity range of 16 to 160 Cst is not sufficient. A vane pump could only be used with a fluid which has a very flat viscosity curve, e.g. fluids for aeroplanes, etc.

From the flow diagram for the pilot operated directional valve, size 10 (see manufacturer's data sheets), it is clear that flow may pass through the valve without large losses. In directly operated directional valves, size 10, the flow limit is max. 120 L/min at 41 Cst and 50 °C. Hence this valve should not be used for this application.

All hydraulic components selected for an application must be examined in this manner to assess their suitability during the design phase or when exchanging components.

In order to ensure that the hydraulic system operates correctly, it is also important to sufficiently dimension the pressure line and return line filters. At a temperature of -10°C (lower temperature limit used in example), a filter which is too small may lead to considerable problems, as the fluid thickens at low temperatures.

If the vane pump mentioned in the example were used, summer operation would be possible. At the beginning of Winter, the vane pump with the mentioned data would undoubtedly mal-function. If variable displacement pumps are used, the conditions of use with respect to viscosity-temperature would change considerably.

Notes

Chapter 4

Hydraulic Pumps

Rudhard Freitag

1. Introduction

The requirements of a pump may be summarised in one sentence:
Hydraulic pumps should convert mechanical energy (torque, speed) into hydraulic energy (flow, pressure).

However, in practice the requirements are much more diverse.

When choosing a pump, the following points must be taken into account:

- Operating medium
- Required range of pressure
- Expected range of speeds
- Minimum and maximum operating temperature
- Maximum and minimum viscosities
- Installation (piping, etc.)
- Type of drive (coupling, etc.)
- Expected life-time
- Maximum level of noise
- Ease of servicing
- Maximum cost

This list could be continued. The variety of requirements, however, does show that every pump cannot fulfil all the criteria to an optimum degree. Hence, a whole range of different design principles exist. One thing that all the types have in common, is that the pumps operate according to the displacement principle. This involves the existence of mechanically sealed chambers in the pumps. In these chambers, fluid is transported from the inlet of the pump (suction port) to the outlet (pressure port). As there is no direct connection between the two ports in the pump, these pumps are very suitable for operating at high system pressures. Hence they are ideal for hydraulics.

2. Basic design

The main types of hydraulic pumps, which operate to the displacement principle are outlined below:

2.1 External gear pump

Volume is created between the gears and housing.

$$V = m \cdot z \cdot b \cdot h \cdot \pi \qquad (1)$$

m = modulus

z = number of gears

b = width of gears

h = height of gears

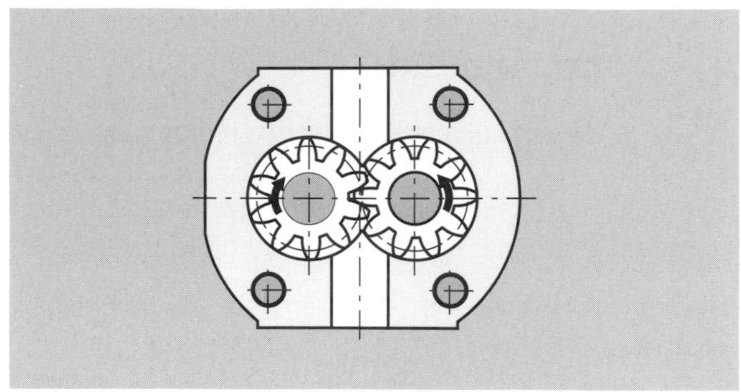

Fig. 1

2.2 Internal gear pump

Volume is created between the gears, housing and spacing/sealing element.

$$V = m \cdot z \cdot b \cdot h \cdot \pi \qquad (2)$$

m = modulus

z = number of internal gears

b = width of gears

h = height of gears

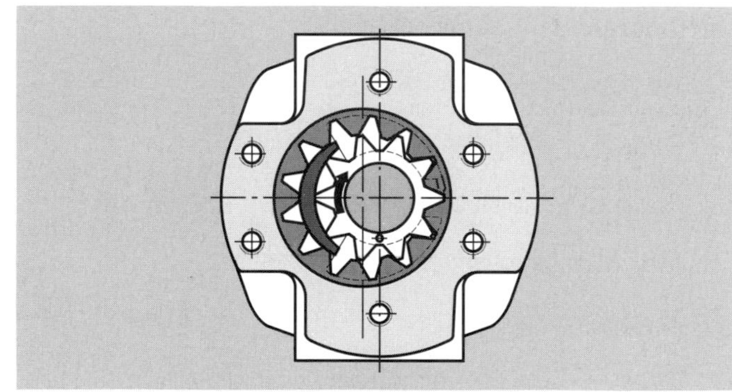

Fig. 2

2.3 Ring gear pump

The rotor has one gear less than on the internally geared stator. Planetary movement of the rotor.

$$V = z \cdot (A_{max} - A_{min}) \cdot b \qquad (3)$$

z = number of rotor gears

b = width of gears

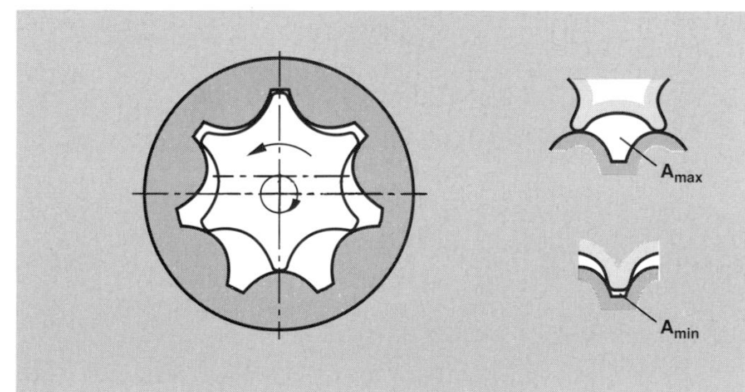

Fig. 3

2.4 Screw pump

The displacement chamber is formed between threads and housing.

$$V = \frac{\pi}{4} (D^2 - d^2) \cdot s - D^2 \left(\frac{\alpha}{2} - \frac{\sin 2\alpha}{2}\right) s \qquad (4)$$

with : $\cos \alpha \doteq \frac{D+d}{2D}$

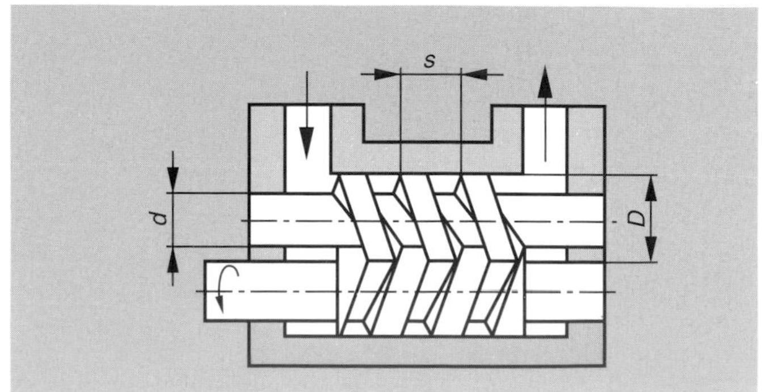

Fig. 4

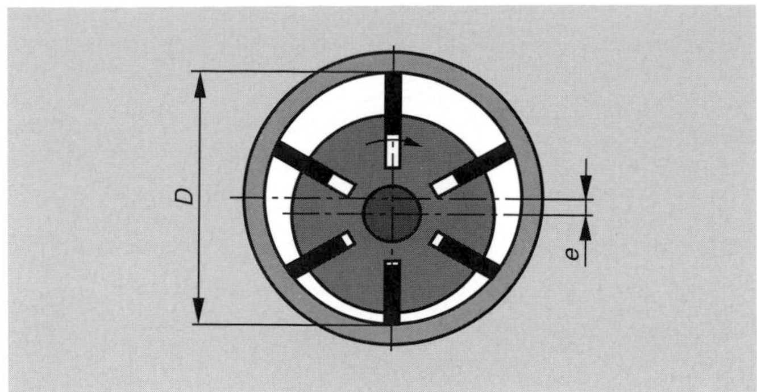

Fig. 5

2.5 Single chamber vane pump

Volume is created between the circular stator, rotor and vanes.

$$V = 2 \cdot \pi \cdot b \cdot e \cdot D \quad (5)$$

b = vane width

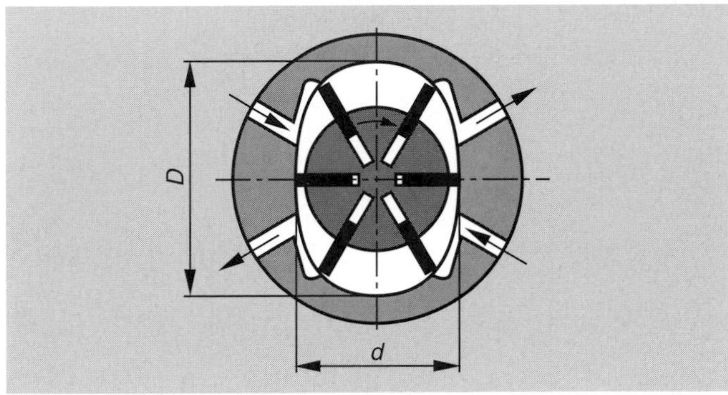

Fig. 6

2.6 Double chamber vane pump

Due to the twin cam forms of the stator, two displacement processes occur per revolution.

$$V = \left(\frac{\pi \cdot (D^2 - d^2)}{4}\right) \cdot k \cdot b \quad (6)$$

b = vane width

k = vane stroke per revolution

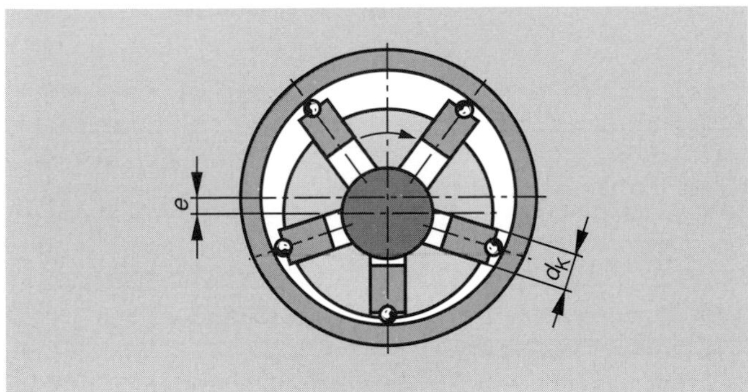

Fig. 7

2.7 Radial piston pump with eccentric cylinder block

The pistons rotate within the rigid external ring. Eccentricity "e" determines the stroke of the pistons.

$$V = \frac{d_K^2 \cdot \pi}{4} \cdot 2e \cdot z \quad (7)$$

z = number of pistons

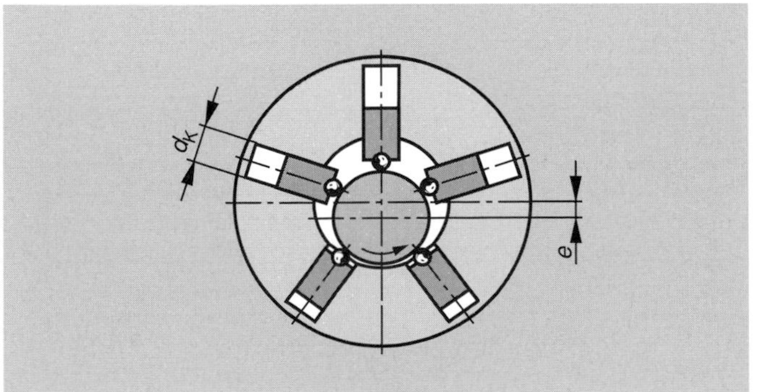

Fig. 8

2.8 Radial piston pump with eccentric shaft

The rotating eccentric shaft causes radially oscillating piston movements to be produced.

$$V = \frac{d_K^2 \cdot \pi}{4} \cdot 2e \cdot z \quad (8)$$

z = number of pistons

2.9 Axial piston pump in bent axis design

Dependent on the swivel angle, the pistons move within the cylinder bores when the shaft rotates.

$$V = \frac{d_K^{\,2} \cdot \pi}{4} \cdot 2\, r_h \cdot z \cdot \sin \alpha \qquad (9)$$

z = number of pistons

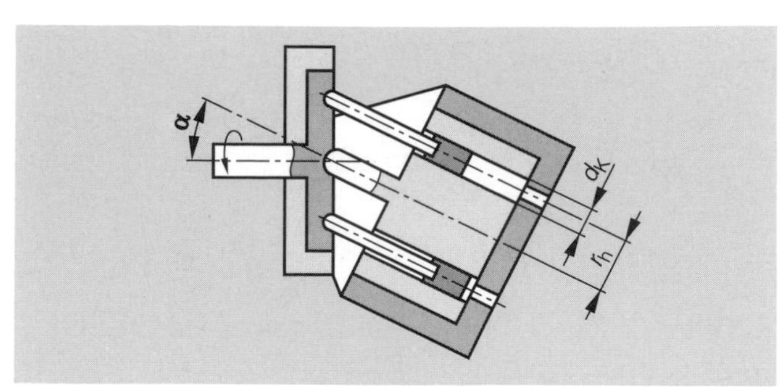

Fig. 9

2.10 Axial piston pump in swashplate design

The rotating displacement pistons are supported by a swashplate. The angle of the swashplate determines the piston stroke.

$$V = \frac{d_K^{\,2} \cdot \pi}{4} \cdot D_K \cdot \tan \alpha \qquad (10)$$

Vane and piston pumps may operate with fixed or variable displacement volumes, but gear pumps only operated with fixed displacement volumes.

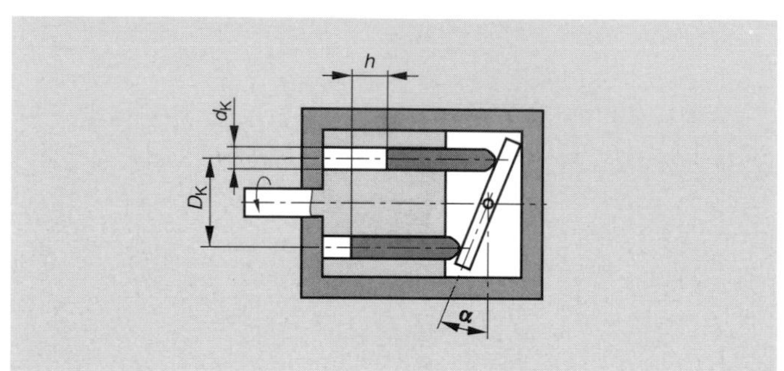

Fig. 10

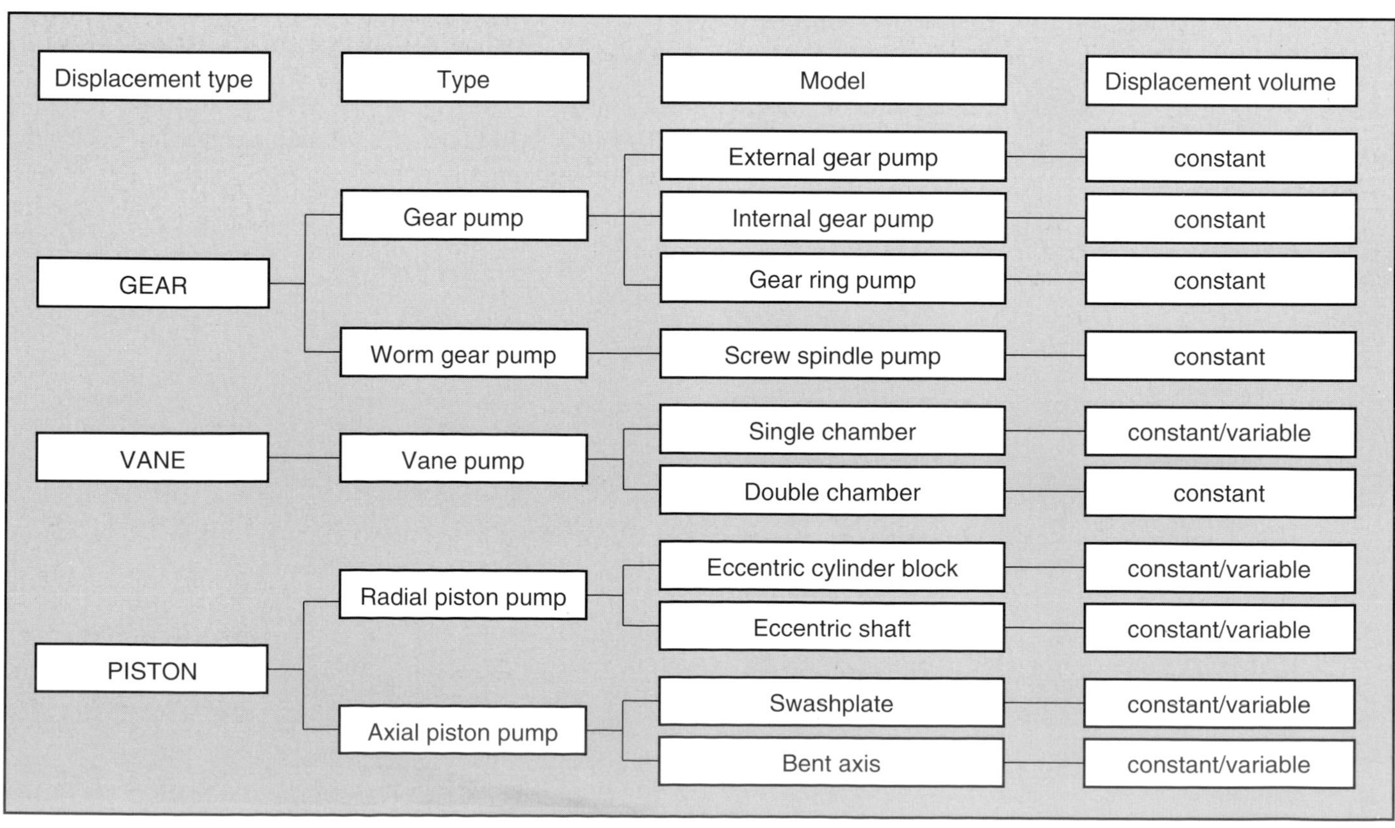

Fig. 11

3. Selection criteria

In the introduction a variety of selection criteria were mentioned for hydraulic pumps. Table 1 summarises the features of the various types of pump.

Depending on the system, a weighting is given:

1 = very good/very large

2 = good/large

3 = satisfactory

4 = poor

Criteria	Type									
	AZP	IZP	ZRP	SSP	FZPE	FZPD	RKPI	RKPA	AKPSA	AKPSS
Useable range of speeds	1	2	2	2	3	3	2	2	2	2
Useable range of pressures	2	2	3	3	3	3	1	1	1	1
Viscosity range	1	2	3	1	3	3	1	1	1	1
Max. noise level	4	1	2	1	2	2	3	3	3	3
Serivce life	3	2	2	1	1	1	2	2	2	2
Price	1	2	2	3	2	2	3	3	3	3

External gear pump = AZP
Internal gear pump = IZP
Gear ring pump = ZRP
Screw spindle pump = SSP
Single chamber vane pump = FZPE
Double chamber vane pump = FZPD
Radial piston pump with eccentric shaft = RKPI
Radial piston pump w. eccentric cylinder block = RKPA
Axial piston pump with bent axis = AKPSA
Axial piston pump with swashplate = AKPSS

Table 1: *Evaluation of hydraulic pumps*

The weightings for each pump must be considered in relation to the other types. As the weighting for the selection criteria depends on the application, this table may only be used as an aid in order to make comparisons when taking such features as age of noise into account.

4. Functional descriptions

4.1 Screw pumps

Screw pumps are similar to internal gear pumps in that their main characteristic is that they possess an extremely low operating noise level. They are therefore used in hydraulic systems in, for example, theatres and opera houses.

Screw pumps contain 2 or 3 worm gears within a housing.

The worm gear connected to the drive has a clock-wise thread and transmits the rotary movement to further worm gears, which each have an anti-clockwise thread.

An enclosed chamber is formed between the threads of the worm gears. This chamber moves from the suction port to the pressure port of the pump without change in volume.

This produces a constant, uniform and smooth flow and hence operation tends to be very quiet.

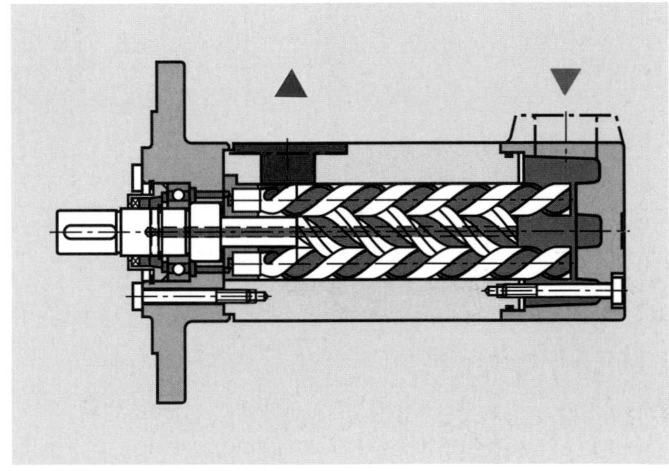

Fig. 12: *Screw pump*

Important parameters

Displacement volume	15 to 3500 cm^3
Operating pressure	up to 200 bar
Range of speeds	1000 to 3500 rpm

4.2 External gear pumps

In particular, external gear pumps are used in large numbers in mobile hydraulics.

The reason for this is the features of this design:

- Relatively high pressure for low weight
- Low cost
- Wide range of speeds
- Wide temperature/viscosity range

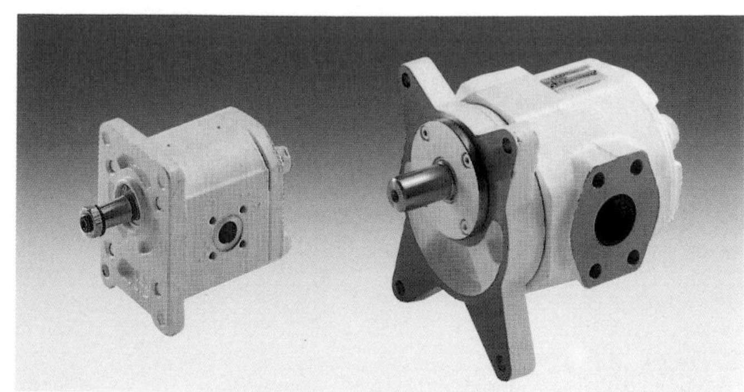

Fig. 14: *Gear pumps G2 and G4*

4.2.1 Function

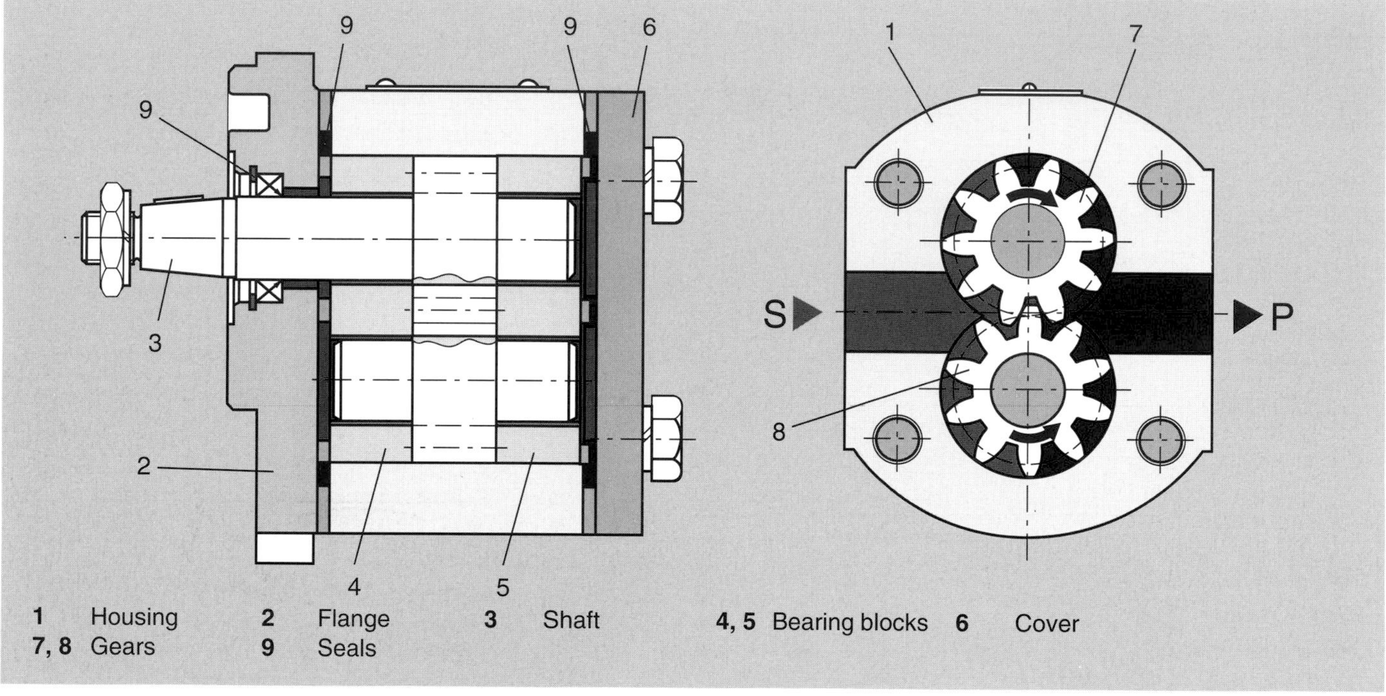

Fig. 13: *External gear pump*

Gear (7) is connected via a coupling with the drive (E motor, diesel engine, etc.). Gears (7) and (8) are positioned in such a way by the bearing blocks (4) and (5) that the gears mesh on rotation with the minimum clearance.

Displacement chambers are formed between the gears, internal walls of the housing and surfaces of the bearing blocks (4) and (5).

When the system is started up, first the air which is in the suction lines is transported from suction side S to pressure side P within the chamber. Hence a negative pressure is produced in the suction line. As this negative pressure increases, fluid rises from the tank into the suction line and up to the pump.

Fluid is fed into the gear chambers and via the pressure port of the pump into the hydraulic system. Hence a pre-requisite for the pump to function is that the gear chambers are sealed to such an extent that air or fluid can be transported with as little loss as possible.

External gear pumps contain clearance seals. Due to this, losses occur dependent on operating pressure from the pressure side to the suction side. So that only very little fluid manages to get through these clearances from the pressure side to the suction side as pressure increases, the rear bearing block (5) is pressed against the rear of the gears via an axial pressure field.

The actual system pressure is present in the pressure field.

Important parameters

Displacement volume	0.2 to 200 cm^3
Max. pressure	up to300 bar (size dependent)
Range of speeds	500 to 6000 rpm

4.3 Internal gear pumps

The most important feature of internal gear pumps is the very low noise level. Hence they are primarily used in industrial hydraulics (presses, machines for plastics and tools, etc.) and in vehicles which operate in an enclosed space (electric fork-lifts, etc.).

Fig. 15: *Internal gear pump GU*

This causes operation to be exceptionally quiet and a very good suction characteristic to be produced.

When the chambers are full, the fluid is transported without change in volume until it reaches the pressure port.

Once a chamber is connected to the pressure port, the space decreases between the gears and the fluid is displaced.

When the gears mesh, their special shape is a positive attribute to their operation, as there is practically no dead zone between the gear rotor and internal gear (in contrast to external gear pumps).

The volume of oil in such dead regions becomes compressed and hence pressure pulses and therefore noise are produced.

Internal gear pumps as described here have practically no pressure pulses and hence are exceptionally quiet.

4.3.1 Function

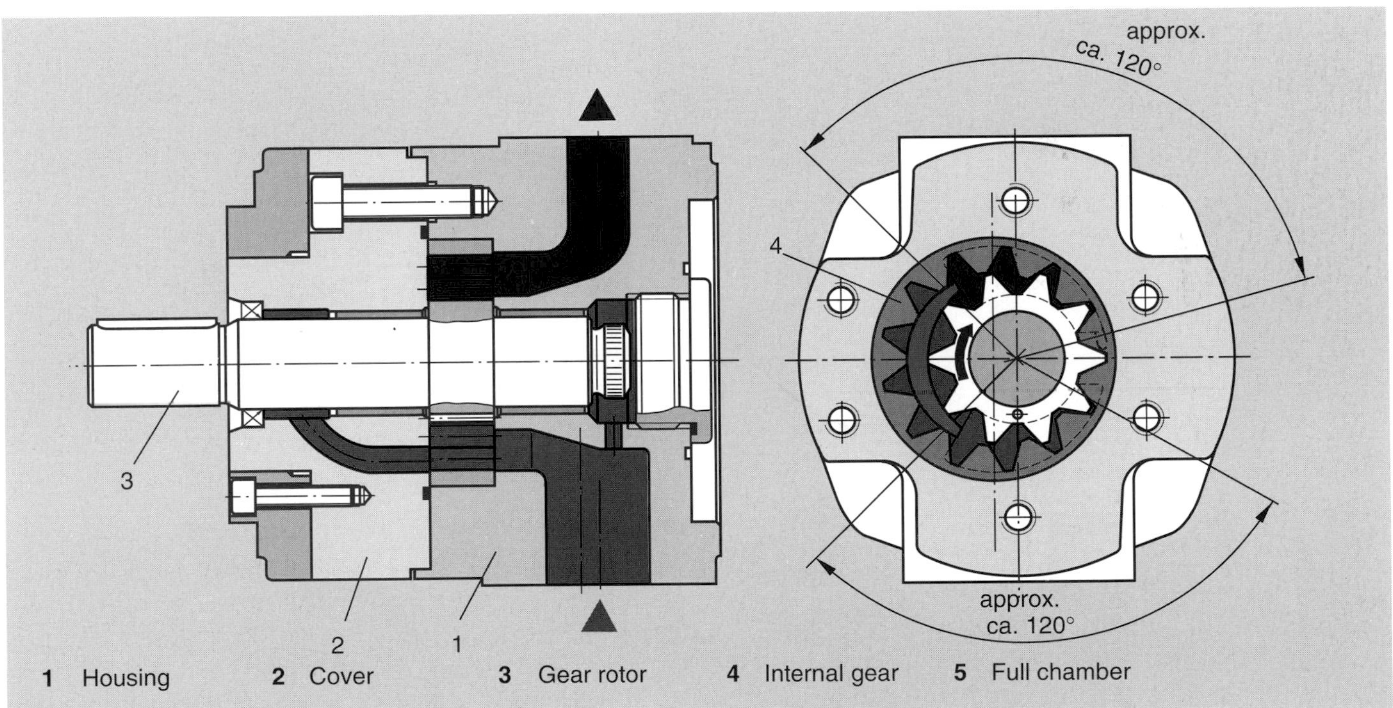

Fig. 16: *Internal gear pump*

The gear rotor is connected to the drive. When the gear rotor and internal gear rotate, the space between the gears increases. The pump "sucks".

This increase in space occurs over an angle of rotation of about 120°C. Hence the displacement chamber is filled relatively slowly.

Important parameters

Displacement volume	3 to 250 cm^3
Operating pressure	up to 300 bar (dependent on size)
Range of speeds	500 to 3000 rpm (dependent on size)

4.4 Radial piston pumps

Radial piston pumps are used in applications involving high pressures (operating pressures above 400 bar): In presses, machines for processing plastic, in clamping hydraulics for machine tools and in many other applications, operating pressures are required of up to 700 bar. It is only radial piston pumps which satisfactorily operate at such high pressures, even under continuous operation.

A valve controlled radial piston pump with eccentric shaft operates as follows:

The drive shaft (1) is eccentric to the pump elements (2). The pump elements consist of piston (3), cylinder sleeve (4), pivot (5), compression spring (6), suction valve (7) and pressure control valve (8).

The pivot is screwed into the housing (9). The piston is positioned with the so-called slipper pad on the eccenter. The compression spring causes the slipper pad to always lie on the eccenter, when the eccentric shaft rotates and the cylinder sleeve to be supported by the pivot.

Fig. 18: *Radial piston pump R4*

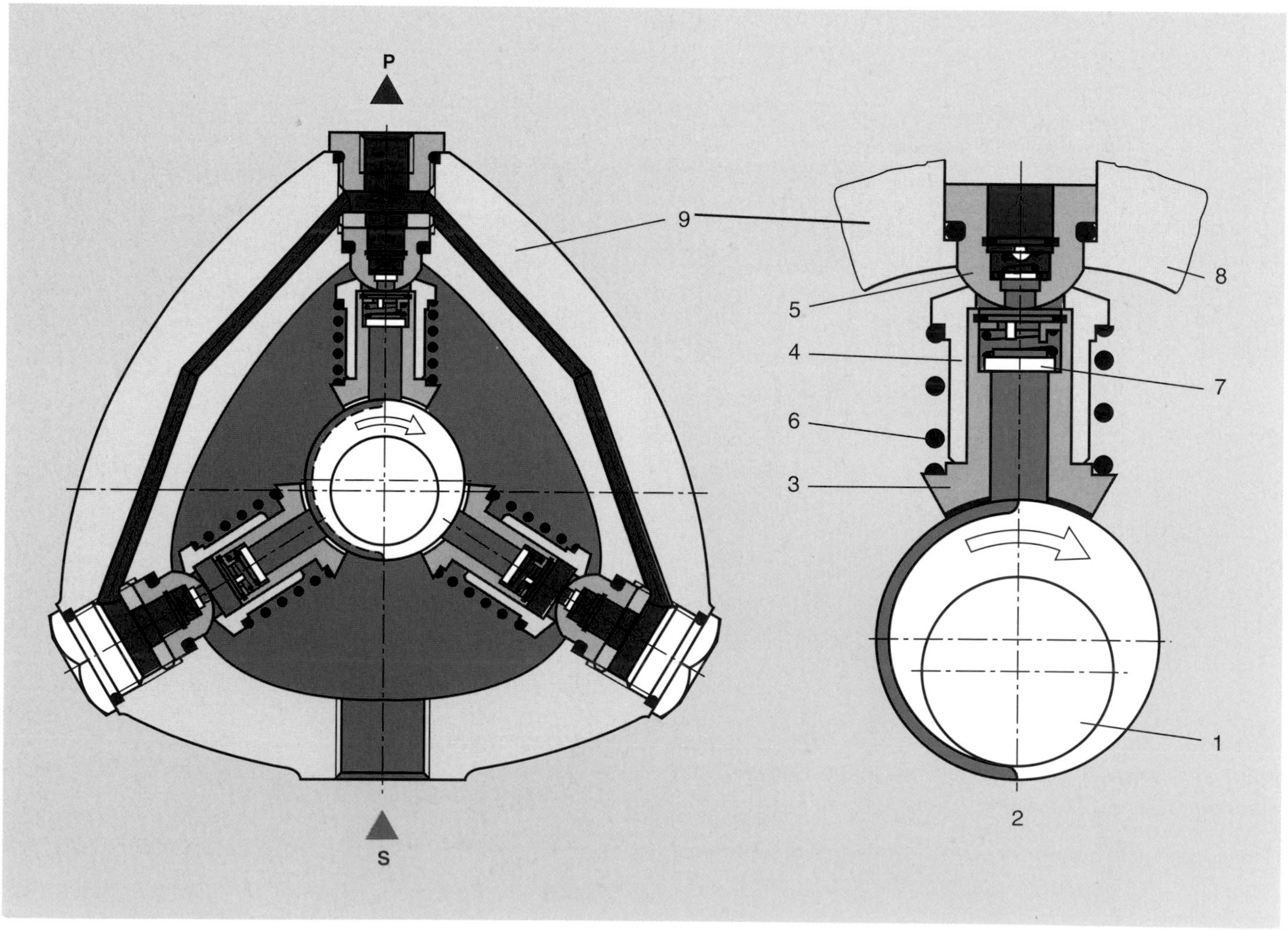

Fig. 17: *Radial piston pump with eccentric shaft*

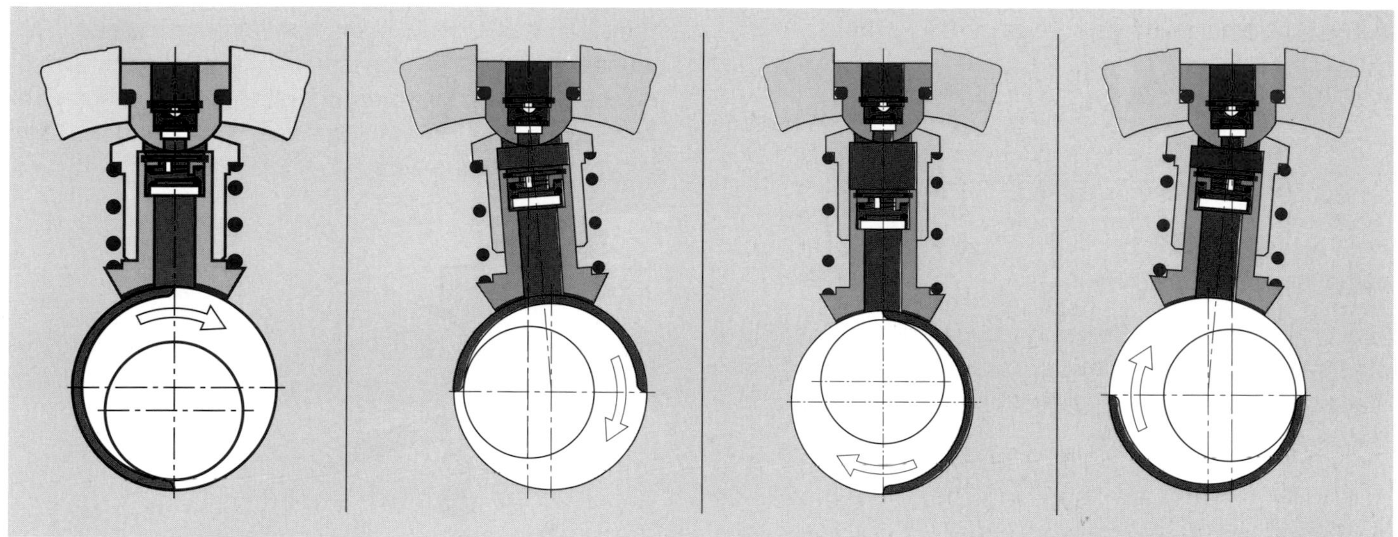

Fig. 19: *Phase 1*
The piston is at the upper idle point. The minimum volume exists in the displacement chamber. The suction valve and pressure control valve are closed.

Phase 2
As the shaft rotates, the piston moves in the direction of the centre axis of the eccentre. The displacement chamber becomes larger and the suction valve opens due to the negative pressure produced. Fluid now flows via the groove in the eccentre and bore in the piston into the displacement chamber.

Phase 3
The piston is at the lower idle point. The displacement chamber is completely full (maximum volume). Suction valve and pressure control valve are closed.

Phase 4
As the eccentre rotates, the piston is moved in the direction of the pivot. Fluid is compressed in the displacement chamber. Due to the pressure produced the pressure control valve in the pivot opens. Fluid flows into the ring channel which connects the pump elements.

In general, piston pumps have an odd number of pump elements. The reason for this is that when the flows of the individual pump elements are added together, this results in a high flow pulsation if there is an even number of elements.

Important parameters

Displacement volume	0.5 to 100 cm^3
Max. pressure	up to 700 bar (dependent on size)
Range of speeds	1000 to 3000 rpm (dependent on size)

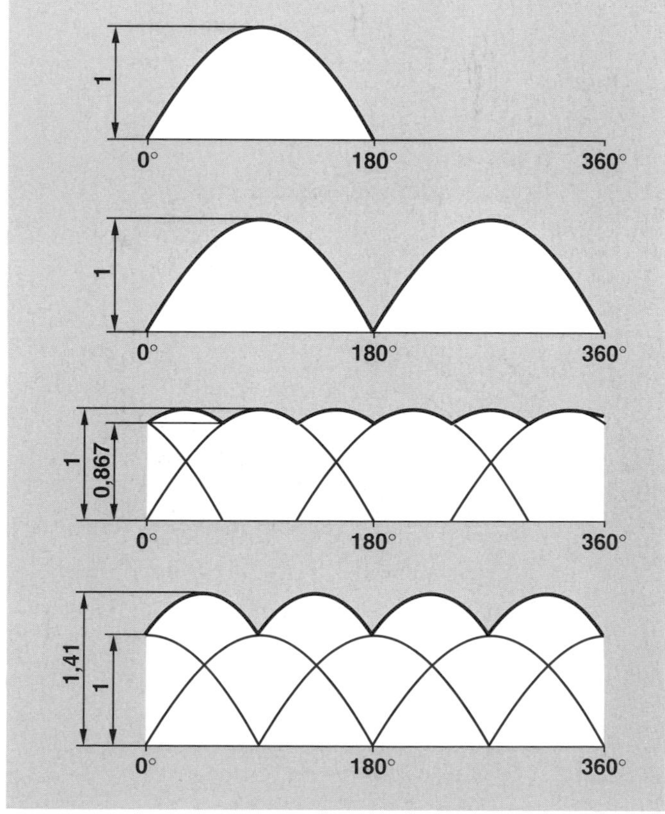

Diagram 1: *Flow pulsation in radial piston pumps with 1, 2, 3 and 4 pump elements*

4.5 Vane pumps

Two types of vane pump may be used:

- single chamber and
- double chamber vane pumps.

Both types have the same main components, i.e. they comprise a rotor and vanes.

The vanes may be radially moved within the rotor. The difference between the two types is in the form of the stator ring, which limits the stroke movement of the vanes.

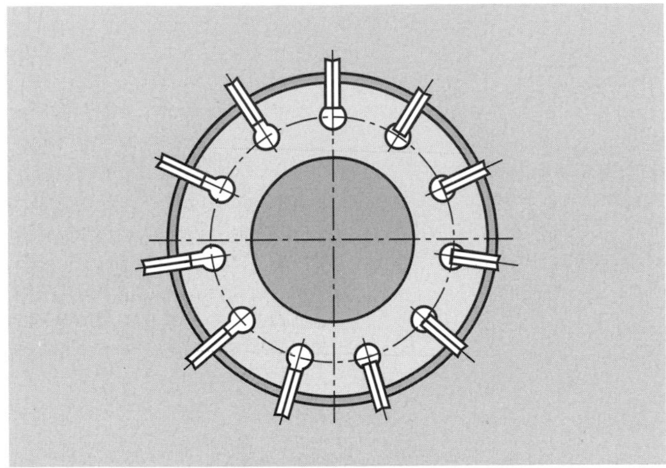

Fig. 20: *Main assembly of vane pump with rotor and vanes*

4.5.1 Double chamber vane pump

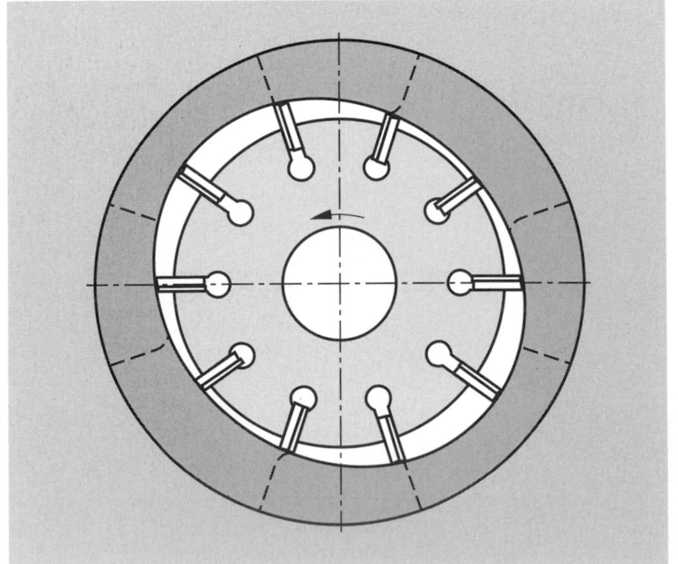

Fig. 21

The stator has a double cam form internal surface. This causes each vane to carry out two strokes per rotation of the shaft. The displacement chambers are created by the rotor, two vanes, internal surface of the ring and the control plate on one side.

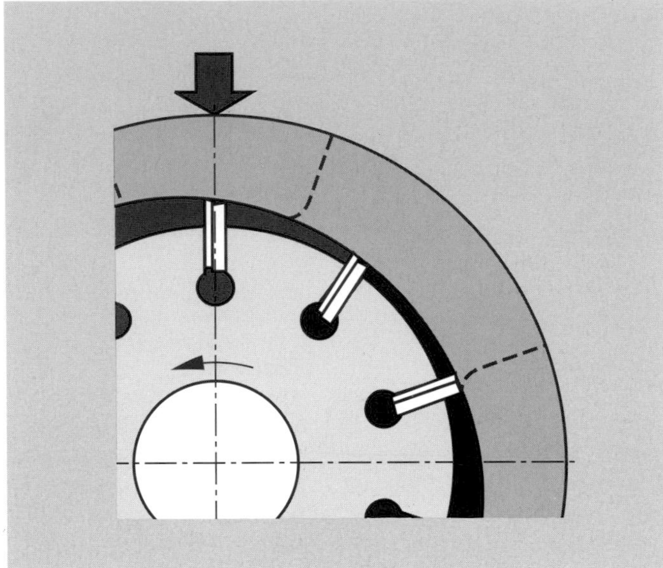

Fig. 22

In the range where the minimum distance between the rotor and ring occurs, the volume in the displacement chambers is also at a minimum. As the rotor rotates, the volume in the displacement chamber increases. As the vanes follow the contour of the ring, every chamber is fairly tightly sealed. A negative pressure is produced. The displacement chamber is connected to the suction side via control slits at the side. As a result of the negative pressure, fluid flows into the displacement chamber.

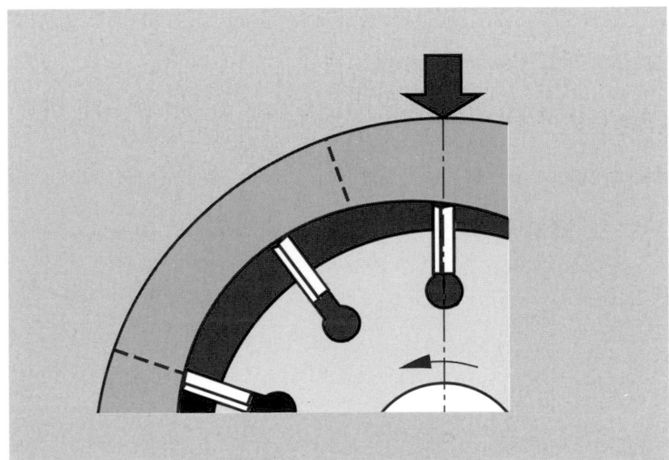

Fig. 23

The maximum volume in the displacement chamber occurs (*Fig. 23*). The connection to the suction side is then interrupted.

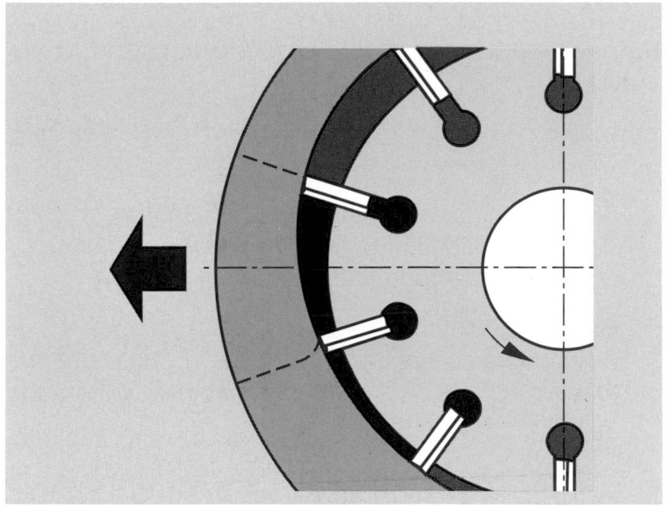

Fig. 24

As the rotor rotates further, the volume in the displacement chamber decreases (*Fig. 24*). Slits in the control disc on the side let the fluid flow via a channel to the pressure port of the pump.

This process is carried out twice per rotation of the shaft.

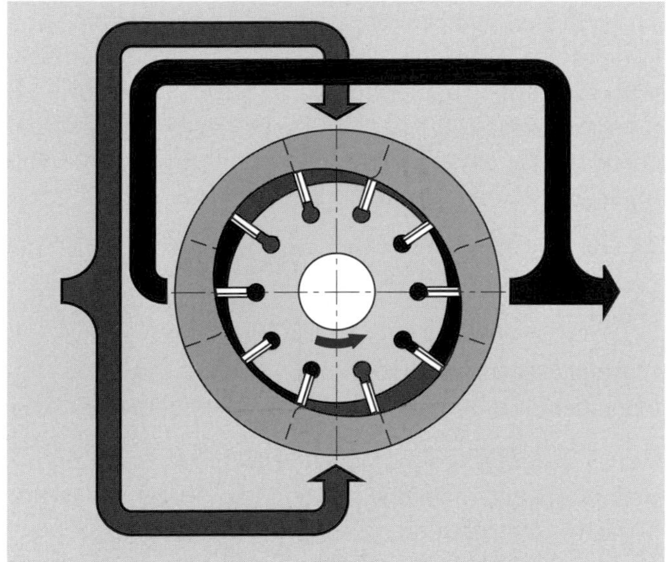

Fig. 25: *Double chamber vane pump*

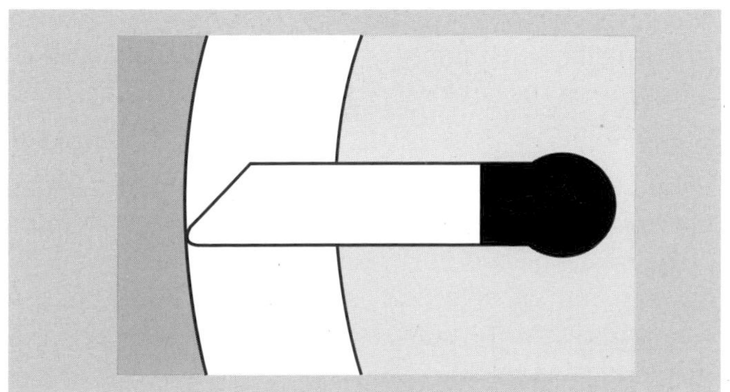

Fig. 26

In order to ensure that the vanes lie correctly on the ring, the chamber behind the vanes must be supplied with oil. This means, that in the pressure range, the total system pressure is behind the vanes.

The vanes are therefore pressed on the ring with a force resulting from pressure x vane area. Above a certain pressure and dependent on the lubrication characteristics of the fluid, the lubricating film between the ring and vanes may be torn away. This leads to wear. In order to reduce the pressing force, vane pumps used at operating pressures of approx. above 150 bar are designed with double vanes.

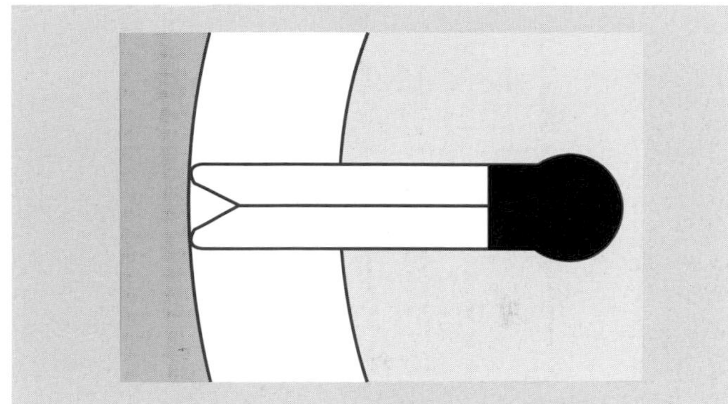

Fig. 27

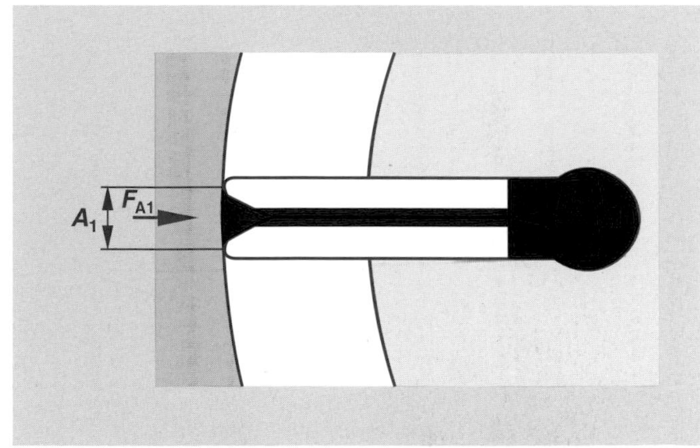

Fig. 28

The fluid under pressure is fed to the chamber between the tips of the vanes via a chamfer or groove. F_{A1} is less than F_A due to the smaller effective area.

The pressing force is hence compensated for to a large extent.

4.5.2 Single chamber vane pumps

The stroke movement of the vanes is limited by a ring with a circular internal form. Due to the off-centre position of the ring with respect to the rotor, the volume is changed within the displacement chambers. The process of filling the chambers (suction) and emptying is in principle the same as for double chamber vane pumps.

Fig. 29: *Vane pumps V5 and V3*

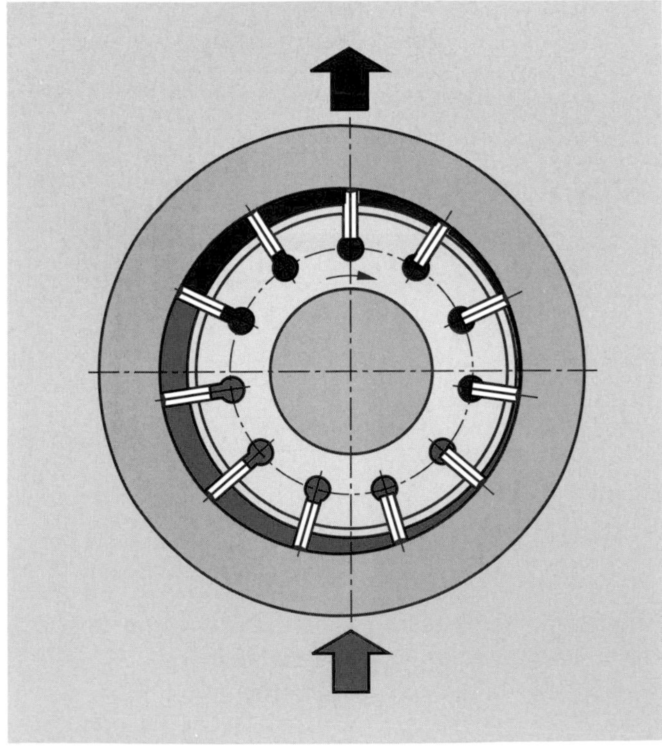

Fig. 30: *Single stroke vane pump*

4.5.2.1 Variable displacement vane pumps

Directly operated vane pumps with adjustable stroke volumes (*Fig. 31*)

The position of the stator ring may be influenced at three positioning devices in this pump:

- Adjustment screw for the stroke volume (1)
  The distance between the ring and the rotor directly determines the feed volume from the pump.
- Height adjustment screw (2)
  Here the vertical position of the stator ring is altered (directly effects noise and dynamic response of the pump).
- Setting screw for max. operating pressure (3)
  The amount of the spring pre-tensioning determines the max. operating pressure.

The pumping action of this pump has already been described under 4.5.2.

Dependent on the resistance in a hydraulic system, a pressure is produced. This pressure is present in the pump in the region marked in red and acts on the internal surface of the ring.

The pressure force in this region may be represented by force vector (F_p). If this force vector is split into its vertical and horizontal components, a large force (F_v) is produced which is removed by the height adjustment screw and a small force (F_h) is produced which acts against the compression spring.

As long as the force of the compression spring (F_f) is greater than the force (F_h) the ring remains in the position shown.

If the pressure increases in the system, the force (F_p) increases and hence (F_v) and (F_h) also increase.

If (F_h) exceeds the spring force (F_f), the ststor ring is moved from its eccentric position to a nearly concentric position. The change in volume in the displacement chambers is reduced until the effective flow at the pump outlet is zero. The pump now feeds only as much oil as required to make up leakage which occurs in the internal clearances within the pump. The pressure in the system is maintained constant by the pump. The amount of pressure may be directly influenced by the pre-tensioning of the spring.

Vane pumps with variable displacements and zero stroke functions (Q = zero) on reaching the set maximum pressure are always designed with a drain case port. The oil removed via this port is that which flows via the clearance within the pump from the pressure region (red) to the housing (pink).

Heat due to friction is removed via the leakage oil and during zero stroke operation the lubrication of internal parts is ensured by this oil.

Important parameters

Displacement volume	5 to 100 cm^3
Operating pressure	up to 100 bar
Range of speeds	1000 to 2000 rpm

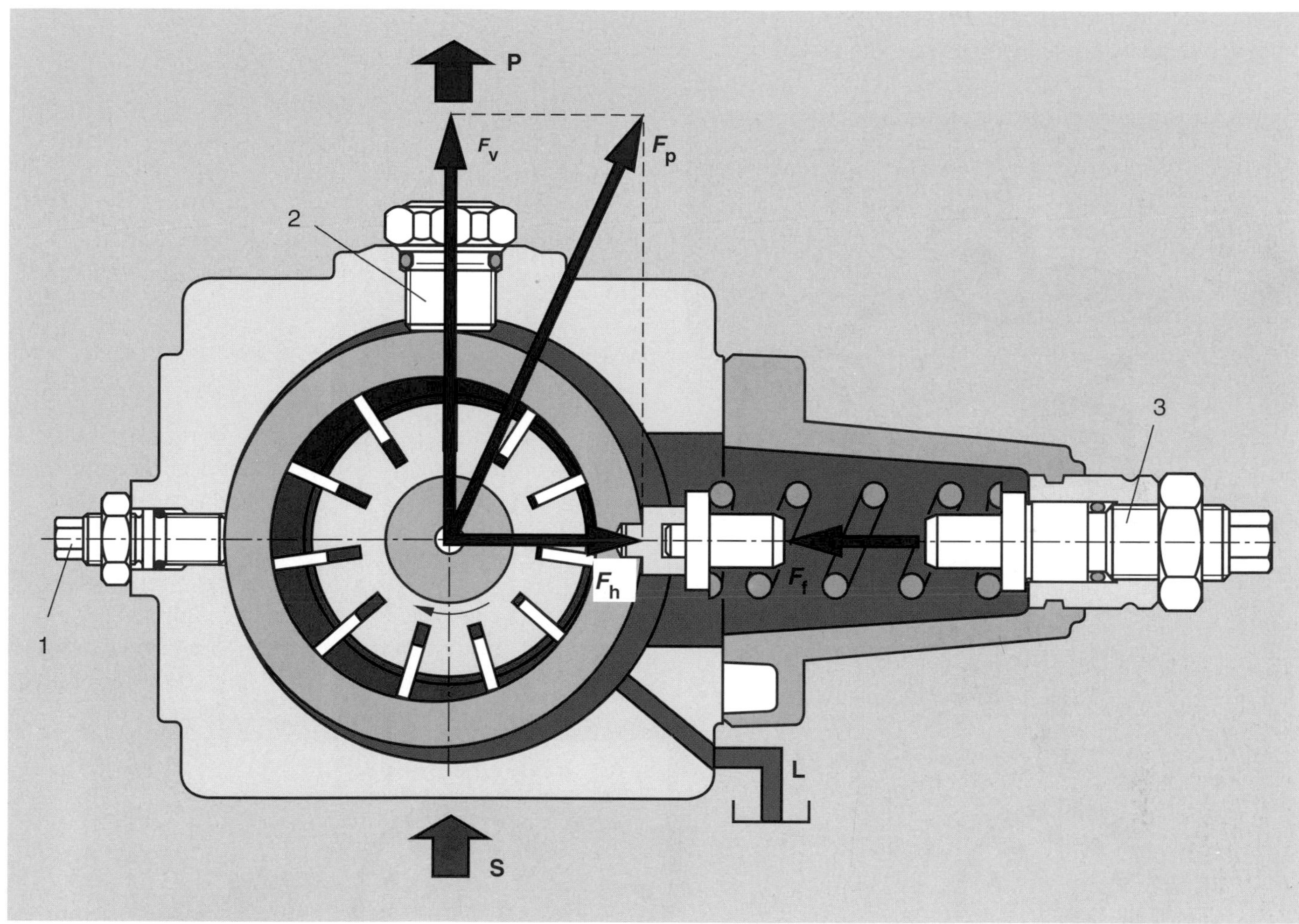

Fig. 31: *Directly operated vane pumps*

Pilot operated vane pumps with adjustable stroke volumes

The basic principle of this pump is very similar to that of the directly operated vane pump. The difference is in the adjustment devices for the stator ring.

Instead of being moved by one or more springs, the stator ring is moved by pressurised positioning pistons.

Fig. 32: *Vane pump V7*

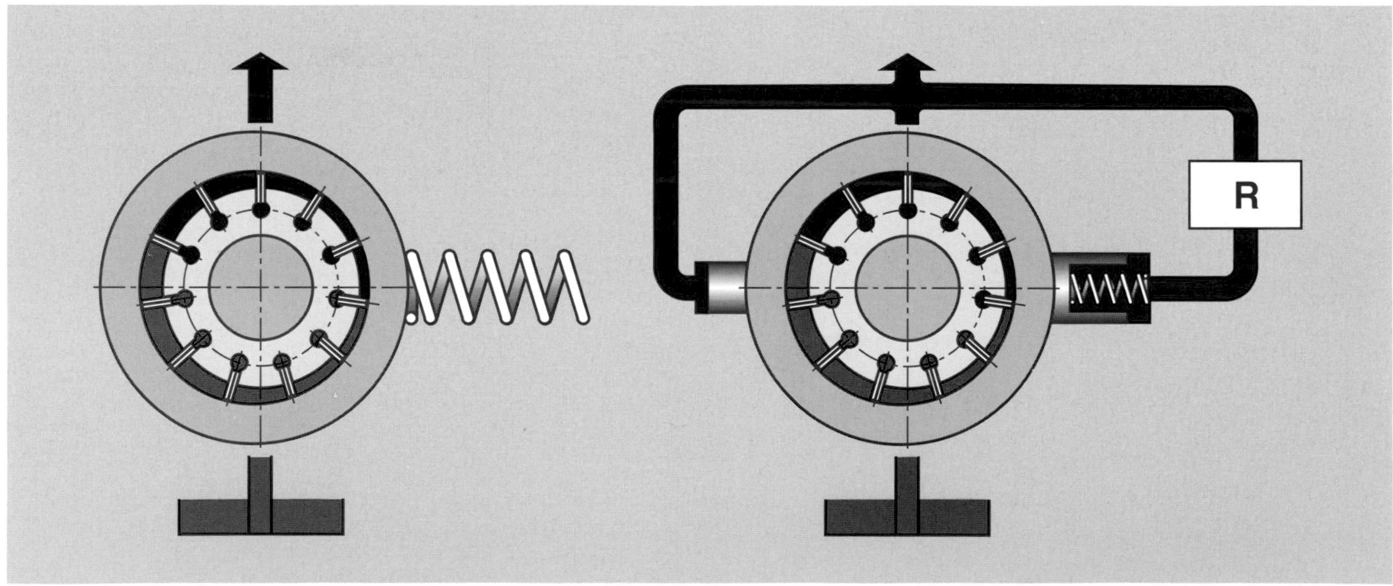

Fig. 33: *Directly operated (left) and pilot operated (right) vane pumps*

The two positioning pistons have different diameters (ratio of areas is approx. 2:1).

Behind the positioning piston with the larger diameter is a compression spring. This spring ensures that the stator ring is in its eccentric position when the pump is started.

The pressure which is formed in the hydraulic system is led via internal channels behind the smaller positioning piston to the controller R and further on to the larger positioning piston.

If the pressures behind both positioning pistons are the same, the stroke ring remains in the position shown due to the difference in areas of the positioning pistons.

4.5.3 Function of pressure controller

The pressure controller determines the maximum system pressure.

Requirements of the pressure controller are as follows:

- High dynamic response
  i.e. pressure controlling processes must take as little time as possible (50 to 500 ms). Dynamic response is dependent on the type of pump, controller and hydraulic system.
- Stability
  All hydraulic systems with controlled pressure tend to oscillate to some degree. The controller must hence represent a good compromise between dynamic response and stability.
- Efficiency
  In the control position a certain amount of pump flow is fed via the controller to tank. This loss should be kept as low as possible, but also it must ensure that the dynamic response and stability of the controller are sufficiently maintained.

4.5.4 Design of pressure controller

The pressure controller comprises a control spool (1), housing (2), spring (3) and adjustment device (4).

In the output position the spring pushes the control spool into the position shown in the controller housing.

Hydraulic fluid reaches the control spool via channels in the pump. The control spool is designed with a longitudinal bore and two cross drillings. Furthermore an orifice limits the flow through the control spool. In the position shown, fluid under pressure flows via the longitudinal bore and the cross drilling to the large positioning piston.

The connection to tank is closed by the control spool.

The actual pressure in the hydraulic system acts against the top surface of the control spool. As long as the force F_p resulting from the pressure is less than the opposing force of the spring F_f, the pump remains in the position shown. The same pressure exists behind both positioning pistons.

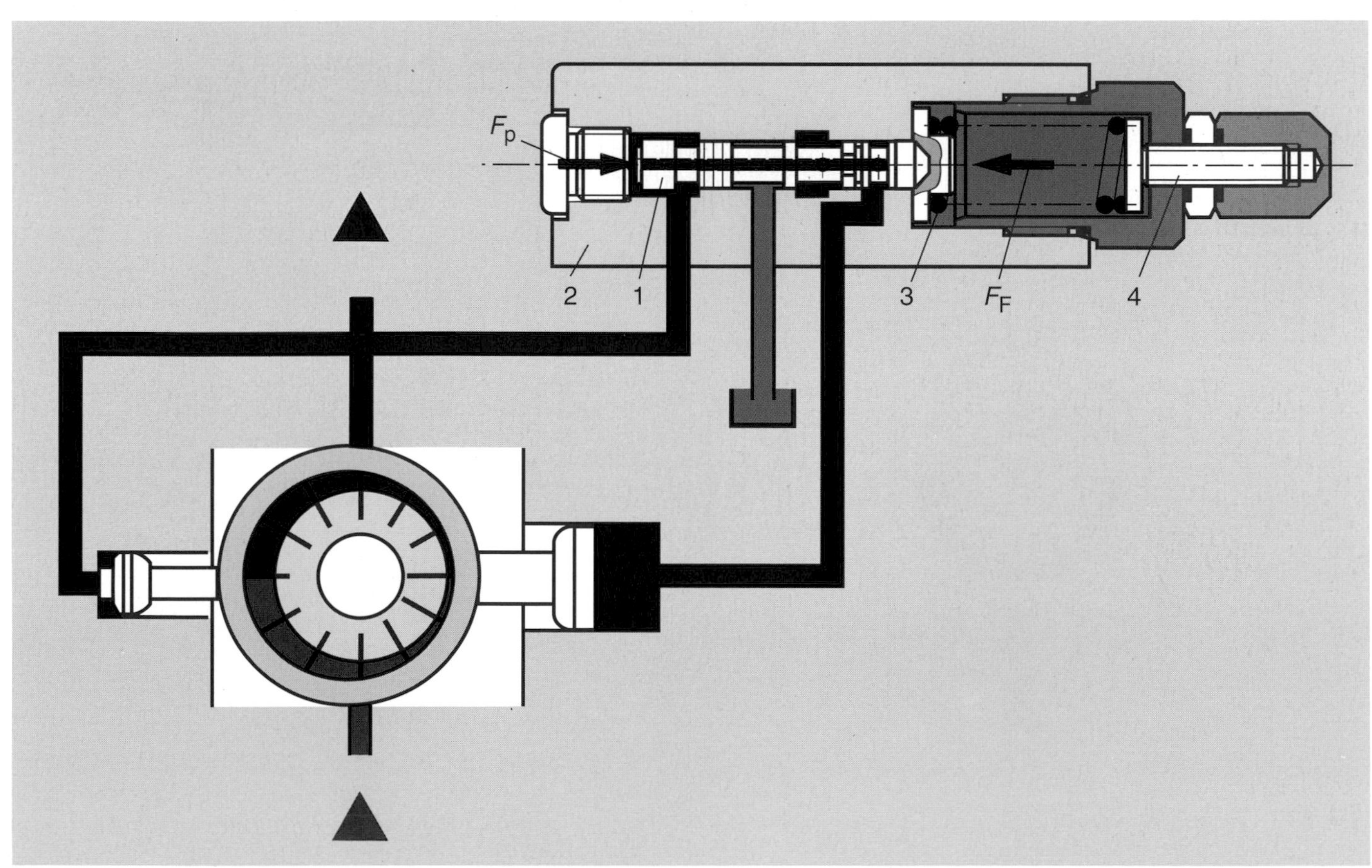

Fig. 34: *Pressure controller, pump delivering fluid. The operating pressure is less than the maximum pressure set at the pressure controller.*

When the force F_p increases as the pressure in the hydraulic system increases, the control spool is pushed against the spring.

The connection to tank in the controller is opened. The fluid flowing away here causes the pressure to decrease behind the large positioning piston. The small positioning piston is still under system pressure and hence pushes the stator ring against the large positioning piston (under reduced pressure) until the ring is nearly in mid-position.

Forces become balanced:
Small positioning piston area x high pressure =
large positioning piston x low pressure

The flow returns to zero, and the system pressure is maintained constant.

Due to this behaviour the power lost in the system is low when the maximum pressure is reached. The fluid does not heat up so much and energy consumption is minimal.

If the pressure decreases in the hydraulic system, the spring in the pressure controller moves the control spool. The connection to tank is hence closed and the complete system pressure builds up behind the large positioning spool.

The forces of the positioning pistons become unbalanced and the large positioning piston pushes the stroke ring back to the eccentric position.

The pump once again delivers fluid to the hydraulic system.

Variable displacement pumps, which operate in this manner, may be designed with any of a series of other control devices, e.g.

- flow controller
- pressure/flow controller
- power controller

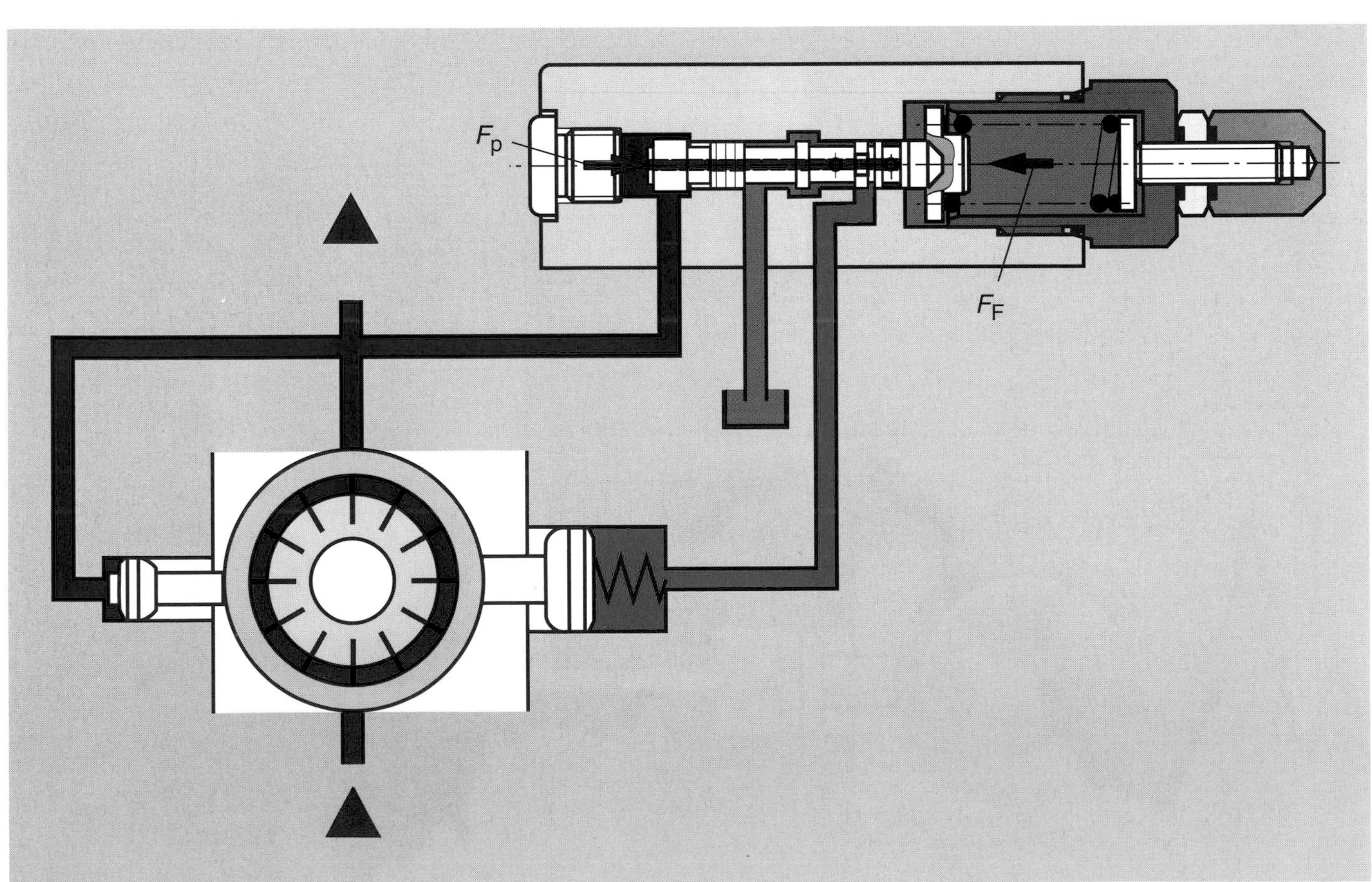

Fig. 35

4.5.5 Flow controller

With flow control the displacement of the pump is matched to a specified value. In order to achieve this, flow is passed through a measuring orifice (throttle, proportional directional valve etc.). The pressure drop at the measuring orifice is taken as the control parameter.

The pressure from the measuring orifice is fed to the top surface to the control spool. This pressure also exists behind the small positioning piston.

The pressure down-stream of the measuring orifice (which is lower than up-stream of the measuring orifice) is fed via a line to the spring chamber of the controller.

At the control spool the forces are balanced. The forces are also balanced at the pistons.

In the position shown, the pressure drop at the measuring orifice is equal to the spring force in the controller.

Pilot oil continually flows away via a control land (X) at the controller, so that a specific pressure is set behind the large positioning piston.

The ring is kept in a stable position.

If (for example) the area of the measuring orifice is increased, the pressure drop is then reduced.

Hence the spring moves the control spool. The opening at the control land is reduced and hence the pressure increases behind the large positioning piston.

The ring is moved in the direction of greater eccentricity and the feed volume of the pump is increased.

Due to the larger feed volume, Δp at the measuring orifice is increased until a stable state is once more achieved.

(Δp at the measuring orifice $\triangleq$ spring force at the controller)

Pressure and flow controllers may be controlled and adjusted by various means (mechanical, hydraulic, electrical).

The combination of flow and pressure controller permits very economic hydraulic drives to be designed (see e.g. load sensing).

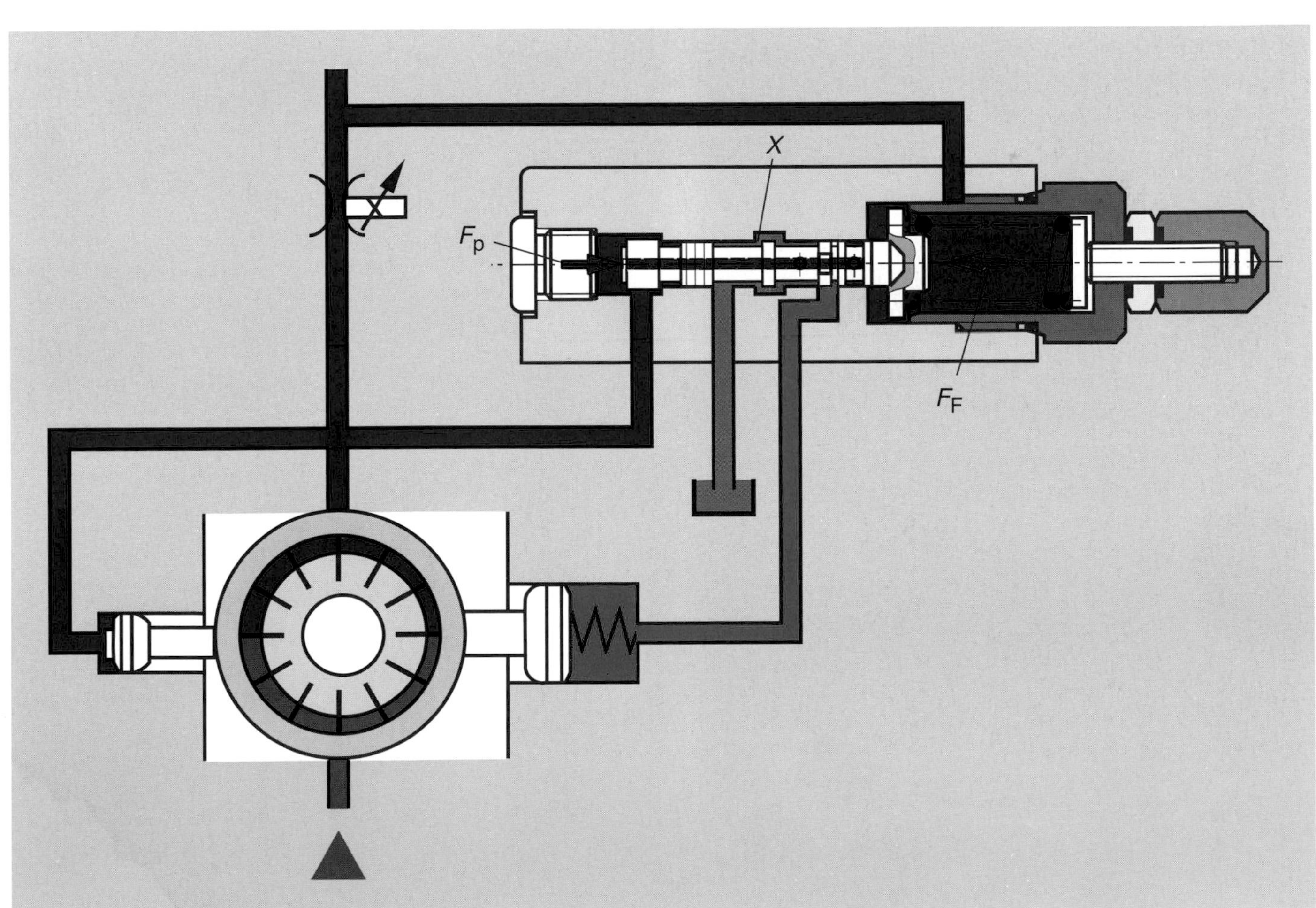

Fig. 36

Notes

Chapter 5

Hydraulic motors

Rudhard Freitag

1 Introduction

Hydraulic motors are used for converting hydraulic energy into mechanical energy.

As with hydraulic pumps, there are a variety of different types and designs of hydraulic motors. As there is no one type which can fulfil all the requirements to an optimum degree, the motor best suited for an application must be decided upon.

Speed

There are only a few motors which may be used at both very low speeds and at high speed of over 1000 rpm.

Hence hydraulic motors may be categorised into
high speed motors (n = 500 to 10 000 rpm) and
slow slow motors (n = 0 to 1 000 rpm).

Torque

The torque produced by the motor is dependent on the displacement and pressure drop at the motor. Slow motors are designed in such a way that large torques are already produced at small speeds. These LSHT (low speed - high torque) motors will be described in a separate section.

Power output

The power produced by a hydraulic motor is dependent on the flow and pressure drop at the motor. As the power is directly proportional to the speed, high speed motors are suitable for applications where a high power output is required.

2 Basic design

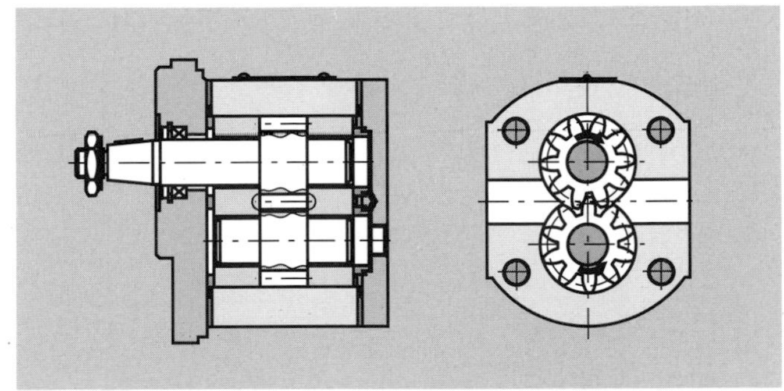

Fig. 1: *Gear motor*

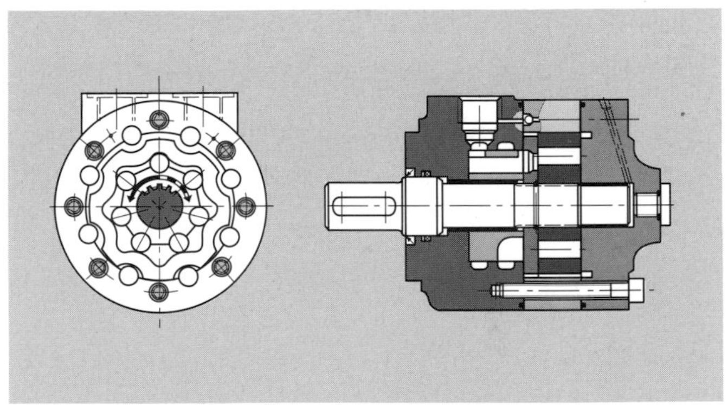

Fig. 2: *Gear ring or epicyclic gear motor*

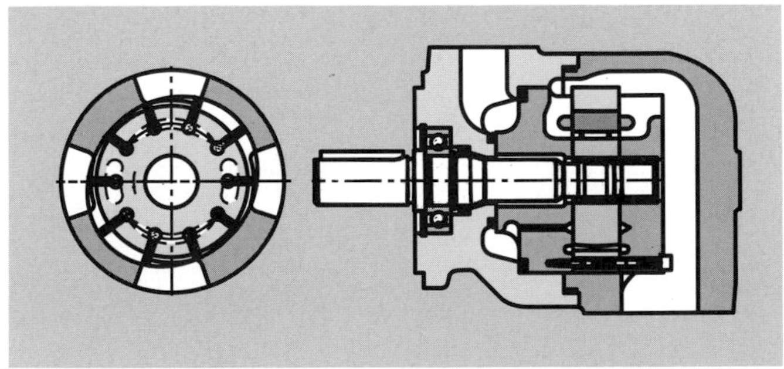

Fig. 3: *Vane motor*

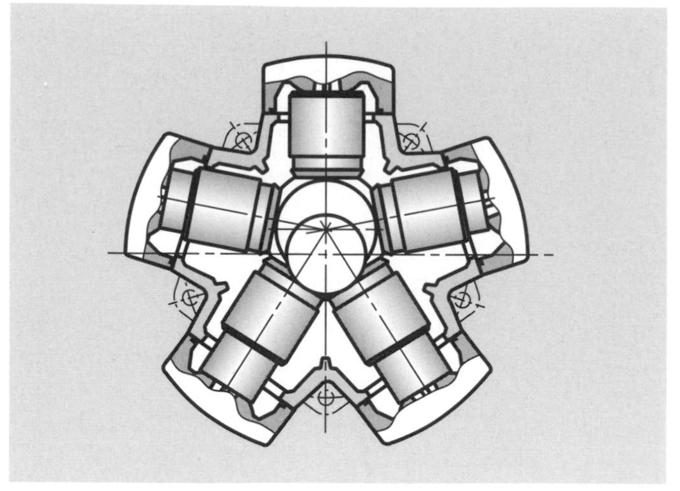

Fig. 4: *Radial piston motor with internal eccenter*

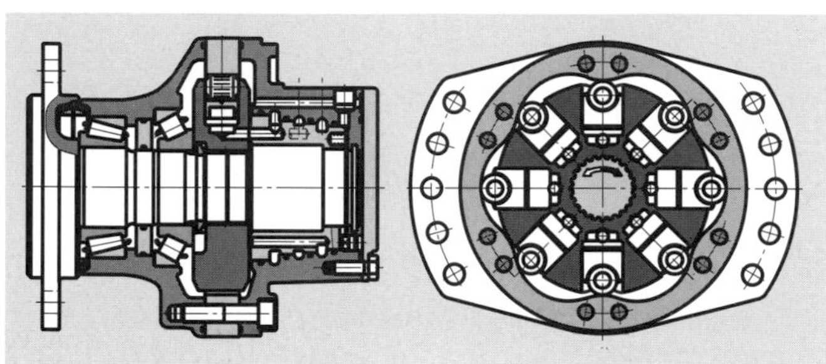

Fig. 5: *Multi-stroke radial piston motor with external cam*

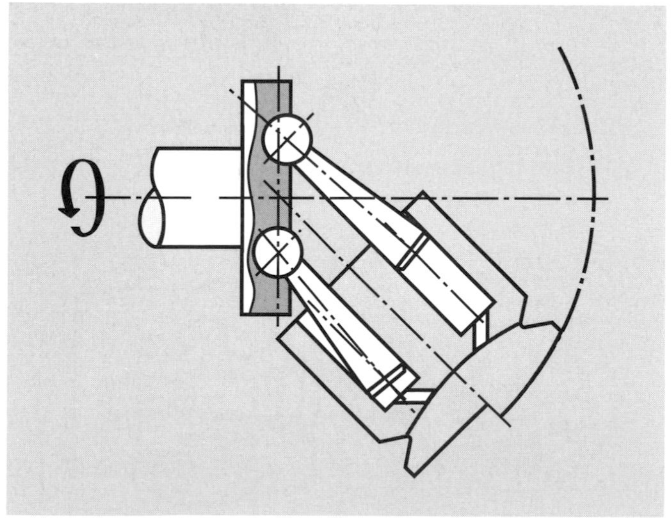

Fig. 6: *Axial piston motor in bent axis design*

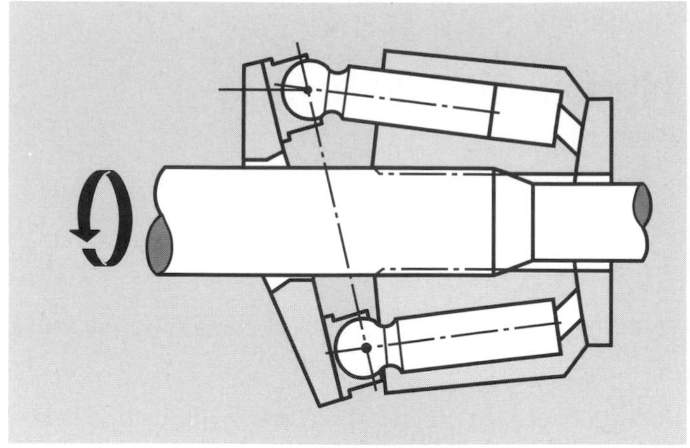

Fig. 7: *Axial piston motor in swashplate design*

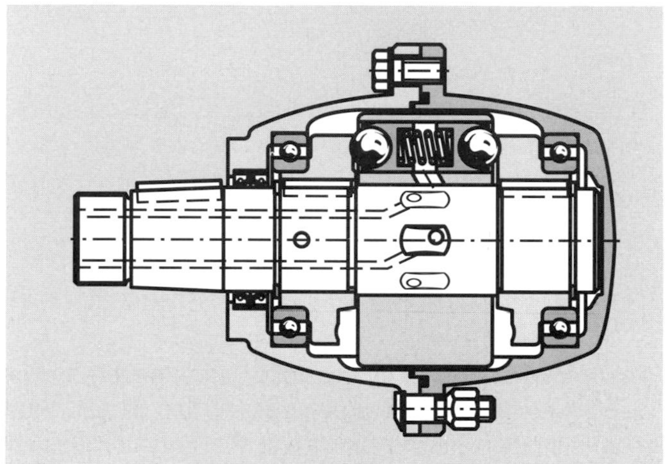

Fig. 8: *Multi-stroke axial piston motor with rotating case*

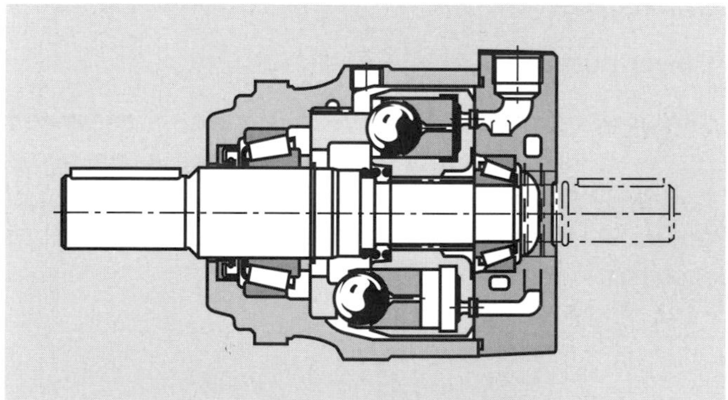

Fig. 9: *Multi-stroke piston motor with rotating shaft*

3 Functional descriptions

3.1 Gear motors

Gear motors are very similar in design to gear pumps (see chapter "Hydraulic pumps"). They are different in that the axial pressure field is different and gear motors have a drain case port, as they are designed for changing directions of rotation.

The fluid flowing to the hydraulic motor acts on the gears. A torque is produced which is output via the motor shaft.

Gear motors are often used in mobile hydraulics and in agricultural machinery to drive conveyor belts, dispersion plates, ventilators, screw conveyors or fans.

Fig. 11: *Gear motors*

Important parameters

Displacement	approx. 1 to 200 cm^3
Max. operating pressue	up to 300 bar
Range of speeds	500 to 10 000 rpm

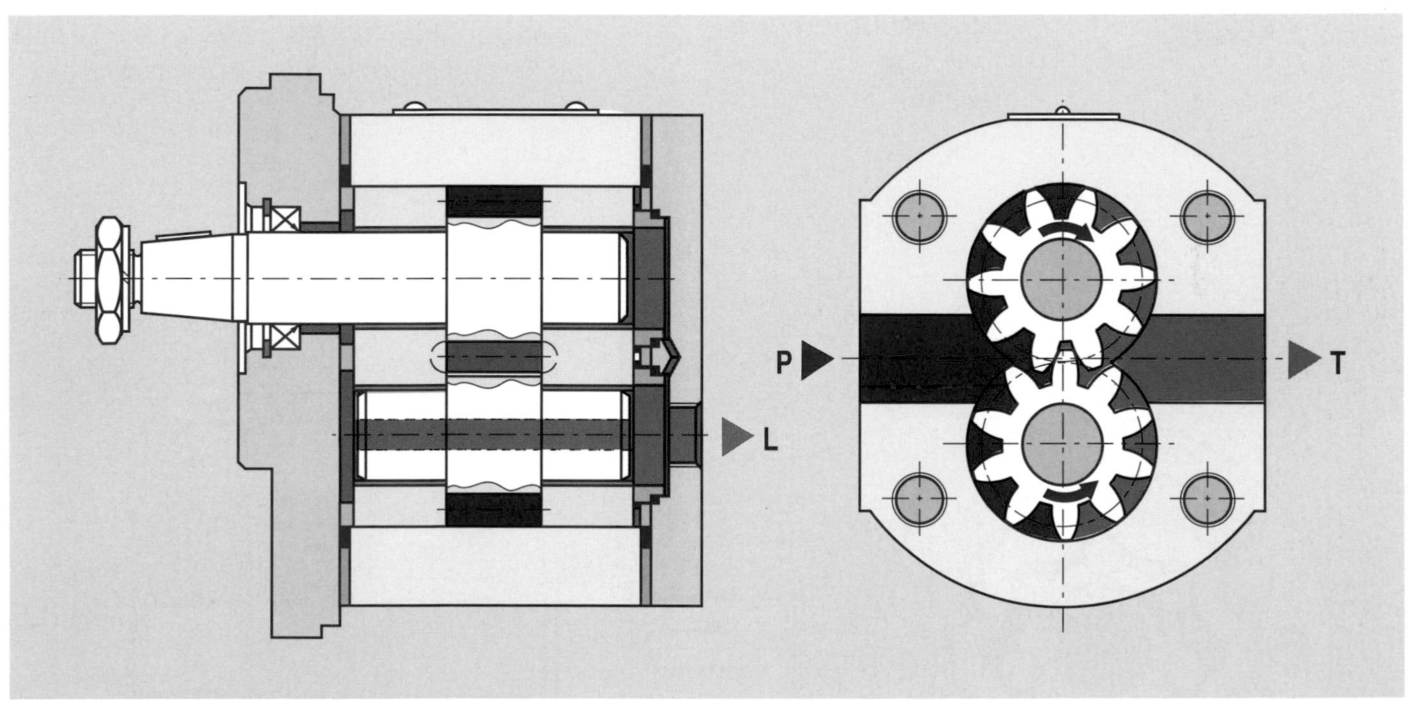

Fig. 10: *Gear motor, type G2*

Gear motors and axial piston motors (see chapter "axial piston machines") are high speed motors. Fast motors are used for speeds of over 500 rpm. For applications requiring low speeds, either high speed motors are used with gears or slow speed motors are used. Slow speed motors or LSHT (low speed - high torque) motors exhibit their best characteristics and efficiencies for speeds of less than 500 rpm.

3.2 LSHT motors (slow speed motors)

3.2.1 Epicyclic gear motors with central shafts

Hydraulic motors, type MZ belong to the group of epicyclic gear motors. Their main feature is to offer large dispacements within small dimensions.

This is achieved due to a large number of displacement processes occurring per revolution of the output shaft.

Fig. 12: *Epicyclic gear motors*

The operation is as follows:

In the commutator (2) which is pressed into the housing (1), fluid is fed to and from the control disc (10) via 2 ring channels (13) and 16 longitudinal bores. The control plate is connected to the shaft (4) via a spline. The rotor (6) and control disc (10) rotate at the same speed.

The connection between commutator (2) and displacement chambers is achieved via control apertures (11) arranged radially in the control disc. The displacement chambers are formed by the internal surface of the internal gear (7), external surface of the rotor (6) and internal rollers (8).

Within the commutator, half of the 16 longitudinal bores are connected to the high pressure and the other half are connected to the low pressure.

All displacement chambers which are currently increasing in volume are connected to the high pressure side via the control plate. All displacement chambers which are currently decreasing in volume are connected to the low pressure side.

The pressure in these chambers produces a force which acts on the rotor, which creates a torque. The internal gear (7) is thus supported by the external castors (9).

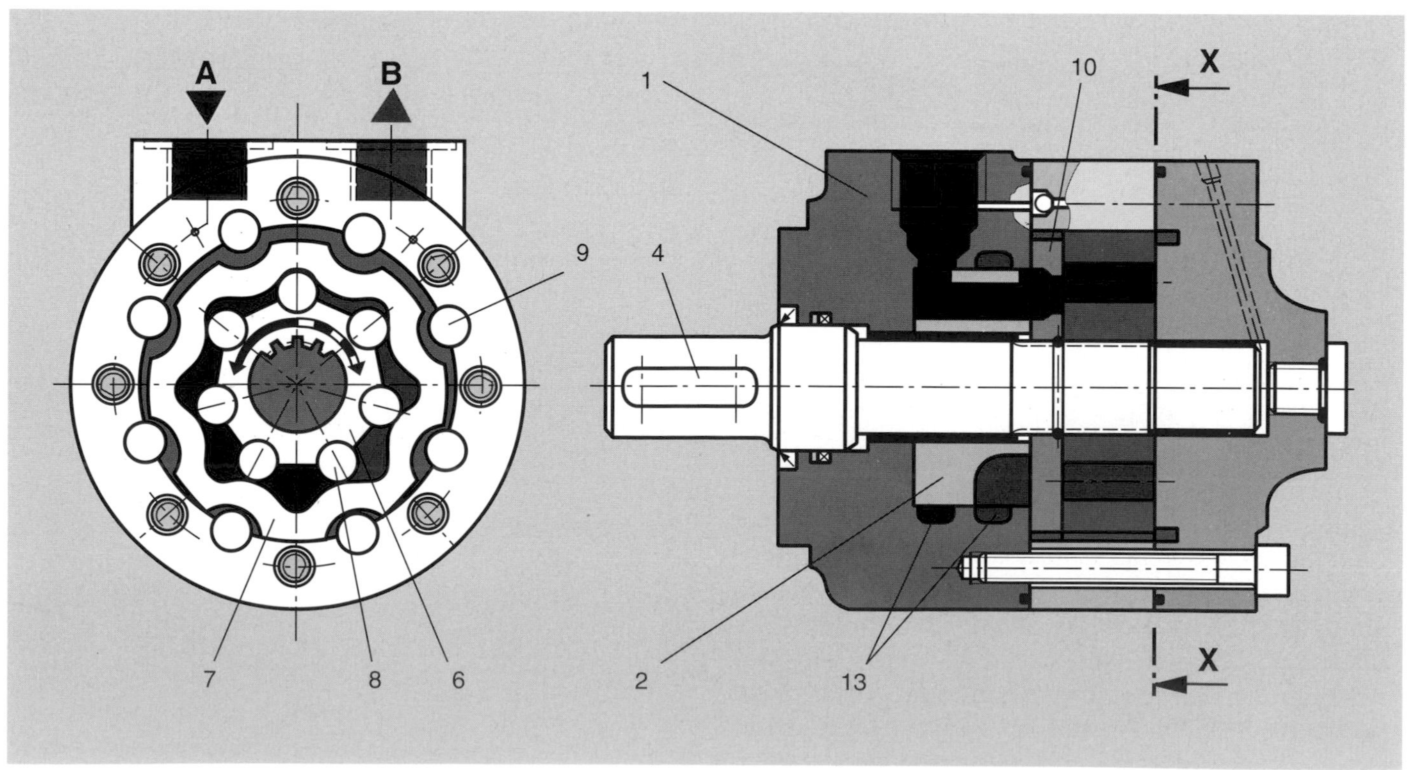

Fig. 13: *Epicyclic gear motor, type MZD*

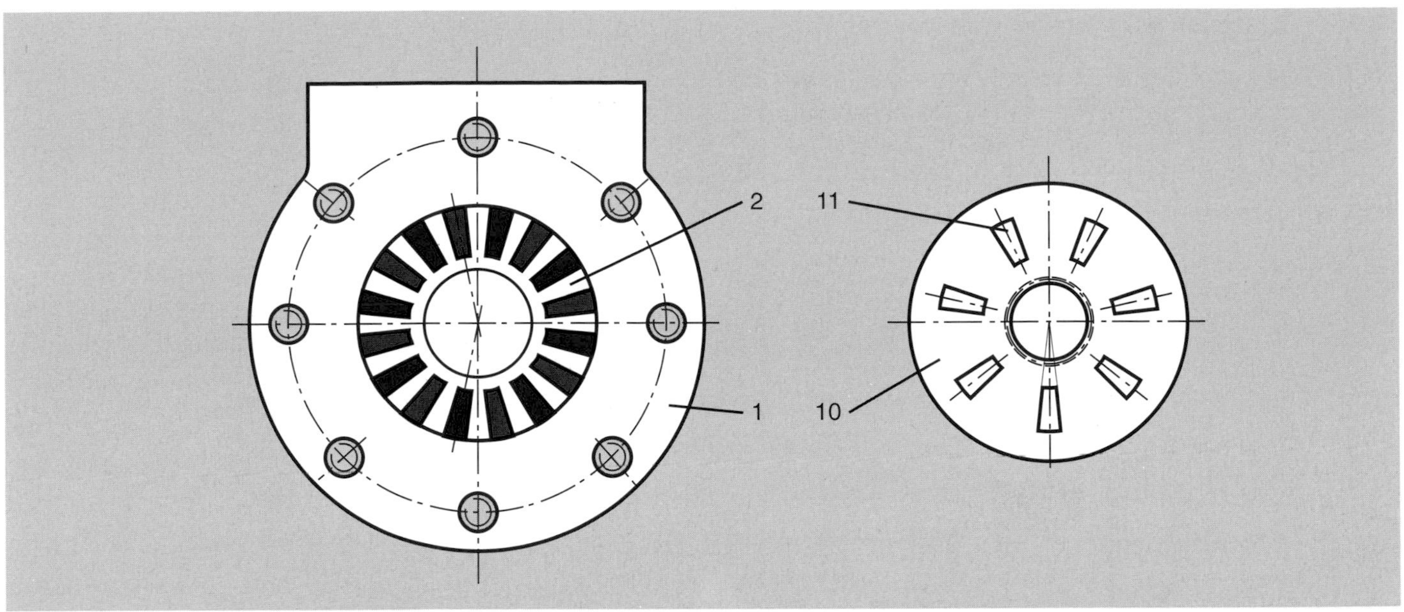

Fig. 14

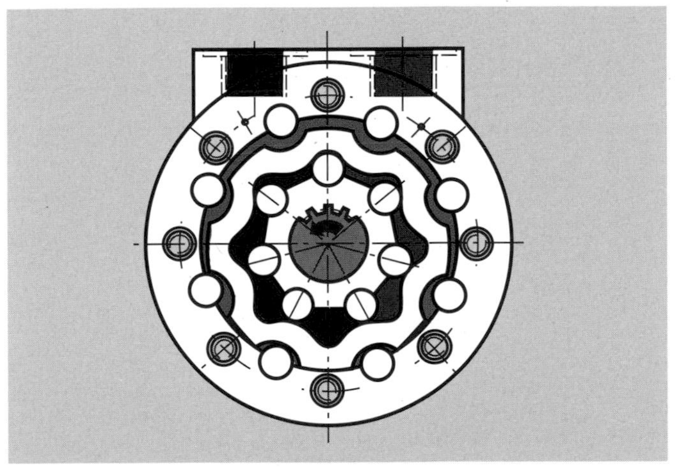

Fig. 15

Each time the largest or smallest chamber volume is produced, the control is reversed. 8 changes in volume occur per chamber per shaft rotation. Thus 7 chambers x 8 = 56 displacement processes take place per revolution. This is the reason for the relatively high displacement which occurs per rotation.

It is possible to mount a holding brake onto the central output shaft or to use the second shaft end for the output of rotational movement (for example) (see *Fig. 16*).

Internal check valves are used to feed internal leakages to the current low pressure side. As the pressure in this region may exceed the permissible value, it is essential that the drain case port is connected to tank.

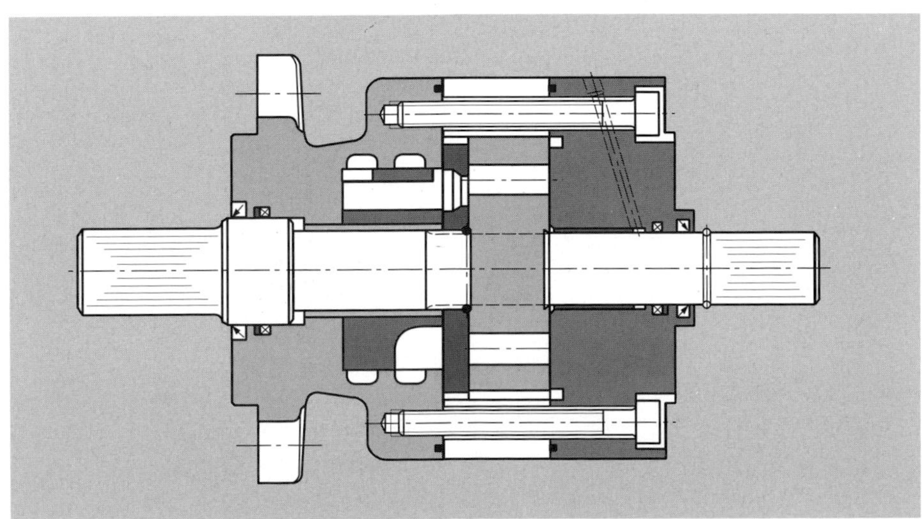

Fig. 16: *Epicyclic gear motor with through shaft, type MZD*

3.2.2 Epicyclic gear motors with drive shafts

In this type of motor, the torque is transferred from the rotating rotor (2) to the output shaft (3) via an internal drive shaft (1) instead of an internal gear.

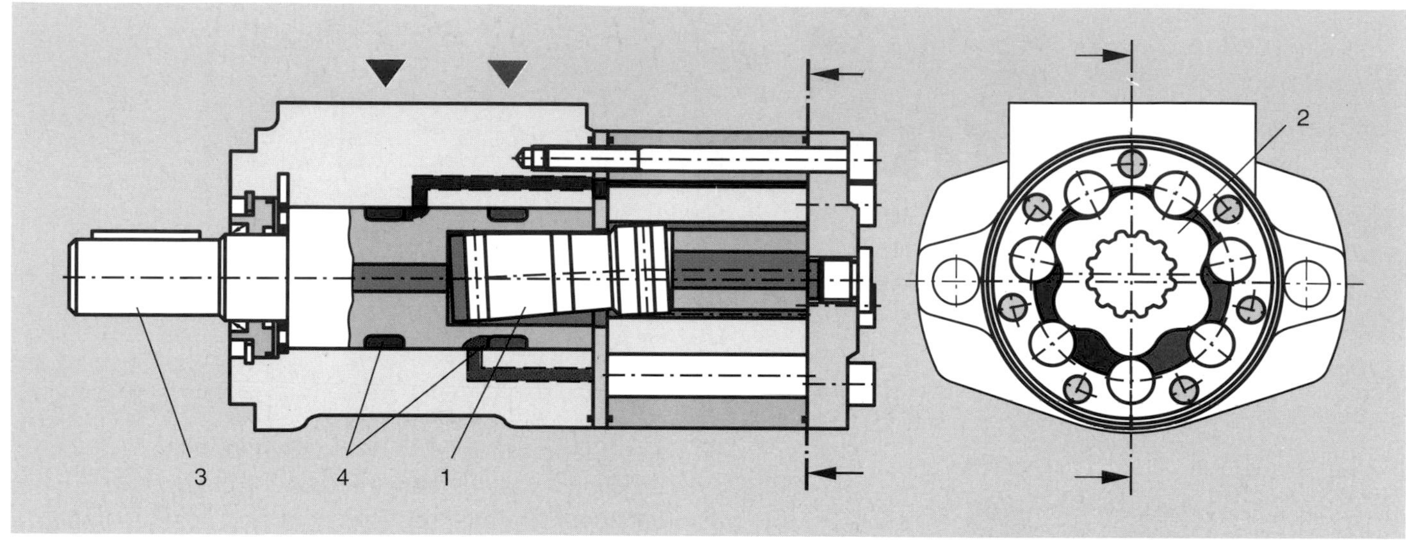

Fig. 17

The operating fluid flowing to the hydraulic motor is distributed in the output shaft via bores (4) and fed to the displacement chambers in the housing via bores. The fluid is returned by the same method.

A large variety of epicyclic hydraulic motors are available.

Important parameters

Displacement: approx. 10 to 1000 cm^3

Max. operating pressure: up to 250 bar

Range of speeds: approx. 5 to 1000 rpm

3.2.3 Basic principle of multi-stroke piston motors

In this type of motor, each piston carries out several operating strokes per rotation of the shaft. Hence high displacements and thus high operating torques are produced in this motor.

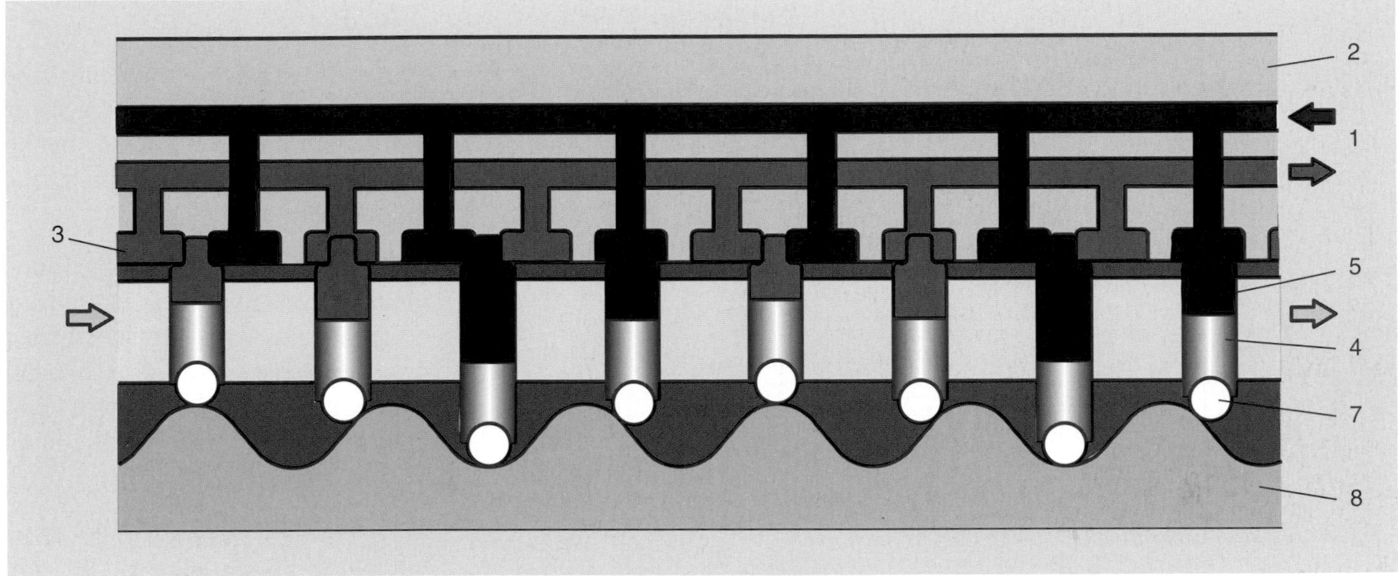

Fig. 18

Control windows (3) are connected to the feed and return sides of the motor via pipe connections (1) and control (2). Depending on the current position, cylinder chambers are either emptied or filled.

The piston is supported by the stroke cam (8) via a ball or roller (7).

The force (F_T) which is converted into torque is dependent on the force F_A (area of the piston x operating pressure) and on the angle of the stroke cam (α).

Depending on the design of motor, the output may be via a rotating housing; the shaft may contain an integrated control and the pipe connections may be permanently connected to the machine (see *section 3.2.3.1*). On the other hand the cylinders and pistons may be connected to the output shaft.

In this case, the control and stroke cam are situated within the fixed housing of the motor (see *section 3.2.3.2 and 3.2.4*).

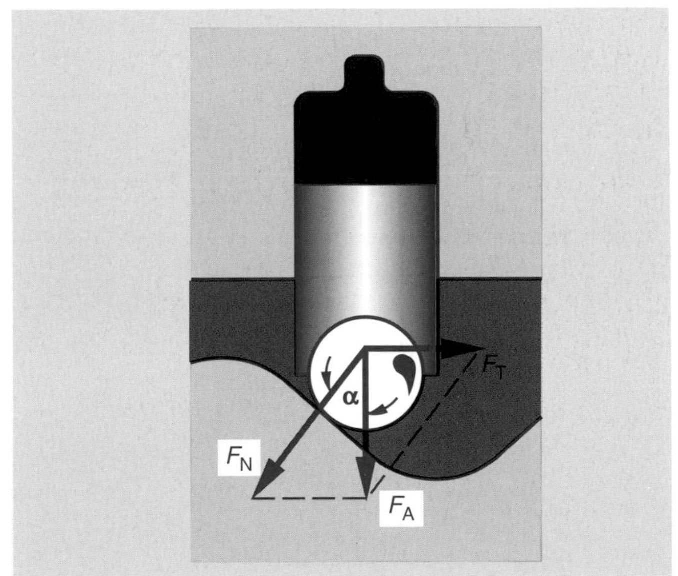

Fig. 19

Multi-stroke hydraulic motors have very good slow speed characteristics and are used in many applications.

3.2.3.1 Multi-stroke axial piston motors with rotating housing

This type of motor only requires a relatively small space for installation.

The control and pipe connections are integrated into the motor shaft.

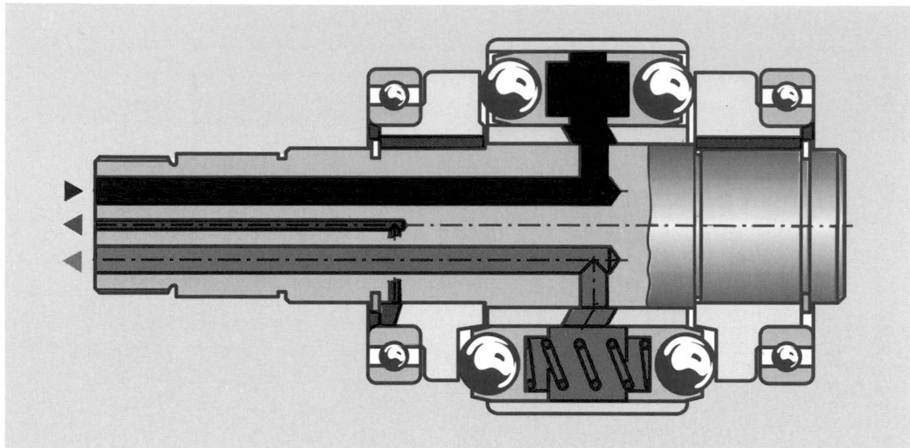

Fig. 20: *Insert motor without housing, type MCA*

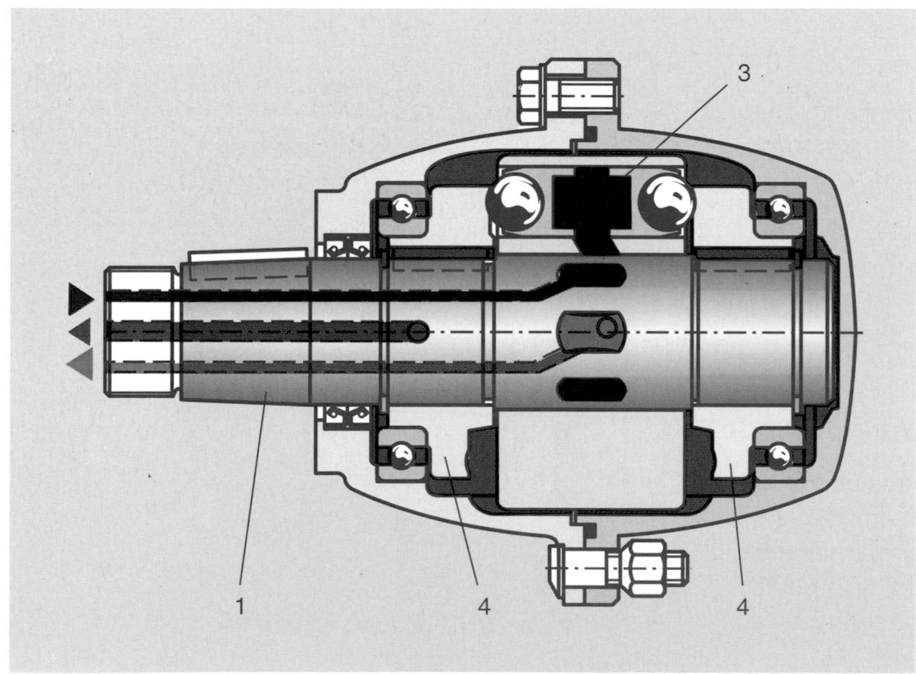

Fig. 21: *Axial piston motor with rotating housing, type MCH*

Two cams (4) are permanently fixed to the shaft (1). The rotor/piston groups are supported axially by the stroke cams and transfer the torque to the rotating housing.

Springs (3) ensure that the pistons maintain contact with the cams in any operating situation. If the springs are removed and if the housing chamber is placed under a low pressure (1 bar) it is possible for these motors to be free-wheeling.

Such motors, due to the small amount of space required for them are very suitable for use in gearbox or winch drive applications.

Important parameters

Displacement:
200 to 1000 cm^3

Max. operating pressure:
up to 250 bar

Range of speeds:
5 to 300 rpm

Max. torque:
up to 3800 Nm

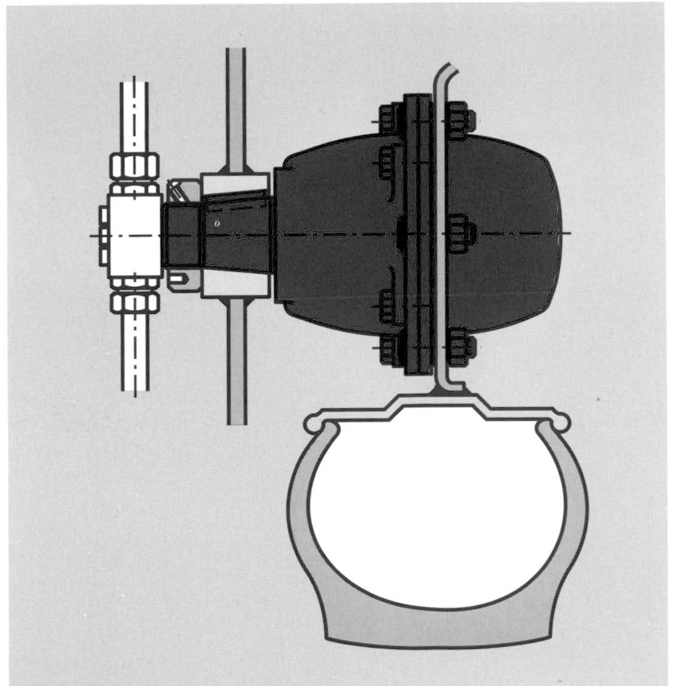

Fig. 22: *Schematic diagram of a wheel drive*

Fig. 24: *Axial piston motors, type MC*

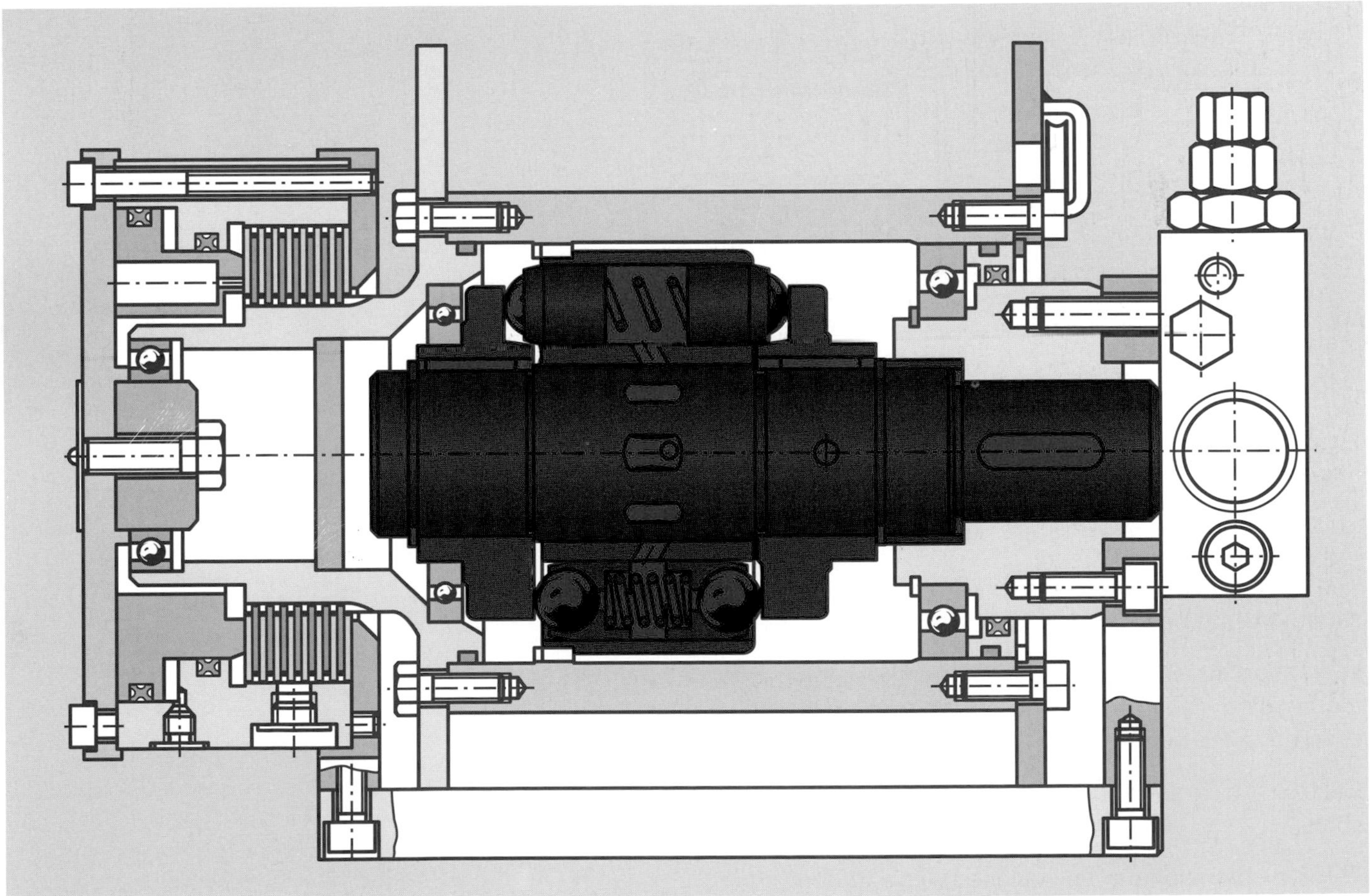

Fig. 23: *Complete winch*

3.2.3.2 Multi-stroke axial piston motors with rotating shaft

Fig. 25: *Axial piston motors, type MCS*

Important parameters

Displacements:	200 to 1500 cm^3
Max. pressure:	250 bar
Range of speeds:	5 to 500 rpm
Max. torque:	up to 5000 Nm

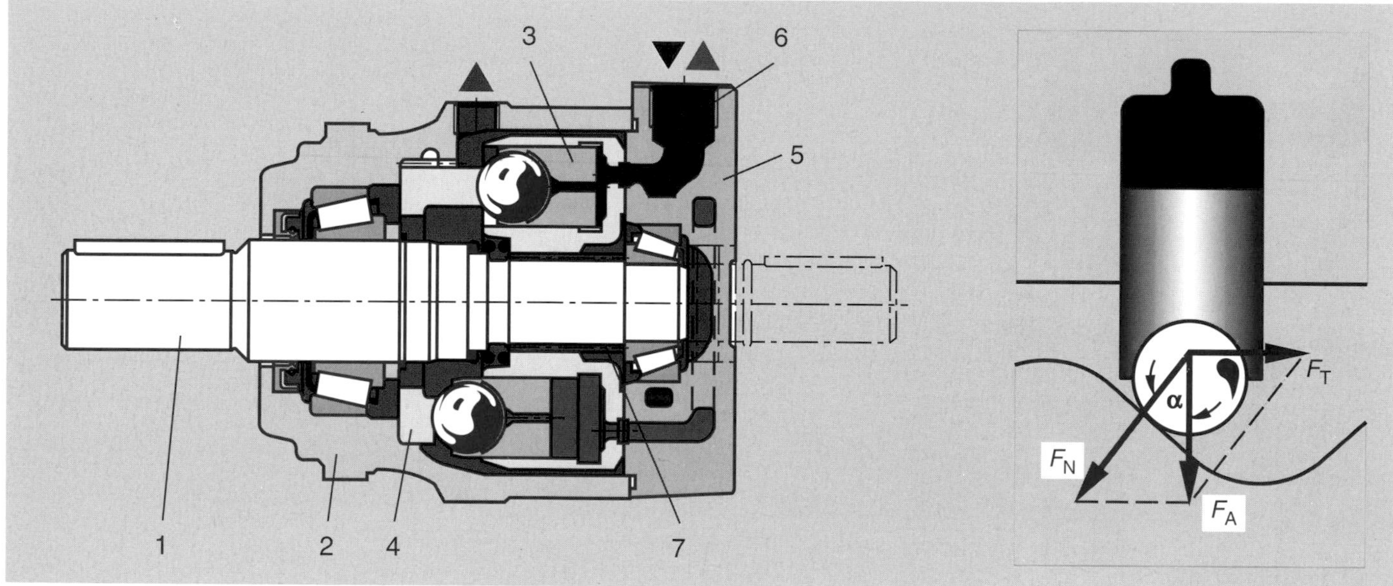

Fig. 26

The control and pipe connections (6) for this motor are situated in the housing (5).

In addition the stroke cam is permanently connected to the housing (2). However, the rotor/piston group (3) is coupled to the output shaft (1) via a spline (7).

Each piston carries out several strokes per rotation of the shaft.

This type of motor may be equipped with a through shaft for a holding brake or for a second output.

3.2.4 Multi-stroke radial piston motors

Fig. 27: *Radial piston motors, type MCR*

In this type of motor the pistons (3) arranged radially are supported via the rollers (8) on the cam (4). The cylinder chamber is supplied with fluid via the axial bores in the control (5). Each piston is loaded and unloaded with fluid as many times per rotation of the shaft as there are number of cams on the cam. The torque resulting from the curve of the cam is transferred from the rotor/piston group (3) to the output shaft (7) via a spline (6).

A tapered roller bearing is integrated into the housing (1), which is capable of receiving high axial and radial forces. A multiple-disc brake (9) may be mounted onto the control housing (2) via a through drive.

If the release pressure decreases below a certain value in the ring chamber (10) of this brake, the plate spring (11) presses the multiple discs together. The brake is hence operated.

If the release pressure exceeds the required value, the brake piston (13) is pushed against the plate spring. The multiple discs are separated and the brake is released.

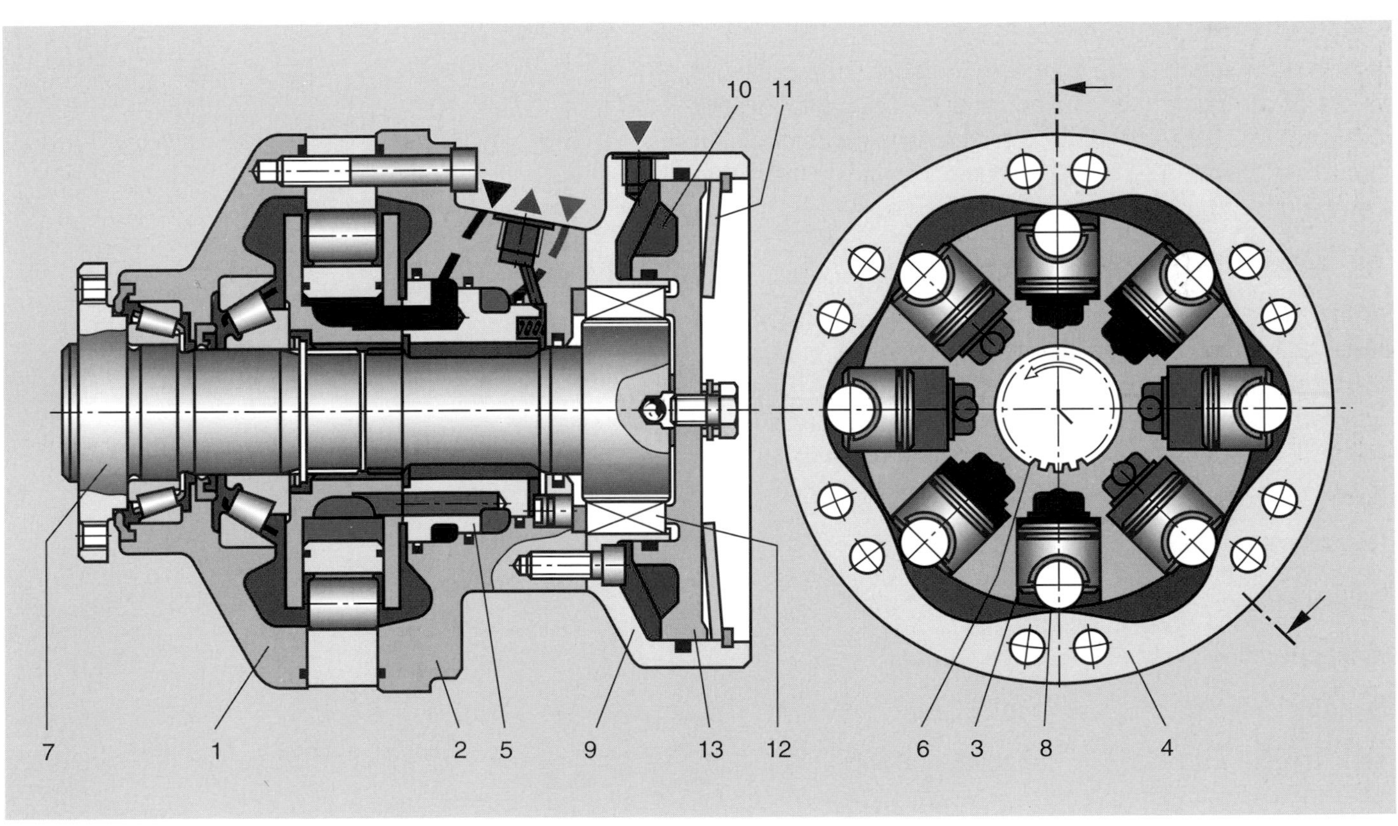

Fig. 28

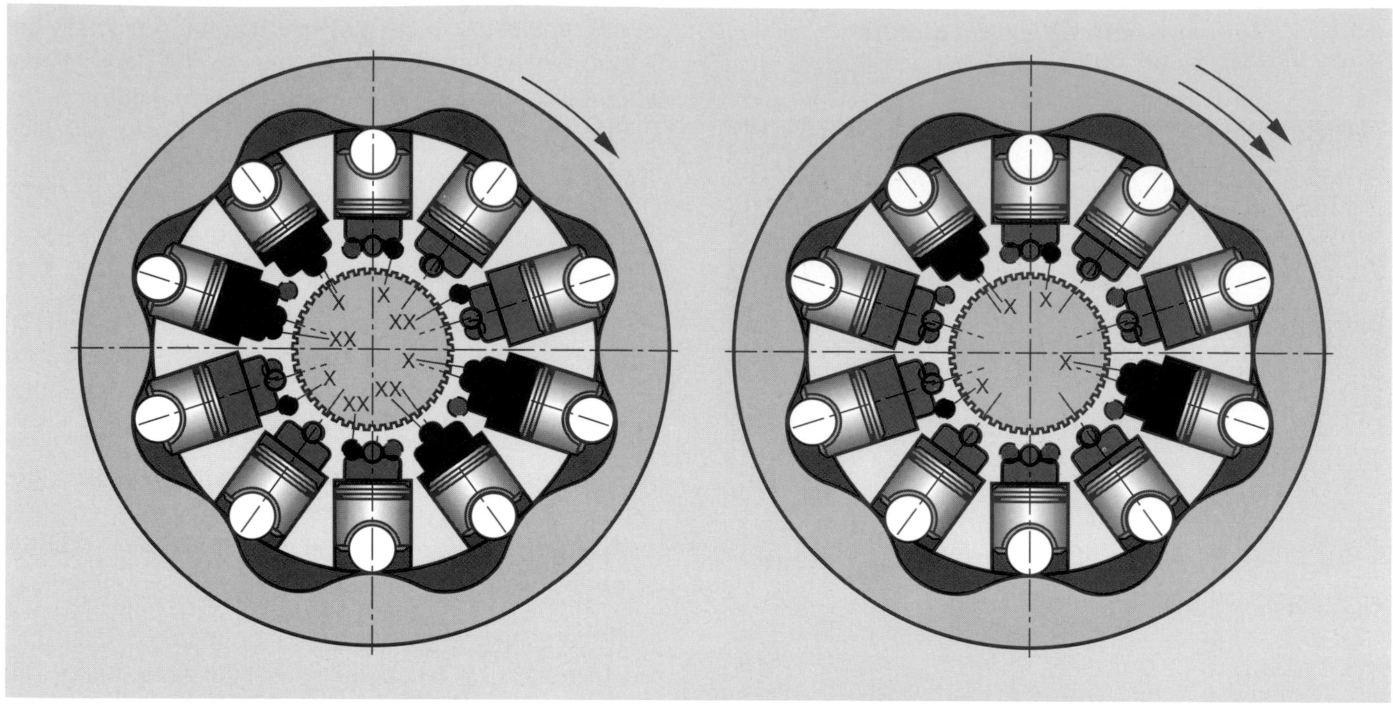

Fig. 29: *Left: set to 100% speed, 100% torque* *Right: set to 200% speed, 50% torque*

Freewheeling

If both ports A and B are connected to a very low pressure and if at the same time the housing is pressurised with a pressure of 2 bar via port "L", the pistons in the rotor/piston group are pushed in. The rollers do not remain on the stroke cam and the shaft end may then freely rotate.

Circuit with half the displacement

With certain models in radial piston motors the displacement may be halved. This is achieved by only half the pistons being supplied with fluid during a stroke. This is due to a valve in the control. The rest of the pistons are connected to the tank side of the motor. When connected in a circuit, this motor runs at twice the speed, but at half the torque.

Important parameters

Displacement: 200 to 8000 cm^3

Max. operating pressure: up to 450 bar

Range of speeds: 1 to 300 rpm

Max. torque: up to 45 000 Nm

3.2.4.1 Radial piston motors (single stroke) with internal eccenter

Fig. 30: *Radial piston motors, type MR*

The cylinder and pistons are arranged in the shape of a star around the central eccentric shaft.

Depending on the position of the eccentric shaft 2 or 3 (6) of the 5 (10) pistons are connected to the feed side (pressure side) and the rest of the pistons are connected to the return side (tank side).

The cylinder chambers are supplied with fluid via control (1).

The control basically comprises control plate (2) and distribution valve (3).

Whilst the control plate is connected via pins to the housing so that it rotates with the housing, the distribution valve rotates at the same speed as the eccentric shaft.

Connection to control plate and hence to the piston chambers is via bores in the distribution valve.

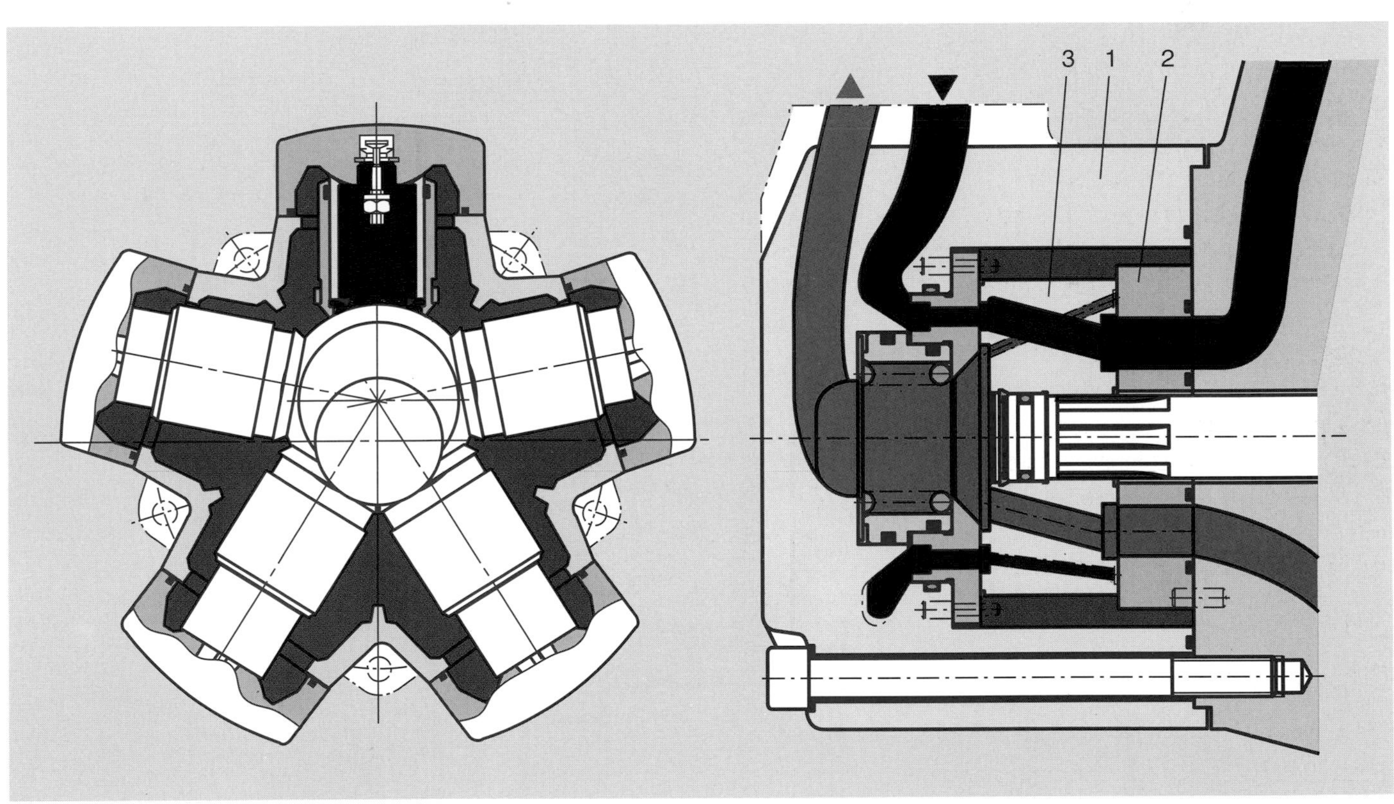

Fig. 31: *Radial piston motor, type MR*

Force may be transferred from the pistons to the eccentric shaft via various methods:

In the model shown in *Fig. 32*, the pistons are within the housing and are supported by special shaped rings on the eccentric shaft.

During rotation of the shaft a relative movement occurs between the piston and ring. In order to minimise friction the contact surface of the piston on the ring is hydrostatically unloaded.

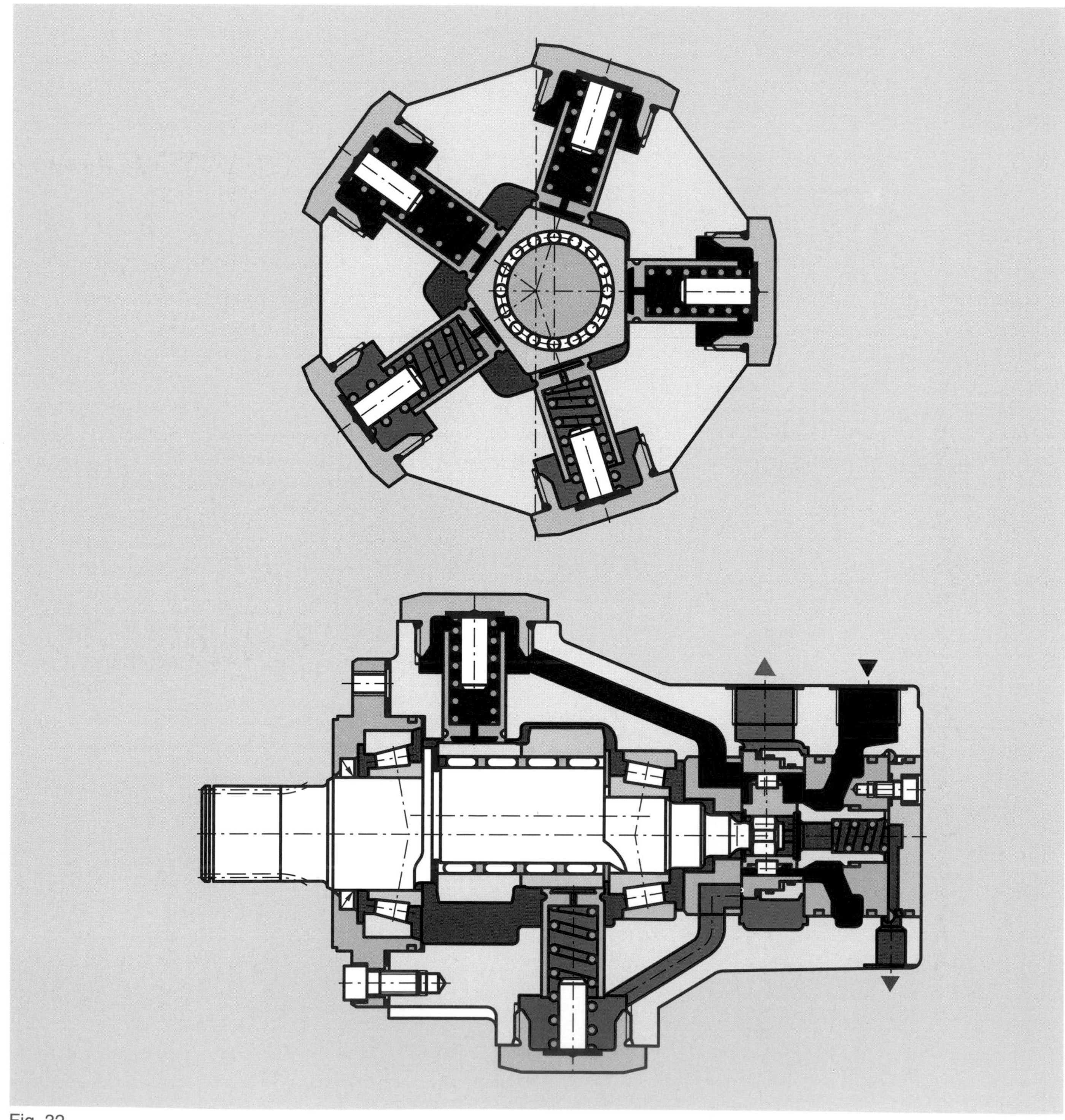

Fig. 32

In another type of model, the operating pressure acts on the eccentric shaft. Pistons and cylinder are supported by spherical surfaces and hence follow the eccentric shaft free of side loads.

The contact surfaces at the eccenter and housing are mostly hydrostatically unloaded, so that friction is minimal. This design is very efficient and has a good slow speed characteristic.

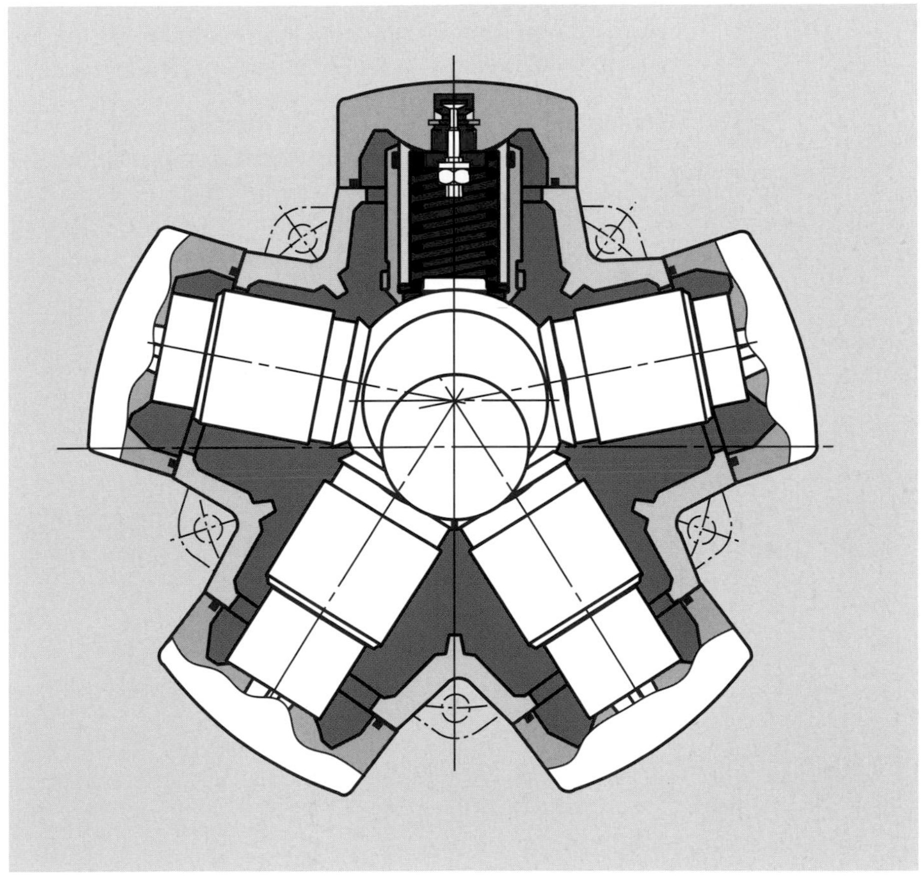

Fig. 33

Important parameters

Displacement:	10 to 8 500 cm^3
Max. pressure:	up to 300 bar
Range of speeds:	0.5 to 2 000 rpm (depending on size)
Max. torque:	up to 32 000 Nm

3.2.4.2 Variable displacement radial piston motors

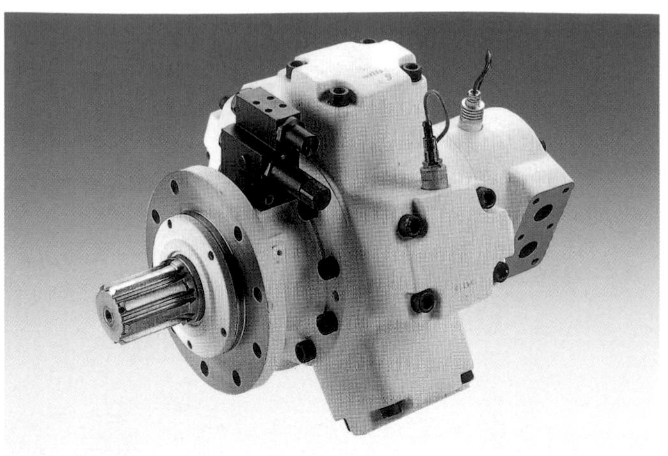

Fig. 34: *Radial piston motor, type MRV*

The basic design of these hydraulic motors is the same as the design described under *section 3.2.4.1.*

The difference to fixed displacement motors is found in the eccentric shaft.

The shaft comprises shaft pivots (1 and 2) and moveable eccenter (3).

The piston chambers within the eccenter (5 and 6) are pressurised via control ports (4). If a higher pressure exists in these piston chambers (6), the eccenter moves in the direction of lower eccentricity. If chamber (5) is places under a higher pressure than chamber (6), the eccenter moves in the direction of the higher eccentricity.

Hence the displacement of the hydraulic motor may be switched between a minimum and maximum value, set by mechanical strokes.

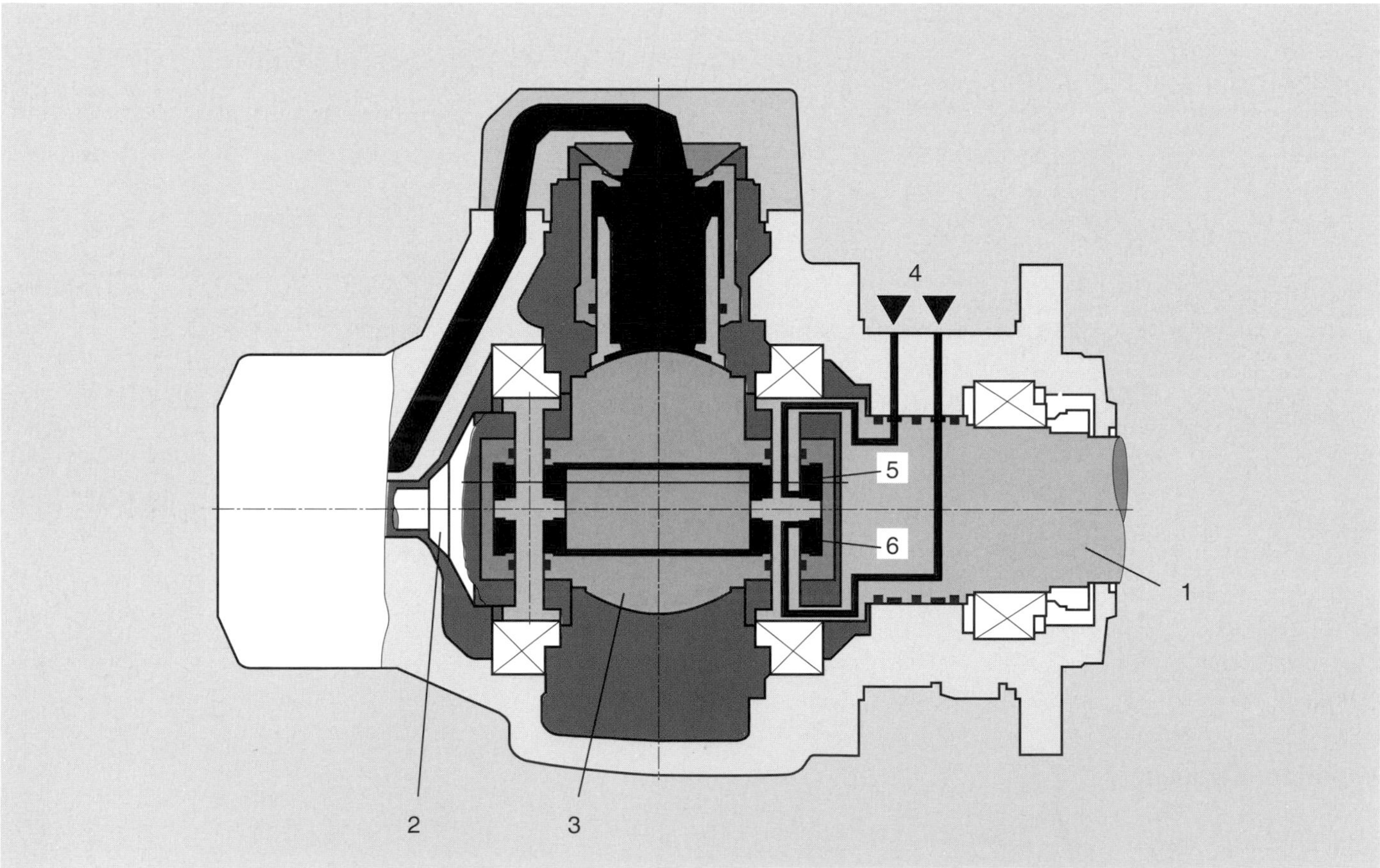

Fig. 35

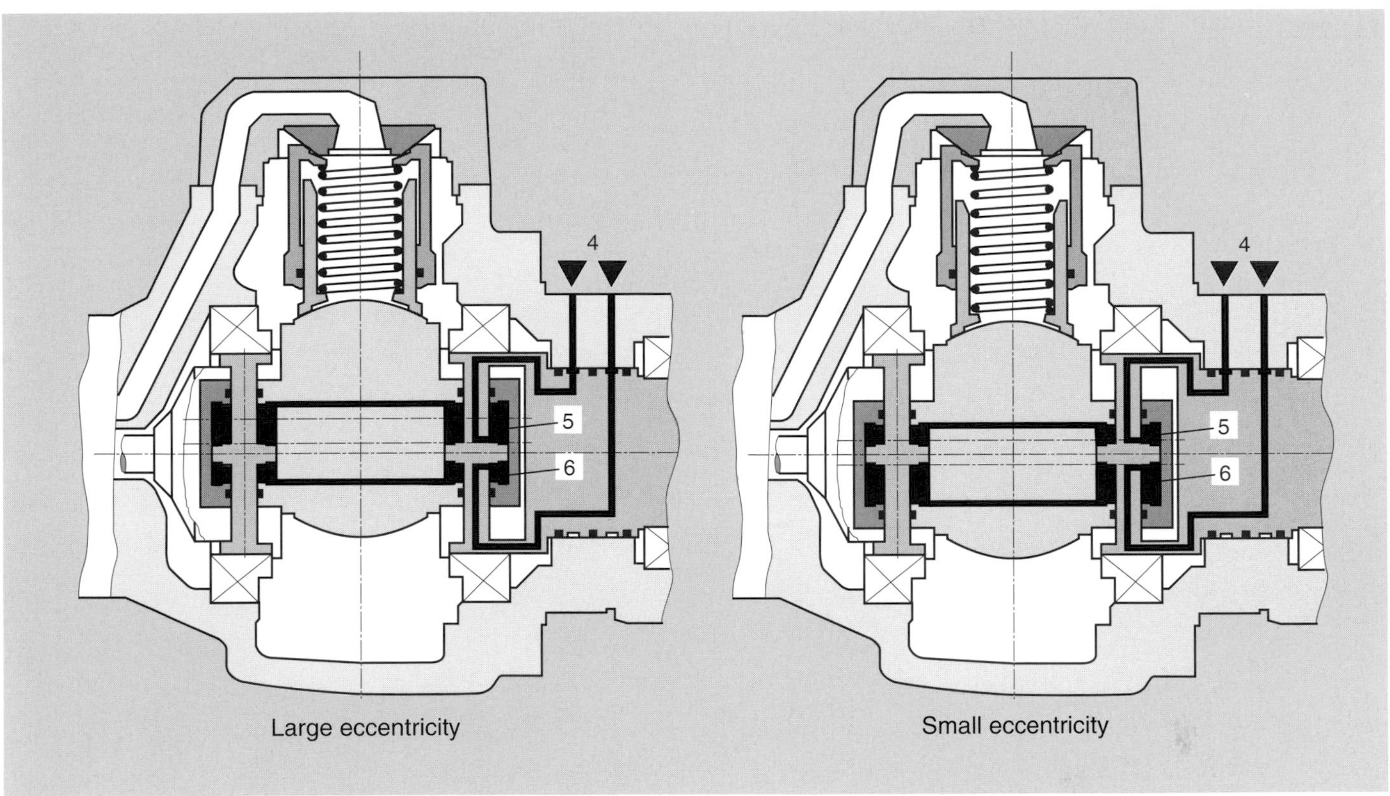

Fig. 36

In order to the displacement to be set smoothly it is necessary for the position of the eccenter to be controlled.

The amount of pendulum movement of the piston is taken as a comparison for the eccentricity.

The positional transducer (3) produces a signal (actual signal) which is compared with the command signal.

If the actual and command signals are not the same, either piston chamber (5) or (6) (depending on whether the deviation is positive or negative) is placed under pressure via a control valve and ports (4). The eccentricity is hence changed in the desired direction.

Radial piston motors with variable displacement together with speed transducers may be used for drives in closed loop control circuits.

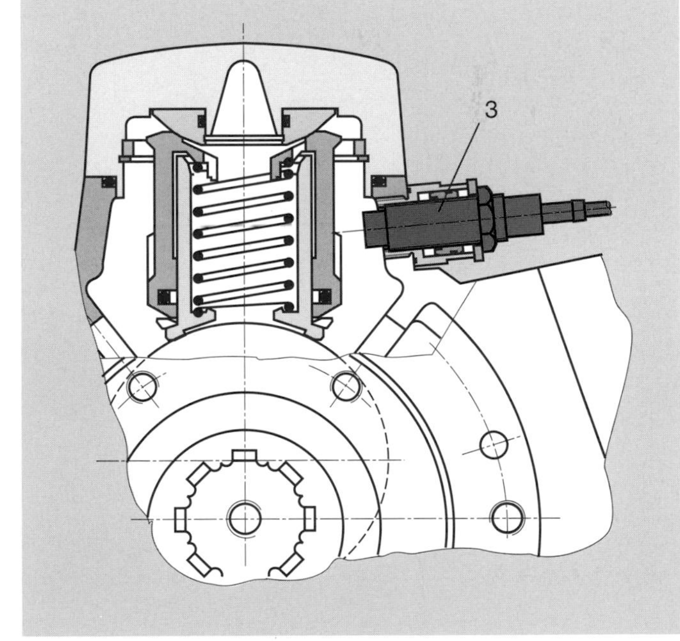

Fig. 37

Important parameters

Displacement:	200 to 5 500 cm^3
Max. pressure:	up to 300 bar
Range of speeds:	1 to 1 000 rpm
Max. torque:	up to 22 000 Nm

Notes

Axial Piston Units

Chapter 6

Axial Piston Units

Udo Ostendorff

1 Introduction

1.1 Circuit types

There are three types of circuits in hydraulics:

– Open loop circuit

– Closed loop circuit

– Semi-closed loop circuit

Open and closed loop circuits will be described in more detail below. The semi-closed loop circuit is a mixture of both types of control circuit and is used in applications where volumes are to be balanced e.g. via anti-cavitation check valves (e.g. when using a single rod cylinder block).

Typical features of open loop are:

- Suction lines
  Large diameters, small lengths
- Directional valves
  Sizes dependent on flow
- Filters/coolers
  Cross-sectional areas/sizes dependent on flow
- Tank size
  Multiple of max pump flow in litres
- Pump arrangement
  Next to or under the tank
- Drive speeds
  Limited by amount of suction
- Unloading in the return line via valves

Typical feature of closed loop circuits are:

- Directional valves
  Small sizes for pilot operation
- Filters/coolers
  Small openings to flow/small sizes
- Tank size
  Small - determined only by flow of auxiliary pumps and system flow
- Speeds
  High limits due to anti-cavitation
- Arrangement/installation position
  Any
- Drive
  Completely reversible through zero position
- Support of loads
  Via drive motor
- Return of braking energy

Axial Piston Units

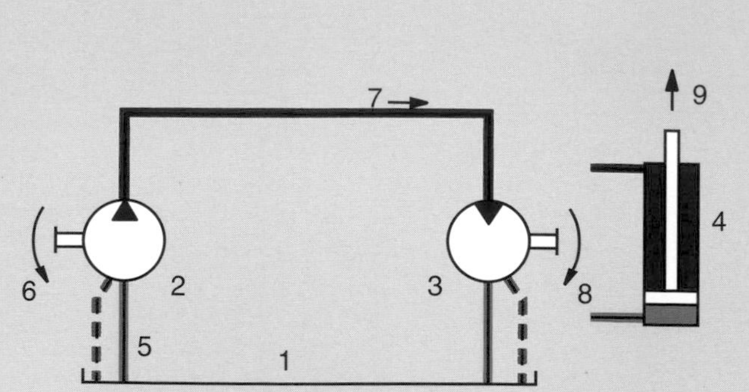

1 Tank
2 Fixed displacement pump
3 Fixed displacement motor
4 Hydraulic cylinder block
5 Suction line
6 Drive speed
n= constant
7 Flow
Q= constant
8 Output speed
n= constant
9 Stroke velocity
v= constant

Basic design with hydraulic pump and hydraulic motor/cylinder block, drive, output and direction of stroke are on one side.

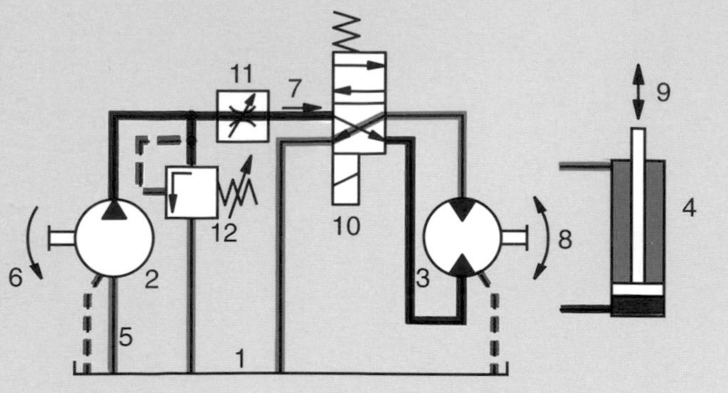

1 Tank
2 Fixed displacement pump
3 Fixed displacement motor
4 Hydraulic cylinder block
5 Suction line
6 Drive speed
n= constant
7 Flow
Q= variable
8 Output speed
n= variable
9 Stroke velocity
v= variable
10 Directional valve
for control of direction
11 Flow control valve
for flow adjustment
12 Pressure relief valve
for protection against overload

By using a flow control valve (11) the output speed (velocity) is made variable. Pressure relief valve (12) protects hydraulic system from overloading.

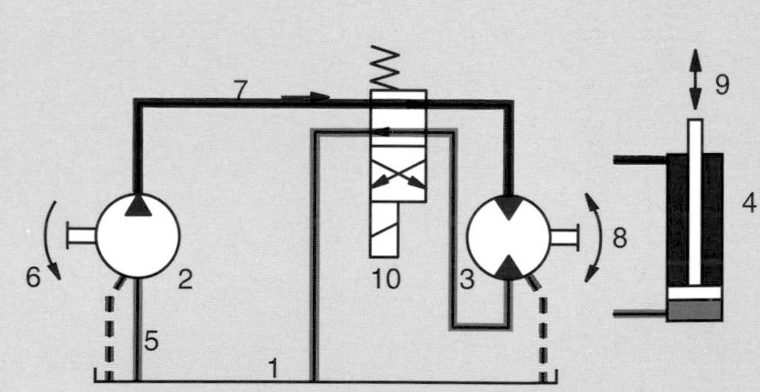

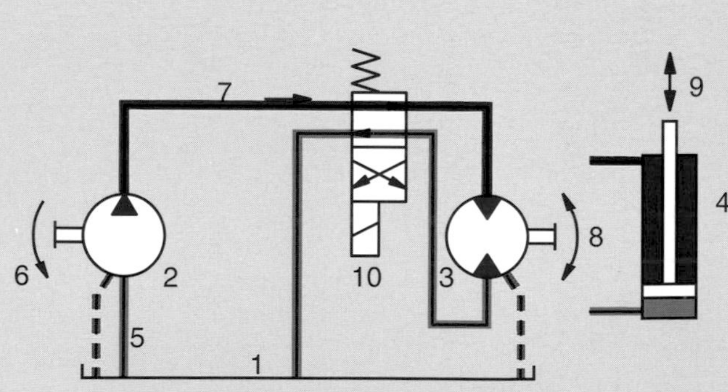

1 Tank
2 Constant displ. pump
3 Constant displ. motor
4 Hydraulic cylinder block
5 Suction line
6 Drive speed
n= constant
7 Flow
Q= constant
8 Output speed
n= constant
9 Stroke velocity
v= constant
10 Directional valve
for control of direction

Due to the directional valve the direction of rotation or movement may be changed at the actuator.

1 Tank
2 Variable displ. pump
3 Constant displ. motor
4 Hydraulic cylinder block
5 Suction line
6 Drive speed
n= constant
7 Flow
Q= variable
8 Output speed
n= variable
9 Stroke velocity
v= variable
10 Directional valve
for control of direction
12 Pressure relief valve
for protection against overload
13 Accessories
such as filtration, cooling etc.

A variable displacement pump replaces the constant displacemnt pump and flow control valve. Further directional valve functions, e.g. free-wheeling circuit of actuator, use of accessories such as filters, coolers etc. complete the hydraulic system.

1.1.1 Open loop circuits

In general, open implies that the suction line of a pump is fed below the surface of the fluid in the tank and the surface of the fluid is in direct contact with the atmospheric pressure (i.e. the surface is not enclosed). The balance of pressures which is ensured between the air in the hydraulic tank and the ambient air, enables the pump to have an excellent suction characteristic. Resistances in the feed line must not cause the pressure to fall below the so-called suction height/suction limit.

Axial piston units are self-aspirating. However in certain individual cases low pressure is fed to the suction side.

In open loop circuits fluid is fed to the actuator via directional valves and returned via the same valves to tank.

The open loop circuit is the standard circuit used in many industrial and mobile applications. Examples range from machine tools and press drives to winch and mobile drives.

Fig. 1: *Open loop circuit*

Axial Piston Units

1.1.2 Closed loop circuit

A hydraulic system is a closed loop circuit when the fluid returning from the actuator is fed straight back to the hydraulic pump.

Pumps have high and low pressure sides and these change depending on the direction of the load.

The pressure is limited on the high pressure side via pressure relief valves, which unload to the low pressure side. The fluid remains in the circuit.

Only the internal leakages from the pumps and motors need to be replaced (depending on operating data).

This occurs via (in general) an auxiliary pump connected directly by a flange to the pump. This auxiliary pump continually sucks fluid from a small tank and delivers sufficient fluid (boost fluid) via a check valve to the low pressure side of the closed loop circuit. The flow which is not required is returned by a boost pump operating in an open loop circuit via a boost pressure relief valve to tank. Due to the low pressure side being replenished, this pump enables higher operating characteristics to be attained.

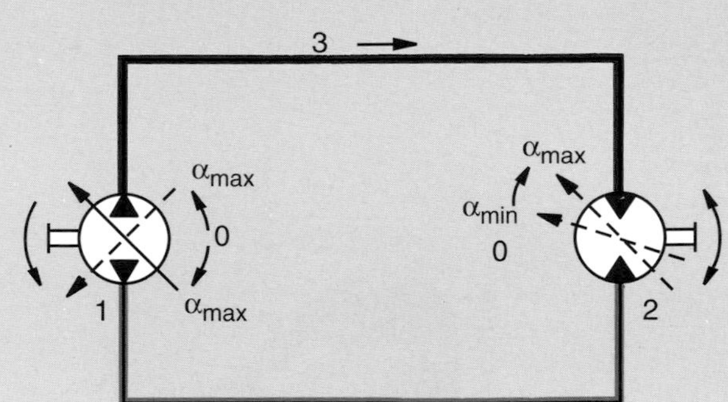

1 Hydraulic pumpe
2 Hydraulic motor
3 Flow
Q= variable

Basic design with variable displacement pump and motor. The pump rotates in one direction only, the motor rotates in both directions (is reversible) The pump swivel angle may be smoothly adjusted through zero, i.e. the direction of flow may be changed. Motor may swivel on one side of centre and is also smoothly adjustable.

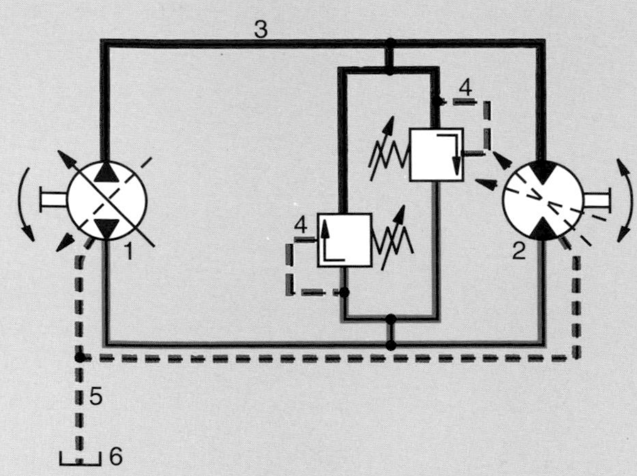

1 Hydraulic pump
2 Hydraulic motor
3 Flow
Q= variable
4 Pressure relief valve for protection against overloading (per pressure side of valve)
5 Drain case line
6 Fluid tank for leakage oil

Leakage from pump and motor is led back to a small tank and must be replaced!

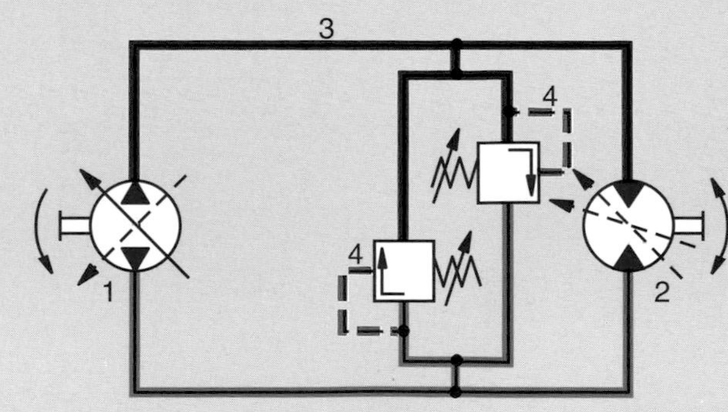

1 Hydraulic pump
2 Hydraulic motor
3 Flow
Q= variable
4 Pressure relief valve for protection against overload (a valve per pressure side)

By using pressure relief valves the maximum pressure is ensured. A pressure relief valve is inserted for each pressure side.

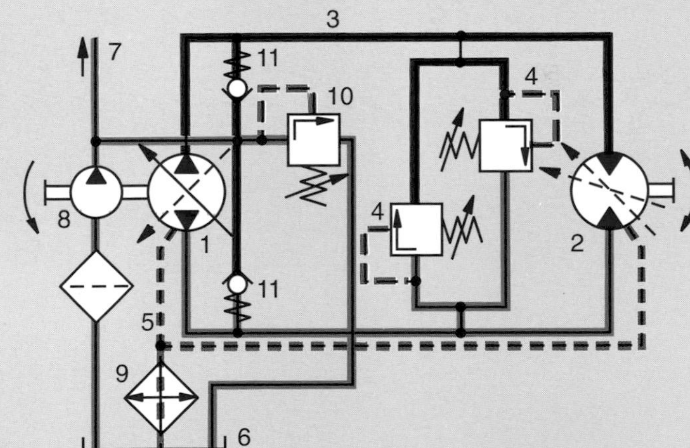

1 Hydraulic pump
2 Hydraulic motor
3 Flow
Q= variable
4 Pressure relief valve for protection against overload (a valve per pressure side)
5 Drain case line
6 Fluid tank for leakage oil
7 For pump control
8 Aux. pump for anti-cavitation
9 Accessories such as filtration, cooling etc.
10 Feed and pressure relief valve
11 Check valve

An auxiliary pump for the replacement of leakage oil and for the control of the pump, check valves for anti-cavitation, protection via a feed / pressure relief valve and use of accessories such as filters, coolers etc. complete the hydraulic system.

Fig. 2: *Closed loop circuit*

2 Basic function

2.1 Bent axis

Fig. 3: *Fixed displacement unit with tapered piston rotary group*

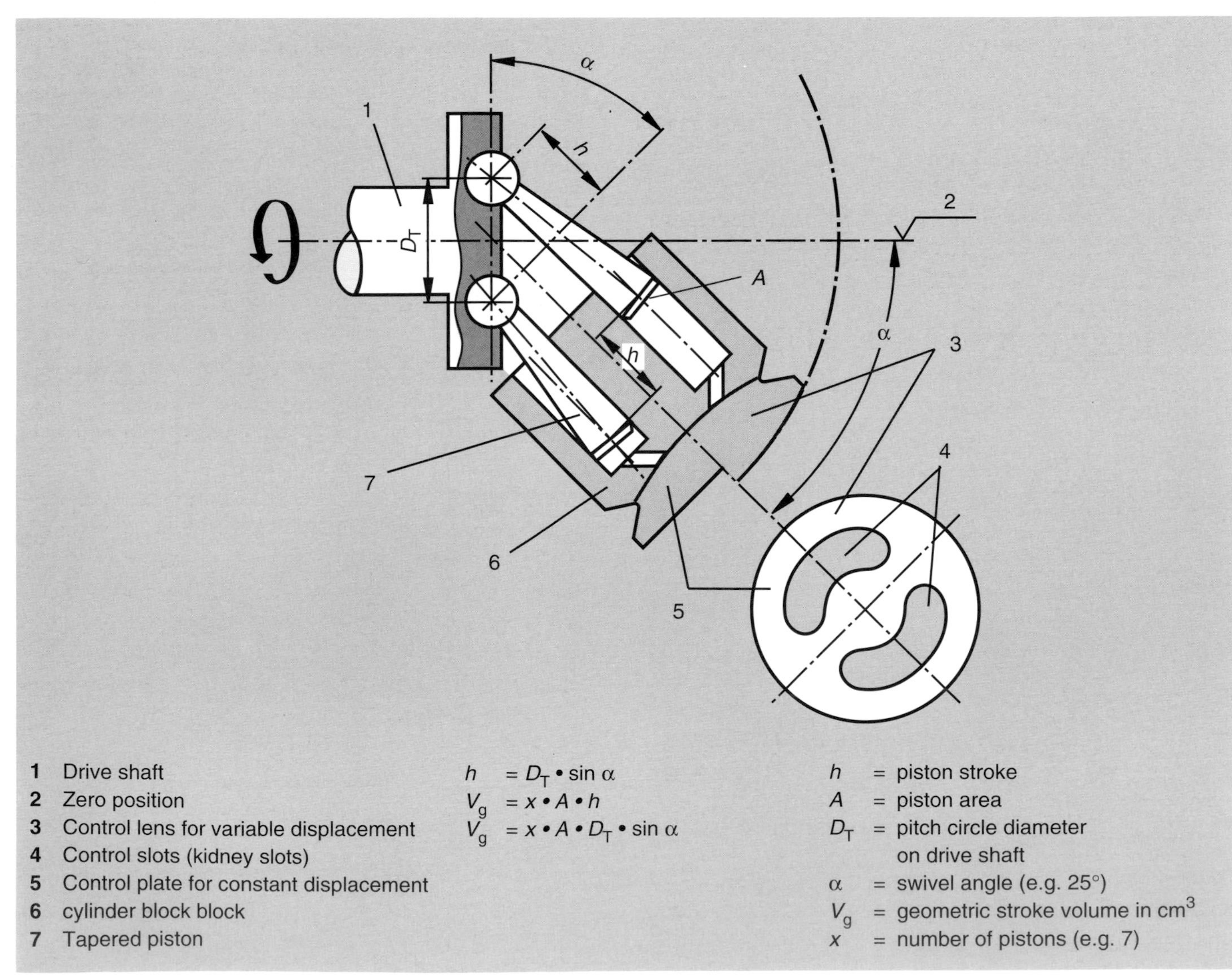

Fig. 4: *Bent axis design with fixed or variable swivel angle*

2.1.1 Bent axis principle

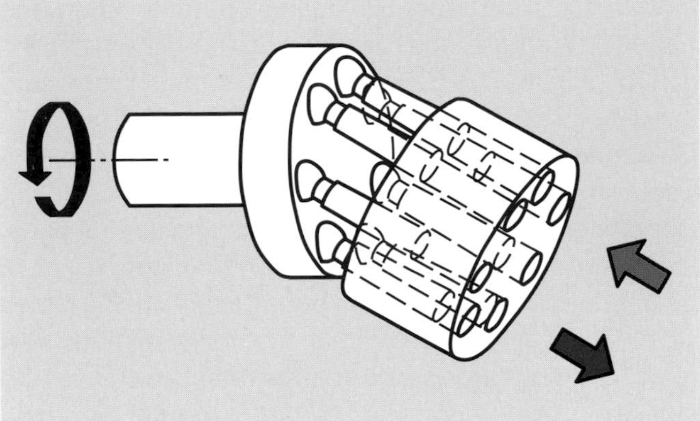

Fig. 5

The bent axis mechanism is a displacement machine, the displacement pistons of which are arranged at an angle to the drive shaft axis.

2.1.1.1 Pump function

As the drive shaft rotates, the cylinder block is caused to rotate by the pivoted pistons. The pistons move up and down within the cylinder block bores. The length of stroke is dependent on the angle of the bent axis. Fluid is fed to the low pressure side (inlet) and then delivered via the pistons on the high pressure side (outlet) to the system.

2.1.1.2 Motor function

In contrast to the pump function, pressurised oil is fed into the inlet. The pistons move up and down within the cylinder block bores. This movement is converted into a rotary movement via the piston ball joint at the drive flange. The cylinder block is caused to rotate by the pistons and an output torque is created at the drive shaft. The fluid emerging from the motor is then returned to the system.

2.1.1.3 Swivel angle

The swivel angle of the fixed displacement unit is set by the housing and hence it is fixed. In a variable displacement unit this angle may be smoothly adjusted between certain limits.

By changing the swivel angle a different piston stroke is obtained and hence an adjustable displacement volume may be produced.

2.1.2 Description of the function by means of an example of a constant displacement unit

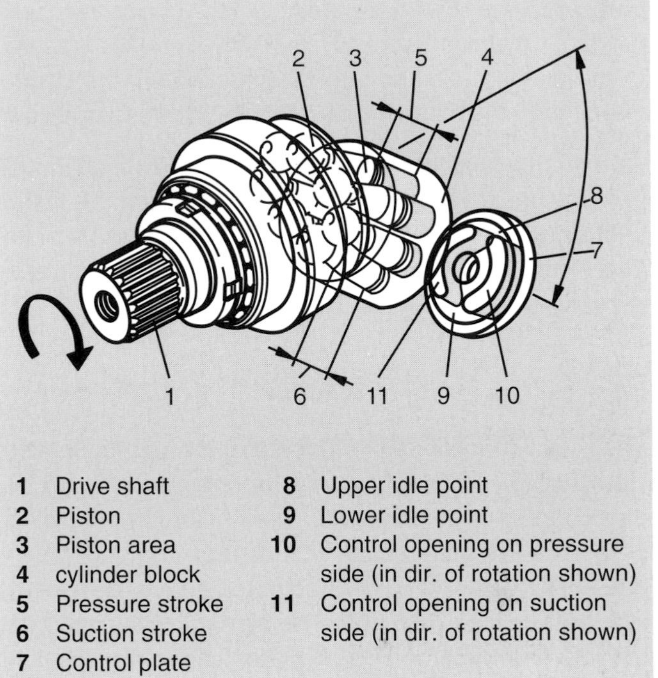

Fig. 6

2.1.2.1 Description

The axial piston units in bent axis design with fixed or variable stroke volumes may operate as hydraulic pumps or as hydraulic motors.

When used as a pump, the flow is proportional to the drive speed and the swivel angle. If the unit is used as a motor, the drive speed is proportional to the flow fed to the unit. The torque received (pump) or produced (motor) increases as the pressure drop increases between the high and low pressure sides. When operating as a pump, the unit converts mechanical energy into hydro-static energy. In contrast, when operating as a motor, the unit converts hydrostatic energy into mechanical energy. In variable displacement pumps or motors the displacement volume, i.e. the pump flow or the suction flow in motors may be varied by adjusting the swivel angle.

2.1.2.2 Operating as a pump in an open loop circuit

As the drive shaft is rotated the cylinder block is made to rotate via seven pistons which are mounted via ball joints in a circle on the drive flange. The cylinder block slides on the spherical control plate, in which there are two kidney shaped control openings. On rotation, each of the seven pistons moves in the cylinder block bores from the upper idle point to the lower idle point and vice versa. They thereby carry out a stroke which is dependent on the swivel angle. The piston movement in the cylinder block bore from the lower idle point to the upper idle point produces a suction stroke. The fluid volume with respect to the piston area and stroke is sucked via the control opening on the suction side into the cylinder block bore.

As the drive shaft is further rotated and the piston moves from the upper idle point to the lower idle point, the fluid is pushed out of the other control opening (pressure side). The pistons are supported under hydraulic pressure by the drive shaft.

2.1.2.3 Operating as a motor

The motor function is the reverse of the pump function. Here fluid is fed through a control opening into the cylinder block bores via the port plate. Three or four cylinder block bores are situated above the control opening on the pressure side and four or three bores above the opening in the return side. One bore may be directly connected to the idle point via the control plate. The force (resulting from the pressure and piston area) which acts on the drive shaft
causes an output torque to be produced.

2.1.2.4 Adjustment (in variable displacement unit)

The swivel angle of the bent axis may be adjusted e.g. mechanically via a positioning screw or hydraulically via a positioning piston. The hydraulic part of the drive cylinder block is moved via a control lens (control plate) and depending on the circuit and whether the operation is mechanical or hydraulic, held in either the zero position or output position. As the angle increases, the displacement volume and torque increase. As the angle decreases these values decrease accordingly. If the angle is zero, the displacement volume is zero. It is usual to have mechanically or hydraulically acting adjustment devices which may be controlled either mechanically, hydraulically or electrically. Well-known examples of these types of control are: handwheel, electronic proportional control, pressure control and power control.

2.1.2.5 General

In both cases of pump and motor operation the torque is created directly on the drive shaft due to the bent axis design. The pistons only produce very small side forces in the cylinder block. This is advantageous for the wear behaviour, efficiency and starting torque. Due to the spherical control plate, the cylinder block is situated on a torque-free bearing. This is because all the forces acting on the cylinder block act on one point. Sideways movements due to elastic deformations do not cause leakage losses to be increased between the cylinder block and control plate. During idle operation and when operation is started, the cylinder block is pushed onto the control plate by the Belleville washers. As the pressure increases, the increasing hydraulic forces are hydraulically balanced so that the resultant forces are maintained within acceptable limits while maintaining a minimum clearance between the cylinder block and contral plate, thus keeping leakage losses to a minimum. A set of bearings is situated on the drive shaft to absorb the forces which occur in axial and radial directions. A radial seal ring and O-rings are used to seal the rotary group from the outside. The complete rotary group is held in the housing via a retaining ring.

2.1.3 Rotary group forces

Representation in force parallelogram of a fixed displacement unit

Forces are resolved at the drive flange, i.e. directly at the drive shaft. The conversion of torque into piston force in pumps or vice versa in motors ensures that the best efficiencies are obtained. Wherever forces must be resolved (e.g. angular displacernent) a loss of efficiency occurs.

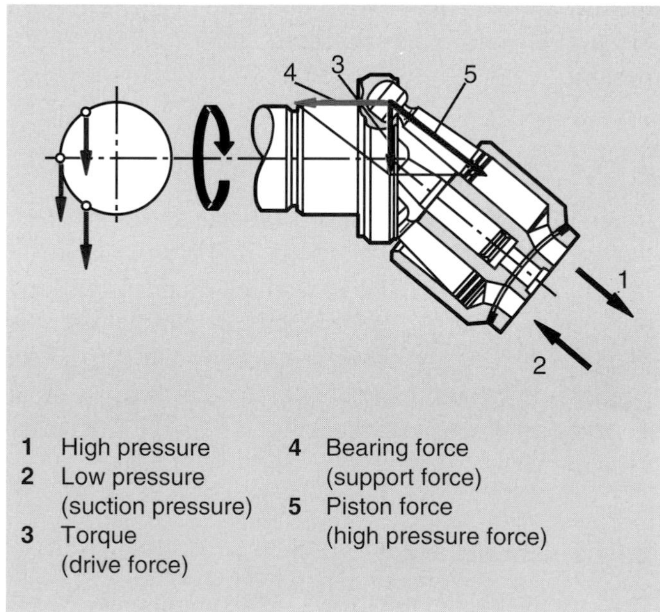

Fig. 7: *Resolution of forces at drive flange of pump*

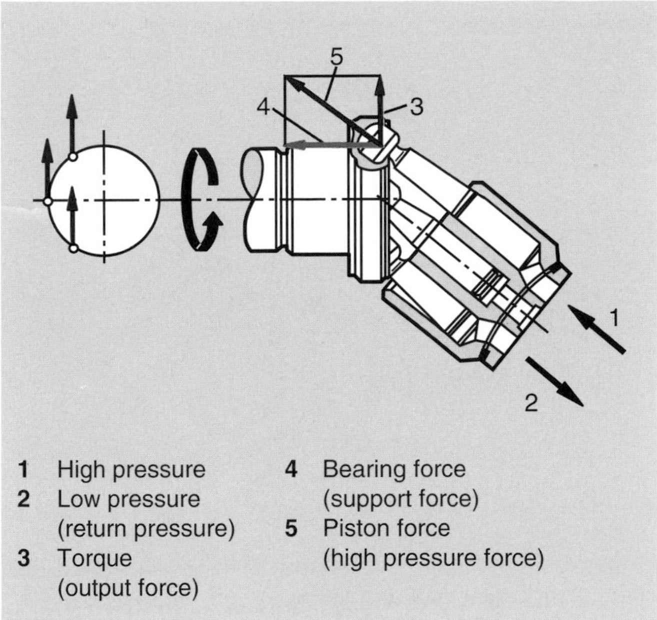

Fig. 8: *Resolution of forces at motor drive flange*

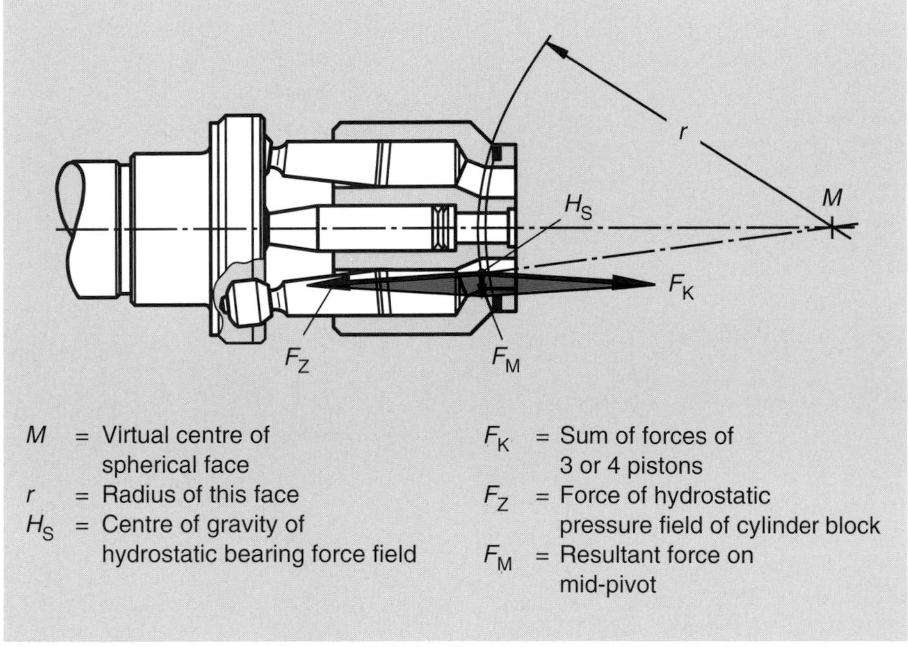

Fig. 9: *Resolution of forces at the control plate with its spherical surface*

In considering torque, a segment of the hydraulic rotary group is removed and simplified until it is illustrated as a pure static example at a swivel angle of 0°.

In practice, dynamic loading processes are present in rotary groups where the swivel angle is greater than zero, as three or four piston surfaces are being continually pressurised with high pressure.

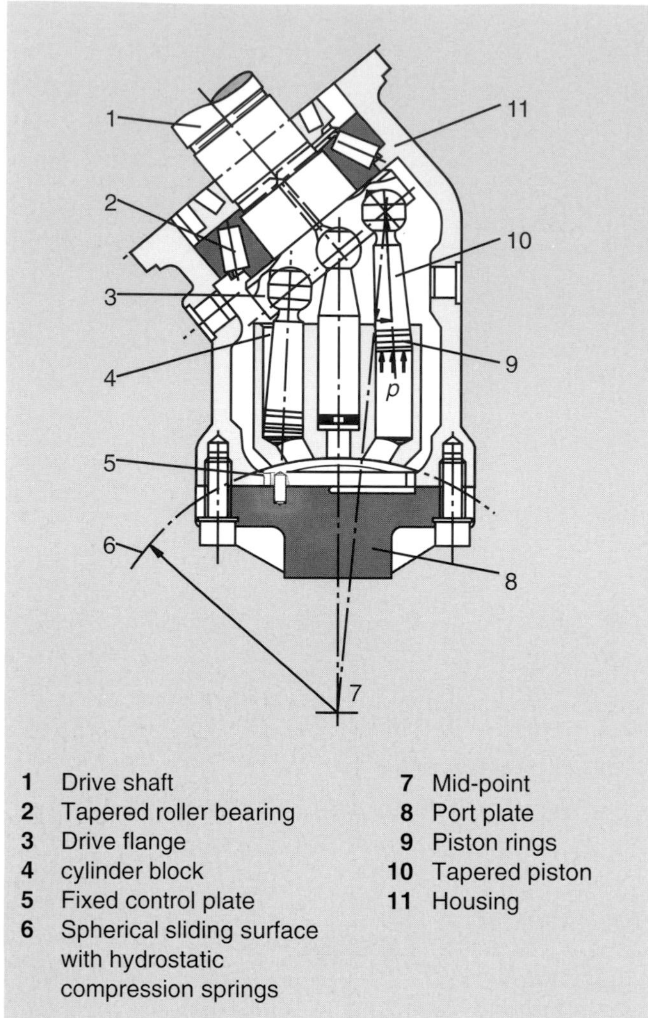

Fig. 10: *Bent axis tapered piston rotary group with 40° fixed swivel angle*

Features:

- Automatic centring
- Cardanless cylinder block drive
- Torque free cylinder block bearings
- Self-centering rotary group
- Spherical control plate
- Taper roller bearings
- Single tapered piston with two piston rings
- Automatic lubrication of bearings
- Force resolution direct at drive flange

2.1.4 Types

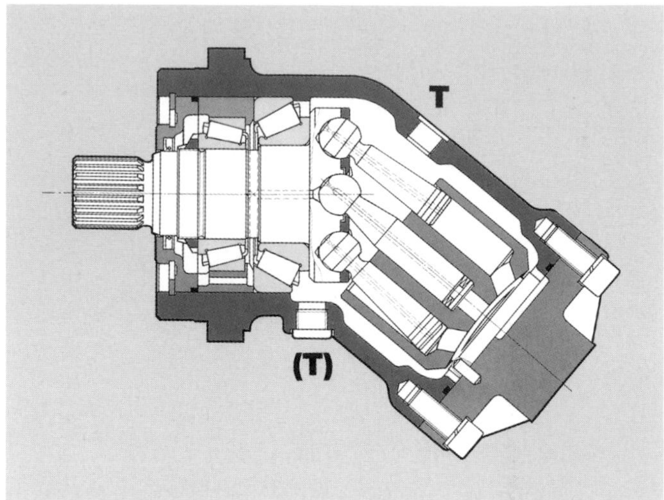

Fig. 11: *Fixed displacement unit, type A2F (fixed swivel angle), as a pump or motor for open and closed loop circuits*

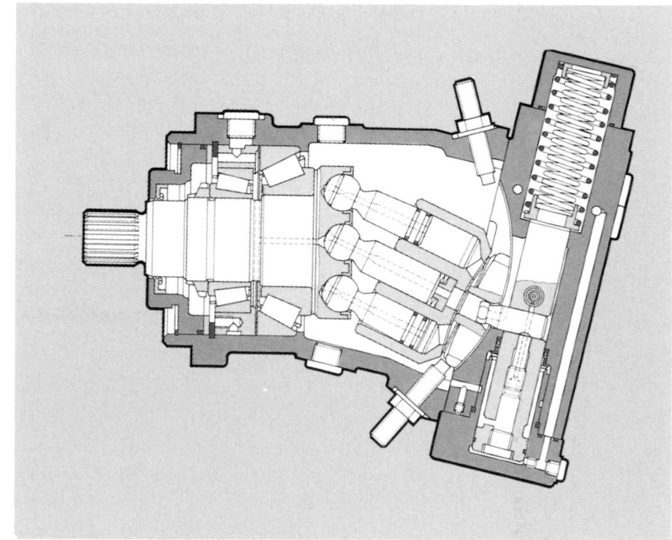

Fig. 12: *Resolution of forces at drive flange of pump*

2.1.5 Symbols

Type	Schematic diagram	Symbol	Description
Fixed displacement motor, type A2FM	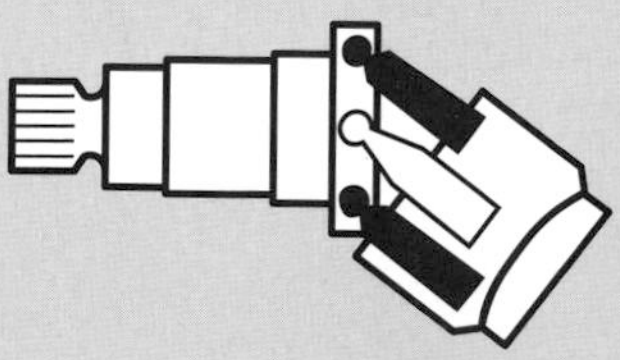	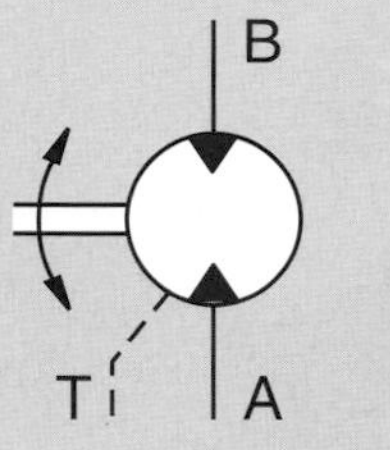 B, T, A	Fixed displacement motor for open and closed loop circuits, fixed swivel angle, both output directions of rotation possible.
Variable displacement motor, type A6VM		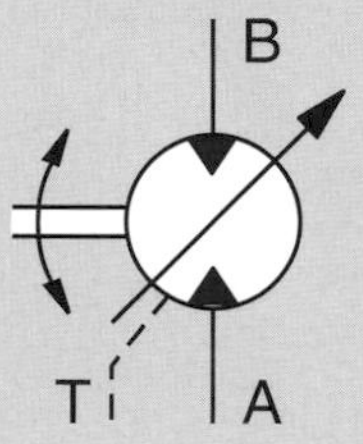 B, T, A	Variable displacement motor for open and closed loop circuits, swivel angle smoothly adjustable (single sided), both output directions of rotation possible.
Variable displacement motor, type A7VO	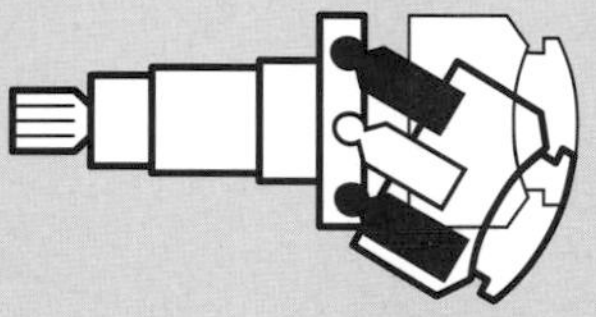	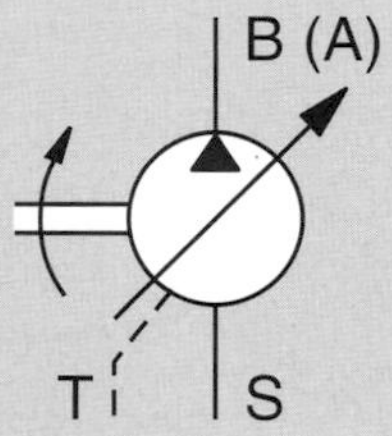 B (A), T, S	Variable displacement pump for open loop circuit, swivel angle smoothly adjustable (single sided), single output direction of rotation possible.
Variable displacement motor, type A2V	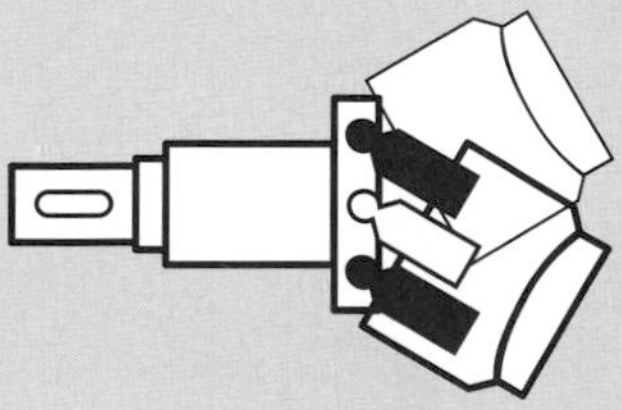	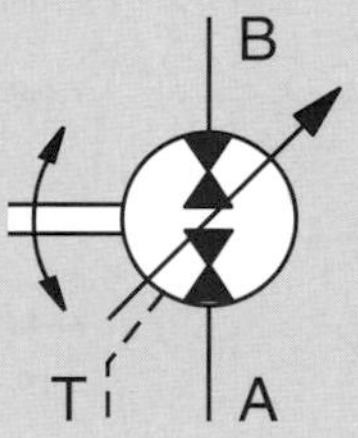 B, T, A	Variable displacement pump, angles may be changed on both sides, swivel angle smoothly adjusted through zero position, both output directions of rotation possible.

Fig. 13

2.2 Swashplate

Fig. 14: *Variable displacement pump with electronic-hydraulic adjustment, speed dependent control and mounted auxilliary pump*

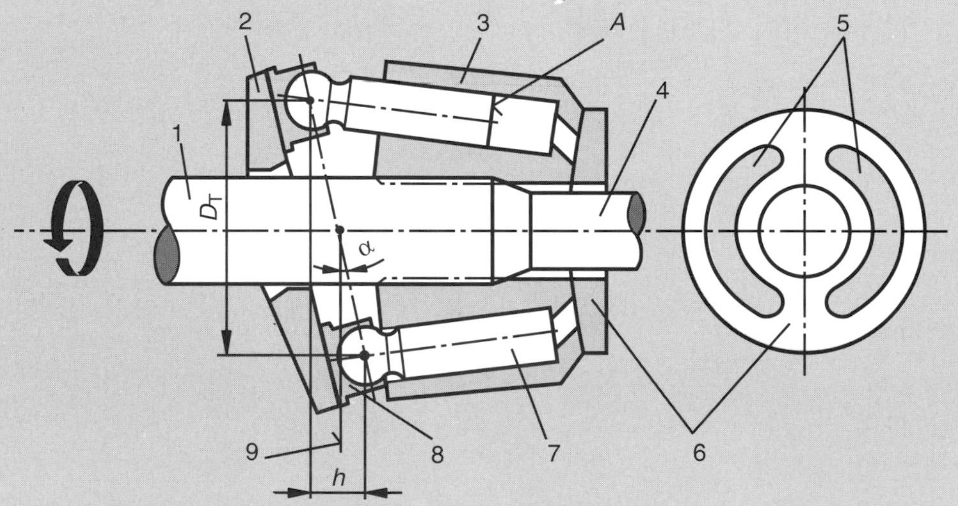

1 Drive shaft
2 Swashplate
3 Cylinder block
4 Through drive
5 Control kidneys
6 Control plate
7 Piston
8 Slipper pad
9 Zero position

$h = D_T \bullet \tan\alpha$
$V_g = x \bullet A \bullet h$
$V_g = x \bullet A \bullet D_T \bullet \tan\alpha$

h = piston stroke
A = piston area
D_T = pitch circle diameter at $\alpha = 0°$
α = swivel angle (e.g. 15°)
V_g = geometric stroke volume in cm^3
x = number of pistons (e.g. 9)

Fig. 15: *Swashplate design with fixed or variable swivel angle*

2.2.1 Swashplate principle

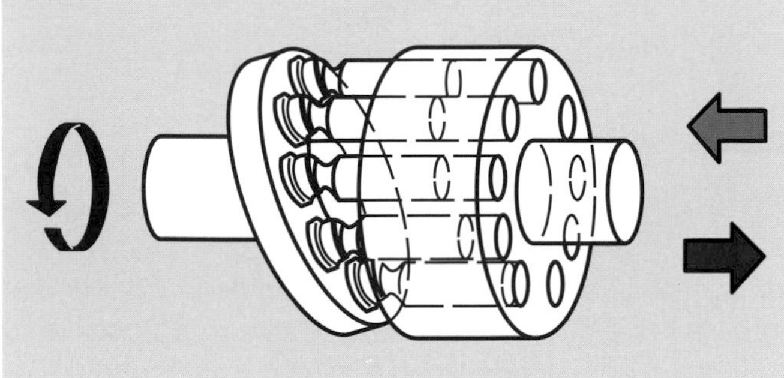

Fig. 16

The swashplate mechanism is a displacement machine, the displacement pistons of which are arranged axially to the drive shaft. The reaction force of the pistons is carried by the swashplate.

2.2.1.1 Pump function

As the drive shaft rotates, the cylinder block is driven by means of splines. The pistons move up and down within the cylinder block bores. This movement is dependent on the angle to the swashplate. Fluid is fed to the pump via the low pressure side (inlet) and then delivered via the pistons on the high pressure side (outlet) into the system.

2.2.1.2 Motor function

In contrast to the pump function, fluid is fed into the inlet. The pistons carry move up and down within the cylinder block bores and turn the cylinder block, which then turns the drive shaft via the connected splines. The fluid is pushed out of the low pressure side (outlet) and fed back into the system.

2.2.1.3 Swivel angle

The swivel angle of the swashplate in the housing in the fixed displacement unit is fixed. In a variable displacement unit the angle of the swashplate may be smoothly adjusted between specific limits. By changing the angle of the swashplate it is possible to change the piston stroke and hence the displacement volume.

2.2.2 Description of the function by means of an example of a variable displacement pump

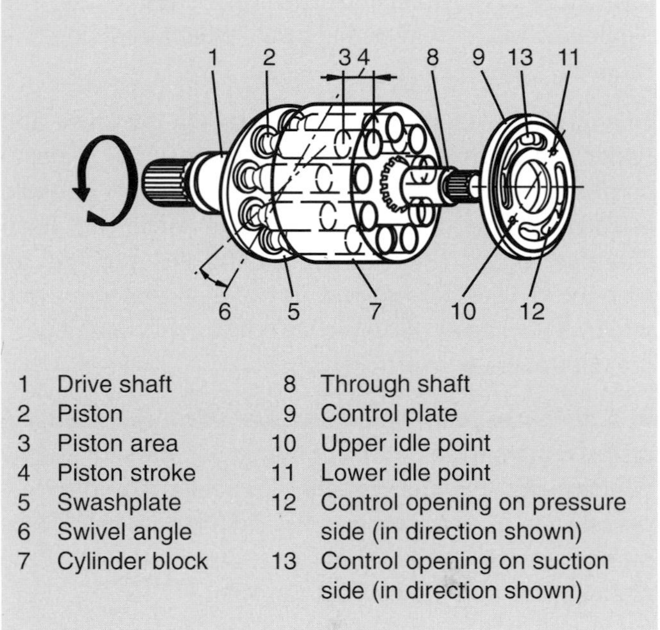

Fig. 17

2.2.2.1 Description

The axial piston units in swashplate design with constant or variable stroke volumes may operate as hydraulic pumps or hydraulic motors.

When operating as a pump the flow being delivered is proportional to the drive speed and swivel angle. If the unit is used as a motor the output speed is proportional to the flow it receives.

The torque received (pump) or produced (motor) increases as the pressure difference between the high and low pressure sides increases.

In pump operation the mechanical energy is converted into hydrostatic energy and in motor operation the hydrostatic energy is converted into mechanical energy.

In variable displacement pumps and variable displacement motors the displacement volume, i.e. the pump or motor flow may be changed by adjusting the swivel angle.

2.2.2.2 Operating as a pump

The drive shaft driven by a drive motor (e.g. diesel engine or electric motor) rotates and drives the cylinder block via splines.

The cylinder block together with its 9 pistons rotates with the drive shaft. The ends of the pistons are held by slipper pads which slide on the face of the swashplate, causing the pistons to move up and down the cylinder bores. The slipper pads are held on the swashplate by means of a retaining plate.

During a rotation each piston moves via the lower and upper idle points back to its starting position. A piston carries out a complete stroke in moving from one idle point to the other (the direction of movement of the piston changes at each idle point). During this process an amount of fluid corresponding to the piston area and stroke is sucked or delivered via both control openings in the control plate.

In a suction stroke, fluid is sucked into the increasing piston chamber, i.e. in effect the fluid is pressurised by atmospheric pressure in open loop circuits or by the boost pressure in closed loop circuits. On the other hand in a pump stroke the fluid is pushed from the piston bores into the hydraulic system.

2.2.2.3 Operating as a motor

The motor function is the opposite of the pump function. In this case, fluid is fed from the hydraulic system to the hydraulic motor. The fluid reaches the cylinder block bores via the control openings in the control plate. Four or five cylinder block bores are situated opposite the kidney shaped control opening on the pressure side. The rest of the cylinder block bores are over the other control opening. These latter bores are connected with the return side or they are partly closed via the connection pin between the control kidneys. By loading the piston, the piston slides down the swashplate. In so doing, it takes the cylinder block which is driving with it. The cylinder block with the nine pistons rotates with the drive shaft and the pistons carry out a stroke movement. The hydraulic pressure creates the torque at the cylinder block and hence the rotation of the drive shaft. The amount of flow being fed to the motor determines the output speed.

2.2.2.4 Adjustment (in variable displacement units)

The angle of the swashplate may be changed e.g. mechanically via a stub shaft or hydraulically via positioning pistons. The swashplate is held lightly in position by roller or friction bearings and its zero position is spring centred. As the swivel angle is increased the displacement volume and torque increase. As this angle is decreased these values decrease accordingly. If the swivel angle is zero, then the displacement volume is zero. It is usual to have mechanically or hydraulically acting adjustment devices, which may be controlled either mechanically, hydraulically or electrically. Well-known examples of these types of control are: electronic proportional control, pressure control (zero stroke control), power control.

2.2.2.5 General

Pumps and motors in the swashplate design are suitable for use in open and closed loop circuits. Due to their design, they are mainly used as pumps in closed loop circuits. The advantage in this is that it is possible to mount auxiliary or additional pumps on the through drive and to make use of the integrated design of adjustment device and valves. In addition, this compact, space and weight saving unit is capable of having a long life, as the slipper pads are on hydrostatic bearings (plain bearings). The force resolution (piston forces/torque) is via the slipper pad on the swashplate. The hydraulic part of the rotary group, i.e. the cylinder block with piston and control plate forms part of a balanced force system. The drive shaft bearings are able to absorb external forces. The principle of the spherical control surface, its lubrication, the pre-tensioning of the cylinder block via plate springs, etc. is comparable to the function of the bent axis rotary group.

2.2.3 Rotary group forces

Representation in force parallelogram of a variable displacement unit

The resolution of the forces takes place at the swashplate in the slipper pads and cylinder block. The piston slipper pads have hydrostatic bearings and hence ensure that the rotary groups have a long service life.

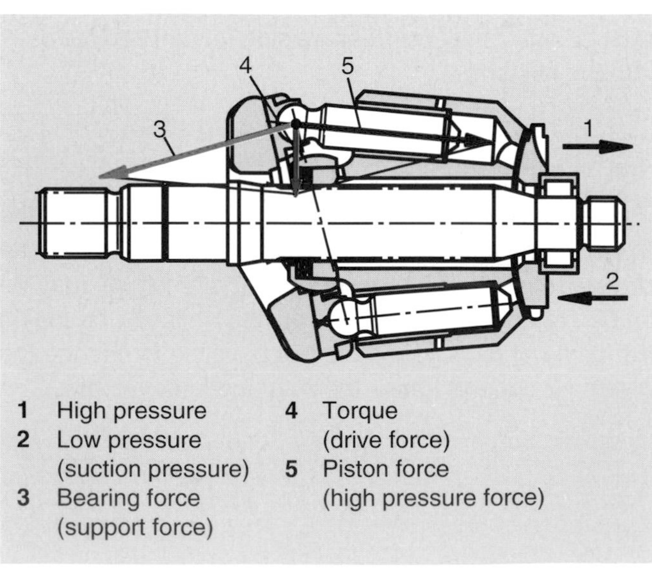

Fig. 15: *Swashplate design with fixed or variable swivel angle*

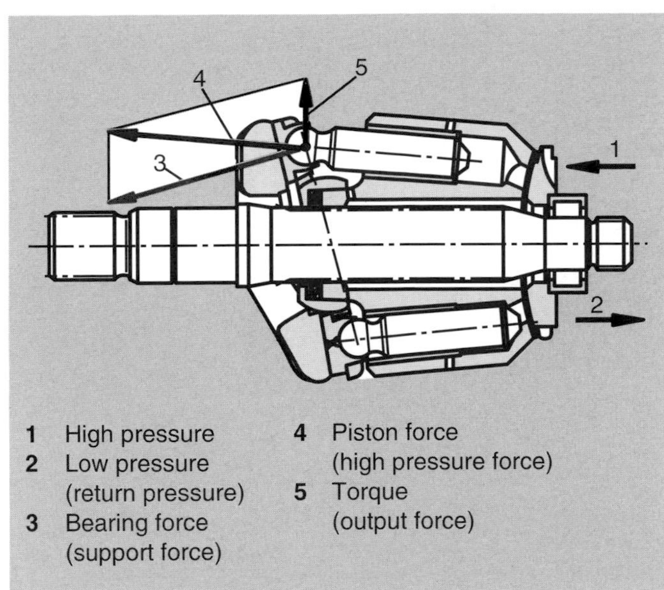

Fig. 19: *Resolution of forces at the swashplate of a motor*

2.2.4 Swashplate rotary group (simplified representation)

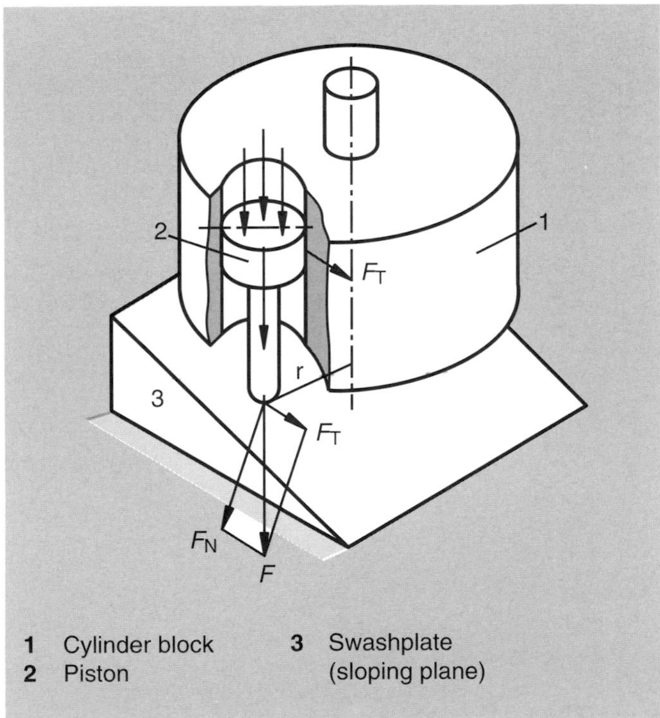

Fig. 20: *Basic components of swashplate rotary group*

2.2.4.1 Swashplate rotary group operating as a motor

As explained in the functional description, the piston is fed fluid from the pump and hence pushed against the sloping surface.

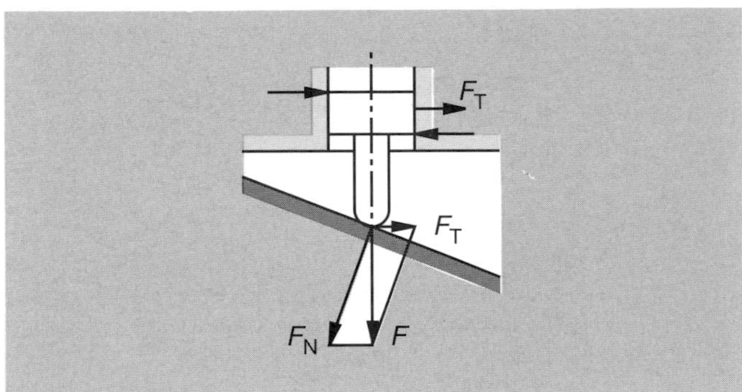

Fig. 21: *Resolution of forces*

Resolving the forces at the point of contact (friction bearing) with the sloping surface, a bearing force and a torque force component (F_N and F_T) are obtained. The piston slides down the sloping surface, carries out a stroke movement and in so doing takes the cylinder block and drive shaft along with it. However, as the piston can tilt (as far as the clearance allows) in the cylinder block bore, a greater frictional resistance occurs at the moment the unit is started than during a normal stroke movement (stick/slip). This double resolution of forces is the reason for the slightly lower initial efficiency of the swashplate as compared with the simple resolution of forces of the bent axis. In practice, this initial efficiency may be important in motor operation, but not in pump operation.

2.2.5 Types

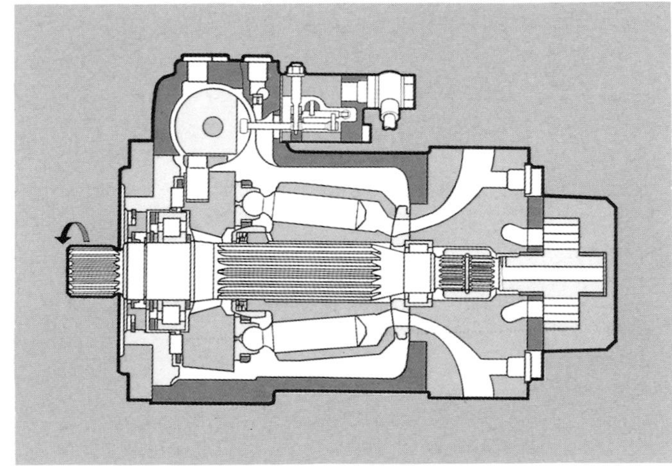

Fig. 22: *Variable displacement pump for closed loop circuit, type A4VG*

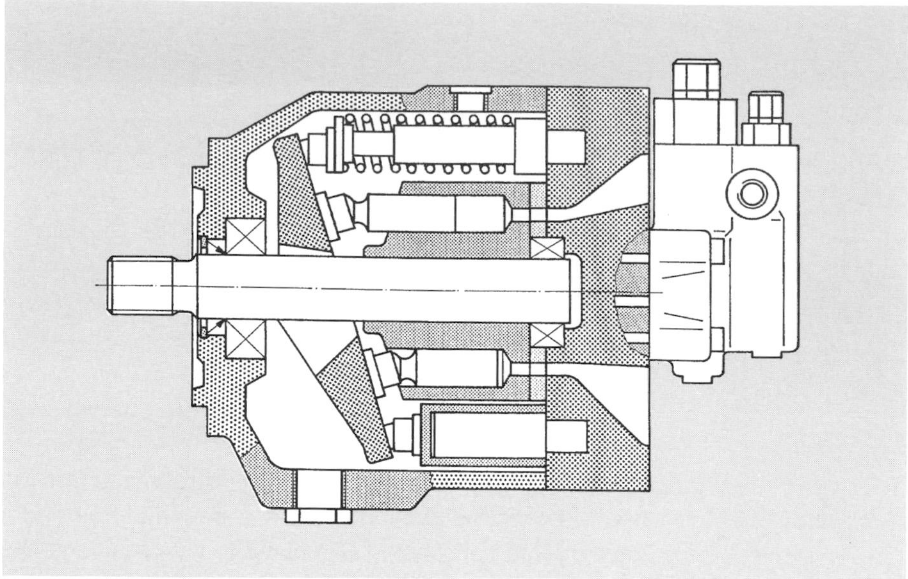

Fig. 23: *Variable displacement pump for open loop circuit, type A10VO*

2.2.6 Symbols

Type	Schematic diagram	Symbol	Description
Variable displacement pump, type A4VG	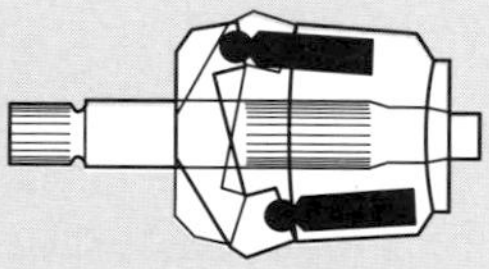	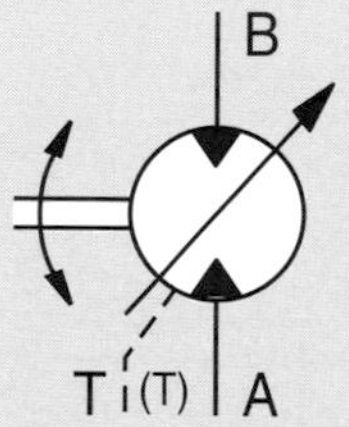 B, T (T), A	Variable displacement pump for closed loop circuit, angles may be changed on both sides, swivel angle smoothly adjusted through zero position, both output directions of rotation possible.
Variable displacement pump, type A4VO	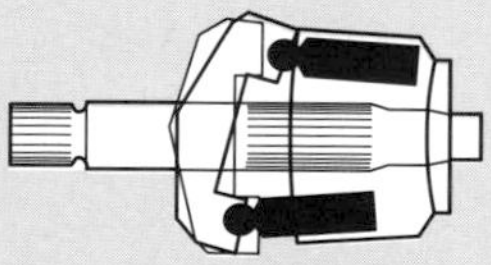	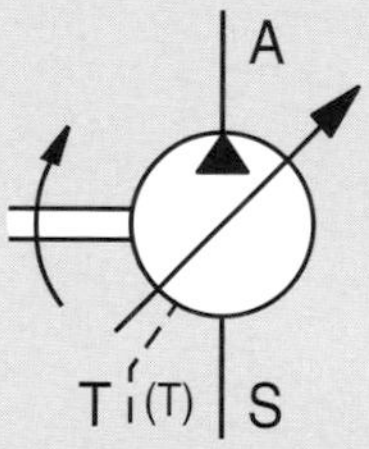 A, T (T), S	Variable displacement pump for open loop circuit, angle may be changed on one side, swivel angle smoothly adjusted, single output direction of rotation possible.
Fixed displacement motor, type A4FM	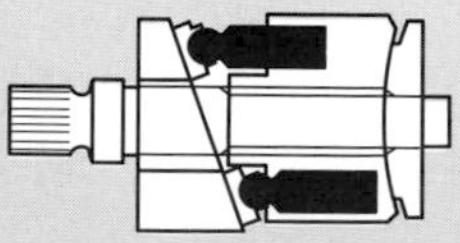	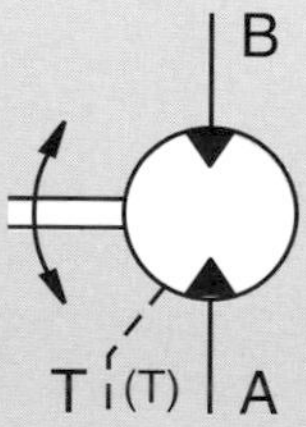 B, T (T), A	Fixed displacement motor for open or closed loop circuit, fixed swivel angle, both output directions of rotation possible.
Variable displacement pump, type A10V	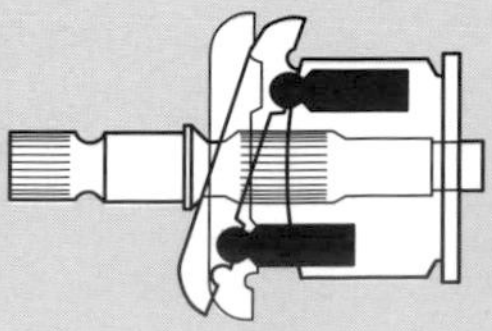	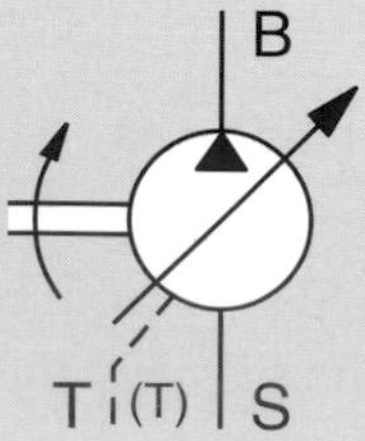 B, T (T), S	Variable displacement pump for open loop circuit, angle may be changed on one side, swivel angle smoothly adjusted, single output direction of rotation possible.

Fig. 24

2.2.8 Basic calculations for axial piston units in bent axis design

Determination of pump size	Fixed displacement pump	Variable displacement pump
Flow in L/min	$Q = \frac{V_g \bullet n \bullet \eta_{vol}}{1000}$	$Q = \frac{V_{g\,max} \bullet n \bullet \sin\alpha \bullet \eta_{vol}}{1000 \bullet \sin\alpha_{max}}$
Drive speed in rpm	$n = \frac{Q \bullet 1000}{V_g \bullet \eta_{vol}}$	$n = \frac{Q \bullet 1000 \bullet \sin\alpha_{max}}{V_{g\,max} \bullet \eta_{vol} \bullet \sin\alpha}$
Drive torque in Nm	$M = \frac{V_g \bullet \Delta p}{20 \bullet \pi \bullet \eta_{mh}} = \frac{1{,}59 \bullet V_g \bullet \Delta p}{100 \bullet \eta_{mh}}$	$M = \frac{V_{g\,max} \bullet \Delta p \bullet \sin\alpha}{20 \bullet \pi \bullet \eta_{mh} \bullet \sin\alpha_{max}}$ $= \frac{1{,}59 \bullet V_{g\,max} \bullet \Delta p \bullet \sin\alpha}{100 \bullet \eta_{mh} \bullet \sin\alpha_{max}}$
Drive power in kW	$P = \frac{2 \bullet \pi \bullet M \bullet n}{60000} = \frac{M \bullet n}{9549}$ $P = \frac{Q \bullet \Delta p}{600 \bullet \eta_{vol} \bullet \eta_{mh}} = \frac{Q \bullet \Delta p}{600 \bullet \eta_t}$	$P = \frac{2 \bullet \pi \bullet M \bullet n}{60000} = \frac{M \bullet n}{9549}$ $P = \frac{Q \bullet \Delta p}{600 \bullet \eta_{vol} \bullet \eta_{mh}} = \frac{Q \bullet \Delta p}{600 \bullet \eta_t}$
Determination of motor size	Fixed displacement motor	Variable displacement motor
Flow in L/min	$Q = \frac{V_g \bullet n}{1000 \bullet \eta_{vol}}$	$Q = \frac{V_{g\,max} \bullet n \bullet \sin\alpha}{1000 \bullet \eta_{vol} \bullet \sin\alpha_{max}}$
Output speed in rpm	$n = \frac{Q \bullet 1000 \bullet \eta_{vol}}{V_g}$	$n = \frac{Q \bullet 1000 \bullet \eta_{vol} \bullet \sin\alpha_{max}}{V_{g\,max} \bullet \sin\alpha}$
Output torque in Nm	$M = \frac{V_g \bullet \Delta p \bullet \eta_{mh}}{20 \bullet \pi} = \frac{1{,}59 \bullet V_g \bullet \Delta p \bullet \eta_{mh}}{100}$	$M = \frac{V_{g\,max} \bullet \Delta p \bullet \eta_{mh} \bullet \sin\alpha}{20 \bullet \pi \bullet \sin\alpha_{max}}$ $= \frac{1{,}59 \bullet V_{g\,max} \bullet \Delta p \bullet \eta_{mh} \bullet \sin\alpha}{100 \bullet \sin\alpha_{max}}$
Output torque in kW	$P = \frac{2 \bullet \pi \bullet M \bullet n}{60000} = \frac{M \bullet n}{9549}$ $P = \frac{Q \bullet \Delta p}{600} \bullet \eta_{vol} \bullet \eta_{mh} = \frac{Q \bullet \Delta p \bullet \eta_t}{600}$	$P = \frac{2 \bullet \pi \bullet M \bullet n}{60000} = \frac{M \bullet n}{9549}$ $P = \frac{Q \bullet \Delta p}{600} \bullet \eta_{vol} \bullet \eta_{mh} = \frac{Q \bullet \Delta p \bullet \eta_t}{600}$

Table 2

Where:

Q	= flow	in L/min
M	= drive torque (pump) output torque (motor)	in Nm in Nm
P	= drive power (pump) output power (motor)	in kW in kW
V_g	= geometric stroke volume	in cm^3
$V_{g\,max}$	= max. geometric stroke volume	in cm^3
n	= speed	in rpm
α_{max}	= max. swivel angle (varies depending on model)	in °
α	= set swivel angle (may be between 0° and α_{max})	in °
η_{vol}	= volumetric efficiency	
η_{mh}	= mechanical-hydraulic efficiency	
η_t	= total efficiency ($\eta_t = \eta_{vol} \bullet \eta_{mh}$)	
Δp	= pressure drop	in bar

2.2.7 Basic calculations for axial piston units in swashplate design

Determination of pump size		Fixed displacement pump	Variable displacement pump
Flow	in L/min	$Q = \dfrac{V_g \cdot n \cdot \eta_{vol}}{1000}$	$Q = \dfrac{V_{g\,max} \cdot n \cdot \tan\alpha \cdot \eta_{vol}}{1000 \cdot \tan\alpha_{max}}$
Speed	in rpm	$n = \dfrac{Q \cdot 1000}{V_g \cdot \eta_{vol}}$	$n = \dfrac{Q \cdot 1000 \cdot \tan\alpha_{max}}{V_{g\,max} \cdot \eta_{vol} \cdot \tan\alpha}$
Drive torque	in Nm	$M = \dfrac{V_g \cdot \Delta p}{20 \cdot \pi \cdot \eta_{mh}} = \dfrac{1{,}59 \cdot V_g \cdot \Delta p}{100 \cdot \eta_{mh}}$	$M = \dfrac{V_{g\,max} \cdot \Delta p \cdot \tan\alpha}{20 \cdot \pi \cdot \eta_{mh} \cdot \tan\alpha_{max}}$ $= \dfrac{1{,}59 \cdot V_{g\,max} \cdot \Delta p \cdot \tan\alpha}{100 \cdot \eta_{mh} \cdot \tan\alpha_{max}}$
Drive power	in kW	$P = \dfrac{2 \cdot \pi \cdot M \cdot n}{60000} = \dfrac{M \cdot n}{9549}$ $P = \dfrac{Q \cdot \Delta p}{600 \cdot \eta_{vol} \cdot \eta_{mh}} = \dfrac{Q \cdot \Delta p}{600 \cdot \eta_t}$	$P = \dfrac{2 \cdot \pi \cdot M \cdot n}{60000} = \dfrac{M \cdot n}{9549}$ $P = \dfrac{Q \cdot \Delta p}{600 \cdot \eta_{vol} \cdot \eta_{mh}} = \dfrac{Q \cdot \Delta p}{600 \cdot \eta_t}$
Determination of motor size		Fixed displacement motor	Variable displacement motor
Flow	in L/min	$Q = \dfrac{V_g \cdot n}{1000 \cdot \eta_{vol}}$	$Q = \dfrac{V_{g\,max} \cdot n \cdot \tan\alpha}{1000 \cdot \eta_{vol} \cdot \tan\alpha_{max}}$
Speed	in rpm	$n = \dfrac{Q \cdot 1000 \cdot \eta_{vol}}{V_g}$	$n = \dfrac{Q \cdot 1000 \cdot \eta_{vol} \cdot \tan\alpha_{max}}{V_{g\,max} \cdot \tan\alpha}$
Drive torque	in Nm	$M = \dfrac{V_g \cdot \Delta p \cdot \eta_{mh}}{20 \cdot \pi} = \dfrac{1{,}59 \cdot V_g \cdot \Delta p \cdot \eta_{mh}}{100}$	$M = \dfrac{V_{g\,max} \cdot \Delta p \cdot \eta_{mh} \cdot \tan\alpha}{20 \cdot \pi \cdot \tan\alpha_{max}}$ $= \dfrac{1{,}59 \cdot V_{g\,max} \cdot \Delta p \cdot \eta_{mh} \cdot \tan\alpha}{100 \cdot \tan\alpha_{max}}$
Drive power	in kW	$P = \dfrac{2 \cdot \pi \cdot M \cdot n}{60000} = \dfrac{M \cdot n}{9549}$ $P = \dfrac{Q \cdot \Delta p}{600} \cdot \eta_{vol} \cdot \eta_{mh} = \dfrac{Q \cdot \Delta p \cdot \eta_t}{600}$	$P = \dfrac{2 \cdot \pi \cdot M \cdot n}{60000} = \dfrac{M \cdot n}{9549}$ $P = \dfrac{Q \cdot \Delta p}{600} \cdot \eta_{vol} \cdot \eta_{mh} = \dfrac{Q \cdot \Delta p \cdot \eta_t}{600}$

Table 1

Where:

Q	= flow	in L/min
M	= drive torque (pump) output torque (motor)	in Nm in Nm
P	= drive power (pump) output power (motor)	in kW in kW
V_g	= geometric stroke volume	in cm^3
$V_{g\,max}$	= max. geometric stroke volume	in cm^3
n	= speed	in rpm
α_{max}	= max. swivel angle (various depending on type)	in °
α	= set swivel angle (may be between 0° and α_{max})	in °
η_{vol}	= volumetric efficiency	
η_{mh}	= mechanical-hydraulic efficiency	
η_t	= total efficiency ($\eta_t = \eta_{vol} \cdot \eta_{mh}$)	
Δp	= pressure drop	in bar

3 Components

3.1 Fixed displacement motors and pumps - bent axis design

Features:

- Direct drive of cylinder block block via tapered pistons
- Tapered pistons with piston rings for sealing
- Robust tapered roller bearings with long lives
- Flange and shaft ends to ISO or SAE standard
- Two drain case ports as standard
- Direct mounting of deceleration valve possible
- Model variations for special applications
- Nominal pressure of up to 400 bar
- Peak pressure of up to 450 bar

3.1.1 Fixed displacement motor

This unit may be used as a motor in both open and closed loop circuits. It is used in mobile and stationary industrial applications, that is, wherever a constant displacement is required for hydrostatic power transfer.

Fig. 25: *Fixed displacement motor, type A2FM*

3.1.2 Fixed displacement pump

The A2FM pump may be converted into an A2FO pump via a suitable port plate. This is suitable for the open loop circuit and its main features are: robust, reliable, long life and low noise (not illustrated).

3.1.3 Fixed displacement pumps for lorries

This pump has special characteristics and connection dimensions suitable for use in trucks. It is designed for a pressure range of 250 to 350 bar. If a change in the direction of rotation is required (e.g. with a different gear box), the direction of rotation of the drive may be changed for the pump in open loop by simply rotating the port plate.

Fig. 26: *Fixed displacement pump for trucks, type KFA2FO*

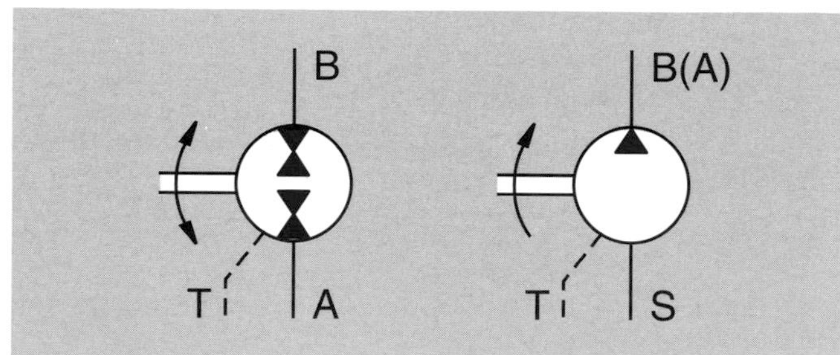

Fig. 27: *Left: Fixed displacement motor/pump for two directions of flow; Right: fixed displacement pump for one direction of flow*

3.2 Variable displacement motors in bent axis design for open and closed loop circuits

Features:

- A larger control range in hydrostatic drives due to the variable displacement motors
- Fulfilment of the requirement of higher speed and high torque
- Reduction of cost by saving on multi-ratio gear boxes or by possibly using smaller pumps
- Low power weight
- Good starting characteristic
- Various control and adjustment devices
- Single sided swivel action
- Nominal pressure is 400 bar
- Peak pressure is 450 bar

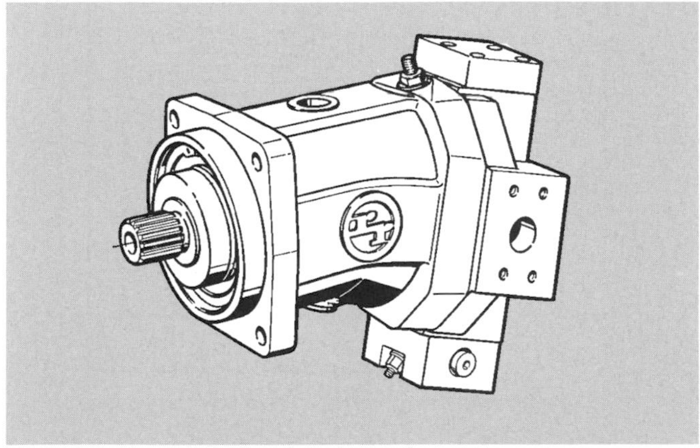

Fig. 28: Variable displacement motor, type A6VM...HA

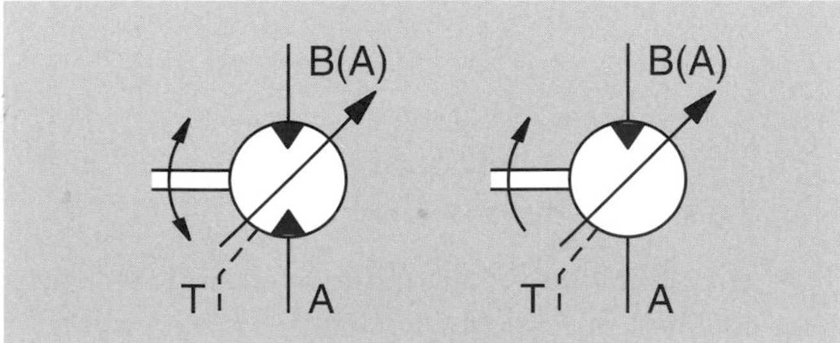

Fig. 29: *Left: Variable displacement motor for two directions of flow; Right: For one direction of flow*

3.2.1 Automatic adjustment device, dependent on high pressure

The A6VM variable displacement motor has a rotary group which operates to the bent axis principle. Torque is produced direct at the drive shaft. The cylinder block is directly driven by the tapered pistons. The rotary group swivel angle is changed by moving the control lens along a circular track via a positioning piston.

Given the condition that pump flow and high pressure must remain unchanged, the following is valid:

- As the angle is decreased, the speed increases and the possible torque decreases.
- As the angle is increased, the torque increases and the possible speed decreases.

The designation "HA" indicates that the adjustment of the motor is dependent on high pressure. The displacement is automatically set, dependent on the operating pressure. Once the operating pressure set at the control valve has been reached (measured internally at A or B), the motor switches over from V_{gmin} to V_{gmax}. The motor remains at the minimum swivel angle below the set value.

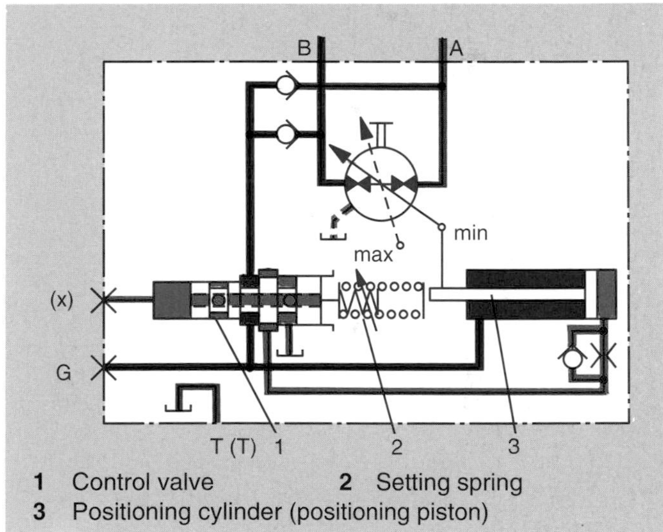

1 Control valve **2** Setting spring
3 Positioning cylinder (positioning piston)

Fig. 30: *High pressure dependent adjustment device*

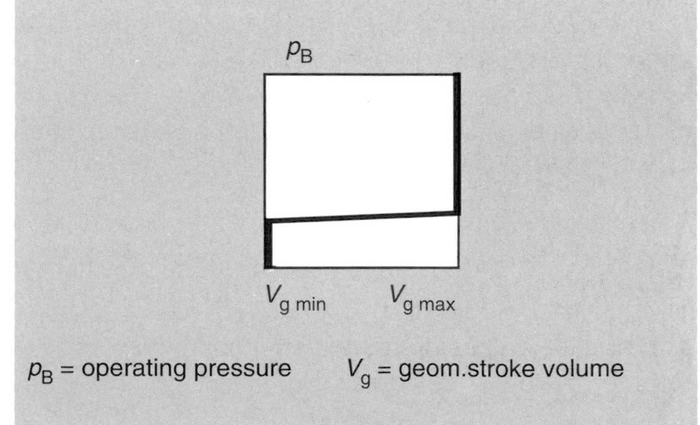

p_B = operating pressure V_g = geom.stroke volume

Diagram 1: *Automatic adjustment dependent on high pressure*

3.3 Variable displacement pump in bent axis design for open loop circuits

Features:

- Axial tapered piston rotary group
- Direct drive of cylinder block block via tapered pistons
- Robust long life bearings
- Flow setting from V_{g0} to V_{gmax}
- Power control with exact hyperbolic operating curve
- Pressure control, hydraulic and electrical adjustment units, load sensing operation possible
- High pressure range up to 350/400 bar
- Used in mobile and industrial applications

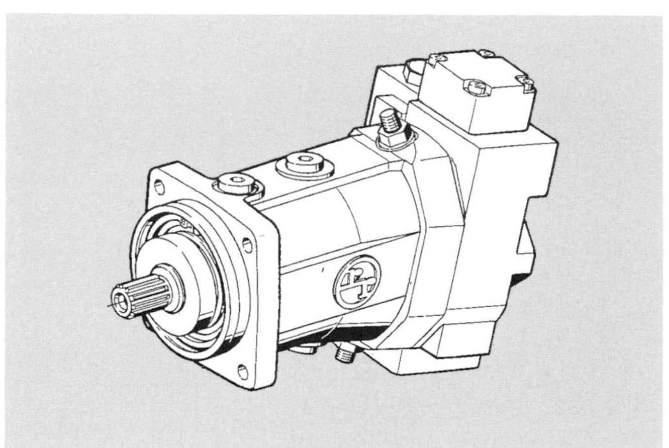

Fig. 31: *Variable displacement pump, type A7VOLR, with power controller built into the port plate*

3.3.1 Application in high pressure range

The A7VO variable displacement pump is a pump with internal leakage oil return for open loop circuits. The rotary group operating to the bent axis principle combines robustness and good self-aspiration. The drive shaft bearings are used to support external forces. If high requirements are made on the input of forces and on the running time, a rotary group is available with extra bearings (A7VTO).

The rotary group swivel angle may be changed by moving the control lens along a circular track via a positioning piston.

If the swivel angle is increased, the pump flow and the required drive torque increase.

If the swivel angle is decreased, the pump flow and the required drive torque decrease. The maximum swivel angle is, for example, 25 or 26.5°; the minimum is 0°. The pump is controlled dependent on the operating pressure or adjusted via external control signals. The required positioning energy is taken from the pressure side.

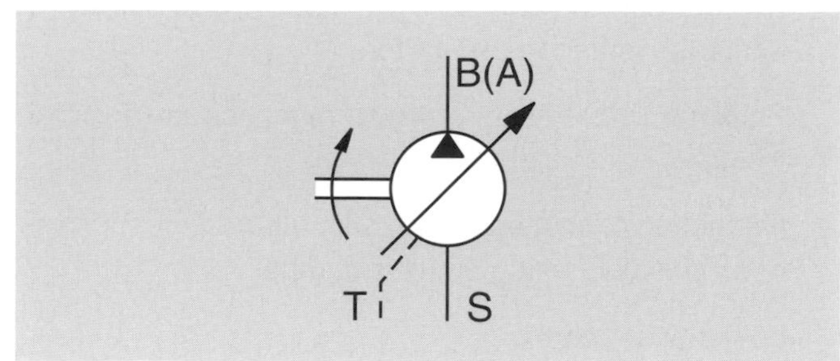

Fig. 32: *Variable displacement pump for 1 direction of flow*

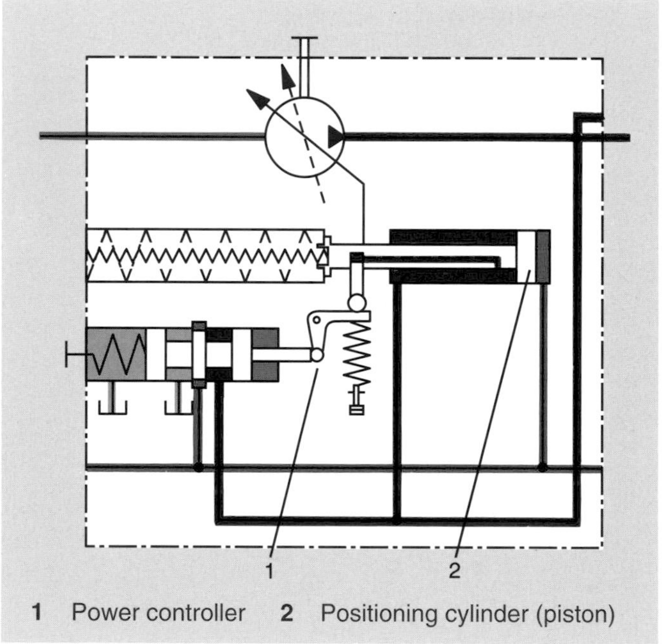

1 Power controller **2** Positioning cylinder (piston)

Fig. 33: *Variable displacement pump with power controller*

3.3.2 Power controller LR (Comparison between spring control/hyperbola control)

The controller ensures that the torque M (Nm) received is kept constant. In connection with a constant speed n (rpm), the function power control is obtained. The mechanical drive power $P = M \cdot n$ (kW) is opposed by the hydraulic output power $P = Q \cdot p$ (kW). Whilst the operating pressure p (bar) is dependent on the load, the flow Q (L/min) may be changed by the swivel angle.

Similarly to a computer, the controller continually multiplies pressure and flow and compares the result with the set value. If a positive deviation occurs the swivel angle is decreased and if a negative deviation occurs this angle is increased. The controller may be set (srewing in of the setting screw = rising set value).

Control is started at the max. swivel angle. The position when control is finished is given by the maximum pressure. In addition, deviating from this, both end values may be limited by strop screws. Be careful: if the maximum set angle is increased there is danger of cavitation in the pump and danger of overspeeding in the motor! If the minimum set angle is increased the drive motor may be overloaded in the high pressure range.

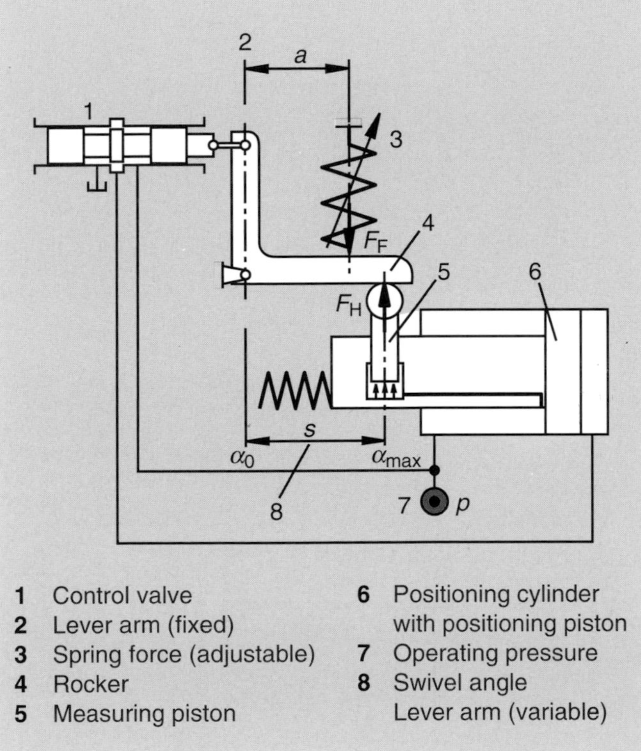

Fig. 34: *Power controller*

The operating pressure acts on a rocker in the positioning piston via a measuring piston. In opposition to this is a spring force (externally set), which determines the power set. If the operating pressure p exceeds the calculated permissible value from the power calculation $P = Q \cdot p$ (kW), the control valve is operated via the rocker and the pump is returned. The flow is reduced until the product of $Q \cdot p$ corresponds to the power available again. The ideal hyperbola has been reached and the drive is not overloaded due to the "power control". Conversely, the pump flow, depending on the operating pressure, may be increased to its max. value via a return spring.

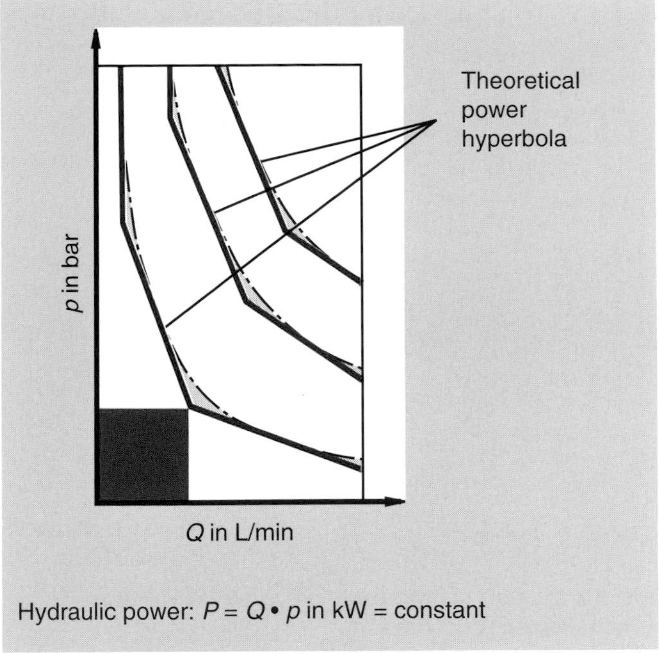

Diagram 2: *p-Q operating curve for a spring controller with aproximate operating curve*

Features:
- Power matching via exchange of spring package
- Slight power losses in shaded regions
- No zero stroke position, i.e. residual flow at high pressure produces heat

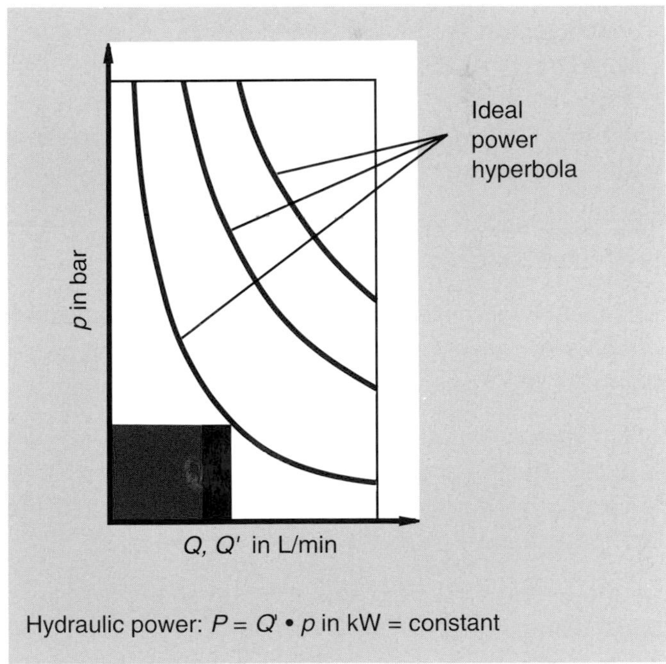

Diagram 3: *p-Q operating curve for a hyperbolic controller with ideal hyperbolic operating curve*

Features:
- Optimum power matching via external smooth adjustable spring force
- Zero stroke position, i.e. no residual flow

3.3.3 Double variable displacement pump with 2 parallel bent axis rotary groups

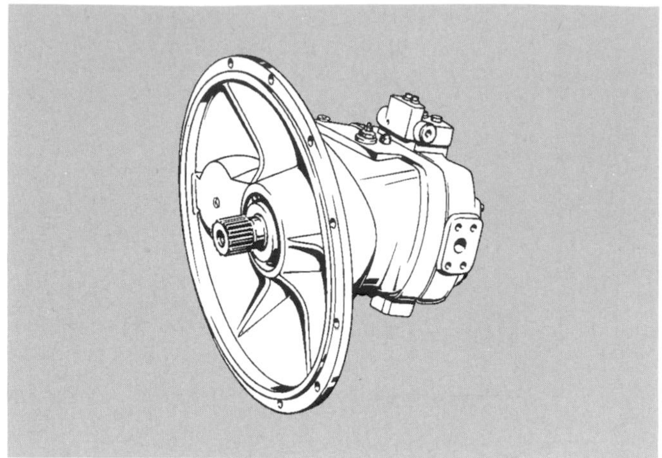

Fig. 35: *Variable displacement pump A8VO...SR with summation power controller*

Two variable displacement pumps - one drive.
This is an advantageous combination of two individual pumps with integral splitter box.

At present, models with an auxiliary drive and/or auxiliary pump for the supply of additional hydraulic circuits are the standard ones used, especially in mobile applications.

To complement the power control of an individual pump (see A7VLR, *fig. 34*), in two parallel circuits the A8VSR pump with summation power control (for example) is installed. This means that the complete drive power is distributed to both circuits in the ratio of their pressures.

The high pressure signal produced in the summator valve is used as a measurement value.

The ideal hyperbolic power operating curve is attained, once the torque forces acting on the rocker of the power controller are balanced.

The hydraulic torque, formed from the high pressure force F_H and the angular displacement s, is only allowed to be as large as the mechanical torque obtained from the set spring force F_F and the fixed lever arm *a*.

As the hydraulic system sets the operating pressure p and the pump can only change its flow Q, this means that when the power is exceeded the pump swivel angle is automatically reduced. The angular displacement is decreased until the hydraulic torque obtained from it is the same as the given mechanical torque.

In practice, individual or combined controls are used. Common variations are e.g. load limiting control, 3 point control, load sensing, etc.

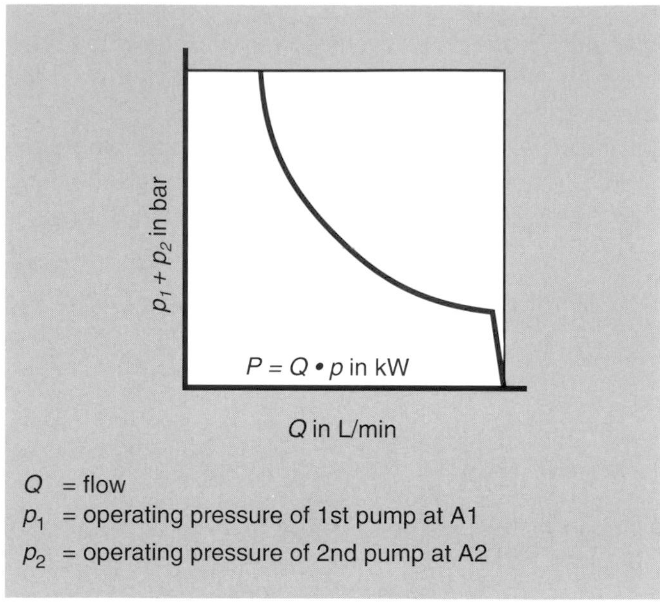

Diagram 4: *p-Q operating curve for summation power controller, hyperbolic controller*

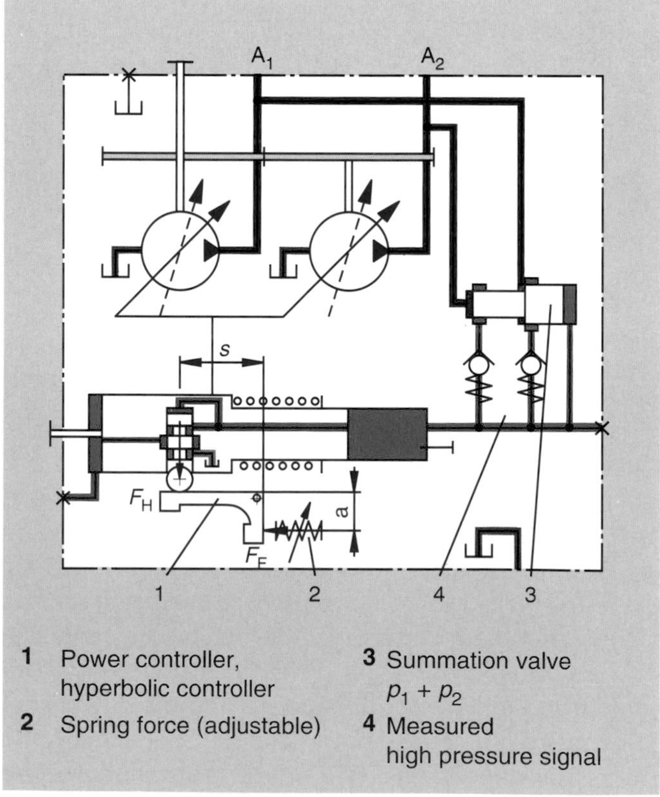

Fig. 36: *Double variable displacement pump with summation power controller*

3.4 Variable displacement pump in bent axis design for universal applications

Fig. 37: *Variable adjustment pump, type A2V*

The A2V variable displacement pump is universally suitable for use in open, closed and semi-closed loop circuits. A variety of controls for varying the displacement are available. The variations with tandem roller bearings or slipper pad bearings (for extremely long bearing lives) are especially preferred for industrial applications. By fitting the A2V with valves and auxiliary pumps, it is turned into the primary power unit A2P.

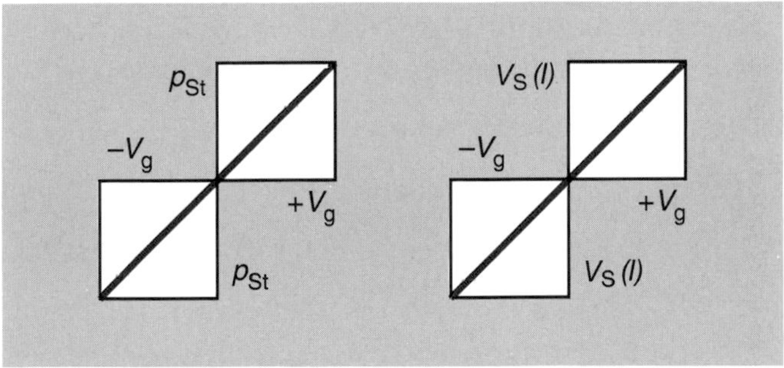

Diagram 5: *Characteristic curves of hydraulic adjustments, left: dependent on pilot pressure, right: dependent on flow (pilot flow)*

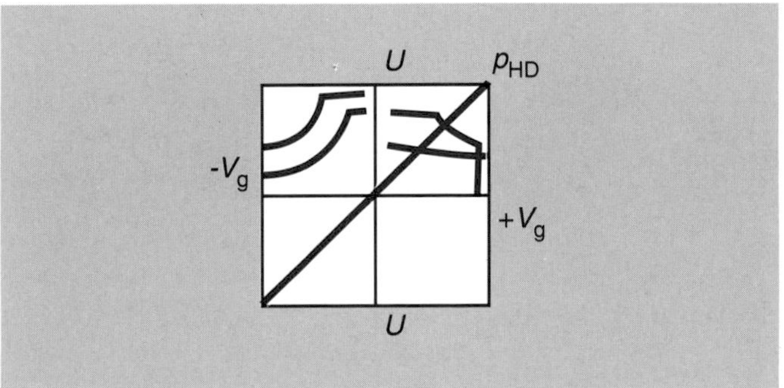

Diagram 6: *Characteristic curve of an electronic adjustment*

3.5 Variable displacement pump in swashplate design suitable for use in medium pressure range in open loop systems

The A10V axial piston pump is used in mobile and industrial fields for pressures of 250/315 bar. The variable displacement pump has the advantage over the fixed displacement pump of saving energy, e.g. by the automatic matching to force (pressure) and velocity (flow) via a combined pressure and feed flow controller.

The advantage of the swahplate design lies not only in the compact design, but also in the low power weight, long life and low noise level. The possibility of mounting further pumps on the through drive must not be neglected as an important feature.

Fig. 38: *Variable displacement pump, type A10VO...DFR*

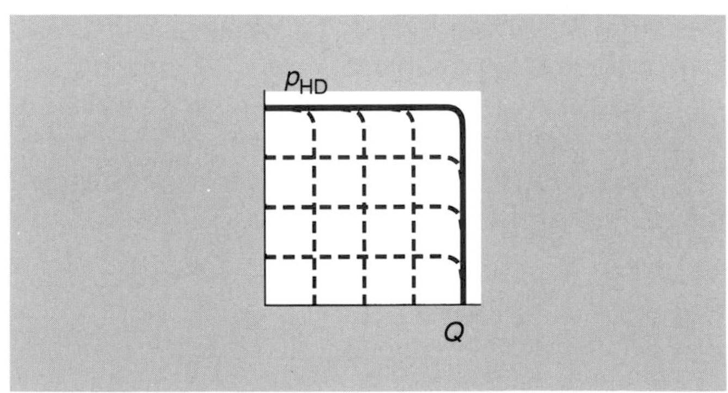

Diagram 7: *Characteristic curve of pressure/feed flow controller*

Legend to diagrams 5, 6 and 7

V_g = stroke volume
p_{HD} = operating pressure
p_{St} = pilot pressure
I = pilot current
U = pilot voltage
V_s = positioning volume
Q = flow

3.6 Variable displacement pump in swashplate design suitable for use in simple mobile applications in closed loop systems

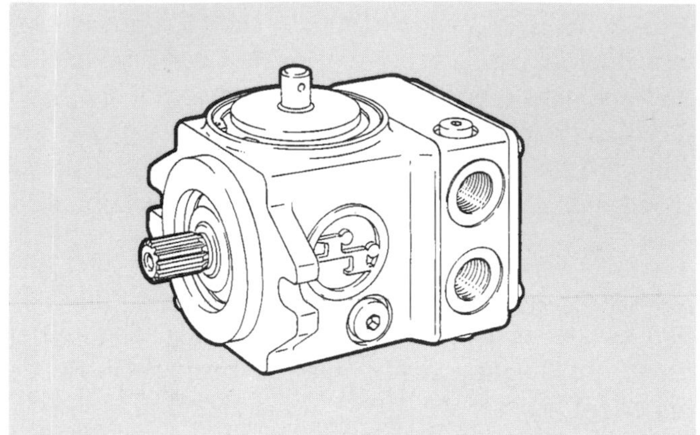

Fig. 39: *Variable displacement pump, type A11VG*

The A11VG hydraulic pump is a variable displacement pump in swahplate design for hydrostatic drives in closed loop circuits. All the valves and auxiliary pump required for it are integrated. Depending on the design, the pump may easily be converted to a multiple pump. The rotary group swivel angle may be directly changed by a rotary stub shaft without power amplification.

In zero position the pump flow is also zero. As zero is passed through, the direction of flow is smoothly changed.

If the rotary stub shaft is manually adjusted, it is directly connected to the bent axis of the rotary group. The angle of rotation of the rotary stub shaft corresponds to the swivel angle of the pump. The displacement torque produced either by hand or foot force is dependent on the high pressure and swivel angle. The limitation of displacement or angle in the positioning mechanism or the possible centring of the zero position must be carried out within the positioning mechanism.

As well as manual adjustment of the rotary stub shaft, hydraulic control mechanisms may also be used.

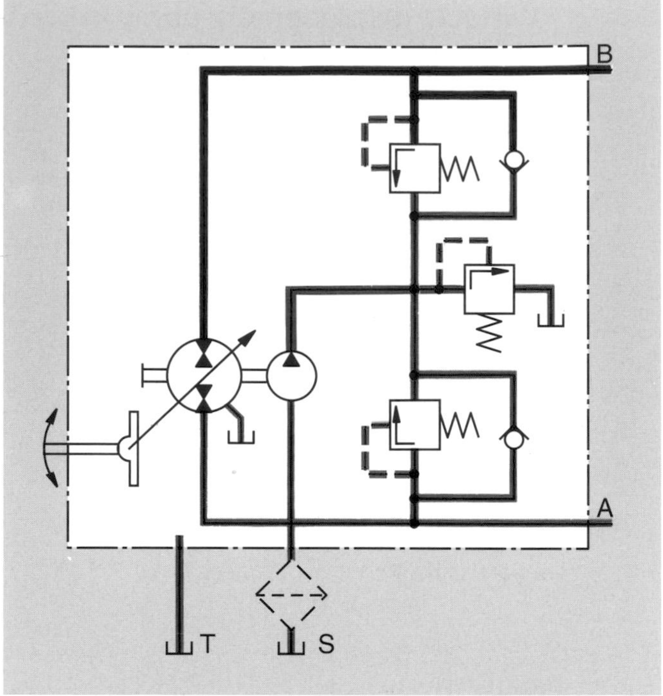

Fig. 40: *Variable displacement pump with adjustment, auxiliary pump and valves*

3.7 Variable displacement pump in swashplate design suitable for use in mobile applications in open loop systems

The control functions of the A4VO shown here may be either operated as combined or individual functions:

- Power control with hyperbolic operating curve
- Pressure control by means of isolating valve
- Load sensing control as Δp control of load pressure signal

Fig. 41: *Variable displacement pump, type A4VO*

3.7.1 Power controller

The power controller controls the flow of the pump dependent on the operating pressure, so that a set drive power at constant drive speed is not exceeded.

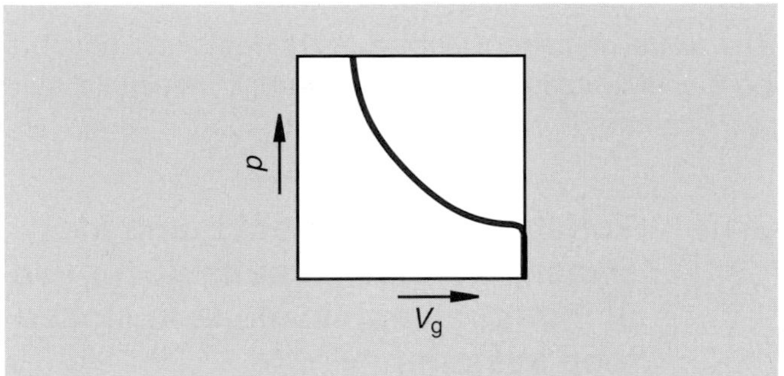

Diagram 8: *Characteristic curve of a power controller*

3.7.2 Pressure controller

The effect of pressure control is to return the pump towards $V_g = 0$ on reaching the max. operating pressure. This function is superimposed on power control.

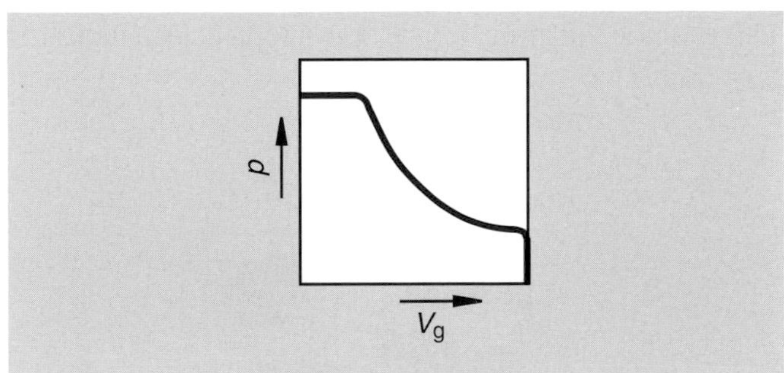

Diagram 9: *Characteristic curve of a power controller with superimposed pressure contol*

3.7.3 Load sensing controller

The load sensing controller operates as a load pressure driven flow consumption controller and matches the pump flow to the flow required from the user. The pump flow is dependent on the opening area of the directional valves, but is not effected by the load pressure in the region below the power operating curve. The power and pressure control are super-imposed on the load sensing function.

Legend to diagrams 8,9 and 10:
p = operating pressure
V_g= geom. stroke volume

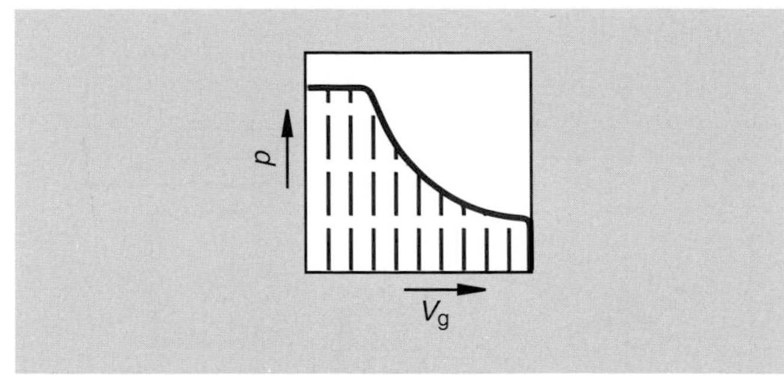

Diagram 10: *Characteristic curve of load-sensing controller*

3.8 Variable displacement pump in swashplate design suitable for use in high pressure mobile gears in closed loop systems

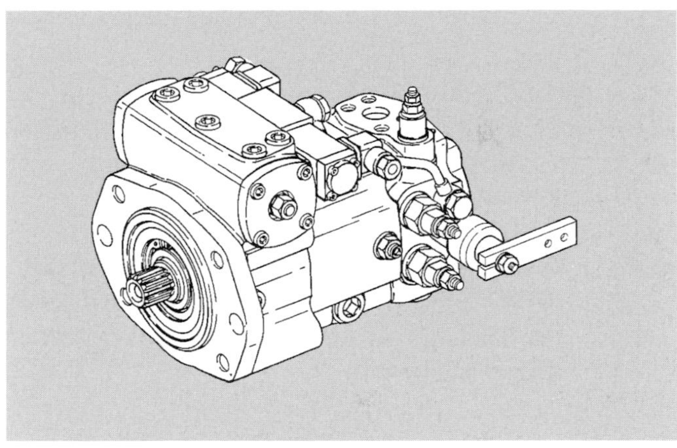

Fig. 42: *Variable displacement pump, type A4VGDA*

Similarly to that described under section 3.6, the pump A4VG is a complete power unit comprising all the components for a closed loop circuit. The unit with hydraulic adjustment with various control devices forms the typical "mobile pump". If this pump is connected to a fixed or variable displacement motor, an automatic vehicle transmission is produced.

This is a speed dependent automatic closed loop system. The pump is effected by the drive speed, operating pressure and electrically by the 2 switching solenoids. Positional energy is taken from the auxiliary circuit. The positional velocity of the pump is damped by throttles.

The speed dependent automatic control system is designed for transmission drives with internal combustion engines. It was taken into account that in internal combustion engines as the speed increases the torque increases and if the engine is loaded a speed pull-down occurs at the torque limit. The power consumption of an internal combustion engine is sufficiently accurately determined by its current speed. If the hydraulic side is suitably adapted, an optimum controlled vehicle transmission is produced.

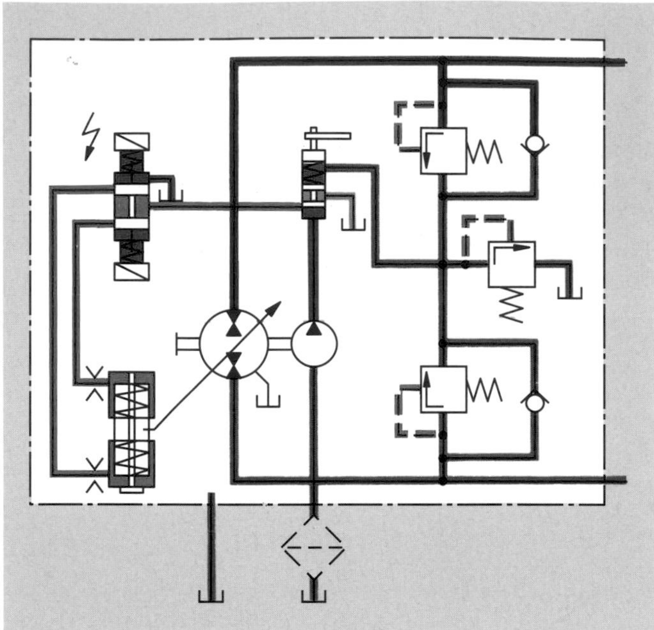

Fig. 43: *Variable displacement pump with adjustment, auxilliary pump and valves*

3.9 Variable displacement pump in swashplate design suitable for use in industrial applications in open loop systems

Fig. 44: *Variable displacement pump, type A4VSO*

This A4VSO pump especially designed for industrial applications has, in addition to the well-known advantages of swashplate design, also the advantage of long service life. Load sensing control and mooring control as well as secondary control may be used with this pump. In connection with a pressure controlled pump and its secondary controlled motor the system of secondary speed control has a high dynamic control response, exact speed control, low losses and energy recovery.

The speed control DS1 controls the adjustment unit so that the required torque is available for the speed demanded.

This torque (under conditions of quasi-constant pressure) is proportional to the displacement volume and hence proportional to the swivel angle.

The swivel angle (position) is measured by an inductive positional transducer and the speed is measured by a tachogenerator.

3.10 Variable displacement pump in swashplate design suitable for use in industrial applications in closed loop systems

Another variable displacement pump in swashplate design is mounted on the unit described in section 3.9, but this unit operates in a closed loop circuit.

When used in industrial applications the A4VSG pump may be made into a complete hydraulic drive with suitable adaption via a valve subplate, auxiliary pump, tank and cooler. It is also possible to create a semi-closed loop circuit by including anti-cavitation check valves. By using these valves it is possible to compensate for the difference in volumes, e.g. in operations using single-rod cylinders.

Fig. 45: *Variable displacement pump, type A4VSG*

3.11 Summary of common adjustment methods in axial piston units

The electronic components (amplifiers) which are used as signal amplifiers are not mentioned in the following list:

The differences between the various types of adjustment are as follows:

- Type of control circuit
- Force transmission (hydraulic or mechanical)
- Operation (direct or pilot)
- Operating curve (position and setting)
- Open loop (without feedback)
  - mechanical: manual
  - mechanical: electrical
  - hydraulic: mechanical
  - hydraulic: electrical
  - hydraulic: hydraulic
- Closed loop (with feedback)
  - hydraulic: mechanical
  - hydraulic: electrical

3.11.1 Pump adjustments

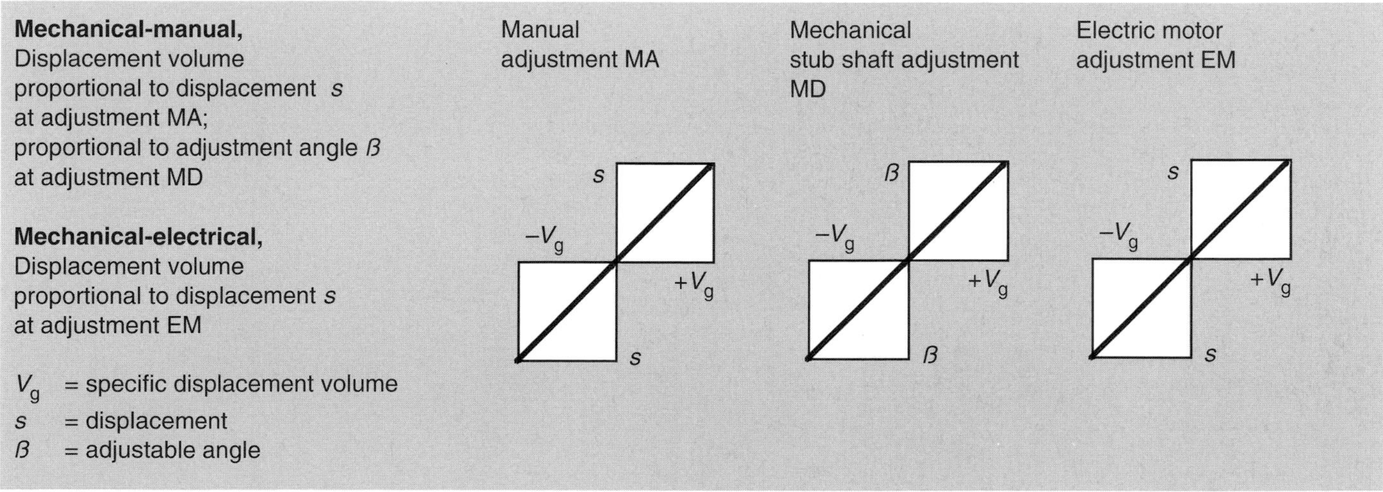

Diagram 11

Hydraulic-mechanical,
Displacement volume proportional to pilot pressure p_{St} at adjustment DG;

proportional to swivel angle β or displacement s (in pumps with reversible operation) at adjustment HW

V_g = specific displacement volume
p_{St} = pilot pressure
β = swivel angle

1) = idle range at zero position

Direct operated hydraulic adjustment pressure dependent DG

p_{St} $-V_g$ $+V_g$ p_{St}

Hydraulic adjustment stroke dependent HW [1)]

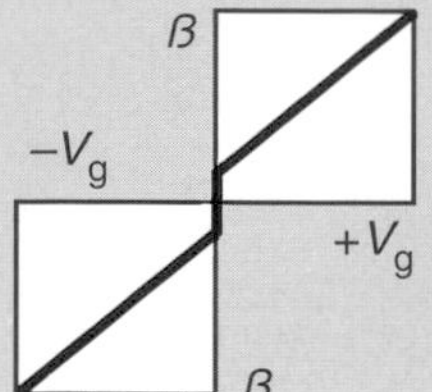

Hydraulic adjustment stroke dependent HW

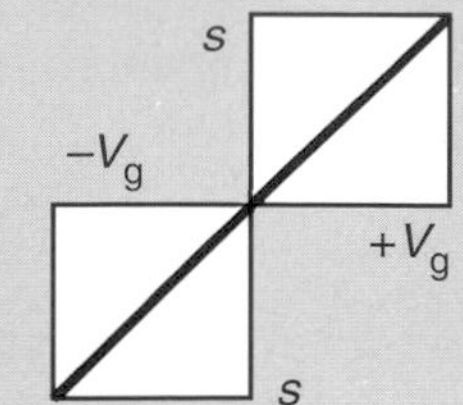

Diagram 12

Hydraulic-hydraulic,
Displacement volume proportional to pilot pressure p_{St} at adjustment HD for pumps in open loop circuits or reversible operation

V_g = specific displacment volume
p_{St} = pilot pressure

1) = idle range at zero position

Hydraulic adjustment pressure dependent HD

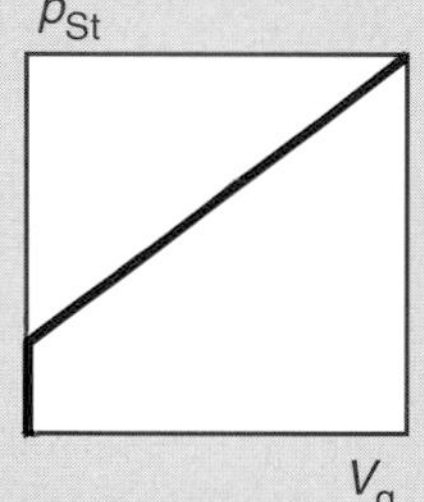

Hydraulic adjustment pressure dependent HD [1)]

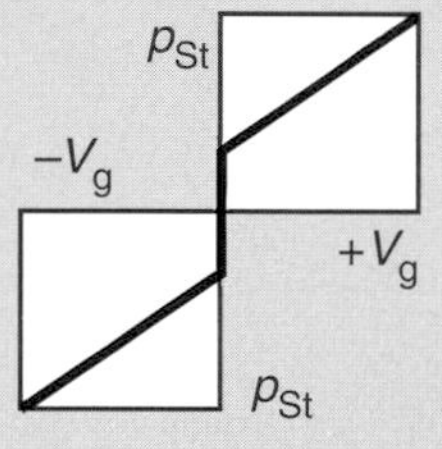

Hydraulic adjustment pressure dependent HD

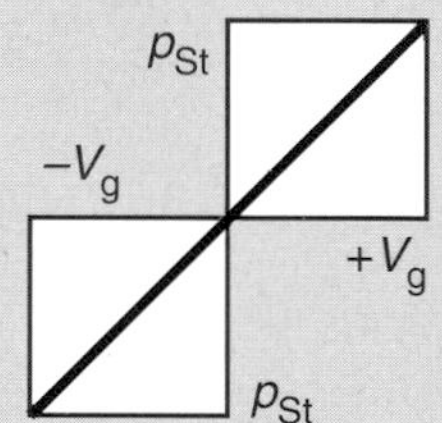

Diagram 13

Hydraulic-electronic,
Displacement volume proportional to pilot current I at adjustment EP and ES in open loop circuits or reversible operation; Adjustment EZ (with switching solenoid) (no diagram)

V_g = specific displacment volume
I = pilot current

Electronic adjustment with prop. solenoid EP

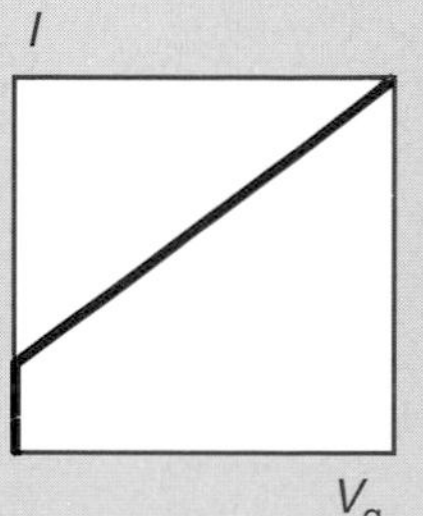

Electronic adjustment with prop. solenoid EP

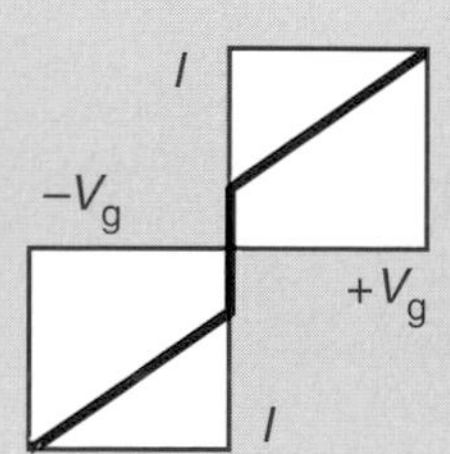

Electronic adjustment with servo valve ES

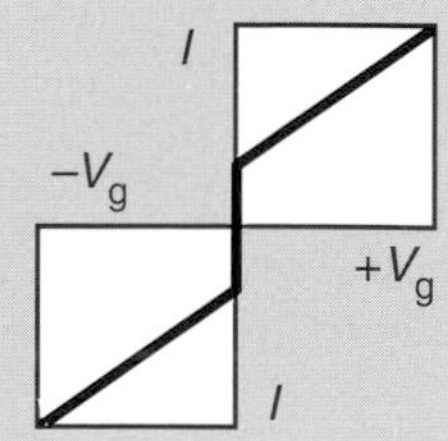

Diagram 14

Hydraulic-dependent on flow,
Displacement volume proportional to positioning oil flow V_S,
Reversible operation at adjustment HM;

Electronic-hydraulic,
Displacement volume proportional to pilot current I at adjustment HS,
Reversible operation with mounted servo valve

V_g = specific displacement volume
I = pilot current
V_S = positioning oil flow

Hydraulic adjustment dependent on flow HM

Hydraulic adjustment with servo valve HS

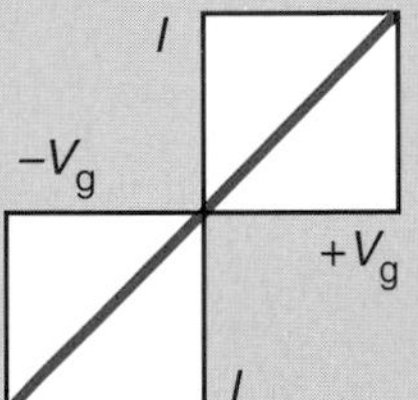

Diagram 15

Hydraulic-dependent on flow,
Displacement volume proportional to pilot voltage U with mounted proportional valve,
Reversible operation,
with electronic amplifier,
Control possible

V_g = specific displacement volume
U = pilot voltage
p_{HD} = high pressure

Electronic adjustment EO

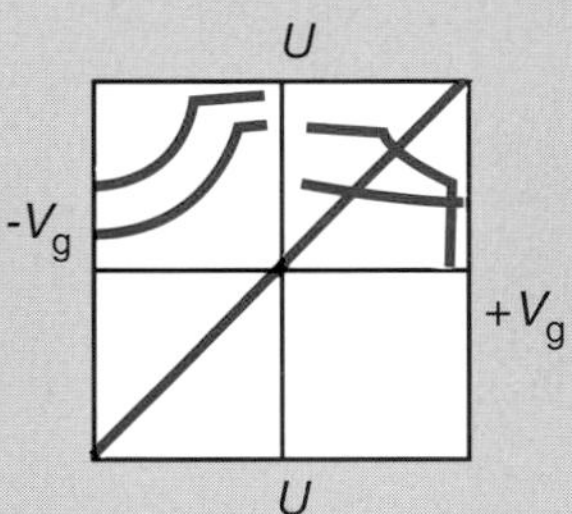

Diagram 16

3.11.2 Pump controls

Hydraulic,
Pressure controller DR
System pressure is held constant, flow is matched.

Flow controller FR
Flow is held constant, even at varying system pressures.

Pressure and flow controller DFR
Pressure and flow are held constant dependent on actuator.

Q = flow
p_{HD} = high pressure

Pressure controller DR

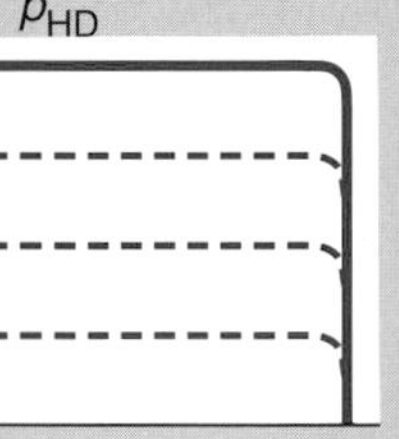

Flow controller FR

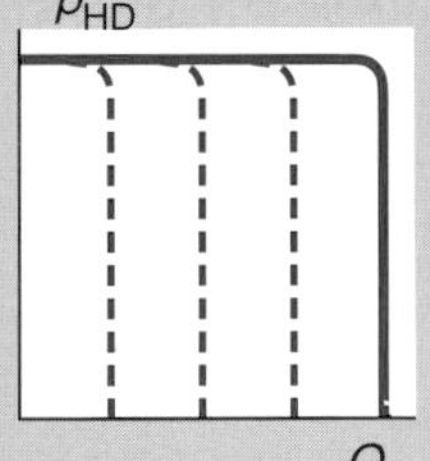

Pressure and flow controller DFR

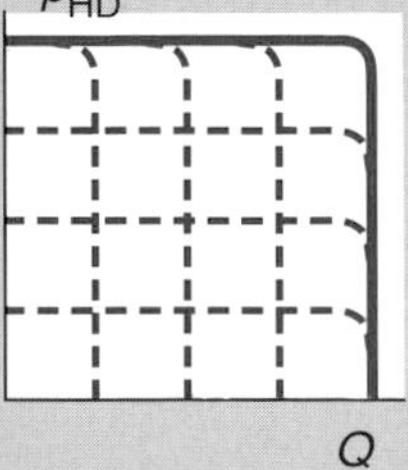

Diagram 17

Hydraulic,
Power regulator LR
Power consumption is held constant.
Power = torque x speed
$P = M \cdot n =$ constant

Summated power controller SR
In parallel operation of two pumps with a drive motor, power is automatically distributed according to the summated pressure.

Pressure, flow and power controller DFLR
A power controller is superimposed on the combined pressure and flow controller.

Pressure controller with load sensing DRS
A pressure controller is superimposed on the load sensing controller. The set flow is held constant by the controller.

Power controller with pressure cut-off and load sensing LRDS
In connection with a power controller the max. drive torque is limited. Pump flow is changed dependent on the actuator.

Q = flow
p_{HD} = high pressure

Power controller
LR

p_{HD}

Q

Total power controller
SR

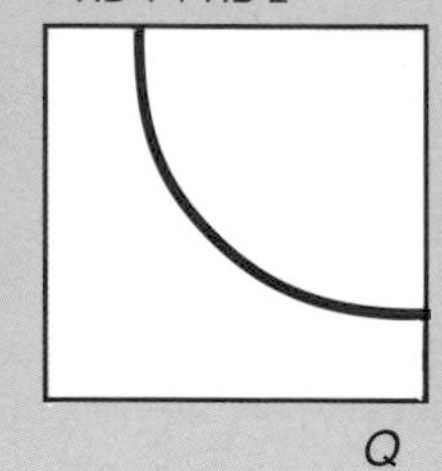

Pressure, flow
and power controller
DFLR

p_{HD}

Q

Pressure controller with
load sensing DRS

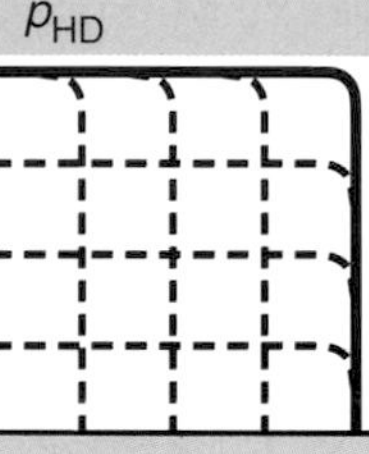

Power controller with
pressure cut-off and
load sensing LRDS

Diagram 18

Electronic
Pressure and flow controller DFE
Pressure and flow are held constant by electronic means dependent on the actuator.

Q = flow
p_{HD} = high pressure
ϟ = electrical signal

Electronic pressure
flow controller
DFE

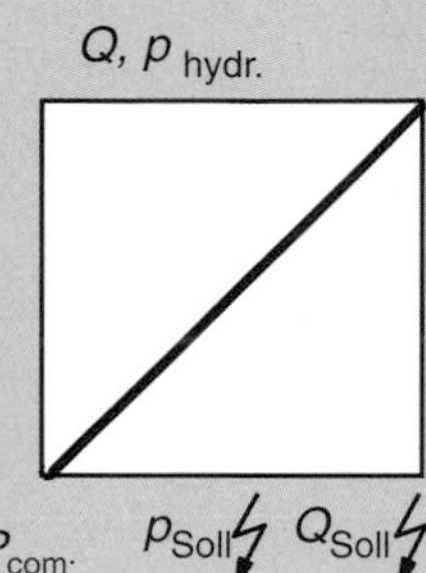

Diagram 19

3.11.3 Motor adjustments

Hydraulic-hydraulic,
Hydraulic adjustment dependent on pilot pressure HD
Displacement proportional to pilot pressure p_{St}

Hydraulic two point adjustment HZ

Hydraulic-electronic,
Electronic adjustment with proportional solenoid EP
Displacement proportional to the pilot current I

Displacement with switching solenoid EZ

V_g = specific displacement volume
p_{St} = pilot pressure
I = pilot current

Hydraulic adjustment dependent on pilot press. HD

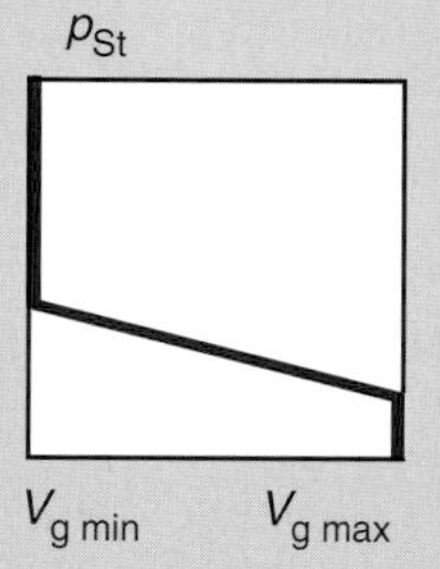

p_{St}
$V_{g\,min}$
$V_{g\,max}$

Hydraulic two point adjustment HZ

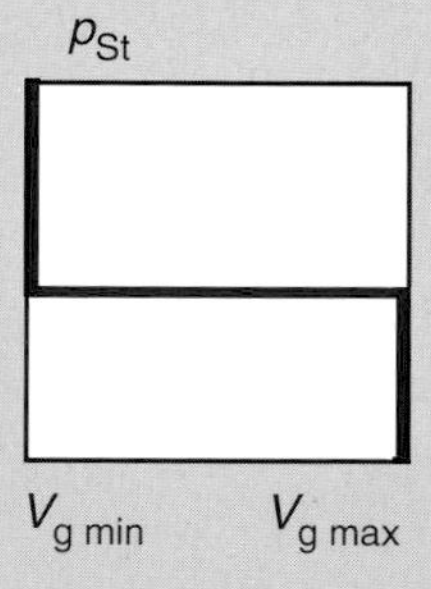

p_{St}
$V_{g\,min}$
$V_{g\,max}$

Electronic adjustment with prop. solenoid EP

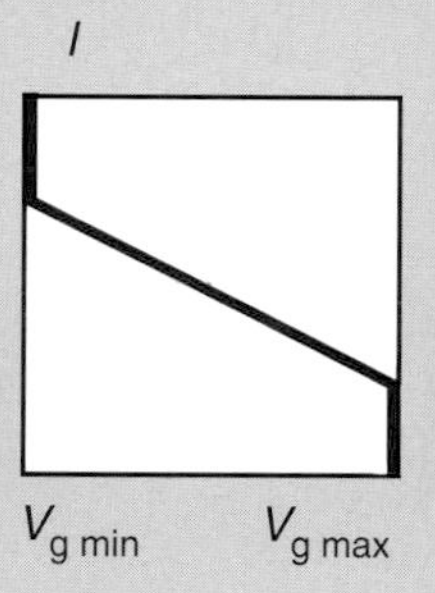

I
$V_{g\,min}$
$V_{g\,max}$

Electronic adjustment with switching solenoid EZ

current added
no current
$V_{g\,min}$
$V_{g\,max}$

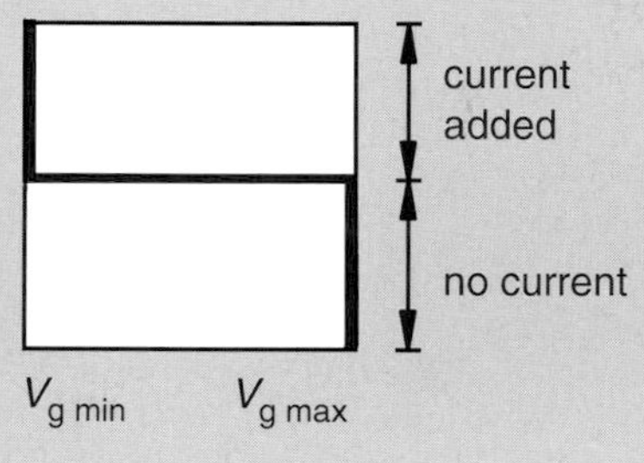

Diagram 20

3.11.4 Motor controls

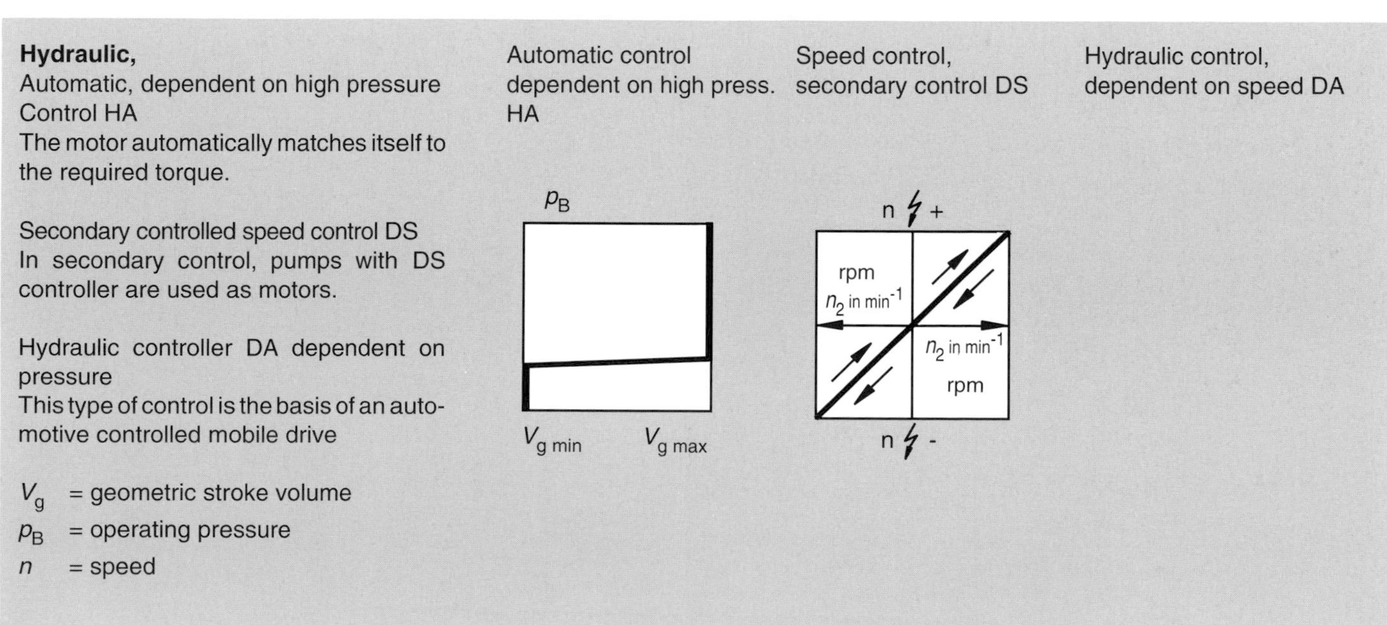

Hydraulic,
Automatic, dependent on high pressure Control HA
The motor automatically matches itself to the required torque.

Secondary controlled speed control DS
In secondary control, pumps with DS controller are used as motors.

Hydraulic controller DA dependent on pressure
This type of control is the basis of an automotive controlled mobile drive

V_g = geometric stroke volume
p_B = operating pressure
n = speed

Automatic control dependent on high press. HA

p_B
$V_{g\,min}$
$V_{g\,max}$

Speed control, secondary control DS

n +
rpm
n_2 in min^{-1}
n_2 in min^{-1}
rpm
n -

Hydraulic control, dependent on speed DA

Diagram 21

Notes

Chapter 7

Hydraulic cylinders

Paul Schwab

1 Cylinders in hydraulic circuits

Nowadays both the hydraulic motor and the hydraulic cylinder are indispensible units in the hydraulic circuit for converting hydraulic energy into mechanical energy. The cylinder is the link between the hydraulic circuit and the working machine.

The hydraulic cylinder is different to the hydraulic motor which carries out rotary movements, in that it carries out translational (linear) movements, through which forces are transferred

Neglecting friction, the maximum possible cylinder force F is dependent on the maximum operating pressure p and the effective area A.

$$F = p \cdot A \text{ in kN}$$

If the working machine carries out linear movements, the following advantages arise for a drive with hydraulic cylinders:

- Simple design of direct drive with cylinders, easily arranged by installation engineer.
- As a rotary movement does not need to be converted into a linear movement, the cylinder drive has a high efficiency.
- Cylinder force remains constant from the beginning to the end of a stroke.
- The piston velocity which is dependent on the flow entering the piston and the area, is also constant over the whole stroke.
- Depending on the model, a cylinder may exert pushing or pulling forces.
- The dimensions of hydraulic cylinders makes it possible to construct drives with large power but small dimensions.

Lifting, lowering, locking and moving of loads are the main applications for hydraulic cylinders.

2 Types of cylinders with respect to functions

Due to their function, it is possible to categorise cylinders into two groups:

- Single acting cylinders
- Double acting cylinders

2.1 Single acting cylinders

Single acting cylinders can only exert force in one direction. The piston can only be returned by a spring, through the weight of the piston itself or by the action of an external force. Single acting cylinders basically have one effective area.

2.1.1 Plunger cylinders

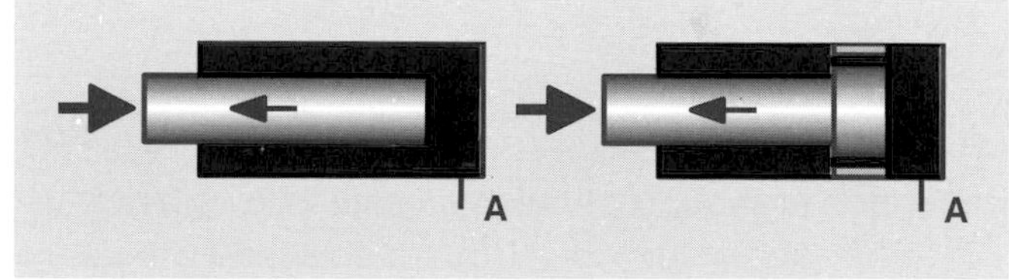

Fig. 1: *Plunger cylinder; left: without internal stop, right: with internal stop (piston guide)*

In this cylinder only pushing forces may be transferred.

Depending on the application, plunger cylinders may be designed with or without an internal stroke limiter. For the model without internal stroke limiter, the pushing force is calculated from the maximum effective piston area and the maximum operating pressure.

It must be noted that for the model with internal stroke limiter only the piston rod area is effective for the calculation of pressure force.

Plunger cylinders are used wherever a definite direction of external force will definitely return the piston to its starting position. Examples of this are upstroke presses, cutter stroke tables and lifting devices.

Pressurising the effective areas via pipe port "A" the piston extends (⇐). Retraction (⇒) of the piston can only occur through the weight of the piston or due to an external force being applied.

2.1.2 Cylinders with spring return

Cylinders with spring returns are used in applications where an external,restoring force does not exist. Return springs may be situated either within the cylinder or mounted onto the cylinder as a separate component. As springs can only carry out limited strokes and exert limited forces, these springs are mainly found in "small cylinders". Applications of this cylinder are pushing cylinders used in installation work or assembly tools used in repairs.

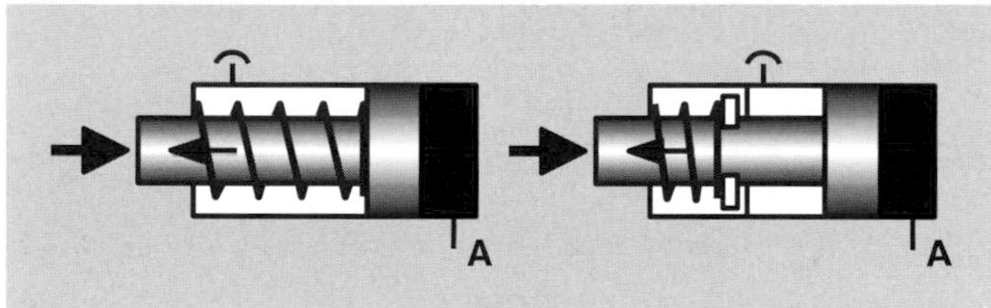

Fig. 2: *Single acting pressure cylinder; left: with internal spring, right: with external spring*

The piston rod is extended (⇐) by means of pressurising the piston area with operating pressure via pipe port "A". The retraction of the piston rod is achieved by means of the return spring.

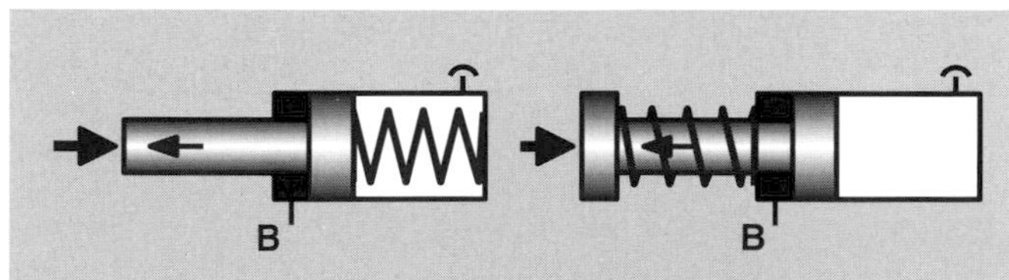

Fig. 3: *Single acting tension cylinder; left: with internal spring, right: with external spring*

By pressurising the effective annulus area with operating pressure via port "B", the piston rod is retracted (⇒). The rod is extended (⇐) by means of the installed return spring.

2.2 Double acting cylinder

Double acting cylinders have two opposing effective areas which are of the same or different sizes. They are fitted with 2 pipe ports which are isolated from each other. By feeding fluid via ports "A" or "B", the piston may transfer pulling and pushing forces in both stroke directions. This type of cylinder may be found in nearly all types of application.

Two categories of double acting cylinder exist: single and double rod cylinders.

2.2.1 Single rod cylinder

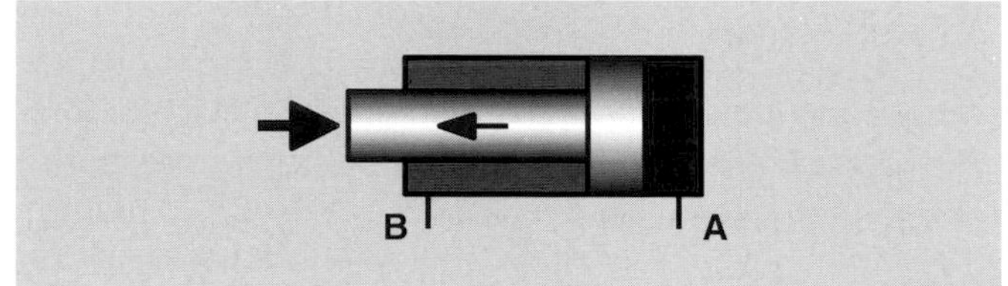

Fig. 4

In most applications cylinders are used with only one piston rod. Single rod cylinders have a piston, which is connected rigidly to a piston rod which has a diameter smaller than that of the piston. In these cylinders the sizes of the effective areas are different. The area ratio of piston area to annulus area is indicated by the factor (φ). The maximum amount of force transferred is dependent on the piston area as the cylinder is extended, on the annulus area as the cylinder is retracted and on the maximum operating pressure. This means that for the same operating pressure the extending force is a factor φ times larger than the retracting force. The chambers being filled are the same length due to the stroke, but because of the differences in piston and annulus areas, their volumes are different. Hence the stroke velocities are inversely proportional to the areas.

This means:

- Large area → slow movement
- Small area → quick movement

2.2.2 Double rod cylinder

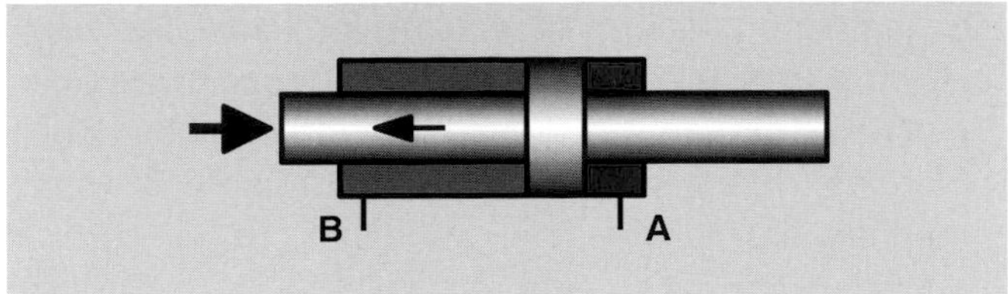

Fig. 5

Double rod cylinders have a piston, which is connected rigidly to two piston rods (often a single continuous through rod) which have diameters smaller than that of the piston. The maximum force transferred is dependent on the annulus areas which are the same size in both directions of movement and on the maximum operating pressure. This means that for the same operating pressure the forces in both directions of movement will be the same size. As the areas and the stroke lengths are the same on both size, the volumes of the chambers being filled must be the same size. Hence, the velocities must also be the same. For special applications, double rod cylinders may be made with different piston rod diameters.

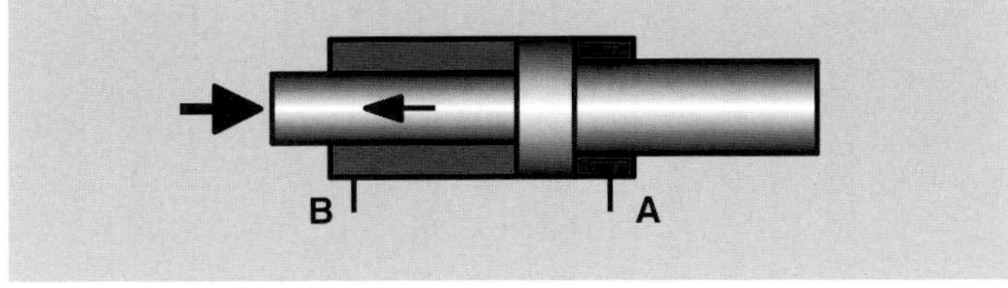

Fig. 6

In this model the forces and velocities (similarly to the single rod cylinder) are in the ratio of the area ratio φ of both annulus areas.

2.3 Special types of single and double acting cylinders

Certain applications exist, where standard single or double acting cylinders may only be used by taking special additional measures involving a lot of effort. The most common of these cases is where long strokes are needed with extremely little installation room or where the largest force is required for the smallest piston diameter. This and other requirements have led to a series of special models being designed, which are partly more difficult and take more effort to produce.

2.3.1 Tandem cylinders

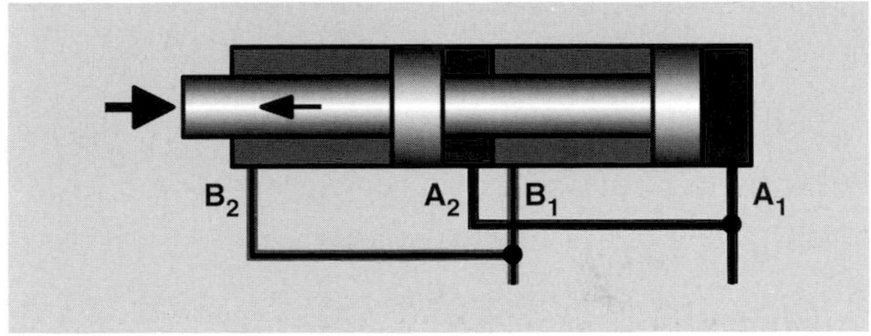

Fig. 7

In double acting cylinders operating in tandem, there are two cylinders which are connected together in such a way that the piston rod of one cylinder pushes through the bottom of the other cylinder to its piston area. By using this arrangement the areas are added together and large forces may be transferred for relatively small external diameters without increasing the operating pressure. However the longer length of this model must be taken into account.

2.3.2 Rapid traverse cylinders

Rapid traverse cylinders are used primarily in presses. In this cylinder, as long as the complete working force is not required, only part of the effective piston area, the co-called rapid traverse piston is placed under pressure.The complete effective piston area is only later connected to the hydraulic pump via a control system by means of pressure control valves or limit switches.

Advantages:

High rapid traverse velocity due to small volume

High pressing force due to large effective piston areas

2.3.2.1 Single acting rapid traverse cylinder

- Rapid traverse (⇐) via port "A1"
- Pressing force (⇐) via port "A2"
- Retracting movement (⇒) via weight of piston itself or through an external force being applied.

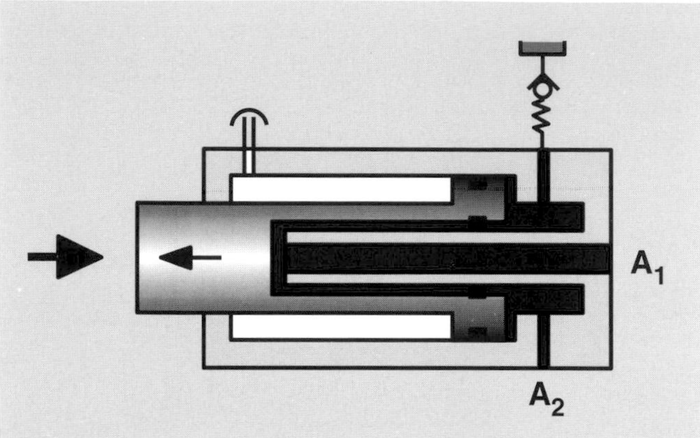

Fig. 8: *Single acting rapid traverse cylinder*

2.3.2.2 Double acting rapid traverse cylinder

- Rapid traverse (⇐) via port "A1"
- Pressing force (⇐) via port "A2"
- Retracting movement (⇒) via port "B".

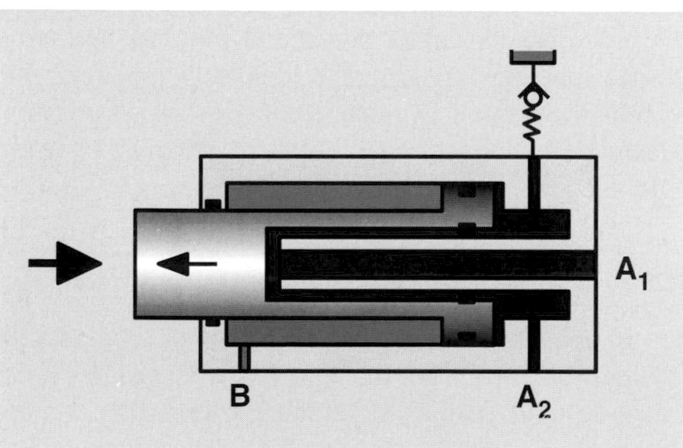

Fig. 9: *Double acting rapid traverse cylinder*

2.3.3 Telescopic cylinder

Telescopic cylinders vary from "normal" cylinders in that they only require a very small amount of space to be installed into when they are retracted in comparison to "normal" cylinders with the same stroke. The reduced space required for installation is due to the piston rods sliding into each other equal to the total length of stroke divided by the number of stages plus the zero stroke measurement (thickness at bottom, guide lengths, seal widths, fixings). This means that the space required for installation is only a little larger than one stage. The retracted length of a telescopic cylinder is normally between half and quarter of the cylinder's stroke. Dependent on the space required for installation these cylinders are available with two, three, four or five stages. Telescopic cylinders are used in hydraulic lifts, tipping platforms, commercial vehicles, lifting platforms, antennas, etc.

2.3.3.1 Single acting telescopic cylinders

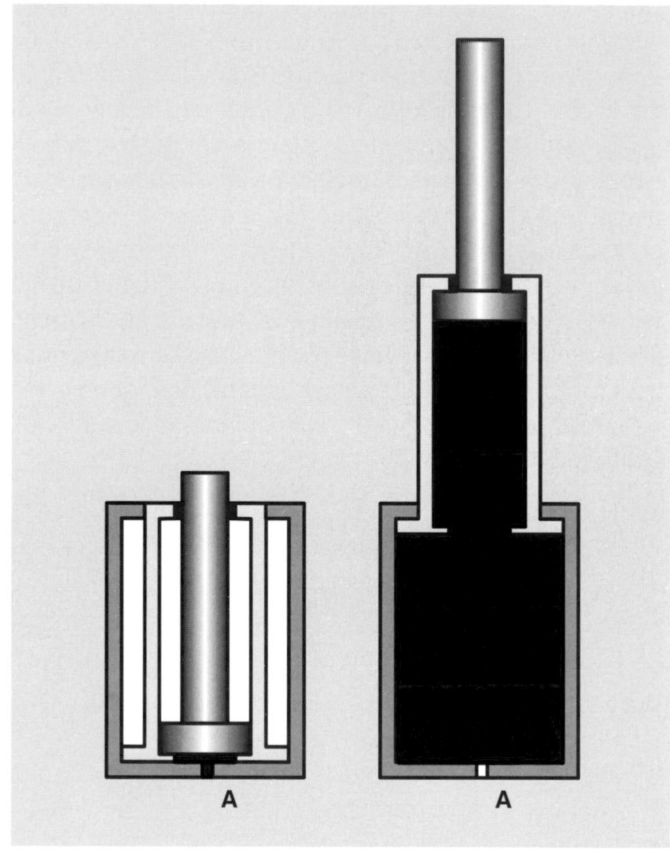

Fig. 10: *Single acting rapid telescopic cylinder*

If the pistons are placed under pressure via port "A", they extend one after another. The pressure is dependent of the size of load and the effective area. Hence the piston with the largest effective area extends first.

At constant pressure and flow the extension begins with the largest force and smallest velocity and finishes with the smallest force and highest velocity.

The stroke force to be used must be designed with the smallest effective piston area in mind. In simple acting telescopic cylinders the order in which the stages are retracted via an external load is reversed. This means, that the piston with the smallest area returns first to its starting position.

2.3.3.2 Double acting telescopic cylinders

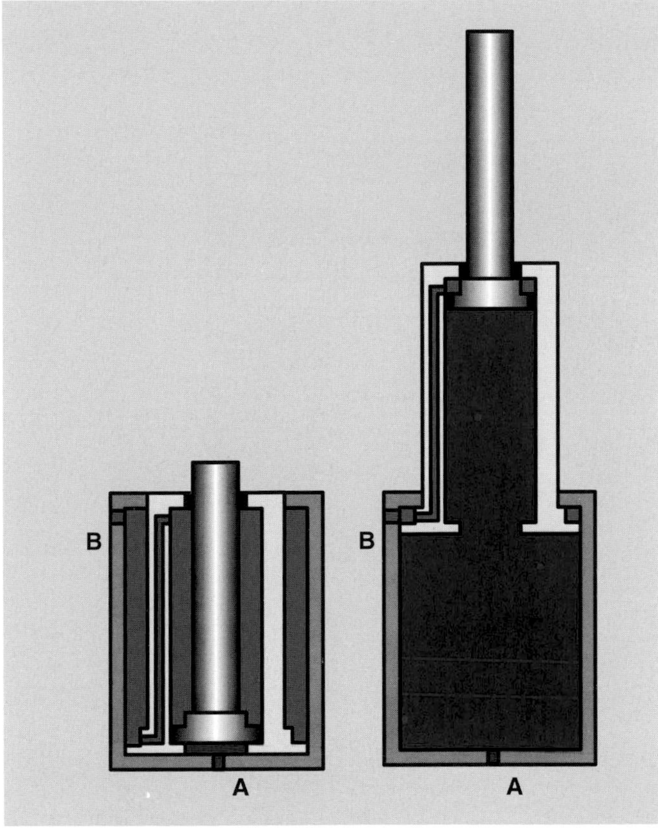

Fig. 11: *Double acting telescopic cylinder*

In double acting cylinders the pistons are extended in the same way as in single acting cylinders. The order in which the individual stages are retracted depends on the size of the annulus area and on the external load. The piston with the largest annulus area first returns to its starting position when it is placed under pressure via pipe port "B". Double acting telescopic cylinders may also be used as synchronised telescopic cylinders. In this model the various stages extend or retract in unison.

3 Basic design

The design of hydraulic cylinders depends to a large extent on the various applications. Cylinders have been developed to suit particular applications. There is a different cylinder design for each of the following examples: machine tools, mobile machines, civil engineering, steel and iron works, etc.

By using the single or double acting single rod cylinder, which is the one mainly used, the most common design principles will be discussed.

There are basically two types of design:

- tie rod cylinders and
- mill type cylinders (screwed or welded design)

3.1 Tie rod cylinder

In tie rod cylinders the top of the cylinder, the cylinder tube and the bottom of the cylinder are all connected together via a tie rod. The main feature of a tie rod cylinder is its especially compact design.

As these cylinders are compact and space-saving they are primarily used in the machine tool industry and in manufacturing devices, such as conveyor belts and machining centres in the car industry.

Fig. 12: *Tie rod cylinders, series CD160 available in a range of diameters and mounting styles*

3.1.1 Individual parts and their names

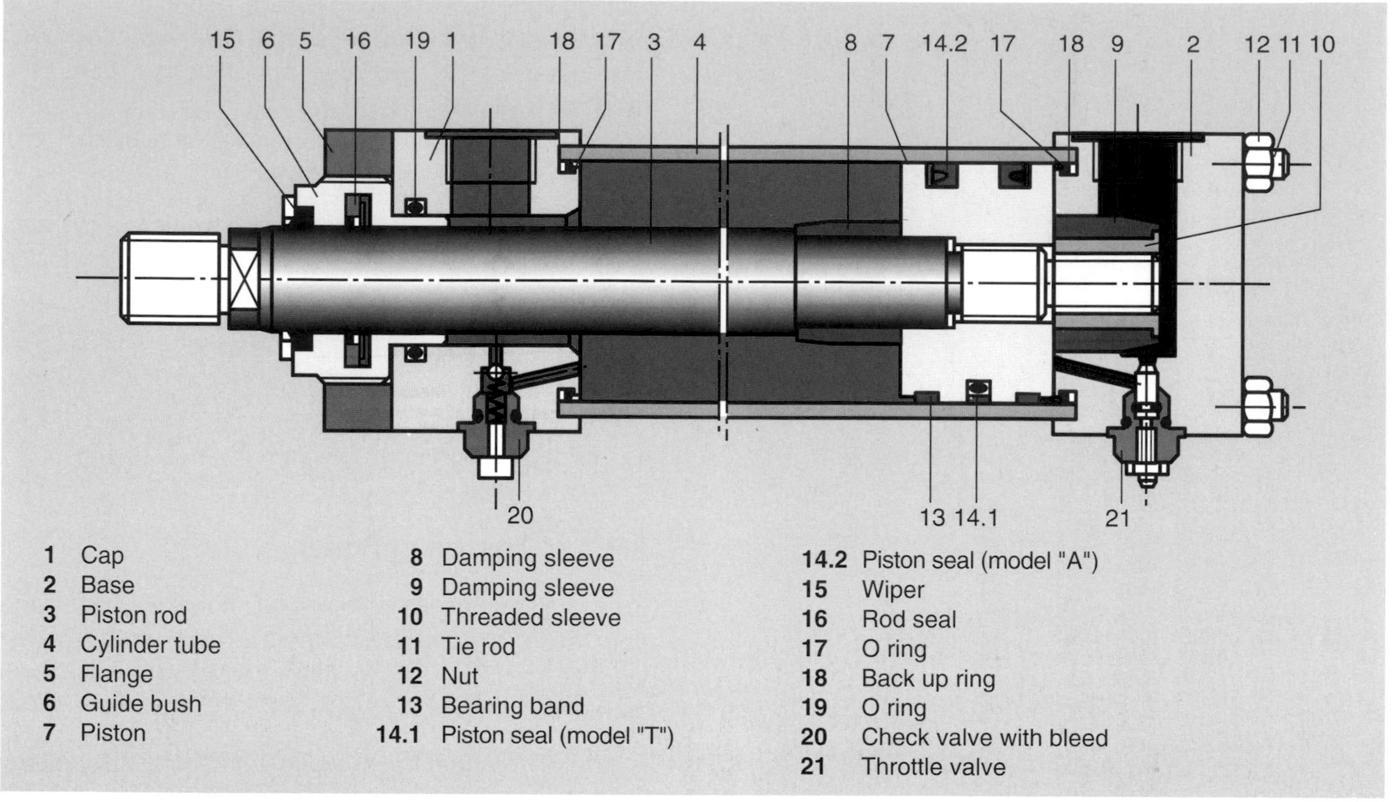

Fig. REF!: *Hydraulic tie rod cylinder with flange mounting*

3.1.2 Design notes

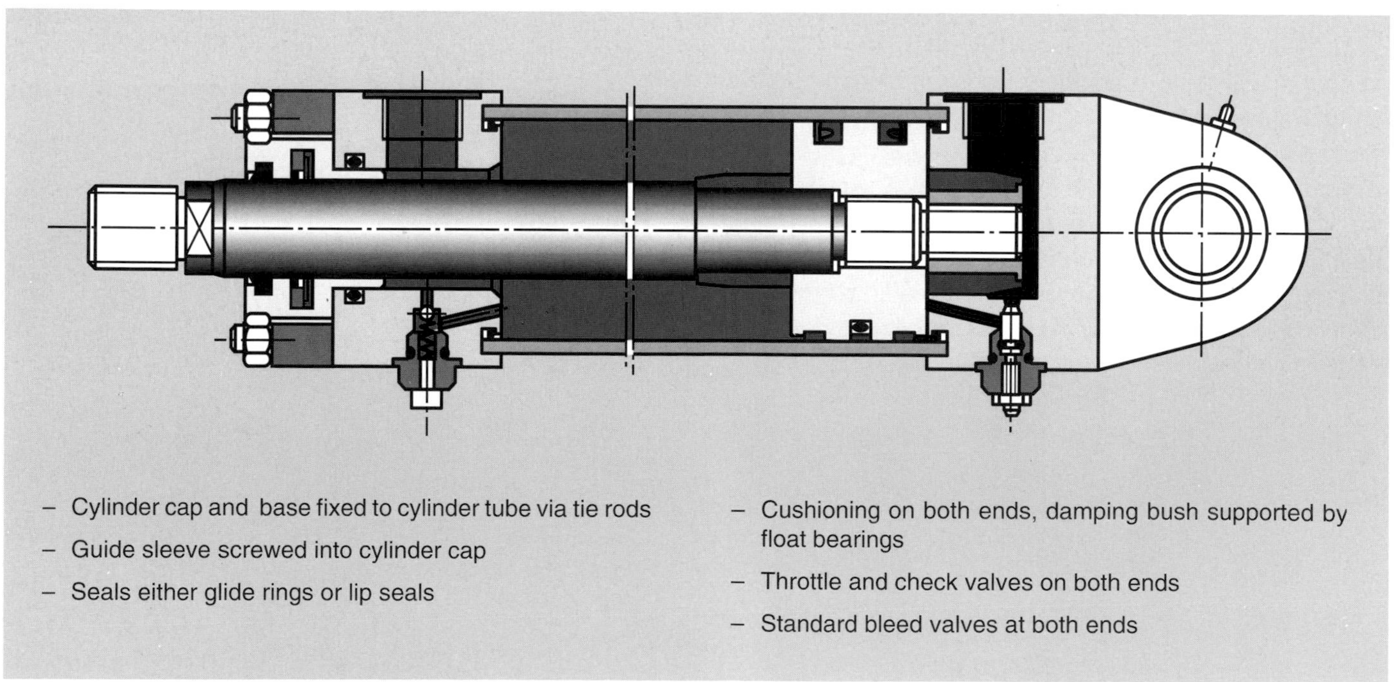

Fig. REF!: *Hydraulic tie rod cylinder with swivel clevis mounting*

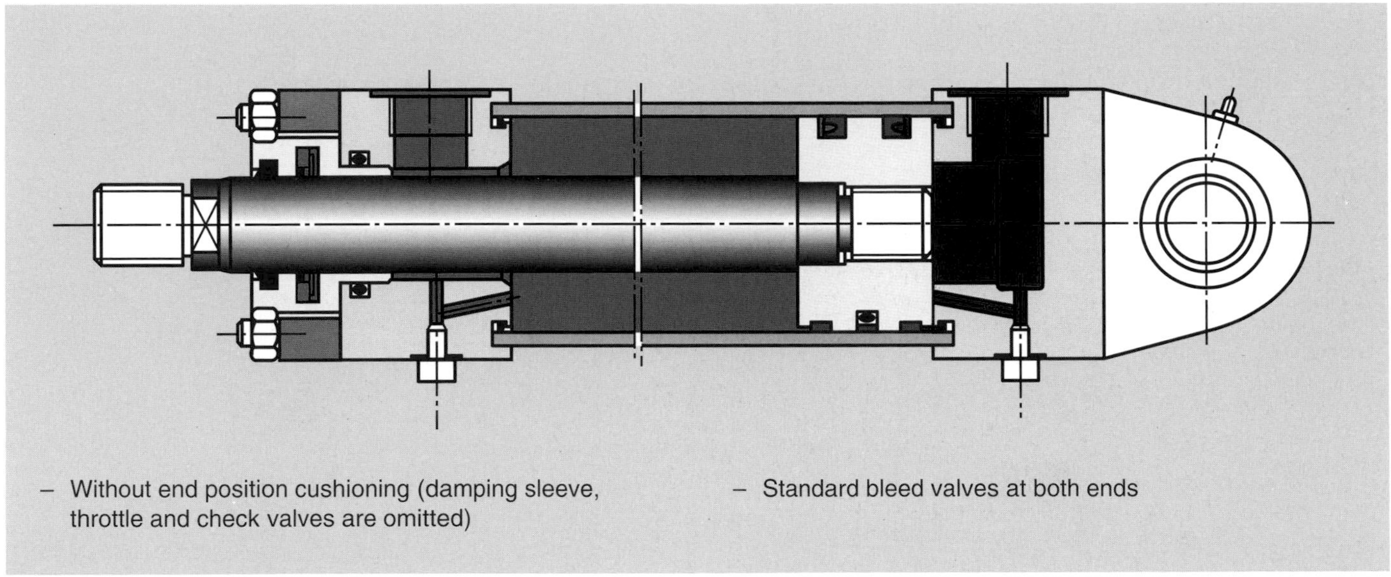

- Without end position cushioning (damping sleeve, throttle and check valves are omitted)
- Standard bleed valves at both ends

Fig. 15

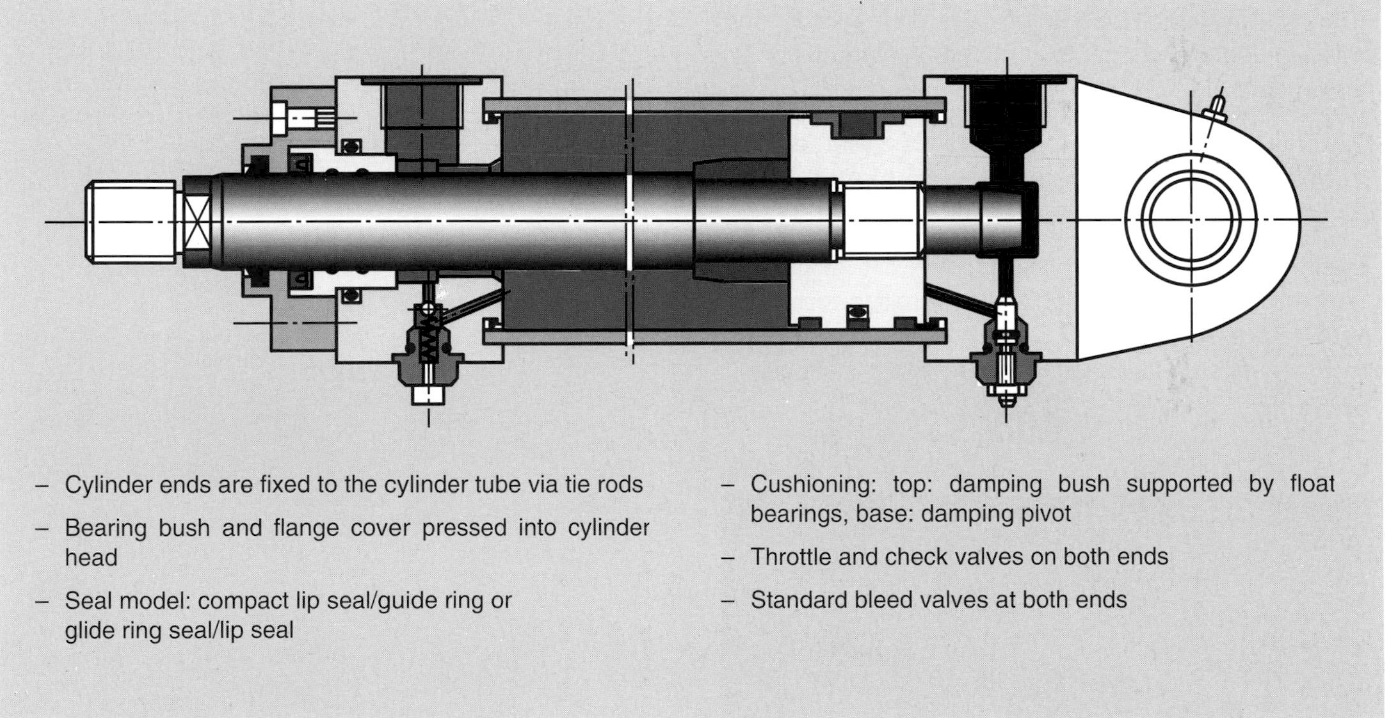

- Cylinder ends are fixed to the cylinder tube via tie rods
- Bearing bush and flange cover pressed into cylinder head
- Seal model: compact lip seal/guide ring or glide ring seal/lip seal
- Cushioning: top: damping bush supported by float bearings, base: damping pivot
- Throttle and check valves on both ends
- Standard bleed valves at both ends

Fig. 16

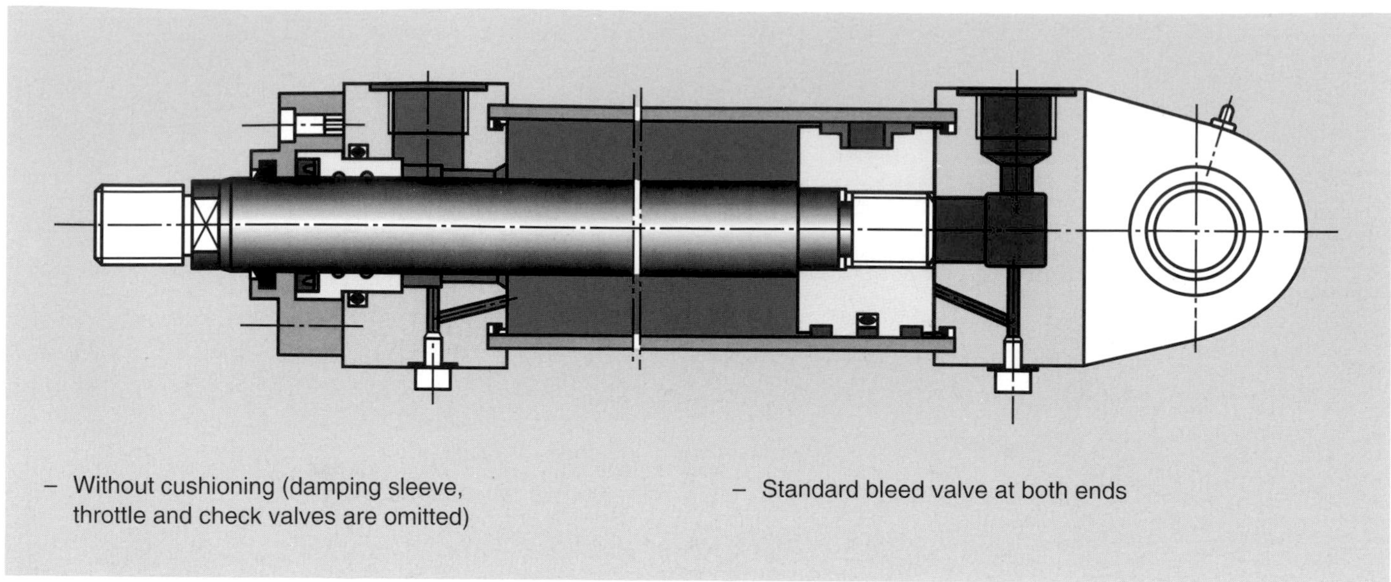

Fig. 17

3.2 Mill type cylinders

In mill type cylinders, the top and base of the cylinder and cylinder tube are connected together via threads or retaining rings.

Due to its robust design, hydraulic cylinders with screwed or welded constructions are also suitable for use in applications with extreme operating conditions.

The main applications of this cylinder are in general mechanical engineering applications, rolling mills, iron works, presses, cranes, mobile machines, civil engineering, ship-building and offshore applications.

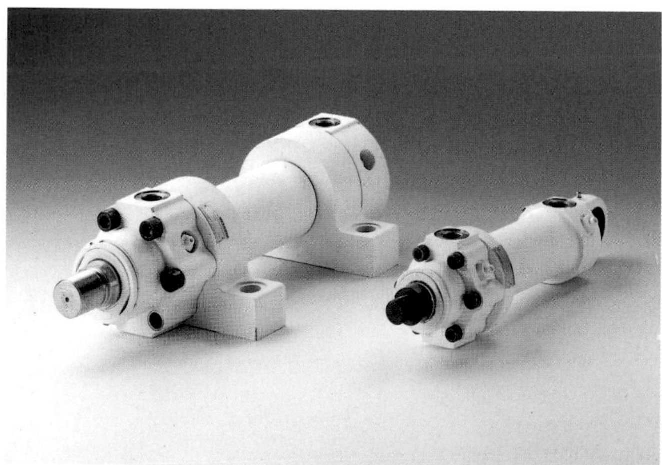

Fig. 18: *Mill type cylinders, series CD 250 and CD 350*

3.2.1 Individual parts and their names

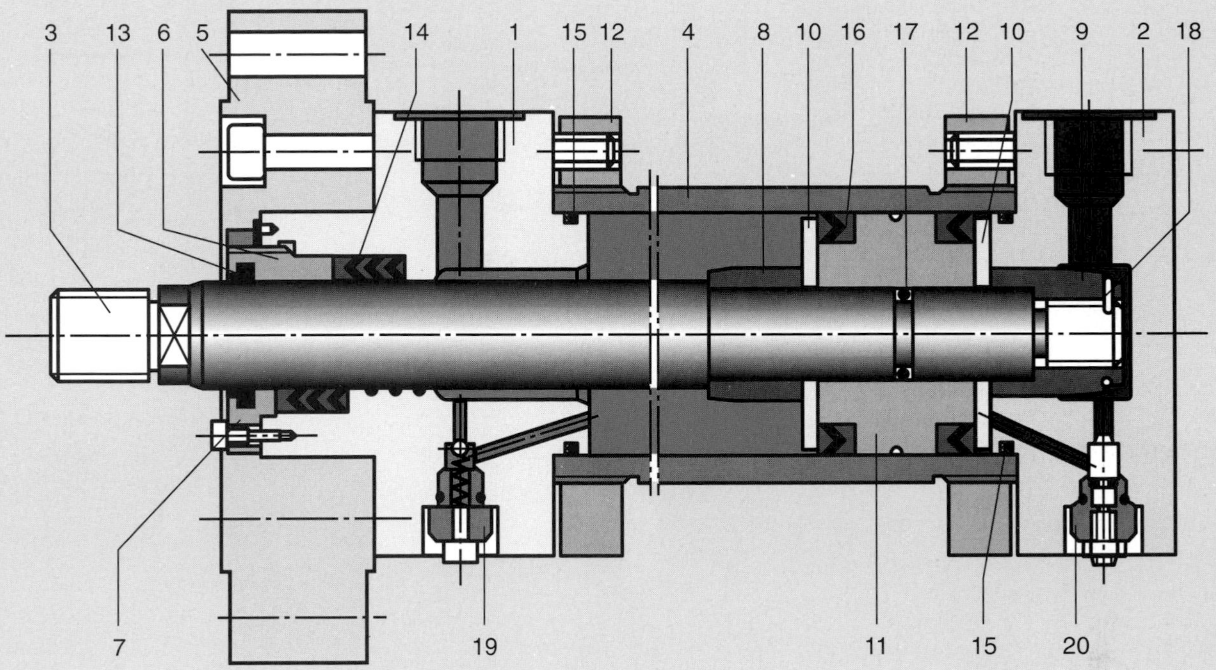

1	Cap	**7**	Cover	**13**	Wiper	**18**	Spring ring
2	Base	**8**	Damping bush	**14**	Rod seal	**19**	Check valve with bleed
3	Piston rod	**9**	Damping bush	**15**	O ring	**20**	Throttle valve
4	Tube	**10**	Retaining plate	**16**	Piston seal (model "A")		
5	Flange	**11**	Piston				
6	Guide bush	**12**	Flange	**17**	O ring		

Fig. REF!: *Mill type hydraulic cylinder with front flange mounting*

3.2.2 Design notes

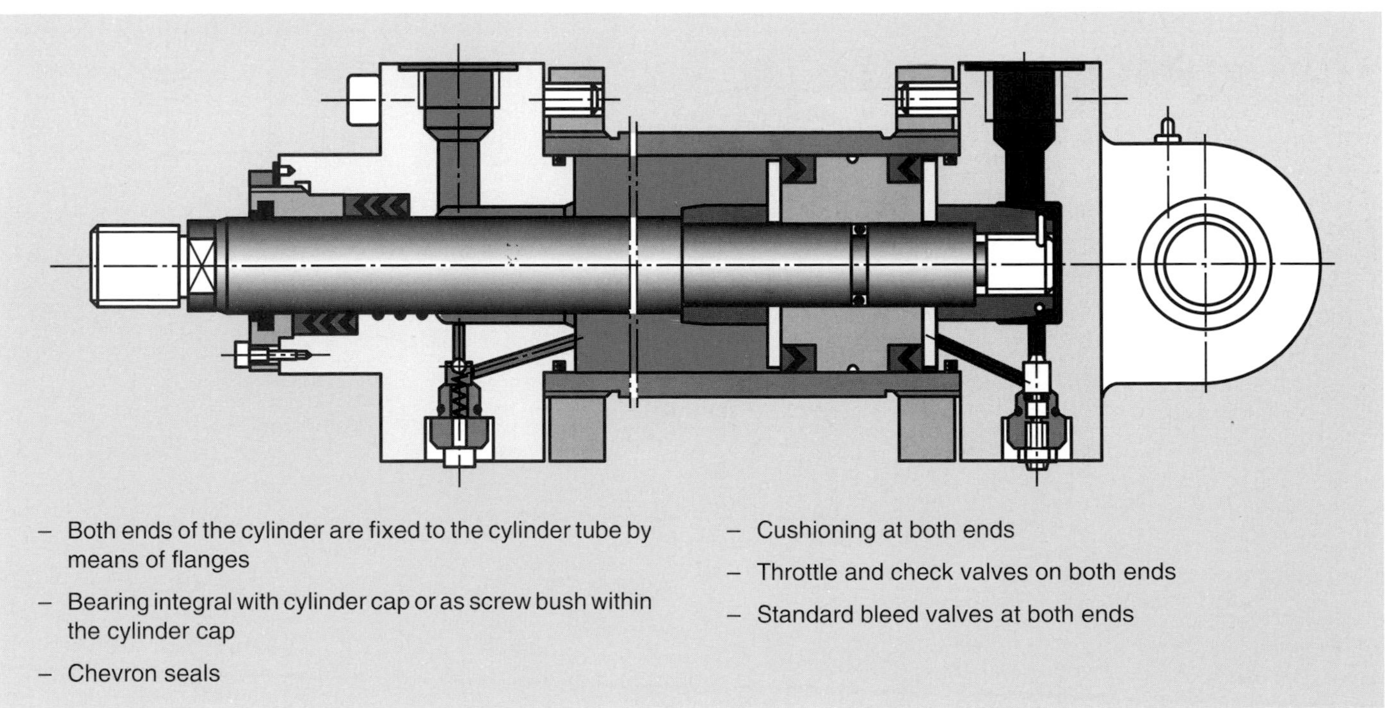

- Both ends of the cylinder are fixed to the cylinder tube by means of flanges
- Bearing integral with cylinder cap or as screw bush within the cylinder cap
- Chevron seals
- Cushioning at both ends
- Throttle and check valves on both ends
- Standard bleed valves at both ends

Fig. REF!: *Mill type cylinder with swivel clevis mounting*

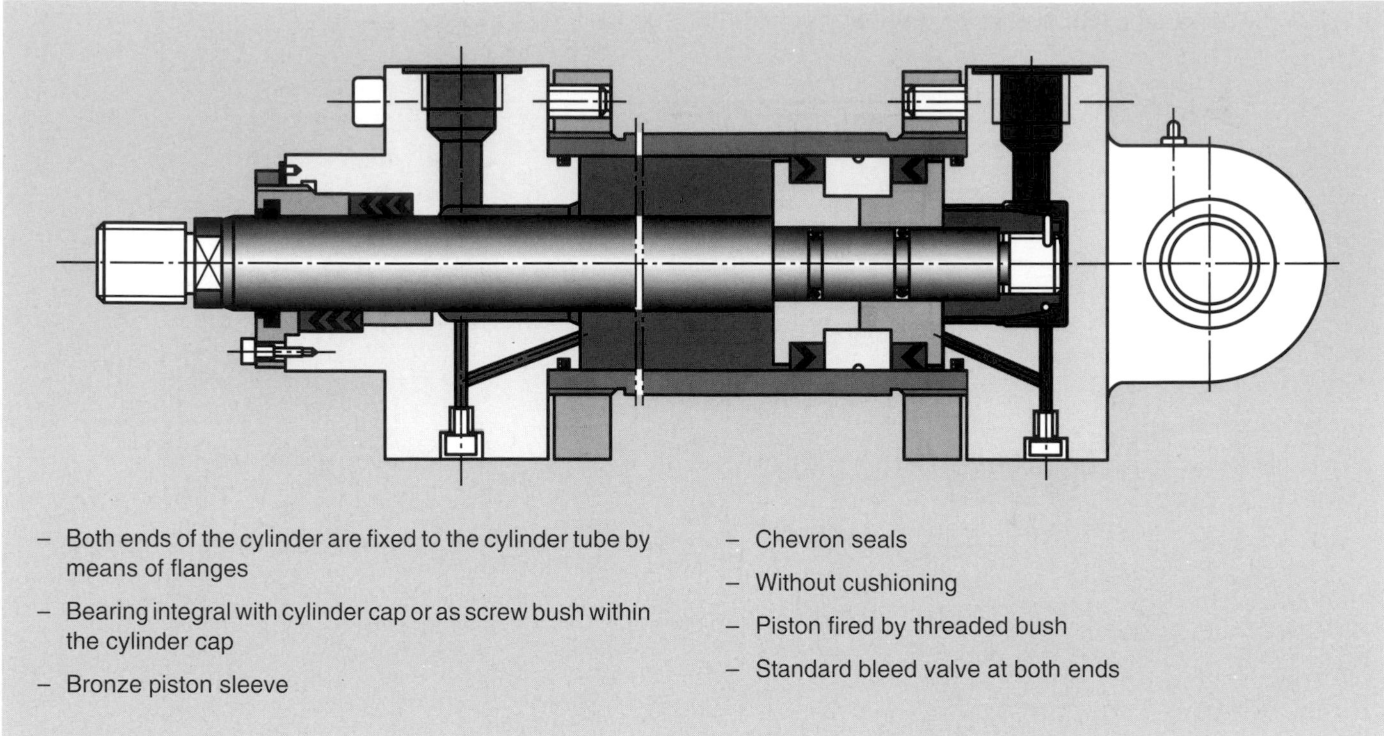

- Both ends of the cylinder are fixed to the cylinder tube by means of flanges
- Bearing integral with cylinder cap or as screw bush within the cylinder cap
- Bronze piston sleeve
- Chevron seals
- Without cushioning
- Piston fired by threaded bush
- Standard bleed valve at both ends

Fig. 21

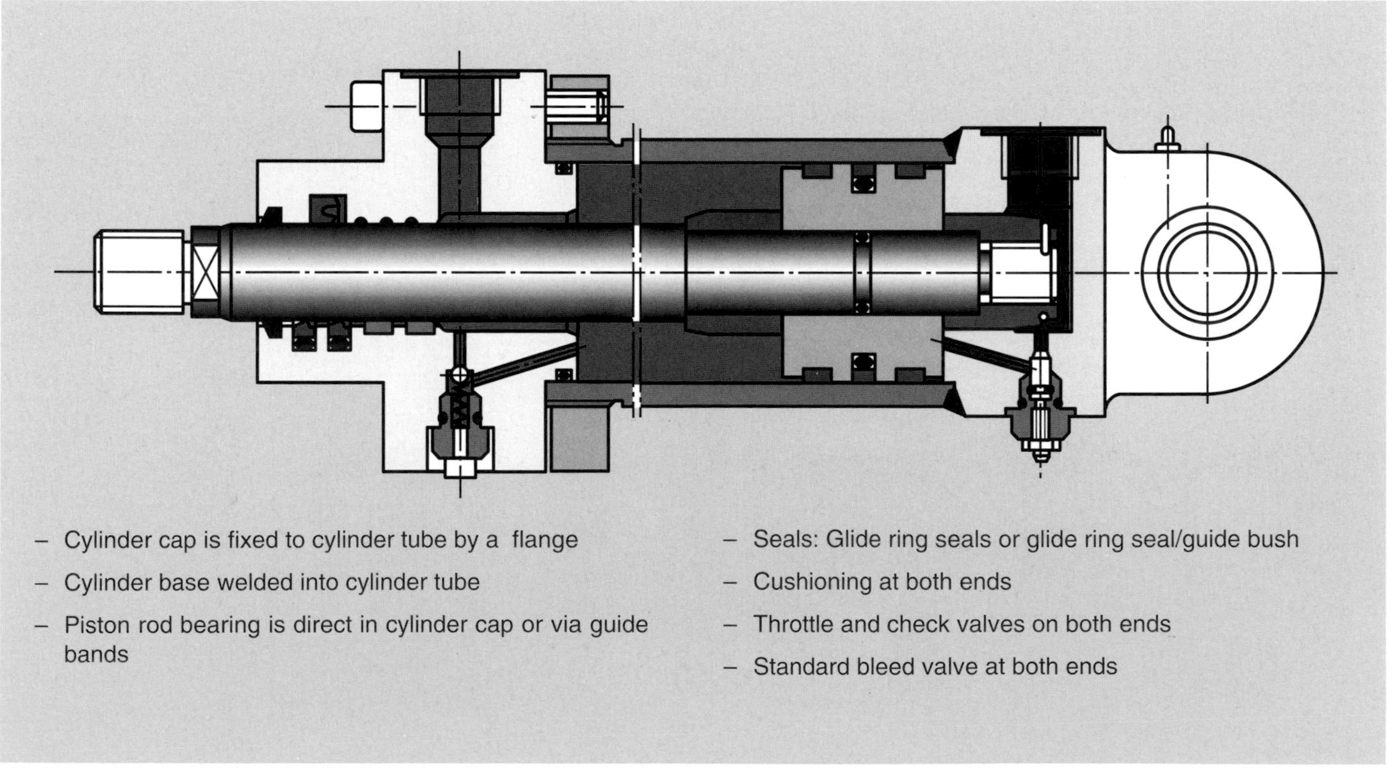

- Cylinder cap is fixed to cylinder tube by a flange
- Cylinder base welded into cylinder tube
- Piston rod bearing is direct in cylinder cap or via guide bands
- Seals: Glide ring seals or glide ring seal/guide bush
- Cushioning at both ends
- Throttle and check valves on both ends
- Standard bleed valve at both ends

Fig. 22

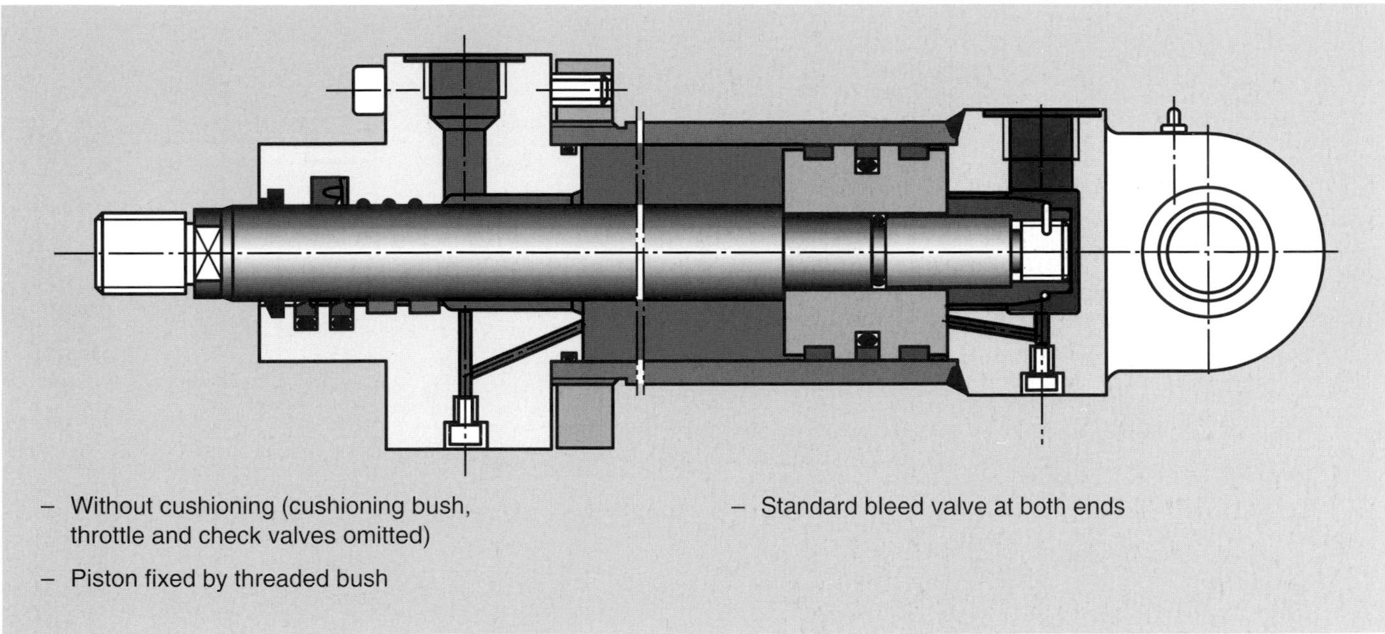
– Without cushioning (cushioning bush, throttle and check valves omitted)
– Piston fixed by threaded bush
– Standard bleed valve at both ends

Fig. 23

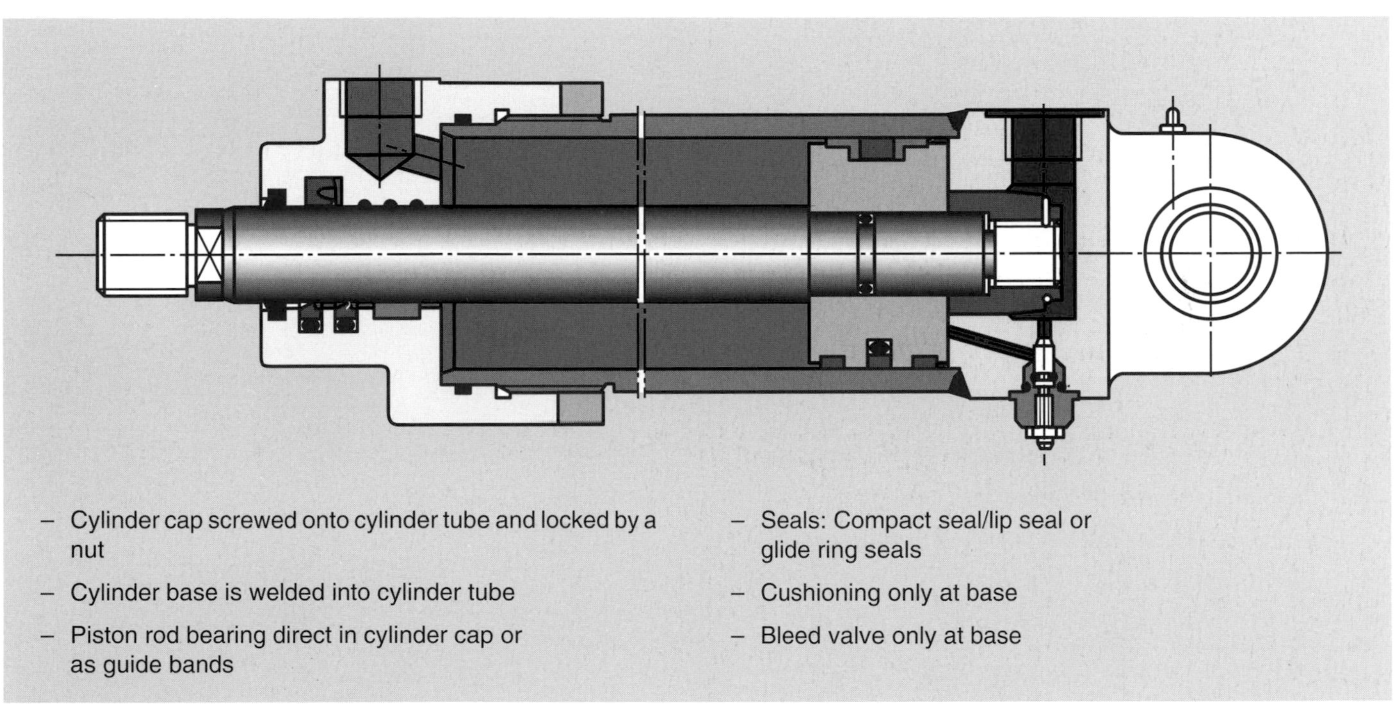
– Cylinder cap screwed onto cylinder tube and locked by a nut
– Cylinder base is welded into cylinder tube
– Piston rod bearing direct in cylinder cap or as guide bands
– Seals: Compact seal/lip seal or glide ring seals
– Cushioning only at base
– Bleed valve only at base

Fig. 24

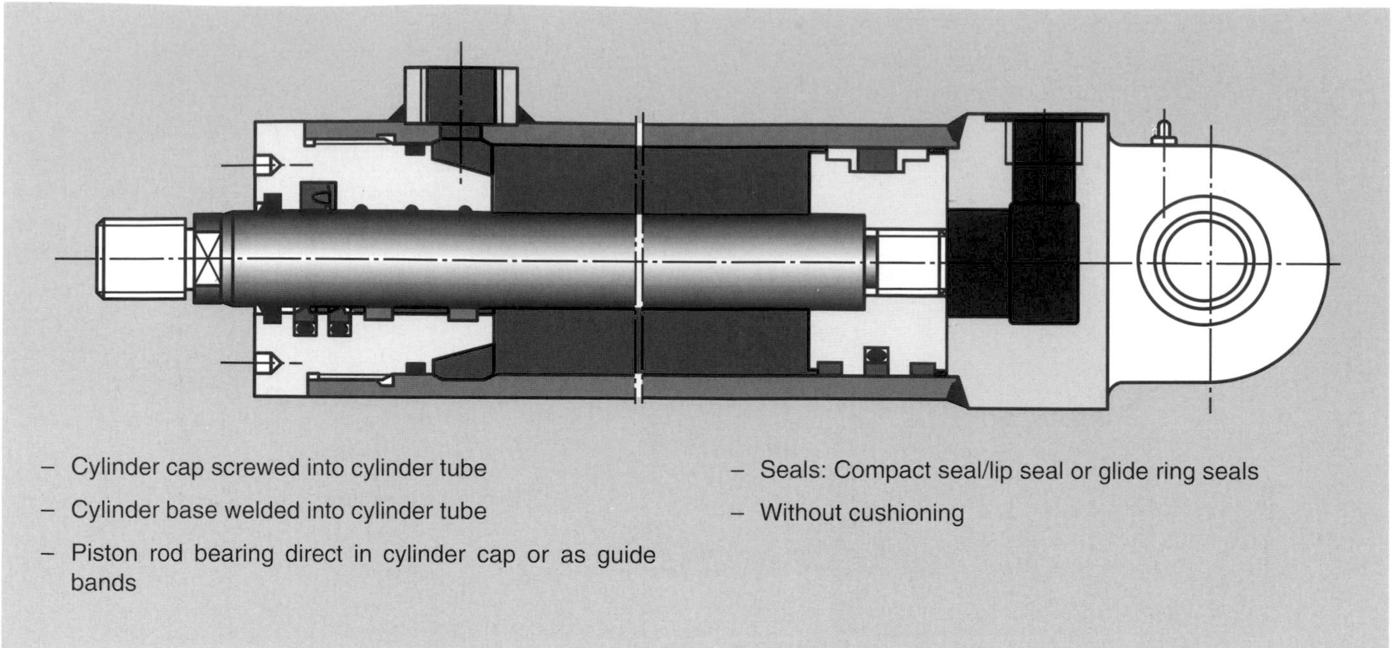

- Cylinder cap screwed into cylinder tube
- Cylinder base welded into cylinder tube
- Piston rod bearing direct in cylinder cap or as guide bands
- Seals: Compact seal/lip seal or glide ring seals
- Without cushioning

Fig. 25

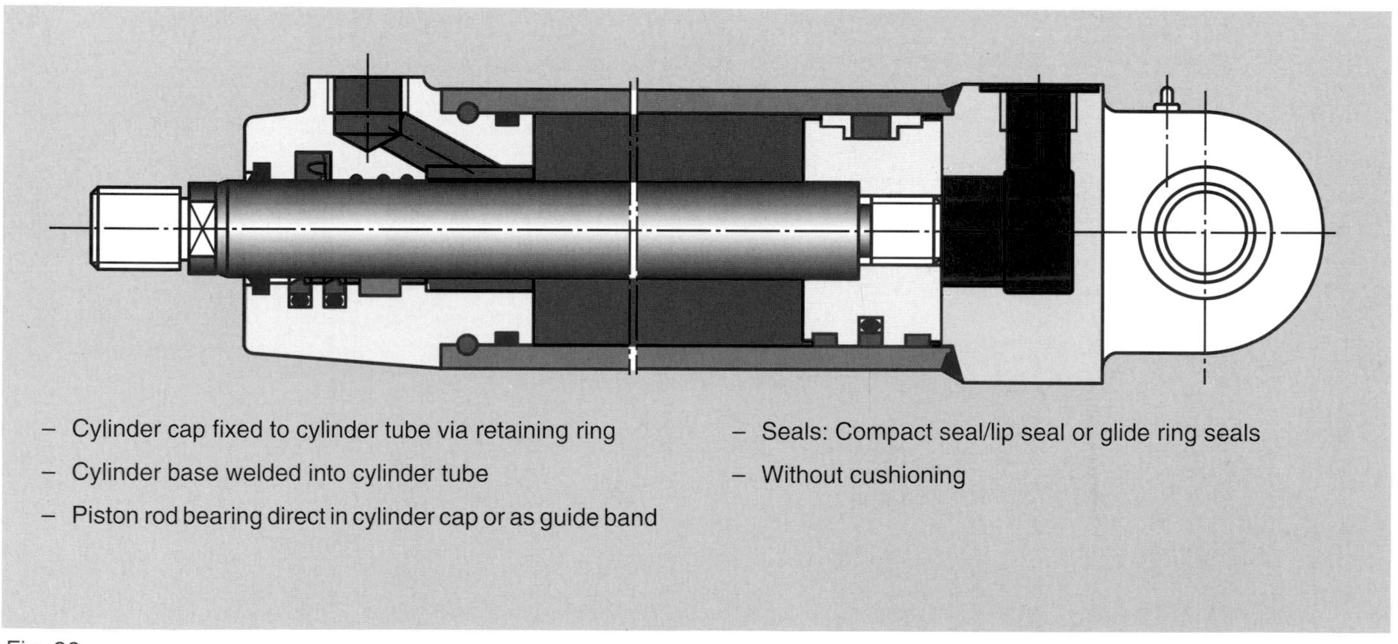

- Cylinder cap fixed to cylinder tube via retaining ring
- Cylinder base welded into cylinder tube
- Piston rod bearing direct in cylinder cap or as guide band
- Seals: Compact seal/lip seal or glide ring seals
- Without cushioning

Fig. 26

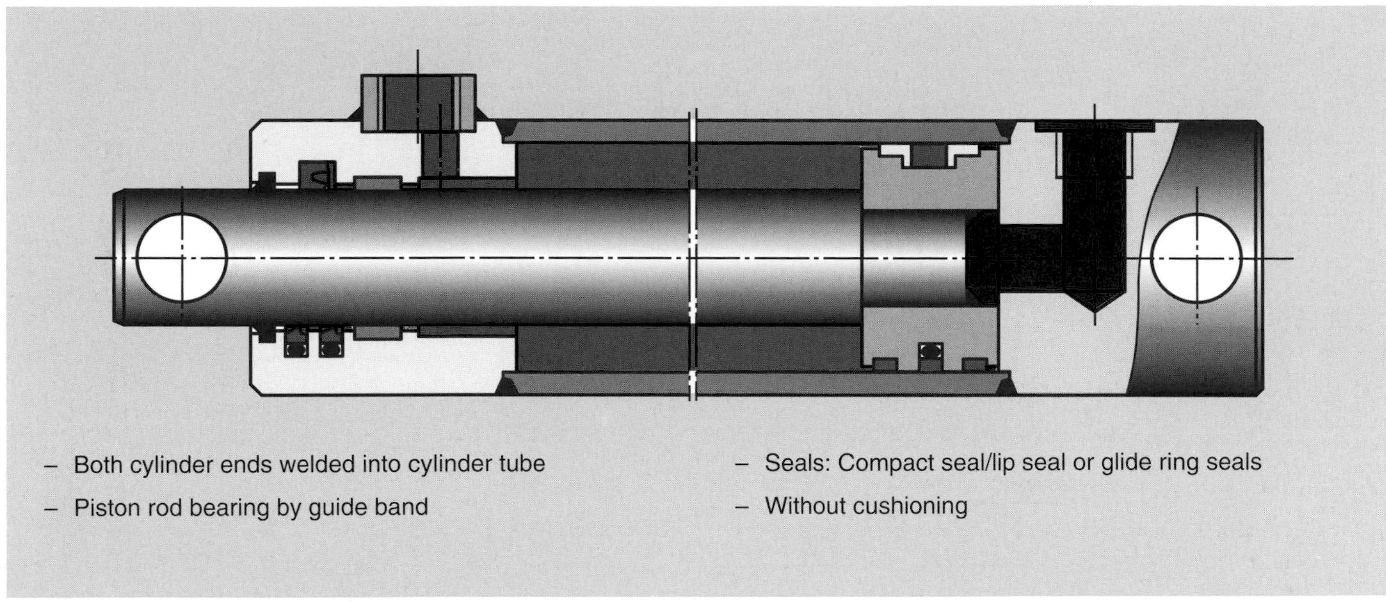

Fig. 27

4 Types of connection and notes on installation

In addition to needing to know the operating pressure, piston and rod diameters, stroke length and pulling or pressing forces, it is necessary to know where the cylinder is to be installed, i.e. what type of mounting it requires.

A number of mounting possibilities for cylinders are shown in *tables 1 and 2*.

When installing hydraulic cylinders various criteria with respect to the type of mounting must be taken Into account. Six of the most commonly used types of mounting with their installation notes are shown in table 3.

Swivel or plain clevis mounting are used at the rear of cylinders for mounting for more than 50 % of cylinders used.

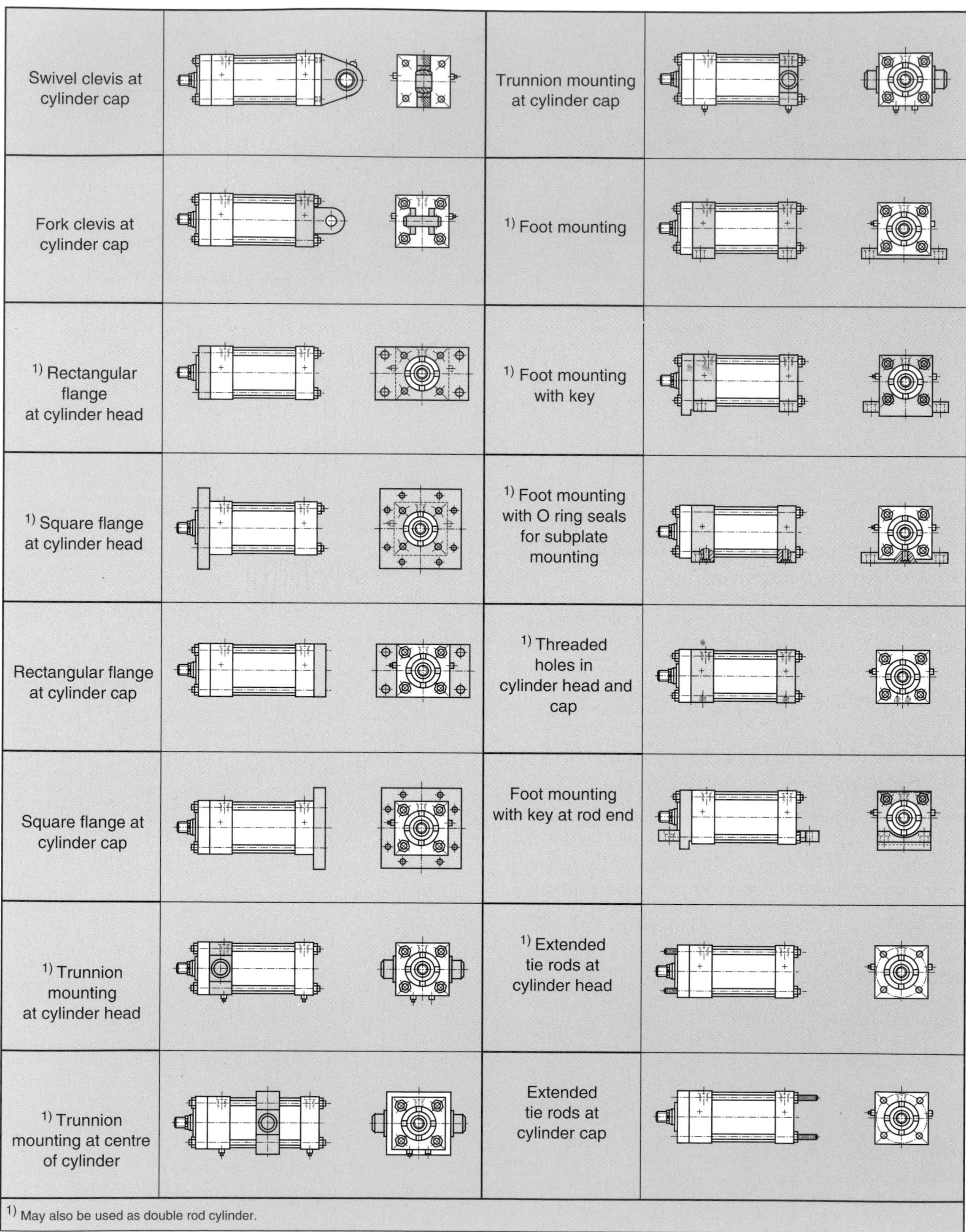

Type of mounting	Drawing	Type of mounting	Drawing
Swivel clevis at cylinder cap		Trunnion mounting at cylinder cap	
Fork clevis at cylinder cap		1) Foot mounting	
1) Rectangular flange at cylinder head		1) Foot mounting with key	
1) Square flange at cylinder head		1) Foot mounting with O ring seals for subplate mounting	
Rectangular flange at cylinder cap		1) Threaded holes in cylinder head and cap	
Square flange at cylinder cap		Foot mounting with key at rod end	
1) Trunnion mounting at cylinder head		1) Extended tie rods at cylinder head	
1) Trunnion mounting at centre of cylinder		Extended tie rods at cylinder cap	

1) May also be used as double rod cylinder.

Table 1: *Types of mounting for tie rod cylinders*

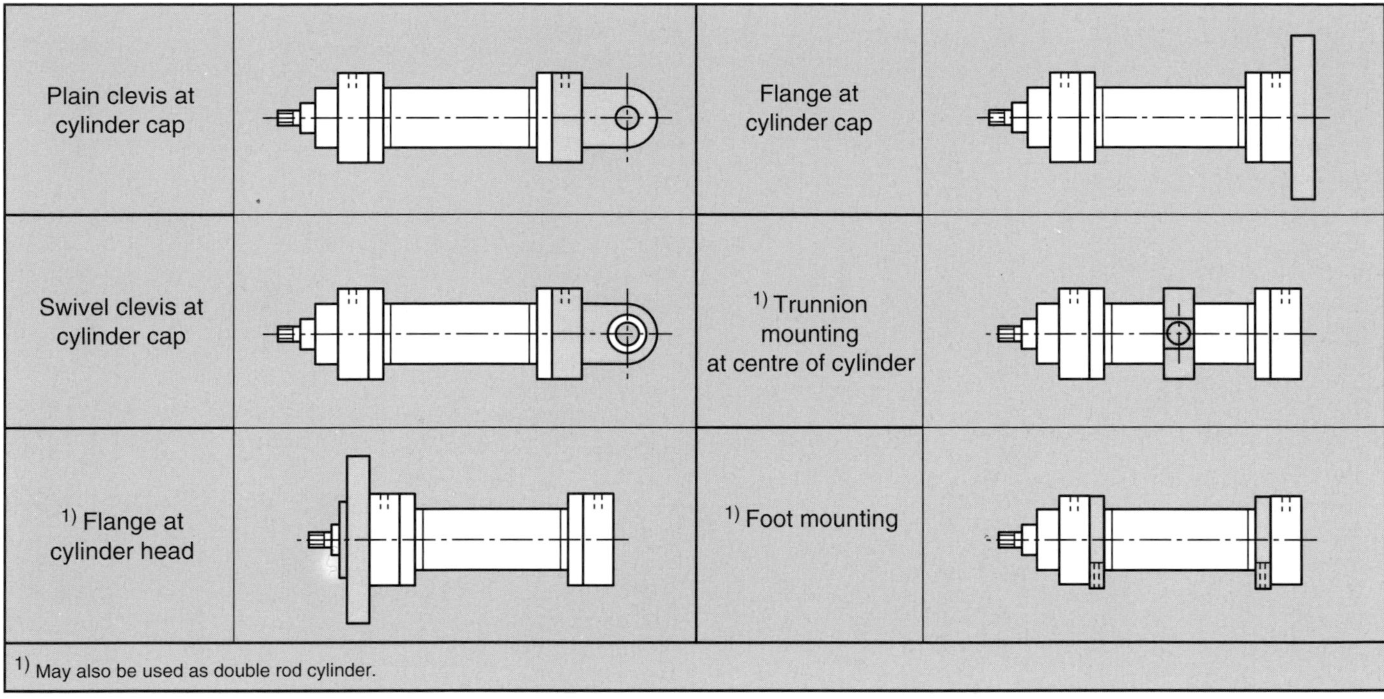

Mounting		Mounting	
Plain clevis at cylinder cap		Flange at cylinder cap	
Swivel clevis at cylinder cap		[1] Trunnion mounting at centre of cylinder	
[1] Flange at cylinder head		[1] Foot mounting	

[1] May also be used as double rod cylinder.

Table 2: *Types of mounting for cylinders with screwed or welded constructions*

Plain clevis bearing at both ends *Note* Axis may only be moved in the direction of clevis	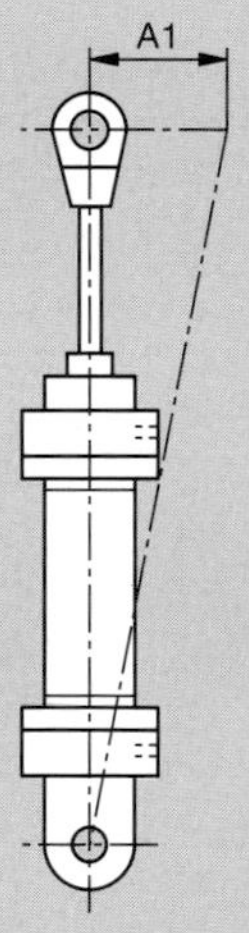	**Swivel clevis at both ends** *Note* Axis may be moved in any direction with tension free installation	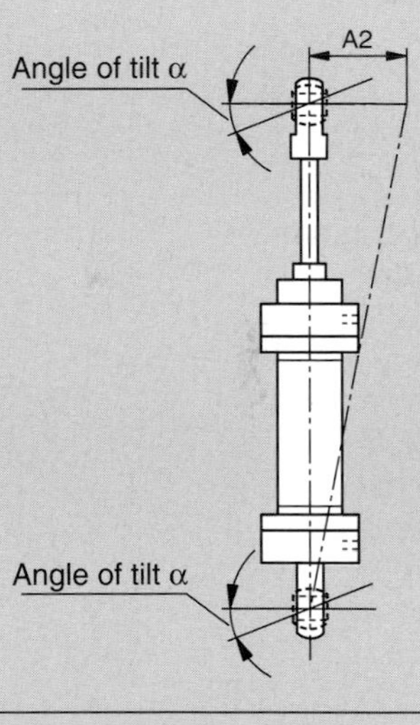
Plain clevis at cylinder base and swivel clevis at rod bearing *Note* Additional inaccuracies in parallelism of both axis pins are compensated for	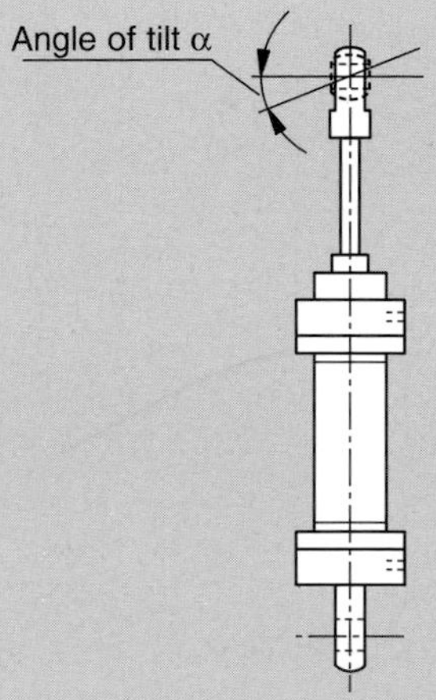		

Table 3a: *Installation notes*

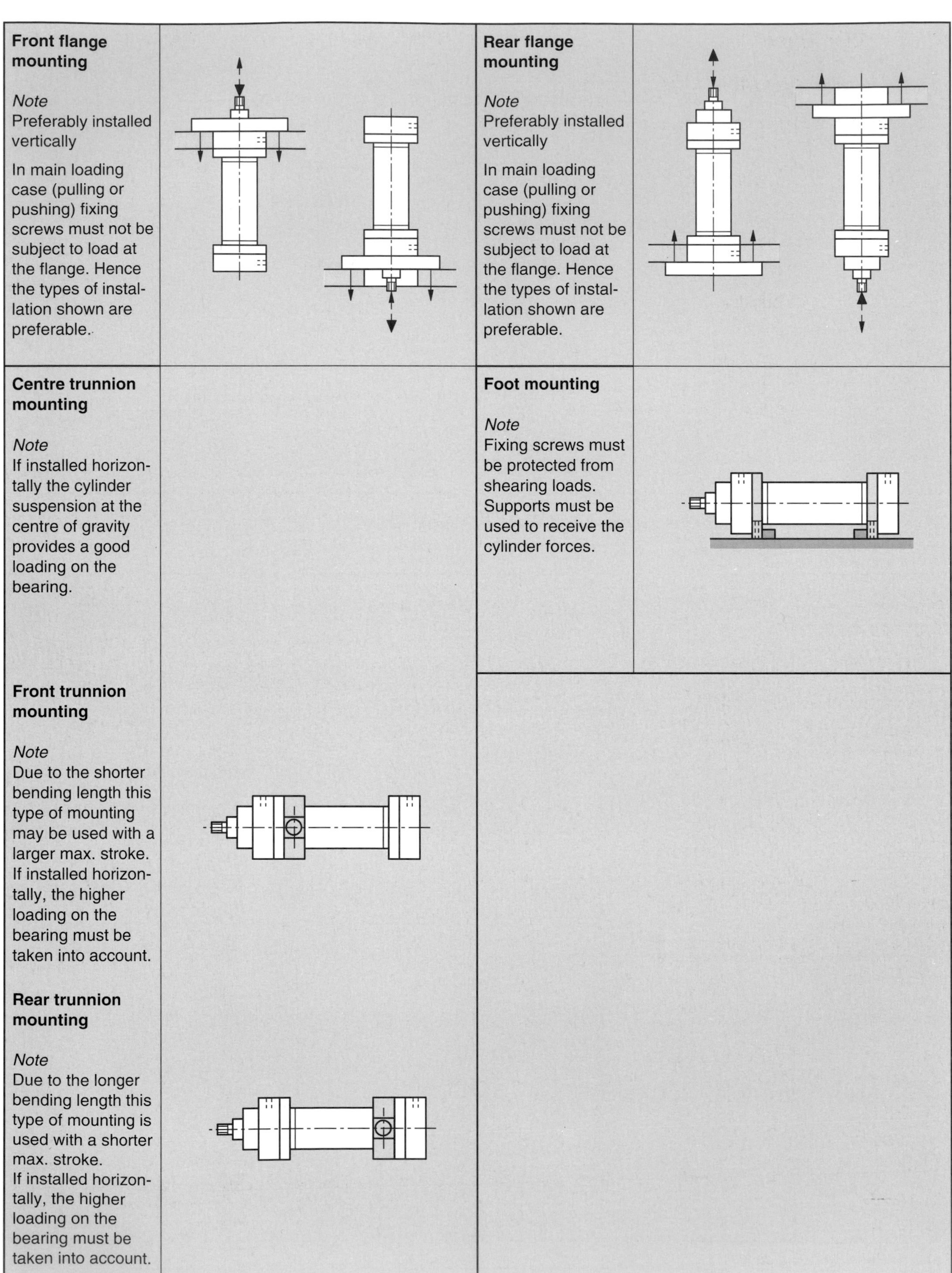

Mounting	Note
Front flange mounting	*Note* Preferably installed vertically In main loading case (pulling or pushing) fixing screws must not be subject to load at the flange. Hence the types of installation shown are preferable.
Rear flange mounting	*Note* Preferably installed vertically In main loading case (pulling or pushing) fixing screws must not be subject to load at the flange. Hence the types of installation shown are preferable.
Centre trunnion mounting	*Note* If installed horizontally the cylinder suspension at the centre of gravity provides a good loading on the bearing.
Foot mounting	*Note* Fixing screws must be protected from shearing loads. Supports must be used to receive the cylinder forces.
Front trunnion mounting	*Note* Due to the shorter bending length this type of mounting may be used with a larger max. stroke. If installed horizontally, the higher loading on the bearing must be taken into account.
Rear trunnion mounting	*Note* Due to the longer bending length this type of mounting is used with a shorter max. stroke. If installed horizontally, the higher loading on the bearing must be taken into account.

Table 3b: *Installation notes*

5 Buckling

5.1 Buckling without side loading

Special problems to do with stability occur when cylinders with long stroke lengths are used.

For the purpose of calculation these cases are divided into areas:

- Non-elastic buckling loads (Tetmajer's calculation) and
- elastic or Hook's buckling loads (its critical limiting load is determined by Euler's equation)

In hydraulic cylinders Euler's calculation is basically the calculation used, as the piston rod may usually be considered to be a slender strut (negligible diameter).

Buckling load and operating load are then calculated as follows:

Buckling load $$K = \frac{\pi^2 \bullet E \bullet J}{s_K^{\ 2}} \text{ in N} \quad (1)$$

i.e. the rod buckles under this load!

Max. operating load $$F = \frac{K}{S} \text{ in N} \quad (2)$$

s_K = free buckling length in mm
E = modulus of elasticity ($2.1 \bullet 10^5$ for steel) in N/mm²
J = moment of inertia for circular cross-section in mm⁴
= $(d^4 \bullet p) / 64 = 0.0491 \bullet d^4$
S = safety factor (3.5)

The length to be used as the free buckling length may be determined from the Euler loading cases (see table 4). In order to simplify the calculation the stiffening due to the cylinder tube is ignored. This provides the required safety margin in standard cylinders, the installation position of which is usually not known, in order to cater for any superimposed bending loads.

Euler's loading case	**Case 1** One end free, one end rigidly connected.	**Case 2** **(Basic case)** Two ends pivoted.	**Case 3** One end pivoted, one end rigidly connected.	**Case 4** Two ends rigidly connected.
Illustration	F, l	F, l	F, l	F, l
Free buckling length	$s_K = 2\,l$	$s_K = l$	$s_K = l \bullet \sqrt{(l/2)}$	$s_K = l/2$
Installation position for cylinder	**Mounting type C, D, F** F, l	**Mounting type A, B, E** F, l	**Mounting type C, D, F** F, l	**Mounting type C, D, F** F, l
Note			Load must be carefully guided, or else possible bracing.	Not suitable, as bracing is to be expected.

Table 4: *Euler's loading cases*

5.2 Buckling with side loading

A particular reference must be made to clevis mounted cylinders (Euler case 2), when used either horizontally or inclined at a large angle.

Besides the pure compression loads, bending occurs due to the weight of the cylinder itself.

Particular attention must be paid to large cylinders with long strokes and which are very heavy.

6 Cushioning

6.1 Cushioning at cylinder base *(Fig. 29)*

The piston (1) is fixed onto the piston rod by means of a cushioning bush.

When the tapered cushioning bush (2) enters the bore in cylinder cap (3), the opening for the fluid leaving the piston chamber (4) decreases until it eventually reaches zero. The fluid from the piston chamber (4) can now only drain away via bore (5) and the adjustable throttle valve (6). The cushioning effect is set at the throttle valve (6). The smaller the opening to flow is, the larger is the effect of cushioning at the end positions.

6.1.1 Adjustable throttle valve for cushioning

The design of the throttle valve stops the throttle screw (7) from being unscrewed when the end position cushioning is set. The setting of the cushioning is protected by means of a lock nut (8).

6.1.2 Check valve with bleed screw

Check valve (9) is used to help the cylinder extend from its starting position. Hence the throttling point is by-passed when the cylinder is extended. Any air in the cylinder may be removed by the bleed screw (10).

In cylinders without cushioning the bleed screw is included as standard.

The throttle valve and the check valve are basically built from the same components and hence they may be interchanged.

6.2 Deceleration force

Cushioning must enable a controlled deceleration (braking) of the stroke velocity in both end positions. When damping starts, all effective energies (formed from product of moving mass and stroke velocity) must not exceed the max. working capability of the damping. The energy being decelerated is converted into heat in the cushioning valve, which works by throttling the fluid flow.

6.2.1 Calculation of deceleration force

The deceleration force of a hydraulic cylinder installed horizontally is calculated as follows:

Extension $F_B = m \bullet a + A_K \bullet p$ (3)

Retraction $F_B = m \bullet a + A_R \bullet p$ (4)

F_B = braking force in N
m = moving mass in kg
a = deceleration in m/s^2 ($a = v^2 / (2 \bullet s)$)
v = stroke velocity in m/s
s = cushioning length in m
A_K = piston area in cm^2
A_R = annulus area in cm^2
p = system pressure in N/cm^2

1 bar ≈ 10 N/cm^2

For vertical stroke movements of the cylinder the weight force (comprising external load, piston and piston rod) must be added or subtracted (depending on the direction of movement) to the braking force F_B.

The cylinder internal friction may be ignored in this calculation.

6.2.2 Calculation of mean cushioning pressure

Under normal circumstances the mean cushioning pressure must not exceed the nominal pressure of the cylinder.

$$p_D = F_B / A_D$$

p_D = mean cushioning pressure in N/cm^2
F_B = deceleration force in N
A_D = effective cushioning area in cm^2

1 bar ≈ 10 N/cm^2

If the calculation produces a cushioning pressure which is too high, either the cushioning length must be made larger or the system pressure must be decreased.

Hydraulic Cylinders

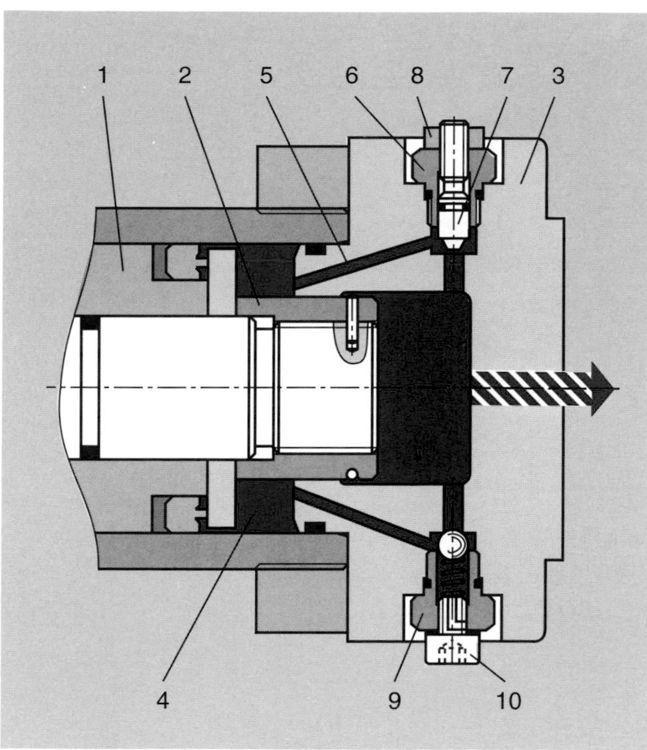

Fig. 29: *Adjustable cushioning at cylinder base*

7 Servo cylinder systems

Servo cylinder systems are a unique sub-group of cylinders.

They are not categorised in accordance with their general techical design as industrial and mobile cylinders are, but instead they are categorised in accordance with the type of bearing of the piston rod (hydrostatic bearing).

Cylinders with hydrostatic bearings are used in applications where low friction and/or high oscillation frequencies with small amplitudes are required.

Servo cylinder systems are primarily used in movement simulators, material and component testing devices and anywhere where the highest of dynamic responses and accuracy of the linear drive is required.

Servo cylinder systems basically comprise the following devices:

- servo cylinder
- servo manifold and
- control electronics

7.1 Servo cylinder

Four characteristics are used to determine which type of cylinder is to be used:

- Permissible amount of friction of cylinder under operating conditions
- Side loads on the piston rod
- Required velocities of the cylinder
- Smallest amplitude or control movements

Dependent on the conditions of use there are basically two designs which are used:

- Servo cylinder with hydrostatic tapered gap bearings of the piston rod without pressurised seals.
- Servo cylinder with full hydrostatic bearings (cavity bearings) of the piston rod without pressurised seals.

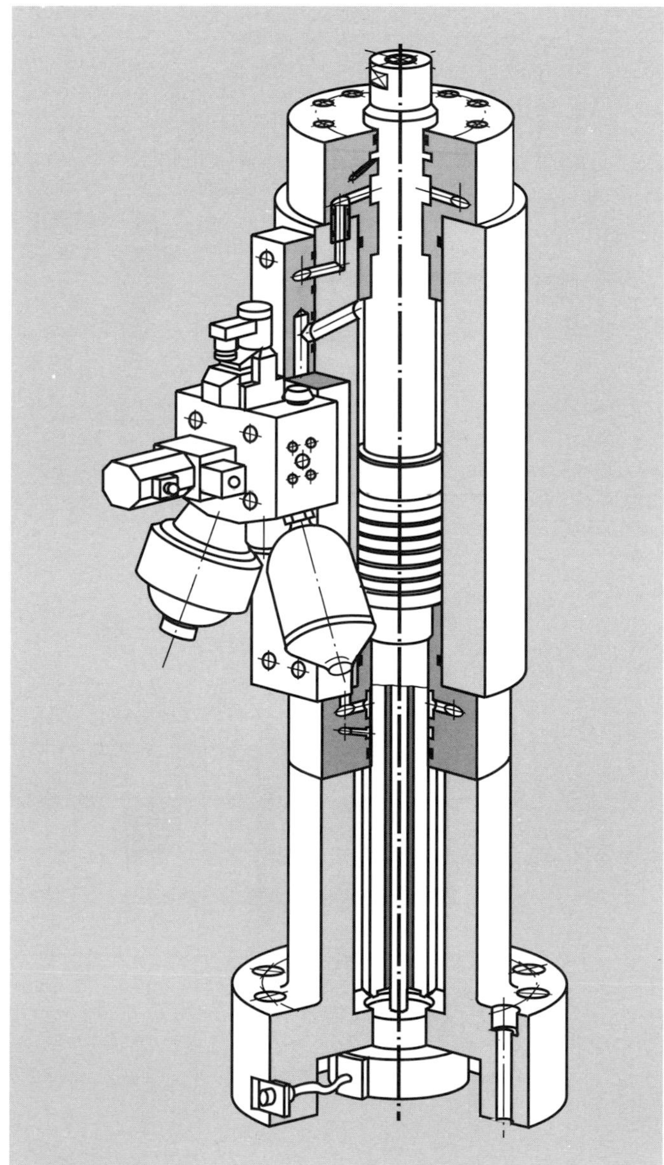

Fig. 30: *Servo cylinder with mounted servo manifold*

7.1.1 Hydrostatic tapered gap bearings

Servo cylinders with tapered gap bearings are used in applications with velocities of up to v_{max} = 2 m/s and small side loads (e.g. effects of mass of cylinder and moments of inertia).

Fig. 31: Servo cylinder with tapered gap bearing

The series is designed for operating pressures of up to 210 bar and for nominal forces of 1 to 4000 kN.

Possible ways of mounting are: clevis bearings at either end, flanges at either end, base mounting or trunnion mounting.

The servo cylinders are supplied with an internal, stationary, inductive positional measuring system as standard. With this measuring system, the piston stroke is measured and the actual value is sent to the control electronics.

The seals built into the servo cylinders are not pressurised by the working pressure. Hence very low friction is produced in this type of bearing. Disruptive stick-slip effects are avoided. These avantageous characteristics are shown in the friction diagrams (*Diagram 1*).

The comparison shows that friction is 3 or 4 times lower in servo cylinders.

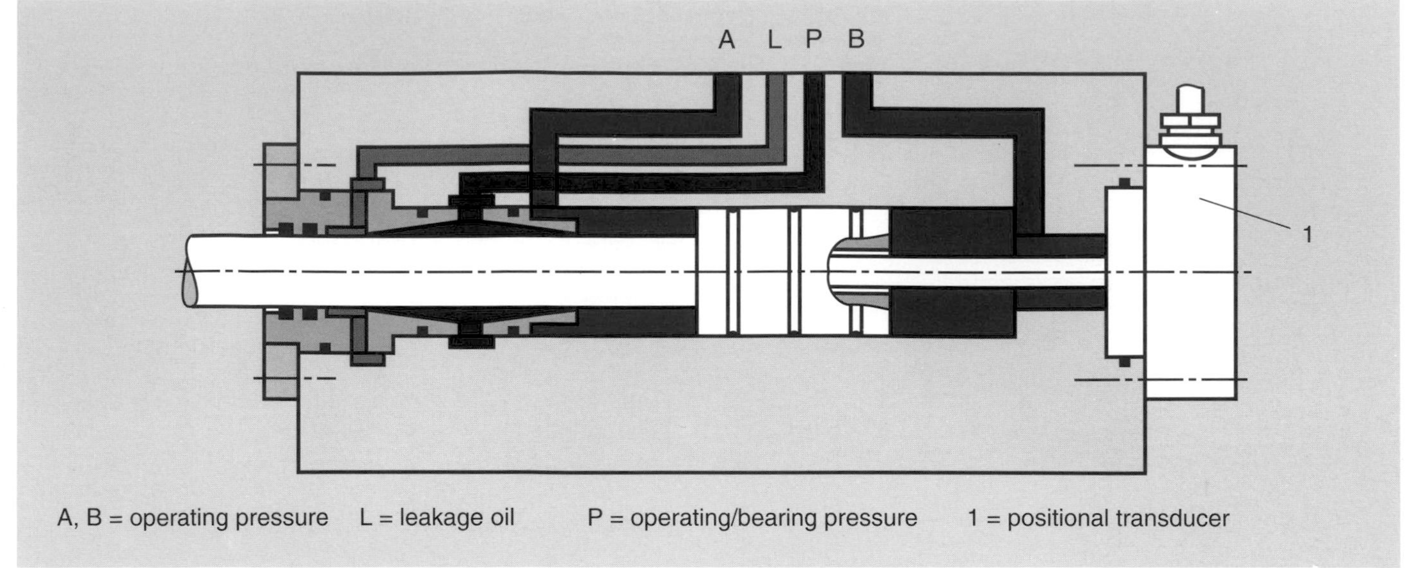

Fig. 32: *Schematic diagram of servo cylinder with hydrostatic tapered gap bearing supporting piston rod*

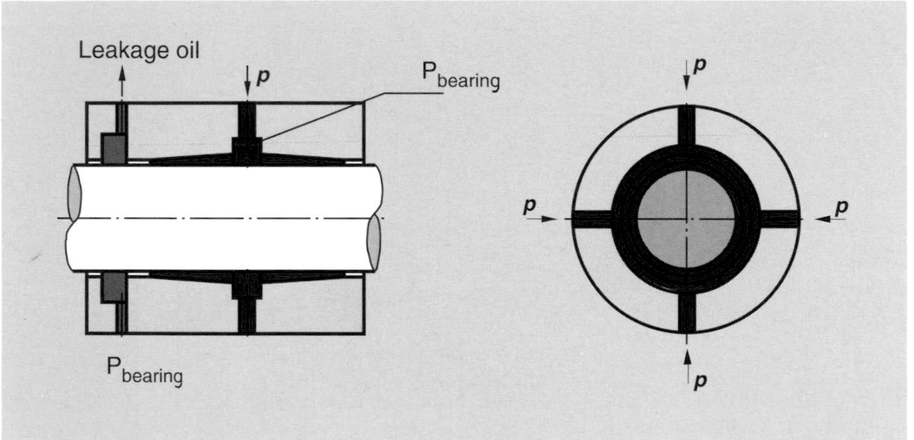

Fig. 33: *Schematic diagram of hydrostatic tapered gap bearing supporting piston rod. The bearing pressure in the taper gap bearing is equivalent to the operating pressure (P)*

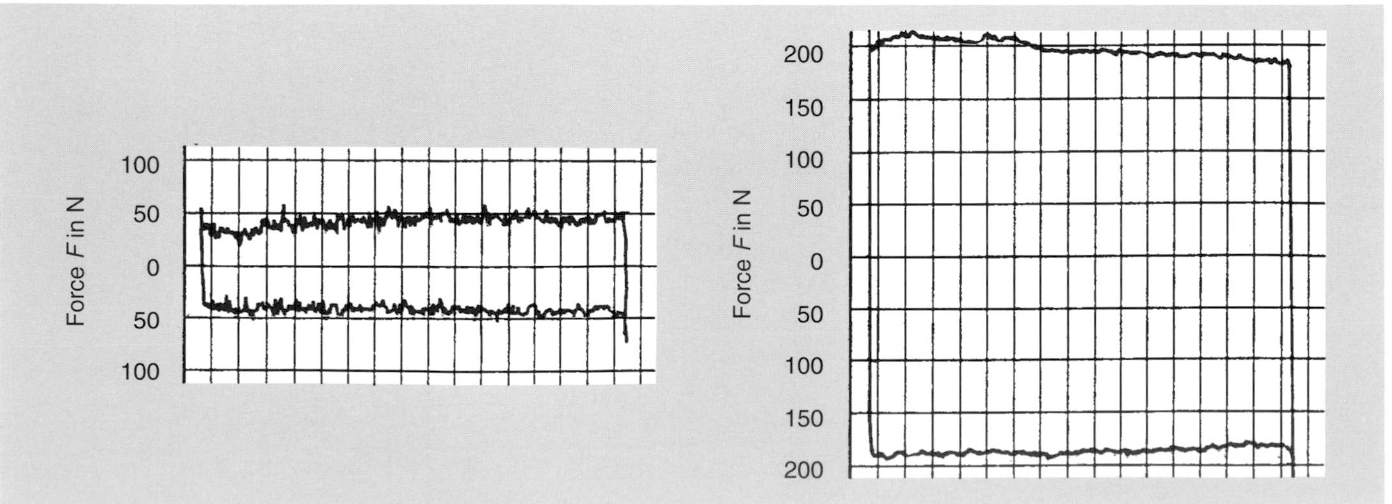

Diagram 1: *Friction measurement at p_{St} = 210 bar, v = 0.1 m/s and s = ± 100 mm; (left) servo cylinder with hydrostatic taper gap bearing, (right) hydraulic cylinder with glide ring seal*

Hydraulic Cylinders

7.1.2 Full hydrostatic bearings (cavity bearings)

In hydraulic cylinders which are used at high as well as low velocities and which may be under high side loads full hydrostatic bearings (cavity bearings) are used.

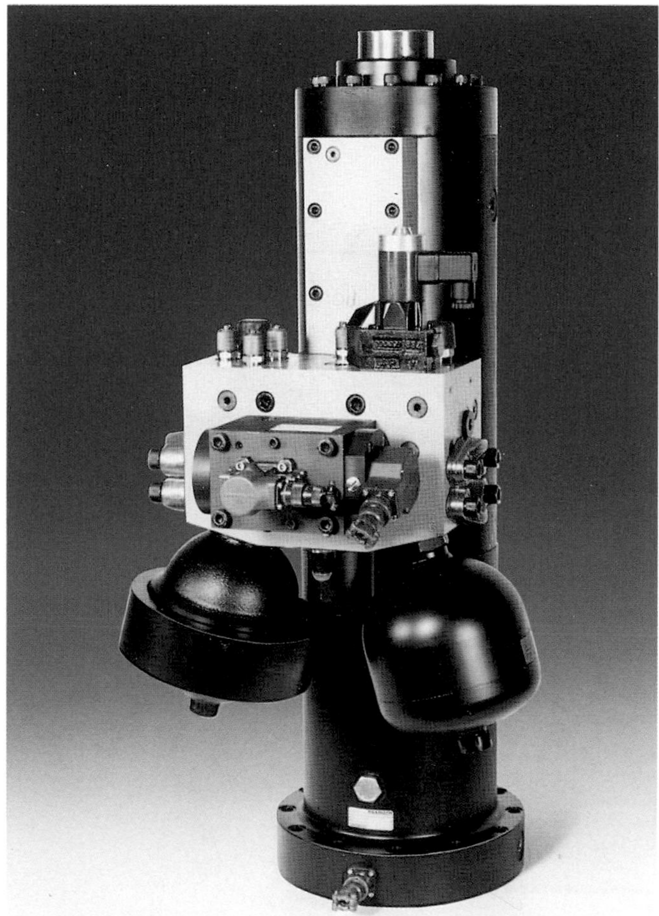

Fig. 34: *Servo cylinder with full hydrostatic bearings (cavity bearings) and mounted servo manifold*

The series is designed for operating pressures of up to 280 bar and for nominal forces of 10 to 10 000 kN.

Possible ways of mounting are: flange at either end or clevis or trunnion mounting. The types of mounting may be combined.

Servo cylinders are supplied with an internal, stationary, inductive positional measuring system as standard. With this measuring system, the piston stroke is measured and the actual value is sent to the control electronics.

This design has four cavities arranged around the circumference of the bearing, which provide the piston rod with four coupled pressure fields hence holding the rod in the central position.

The bearing pressure in the cavity is equivalent to 50% of the operating pressure (*P*) if the effect of the side loading is ignored. If a side load acts on the piston rod, the bearing pressure is increased in the opposing cavity. Hence the piston rod is still held in the central position.

The amount of friction occuring in full hydrostatic bearings (cavity bearings) is the same as for tapered gap bearings (shown in *diagram 1*). However this amount of friction is also valid in cavity bearings under side loads, as the piston rod is not able to rub against the bearing surfaces and hence friction remains at a constant low level.

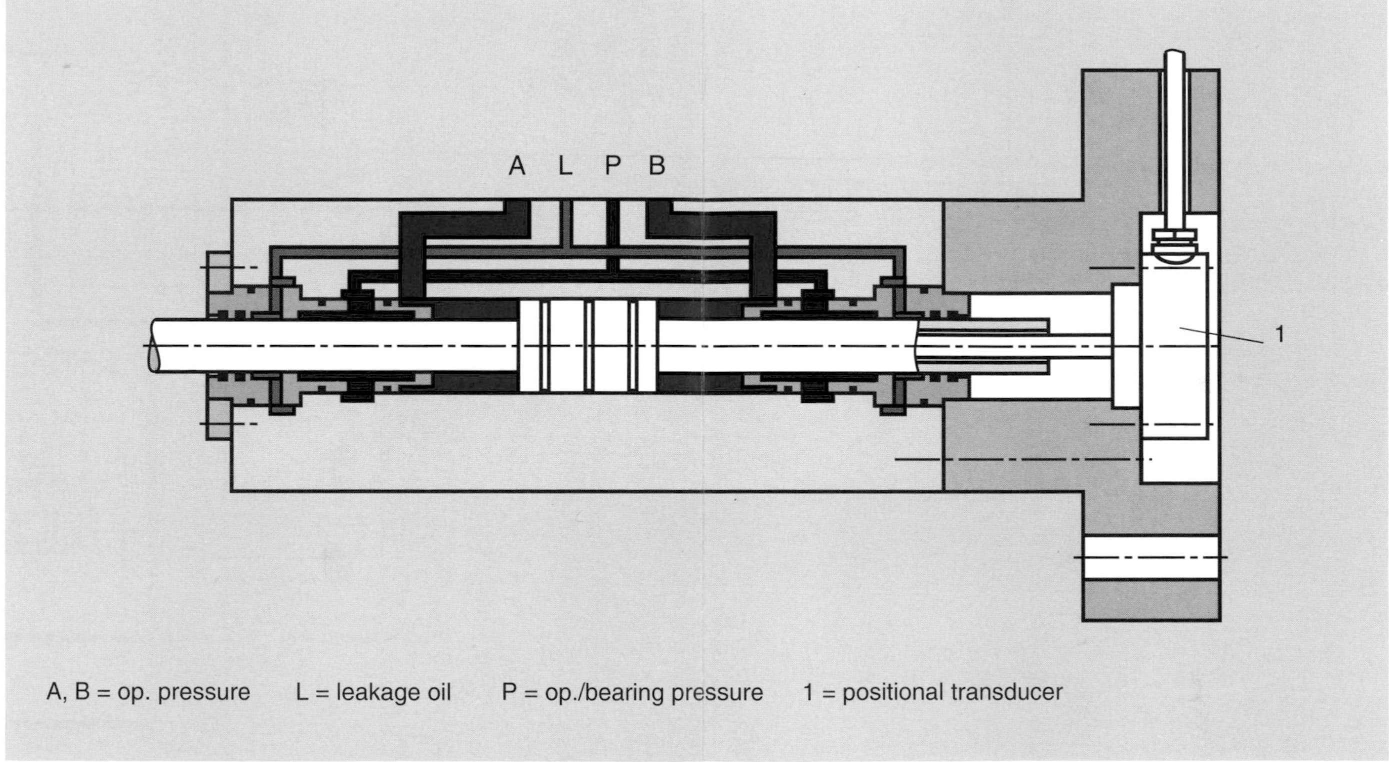

Fig. 35: *Schematic diagram of servo cylinder with full hydrostatic bearings (cavity bearings) supporting the piston rod*

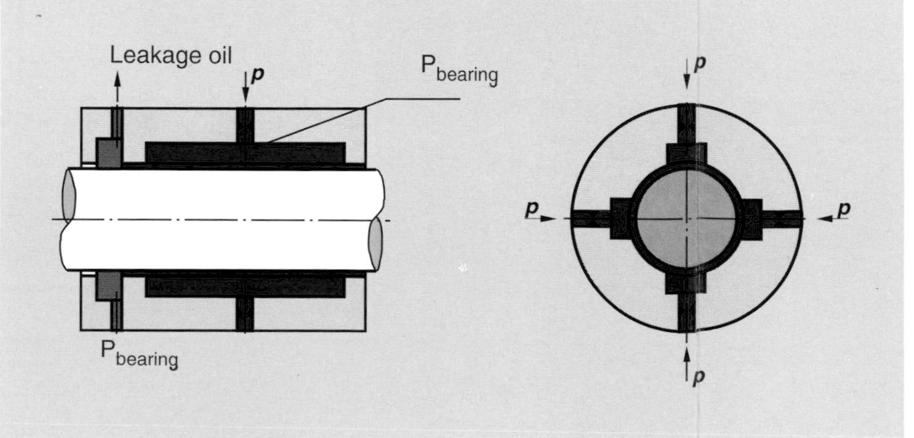

Fig. 36: *Schematic diagram of full hydrostatic bearings (cavity bearings) supporting the piston rod*

7.2 Servo manifold

In order not to unnecessarily reduce the good dynamic characteristics of hydraulic drives, the pipe lengths between the control and servo cylinder must be kept as short as possible. In order to achieve this, the servo manifold is mounted directly onto the servo cylinder.

The piping to the power unit or to the isolating system is via a servo manifold. Additional functions, such as force limiting, pilot oil and bearing oil filtration and pressure storage are included within this manifold.

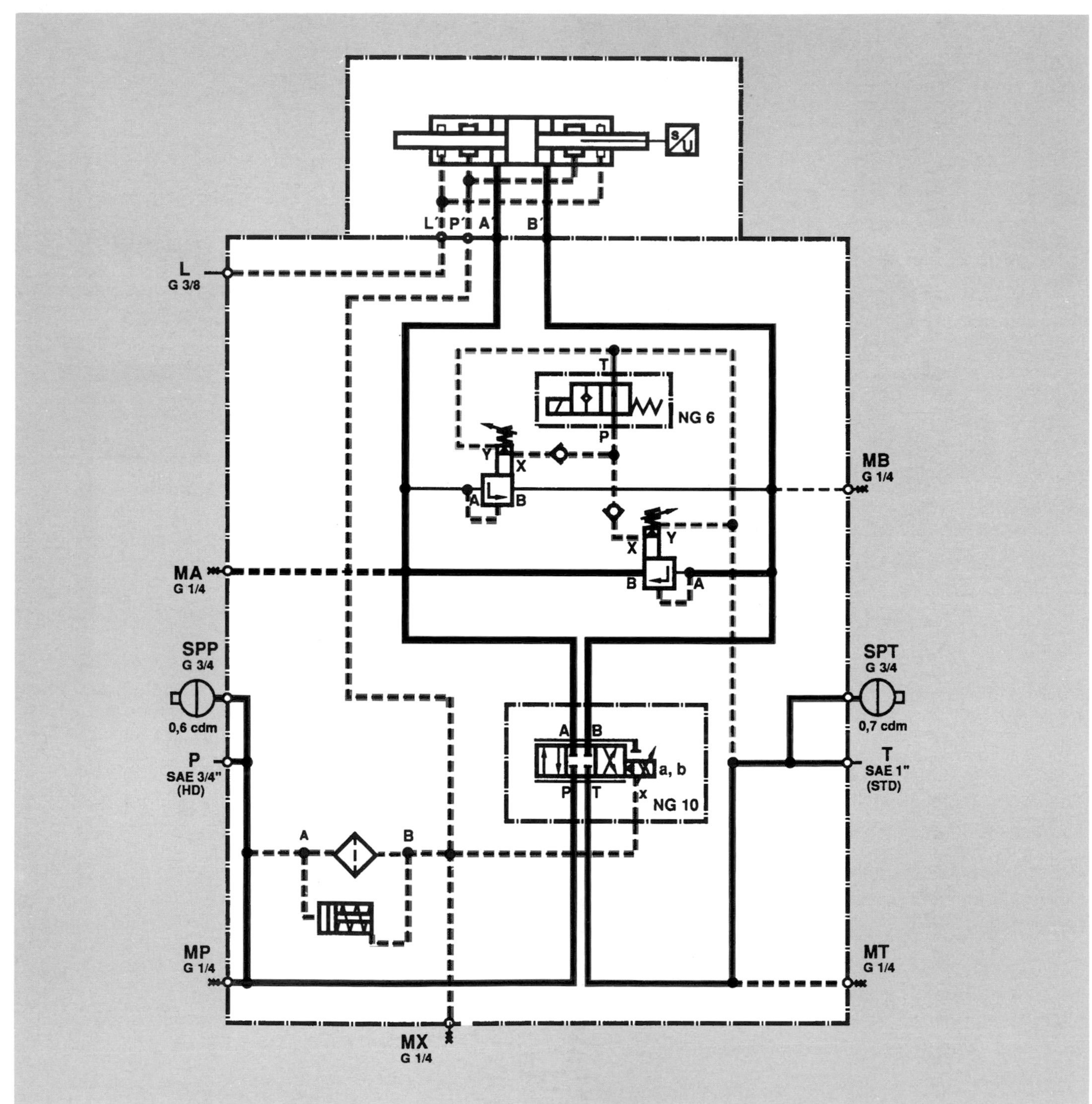

Fig. 37: *Typical circuit diagram of a servo cylinder with mounted servo manifold*

Notes

Notes

Chapter 8

Rotary Actuators

Paul Schwab

1 General

Rotary actuators output a swivel movement via a shaft when pressurised with fluid regardless of the type or design of the unit. The angle the rotary actuator moves through is limited by fixed or adjustable stops. Hence the range of applications in which rotary actuators may be used is limited.

The compact and robust design and the possibility of transferring large torques makes the rotary actuator particularly useful for applications under rough operating conditions.

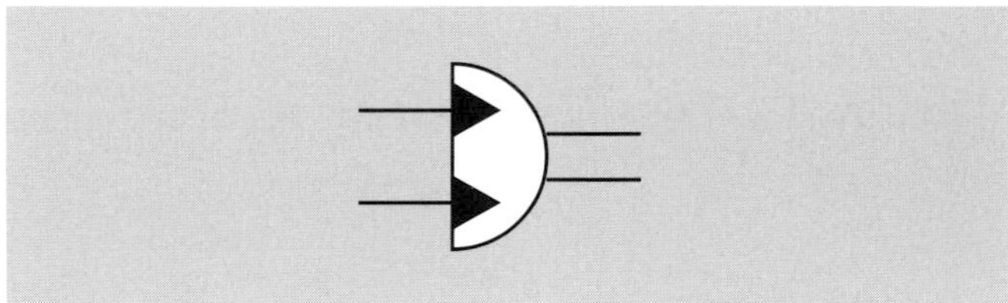

Fig. 1

2 Types

In a similar way to hydraulic motors with rotating output movements, rotary actuators may be categorised into

- vane type
- radial/tangential piston types and
- axial piston types.

2.1 Vane model

The vane rotary actuator is particularly economically designed, as a round housing may be used due to the way the central output shaft with single or double rotary vanes has been designed.

In addition a through shaft may be used in this drive in order to add on another output or display devices.

Vane rotary actuators may rotate through an angle of up to 280°.

Torque is produced by pressurising the rotary vanes with fluid and is maintained constant over the whole swivel range.

By using double vanes the torque produced may be doubled, but the swivel range is then decreased by about 60%.

Fig. 2: *Vane type rotary actuator with single vanes*

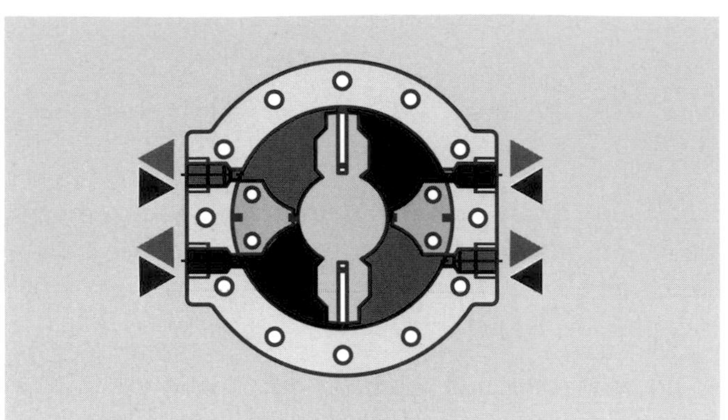

Fig. 3: *Vane type rotary actuator with double vanes*

2.2 Rotary piston/rotary actuator

In this model the fluid acts on the piston which has been lengthened to accomodate helical external splines of about 45° gradient. The helix angles of these two splines are opposed. As one of these splines is restrained by mating splines within the rear housing and the other is similarly restrained within the output shaft, a linear motion of the piston causes the output shaft to rotate.

Rotary piston/rotary actuators may move through a swivel angle of up to 720°.

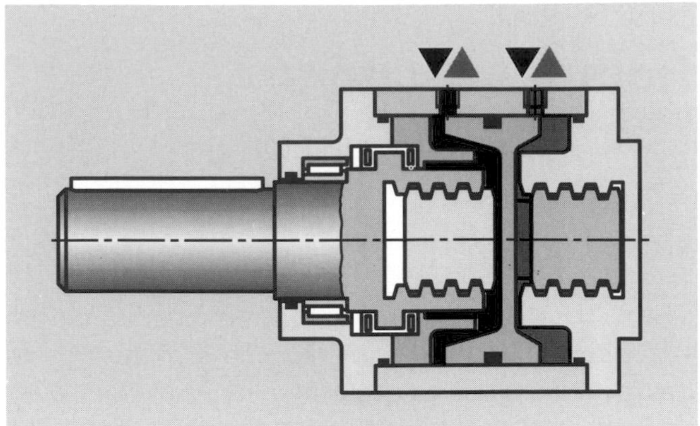

Fig. 4: *Rotary piston/rotary actuator with drive pivot operated by means of a thread*

2.3 Parallel piston/rotary actuator

In parallel piston/rotary actuators two pistons moving in parallel to each other are alternately pressurised with fluid. The force produced in this way is transferred to the output shaft via piston rods (similar to the way in which combustion engines work). These piston rods act at a tangent to the rotating output shaft.

Parallel piston/rotary actuators may move through a swivel angle of up to 100°.

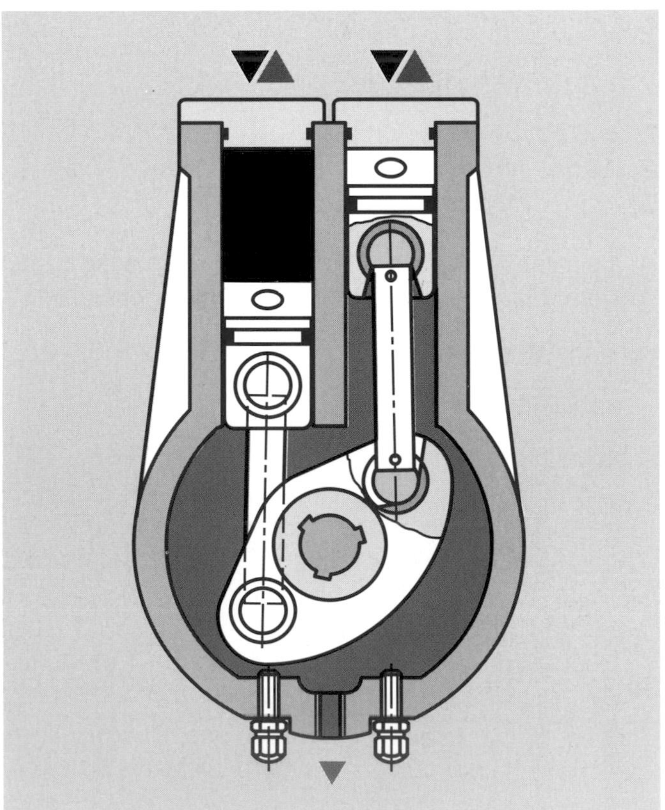

Fig. 5: *Parallel piston/rotary actuator*

2.4 In-line piston/rotary actuator with connecting rod drive

The design of an in-line piston/rotary actuator is similar to that of a double acting double rod cylinder without protruding piston rod ends.

The central piston part drives the output shaft via a connecting rod drive system. Piston, connecting rod and crankshaft are all situated in a sealed housing which is held together by flanges.

In-line piston/rotary actuators with connecting rod drives may move through a swivel angle of up to 180°.

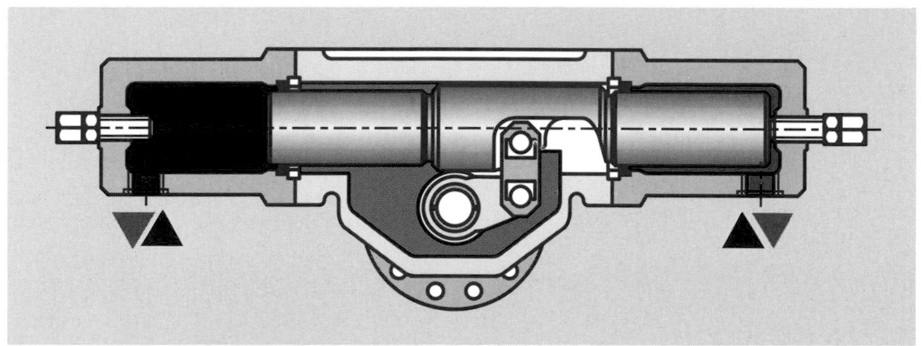

Fig. 6:
In-line piston/rotary actuator with connecting rod drive

2.5 In-line piston/rotary actuator with rack and pinion drive

In this design, the central part of the piston is formed into a rack. The interlocking pinion produces the output torque. A through shaft is possible with this model. Depending on the pinion ratio, swivel angles of 90, 140, 180, 240, 300 or 360° or even more may be achieved.

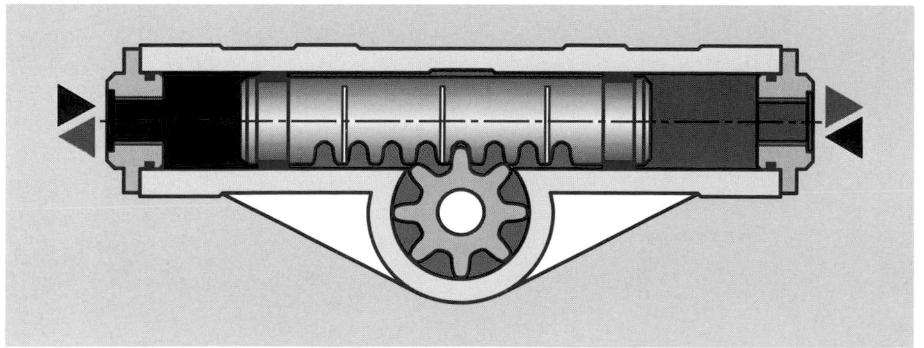

Fig. 7:
In-line piston/rotary actuator operated via double rod cylinder and rack and pinion output

Notes

Chapter 9

Accumulators and Accumuator Applications

Martin Reik

1 General

The main task of an accumulator is to take a specific amount of fluid under pressure from the hydraulic system and store it until it is required within the system.

As the fluid is under pressure, accumulators are treated as pressure vessels and must be designed taking into account the max. operating pressure. However, they must also pass the accepatance standards in the country in which they are being used.

In order to store energy in accumulators, the fluid in an accumulator is weight or spring loaded or pressurised by a gas (*Fig. 1*).

Therefore a balance is maintained between the pressure in a fluid and the opposing pressure produced by the weight, spring or pressure created from the gas.

Weight and spring loaded accumulators are only considered for special industrial applications and hence are of little importance. Gas pressurised accumulators without a separating element are seldom used in hydraulic systems due to the fluid taking in gas.

In most hydraulic systems hydro-pneumatic (gas pressurised) accumulators with a separating element are used.

Depending on the type of separating element used, accumulators are categorised into bladder, piston and membrane accumulators. These accumulators will be described in more detail in the following sections.

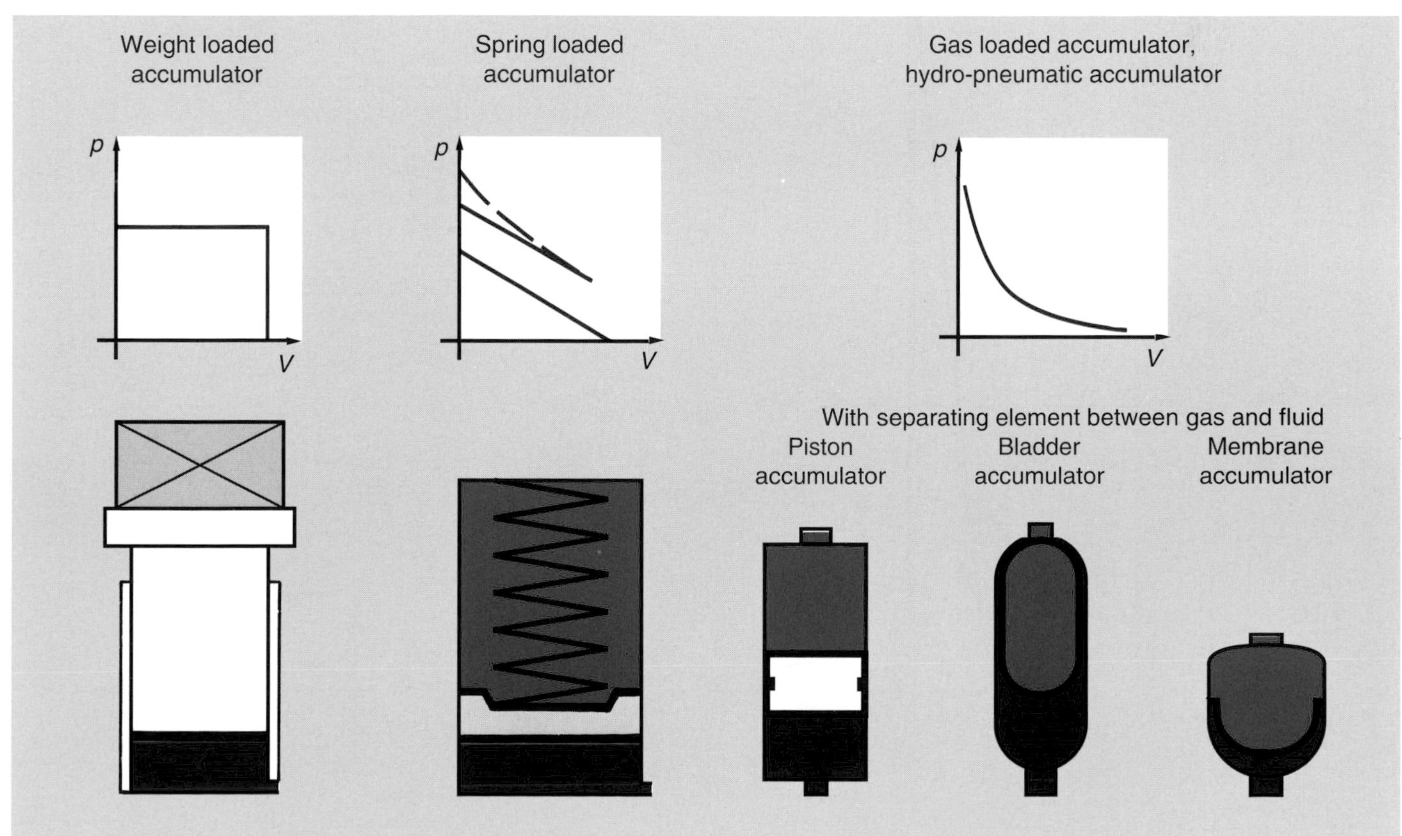

Fig. 1: *Varying features of different accumulators*

2 Function

Accumulators have to carry out various functions in a hydraulic system, e.g.

- Energy storage
- Fluid reserve
- Emergency operation
- Balance of forces
- Damping of mechanical shocks
- Damping of pressure shocks
- Compensation of leakage oil
- Damping of shocks and vibrations
- Damping of pulses
- Vehicle suspension
- Reclaiming of deceleration energy
- Maintaining constant pressure
- Compensation of flow (expansion tank)

2.1 Energy storage

The diagram (*diagram 1*) showing the power required in a plastic injection moulding machine clearly illustrates that max. power is only required for a short period in the tool when it is operating at a high injection velocity. However, sufficient pump power must be available for this short period of maximum power.

By using accumulators the pump power may be decreased to the mean power required. The smaller flow of the pump fills the accumulator during an operation cycle when the required flow for the system is smaller than the flow from the pump. If the max. flow is required, the difference to the flow from the pump is taken from the accumulator.

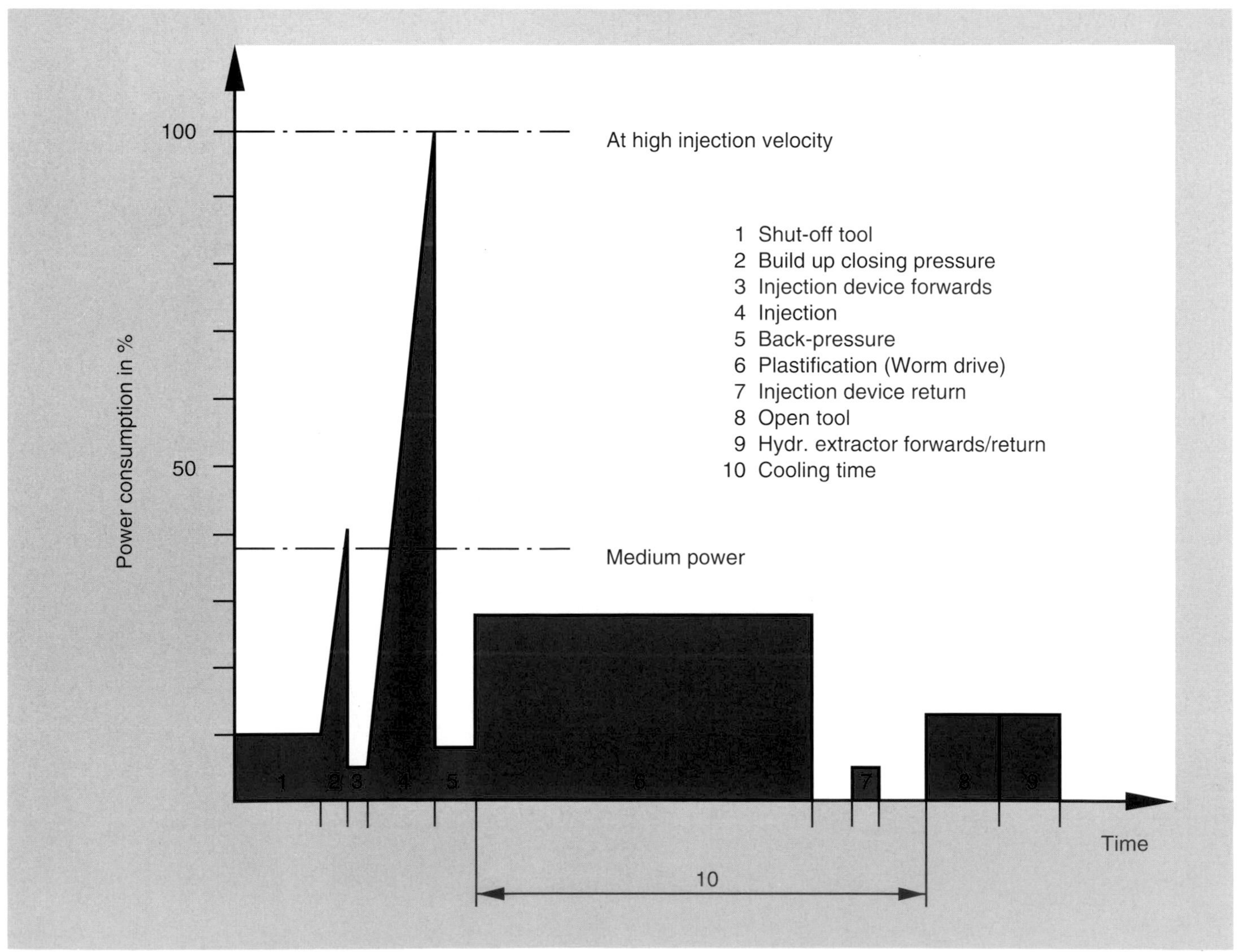

Diagram 1: *Power diagram for an injection moulding machine*

Some of the features of this are:

- Possibility of using smaller pumps
- Lower installed power
- Less heat produced
- Simple servicing and installation

In addition, damping of pressure shocks and pulses (depending on the system) is provided. This increases the service life of the complete system.

By using accumulators, energy is saved.

In hydraulic systems which briefly require a large amount of oil or short cycles, accumulators must be used in order to achieve an economic solution.

2.1.1 Examples of applications

2.1.1.1 Several actuators with varying oil requirements

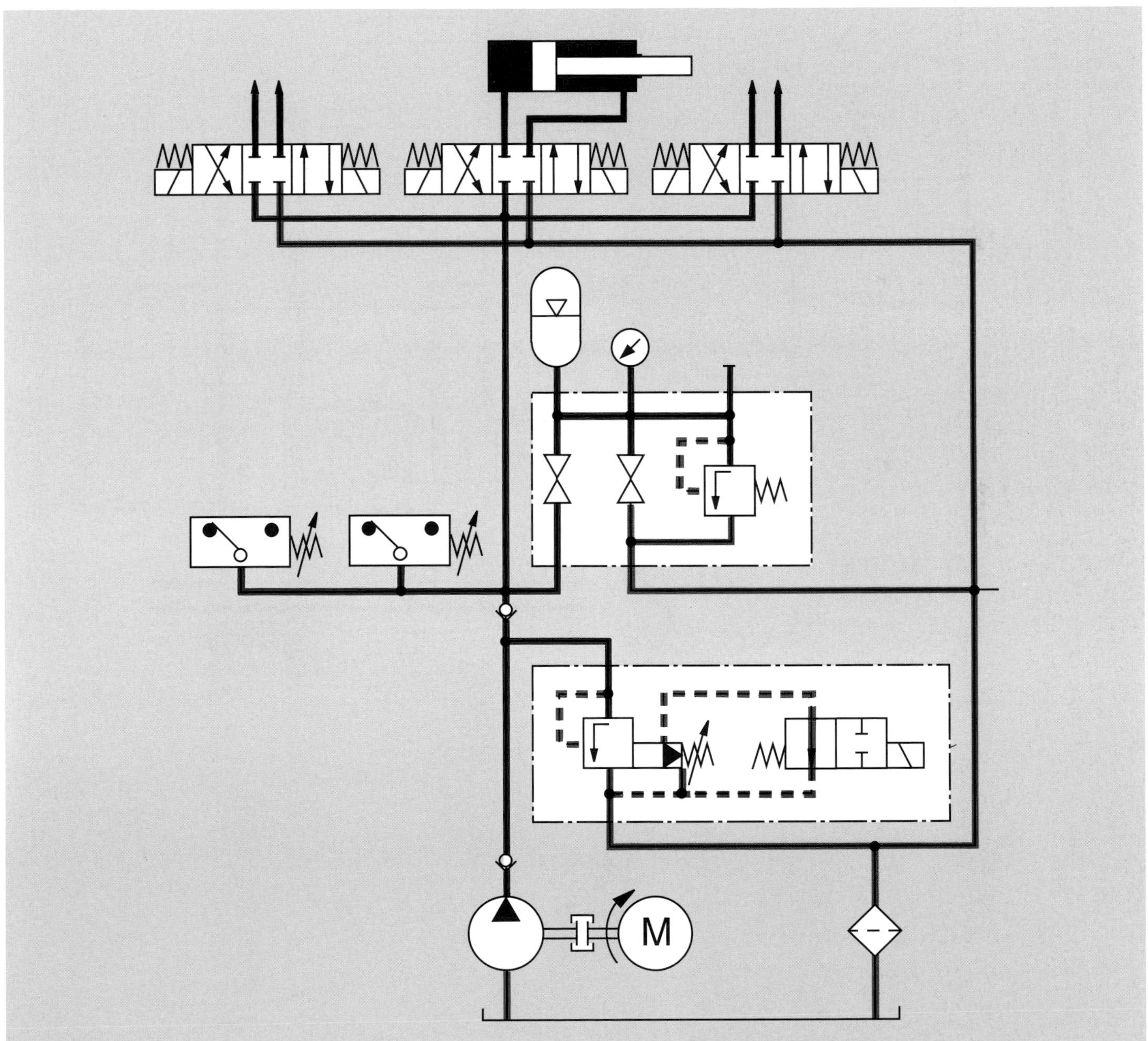

Fig. 2: *Energy storage in an injection moulding machine*

2.1.1.2 Shorter cycles (e.g. in machine tools)

By placing an accumulator directly in front of the actuator the inertia of the fluid column is overcome more quickly than it would be if all the fluid had to pass through the drive unit. Hence the system may be started up more quickly. In addition the accumulators equal out the varying fluid requirements of the actuators.

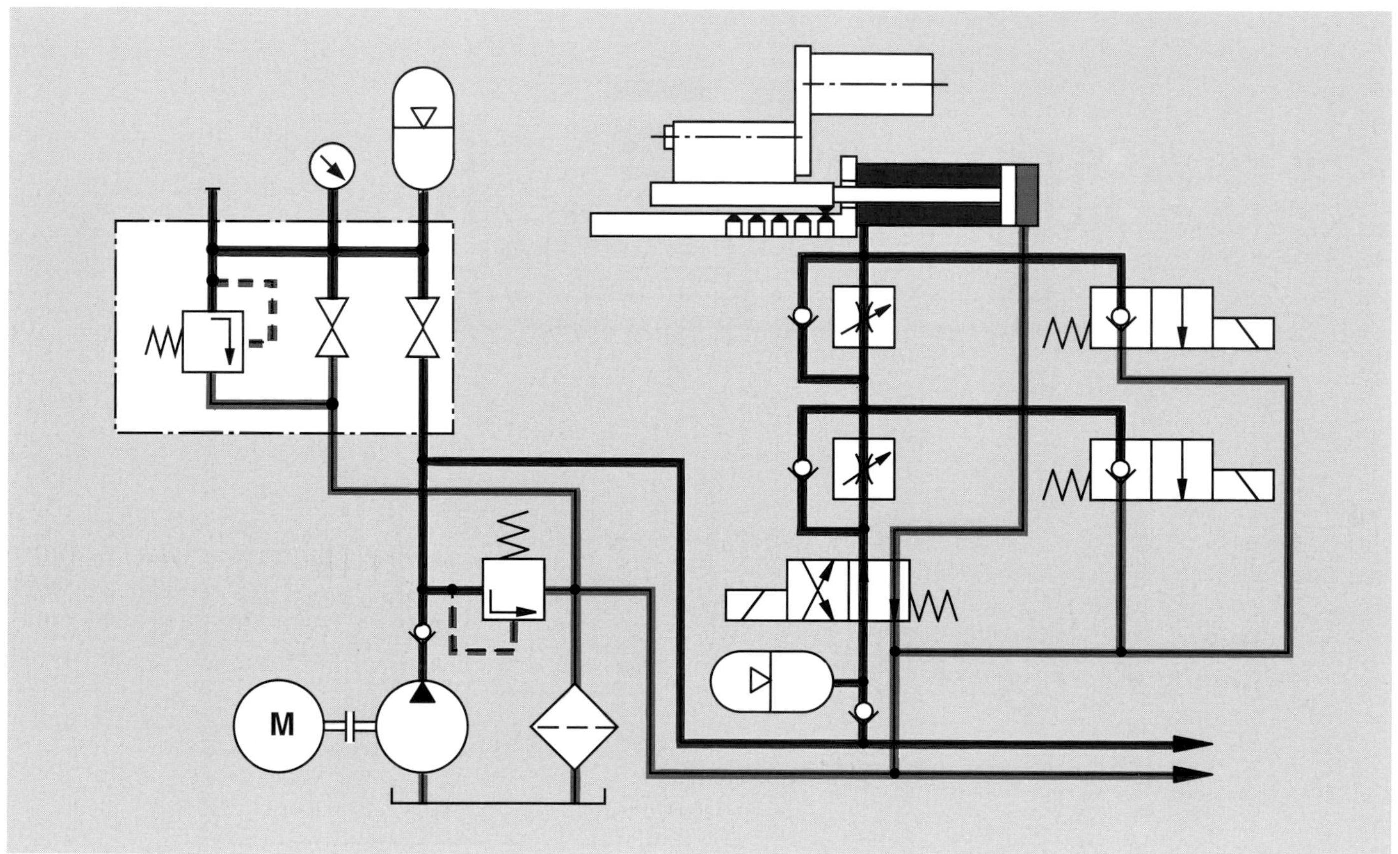

Fig. 3: *Energy storage in machine tools*

2.1.1.3 Decrease in the time taken for a stroke

In order to rationalise production in pressing and punching operations, long and fast approach strokes are required in minimum time. The actual working process is then carried out at low velocity and at high pressure.

Under light running conditions, pump I (low pressure pump), pump II (high pressure pump) and the accumulator all deliver fluid, so that the desired high velocity is obtained.

As the pressure rises towards the end of the approach stroke, check valve (A) closes. Now only pump II delivers fluid with a low flow and at a high pressure. Pump I meanwhile recharges the accumulator.

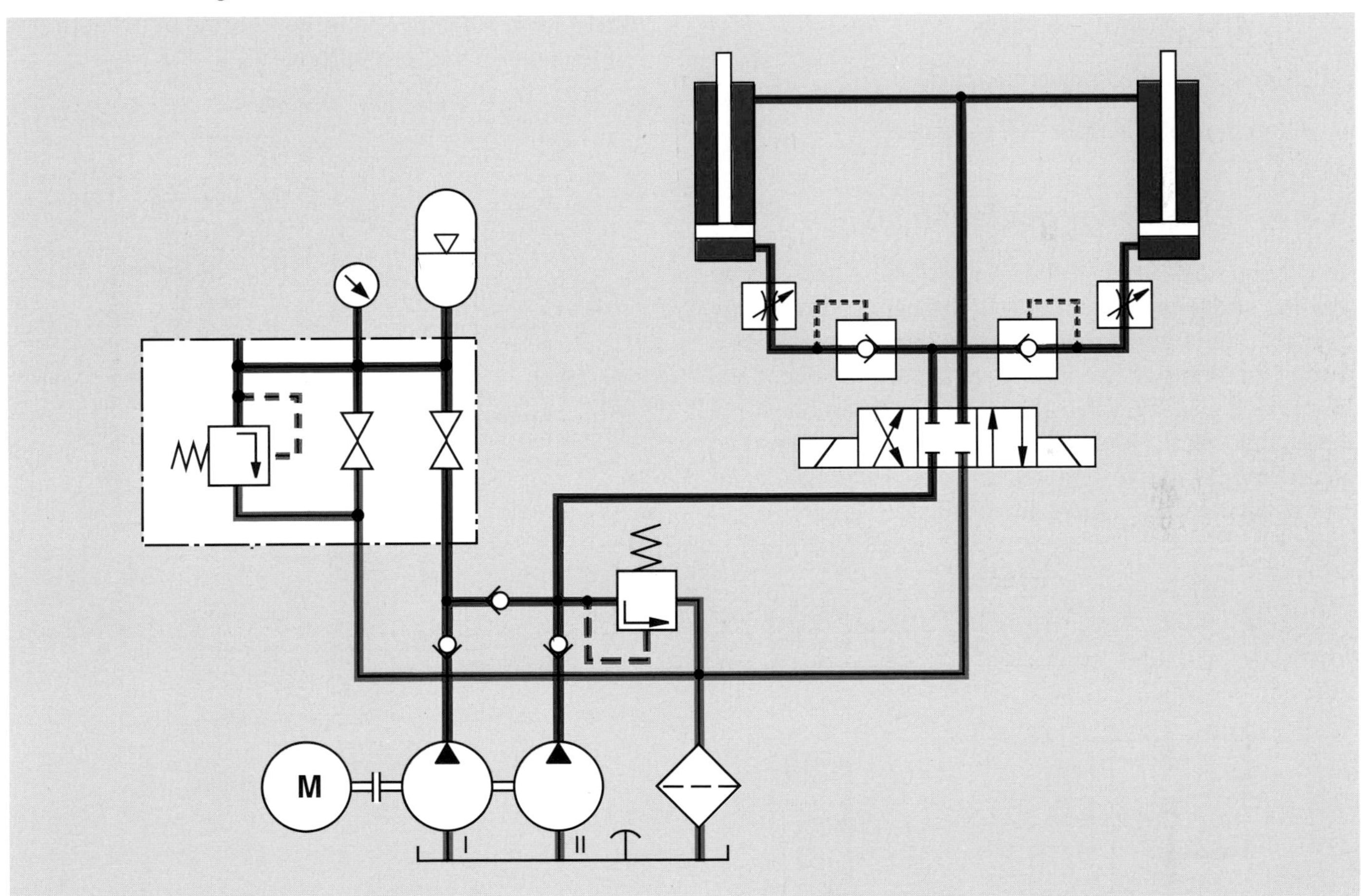

Fig. 4: *Energy storage to decrease stroke time*

2.2 Fluid reserve

If the accumulator is used as a safety element, it does not operate as an energy source during normal operation of the system. It is however always connected directly to the pump. By using leak tight isolating elements, the stored energy may be held indefinitely and is immediately available if required.

Safety systems using accumulators are used in hydraulic systems for emergency operation, in order to carry out specific actions when faults occur.

Some examples of actions to be undertaken are:

- Closing of partitions, flaps and switches
- Operation of sliding contacts
- Operation of high power switches
- Operation of quick shut-off systems

2.3 Emergency operation

In emergencies, e.g. if the power fails, a working or closing stroke is carried out with the help of the energy present in the accumulator. In *Fig. 5* an example of a circuit for emergency operation is shown. If power fails, the spring causes valve (1) to close and return to its original position. Hence the accumulator and piston rod side of the cylinder are connected. The oil under pressure in the accumulator causes the piston to retract.

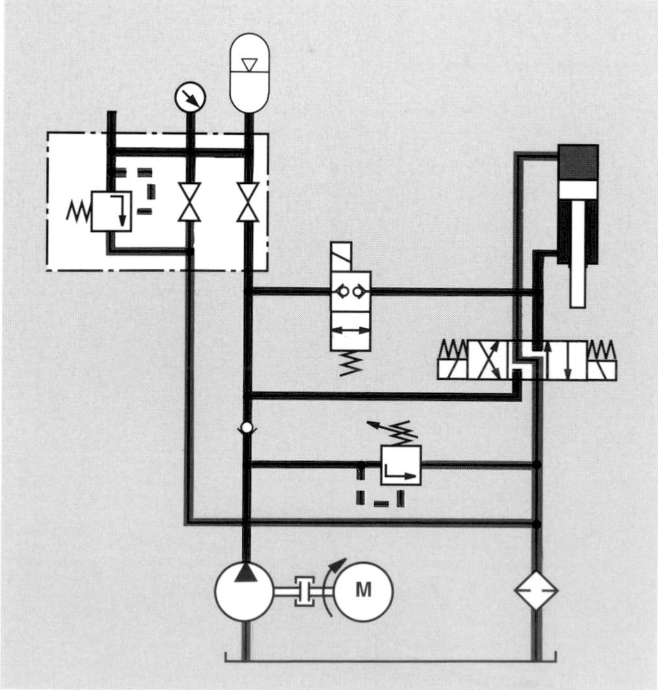

Fig. 5: *Emergency operation of cylinder*

Another application of emergency operation using accumulators is when an operating cycle which has started needs to be completed when a pump or valve malfunctions.

The main features of emergency operation using accumulators are:

- Direct availability
- Unlimited endurance
- No fatigue
- No inertia
- Highest safety achieved for little servicing.

Short-term storage of a large volume of pressurised oil for use on system failure.

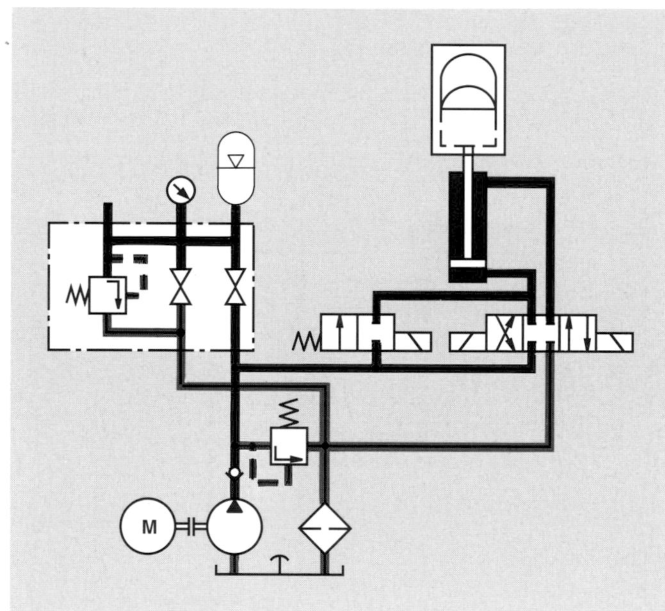

Fig. 6: *Extension of cylinder during system failure*

Emergency braking

Accumulators may be used for the emergency operation of brakes and doors in mountain railways, cable cars, motor cars, etc. The accumulators are filled either by motor pumps or hand pumps within the station. Hence accumulators always have sufficient energy available in order for ermergency braking to be carried out.

Often the control system is reversed, i.e. a spring force operates the brake and the brake cylinders are kept in the "off" position in opposition to this spring force by means of the accumulator.

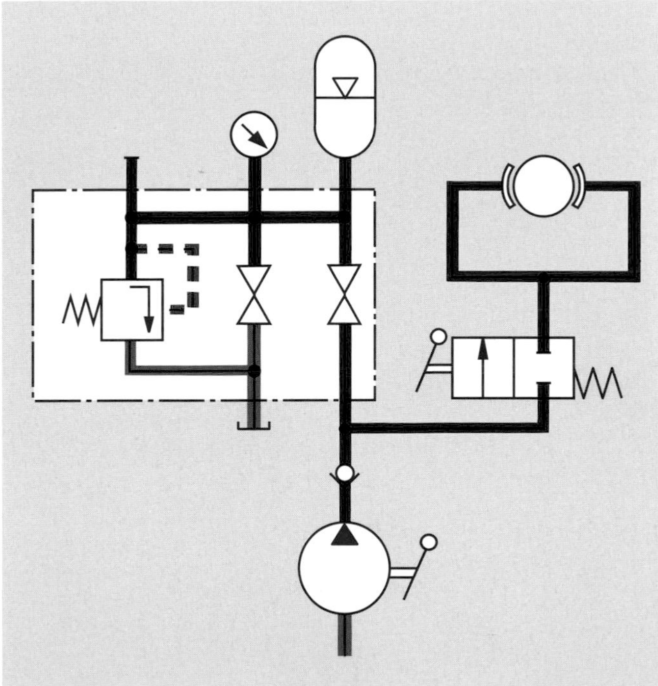

Fig. 7: *Emergency braking in cable cars*

Emergency lubrication

In order to maintain the lubricating film on bearings, these must be continually supplied with lubricating oil. This means, that the lubricated positions are always under pressure. If the lubricating oil pump fails, the pressure can be kept constant by means of the accumulator until the machine has stopped or until a built-in auxilliary pump has built up the required pressure.

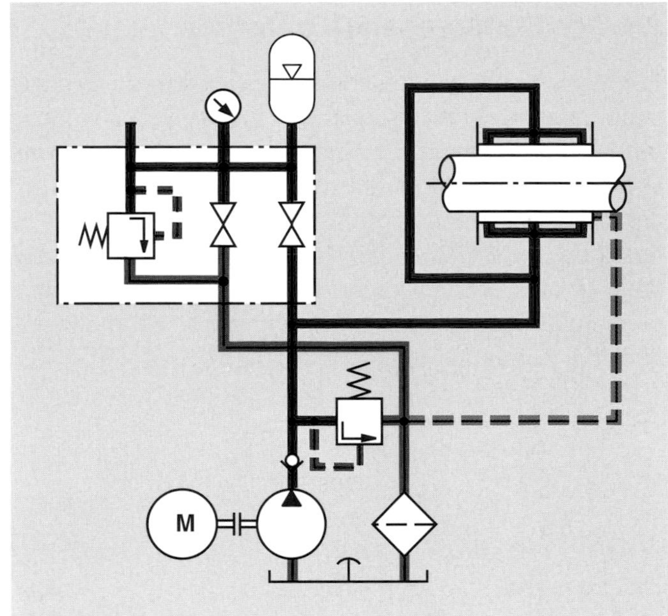

Fig. 8: *Emergency operation of bearings*

Avoidance of interruptions in operation during a working cycle.

If power fails in the middle of an operating cycle of a production machine, this may lead to expensive interruptions occuring in operation. In such cases accumulators can make sure that the cycle which has started is completed.

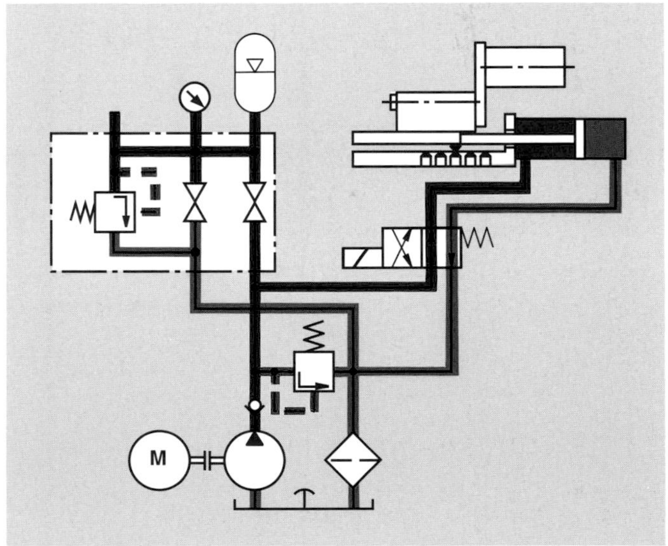

Fig. 9: *Use of accumulators to prevent interruptions in operation*

2.4 Compensation of forces

Forces or displacements may be compensated by using accumulators. This is required in a continuous working process, for example, in rolling tilting may occur due to the varying load of the deformed material. If the roll forces are corrected a continous strip of the same thickness is obtained. In *Fig. 10* a circuit is shown for the counterbalancing of a machine tool. Included are the relevant accumulators and the safety and shut- off manifolds which are mounted directly on to them.

The following features must be mentioned:

- Soft balancing of forces and hence low stressing on foundations and frame
- Saving of counterweights and hence reduction in weight and space required for installation.

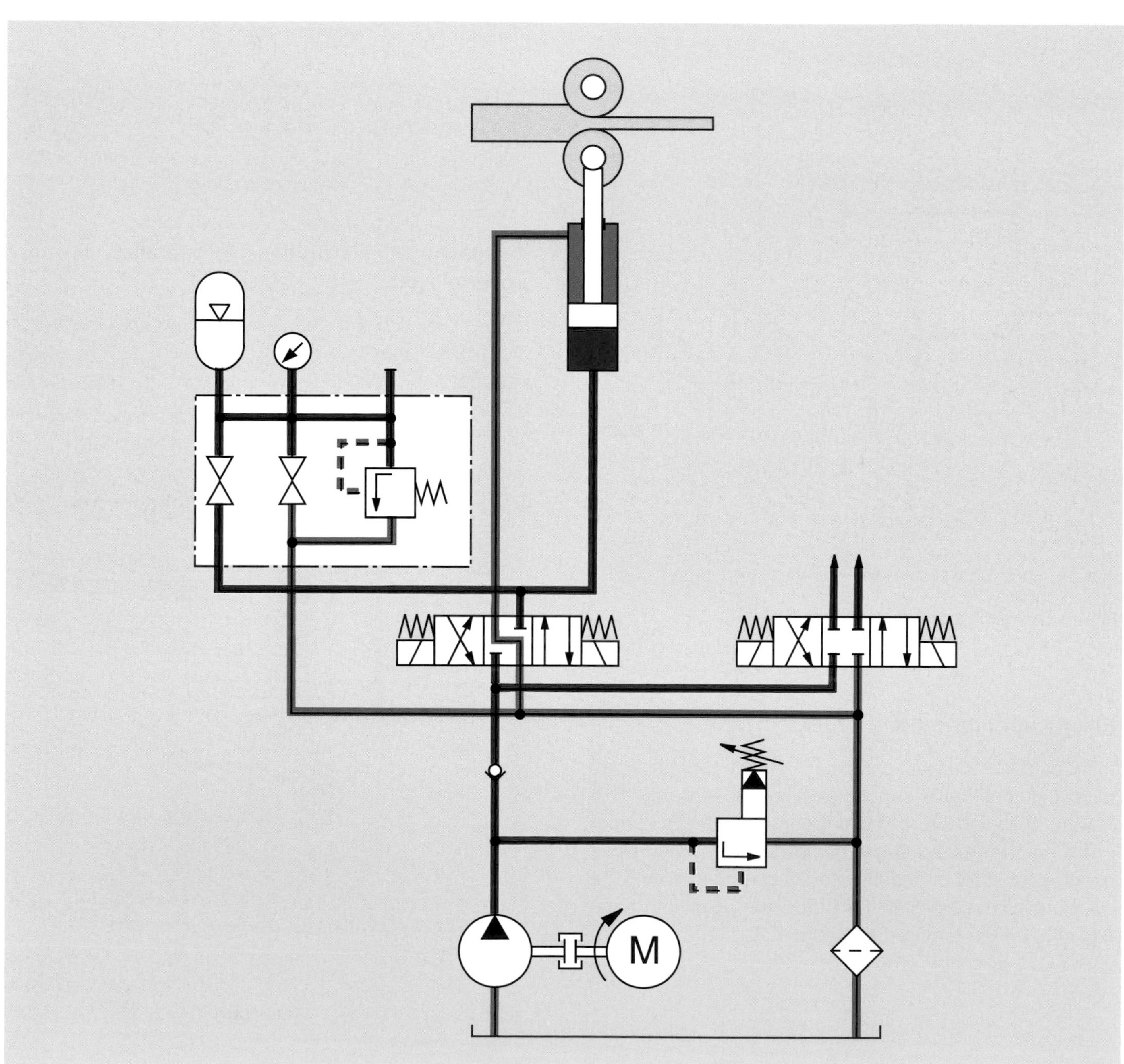

Fig. 10: *Balancing of rolls in the manufacture of sheet metal*

2.5 Compensation of leakage oil

The pre-tensioning force in a hydraulic cylinder may only be maintained if the losses due to leakages in the system are compensated for. Accumulators are especially suitable for this. A circuit diagram for compensation of leakage oil is shown in *fig. 11*. It may be seen from the diagram that the leakage oil from the accumulator is pushed into the piston chamber. Once the pressure decreases below a set value in the accumulator, the pump is reconnected to fill the accumulator up again with fluid.

The features of this are:

- No continuous operation of pumps
- Low level of heat produced and hence low operating costs
- Long service life for the system

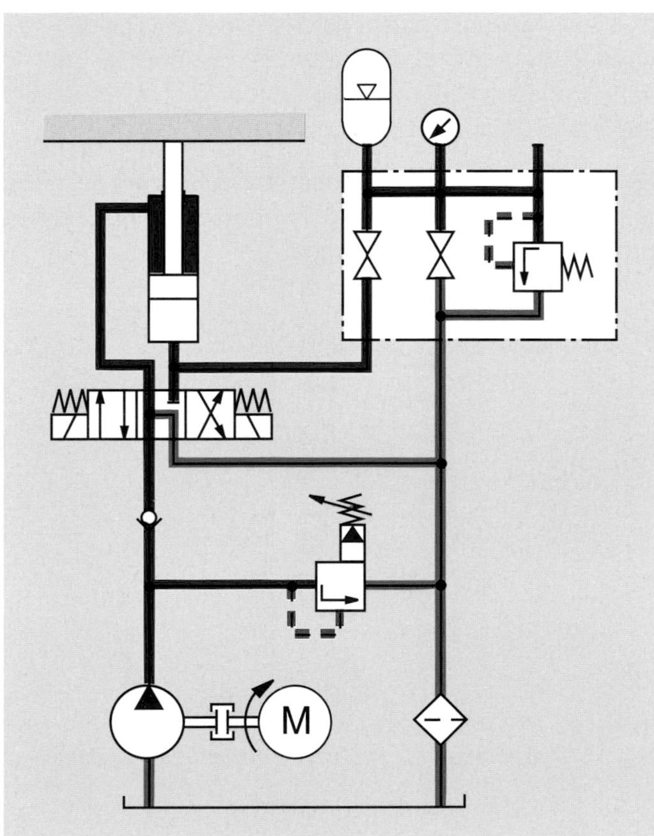

Fig. 11: *Leakage oil compensation*

2.6 Damping of shocks and vibrations

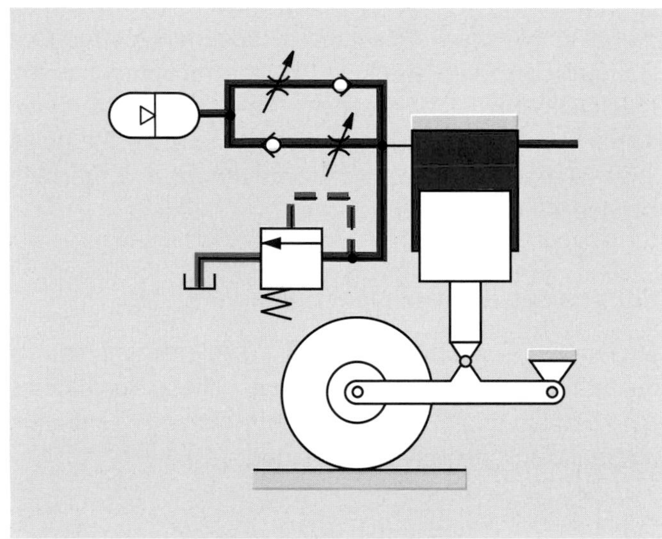

Fig. 12: *Accumulators as spring elements*

Pressure fluctuations may occur in hydraulic systems if the state of flow of the fluid changes due to varying processes dependent on the system.

Causes of this may include:

- Non-uniformity within a hydraulic pump
- Spring-mass systems (pressure compensators in valves). Abrupt connection of chambers with varying levels of pressure.
- Operation of shut-off and control valves with short opening and closing times
- Connection processes involving distributor pumps

In conjunction with the above, flow and pressure fluctuations occur dependent on the operation which have a negative effect on the service life of all the components within a system.

Fluctuations in pressure may be separated into pressure shocks and pulsations depending on the cause. In order to ensure that operation is not adversely affected by these fluctuations, it is necessary to determine the size of pressure fluctuation when designing a system and hence select suitable damping methods. There are many ways of damping pressure fluctuations, but hydraulic dampers have been found to be particularly suitable for use in hydraulic systems.

It is recommended that pulsation damping devices are used in order to meet the requirements of a machines with respect to high power and short pulse time and also good damping of noise. This type of accumulator reduces fluctuations in flow produced by the movement of the machine and also reduces the transfer of these fluctuations to resonating devices. Therefore the noise level is reduced. In addition, component and machine service life is increased.

For positive displacement pumps (*Fig. 13*)

Depending on the type of displacement pump fluctuations may occur in the flow. These fluctuations cause noise and vibrations to be produced. Hence the hydraulic system may be damaged.

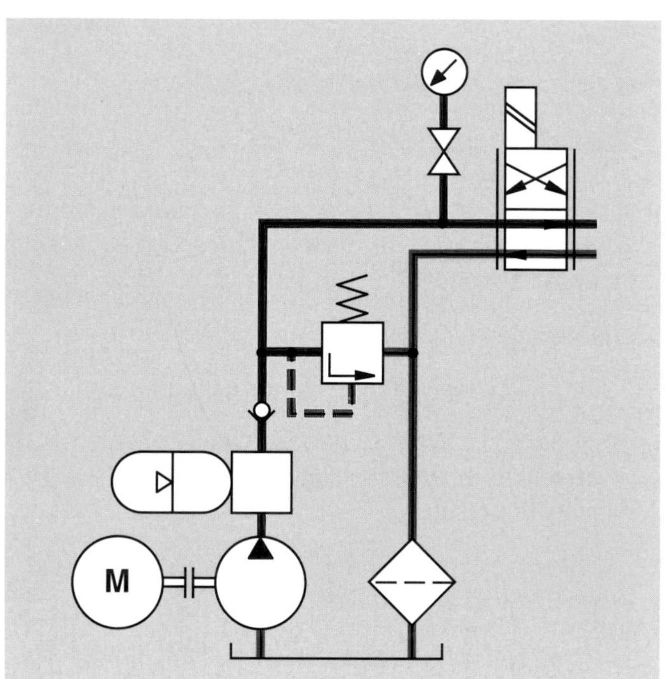

Fig. 13: *Use of pulsation damping elements in positive displacement pumps*

For fast-switching control valves (*Fig. 14*)

So that the positions in valves (e.g. servo and proportional valves) can be quickly but smoothly varied, accumulators need to be installed on both sides of the valves. In addition negative pressure peaks, which may for example damage the pressure line filters in the hydraulic system, may be avoided.

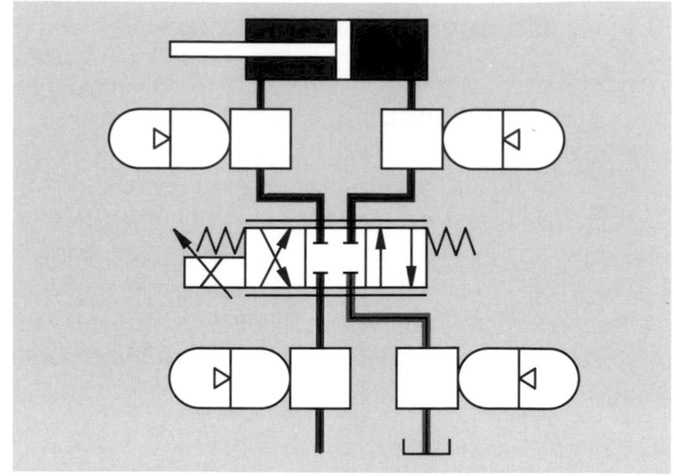

Fig. 14: *Use of pulsation damping elements in hydraulic systems with proportional or servo valves*

For pressure oscillations (*Fig. 15*)

In most hydraulic systems pressure oscillations are created by serveral hydraulic components or due to varying loads in the hydraulic system, e.g. movement of the scoop on an excavator.

By using accumulators, components which are sensitive to pressure oscillations (e.g. hydraulic pumps) may be protected from being damaged.

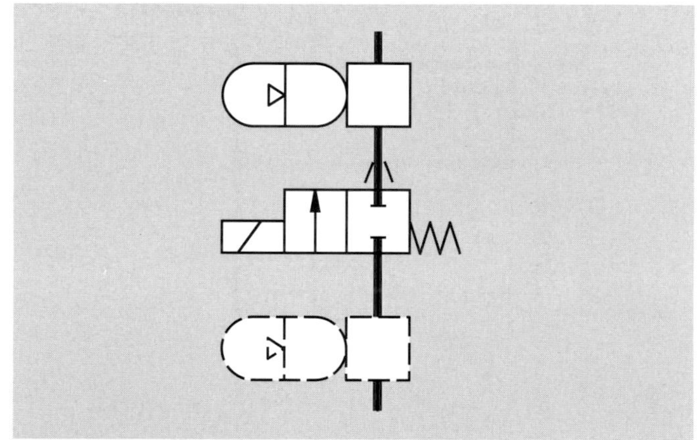

Fig. 15: *Pulsation damping element downstream of pump*

In on- off situations (*Fig. 16*)

Pressure shocks are created when a large flow is quickly introduced into a return line. These shocks may damage oil coolers and return line filters.

In addition, valves, pipe lines and fittings may be damaged due to pressure shocks, if a column of moving fluid is abruptly stopped. This happens, for example, when an emergency shut-off occurs.

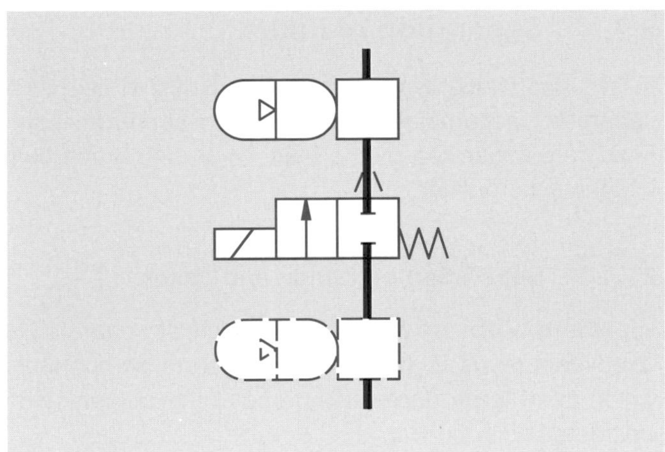

Fig. 16: *Use of pulsation damping elements to damp pressure shocks*

For hydraulic springs

Accumulators may be used as hydraulic springs to dampen shocks and vibrations.

In this case the compressible gas in the accumulator is used as a spring.

Applications for hydraulic springs are:

– Chain tensioning (*Fig. 17*)

Accumulators are used to tension machine and vehicle chains in order to avoid transfer of shocks from the drive chain.

– Tensioning of transmission and suspension cables (*Fig. 18*)

Low tolerances are required in the lengths of wire for cable cars and lifts (for example) so that they may be operated without disturbances.

By using accumulators, the different lengths of wire for up and down hill movements of cable cars or the temperature fluctuations and varying loads in lifts, may be compensated for.

The required tolerances for the lengths of cables and pulling forces is maintained.

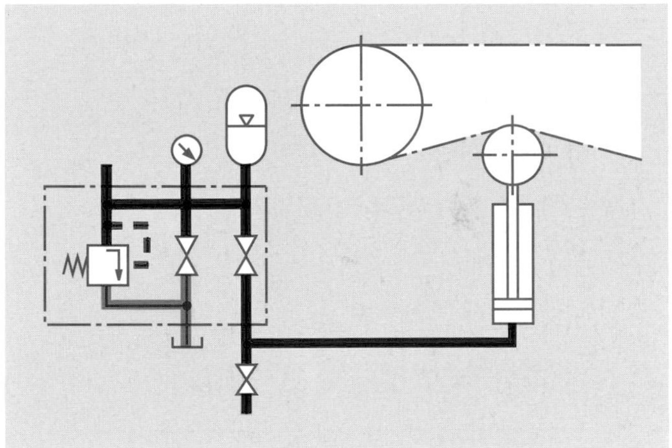

Fig. 17: *Use of accumulator to tension a chain in a machine tool*

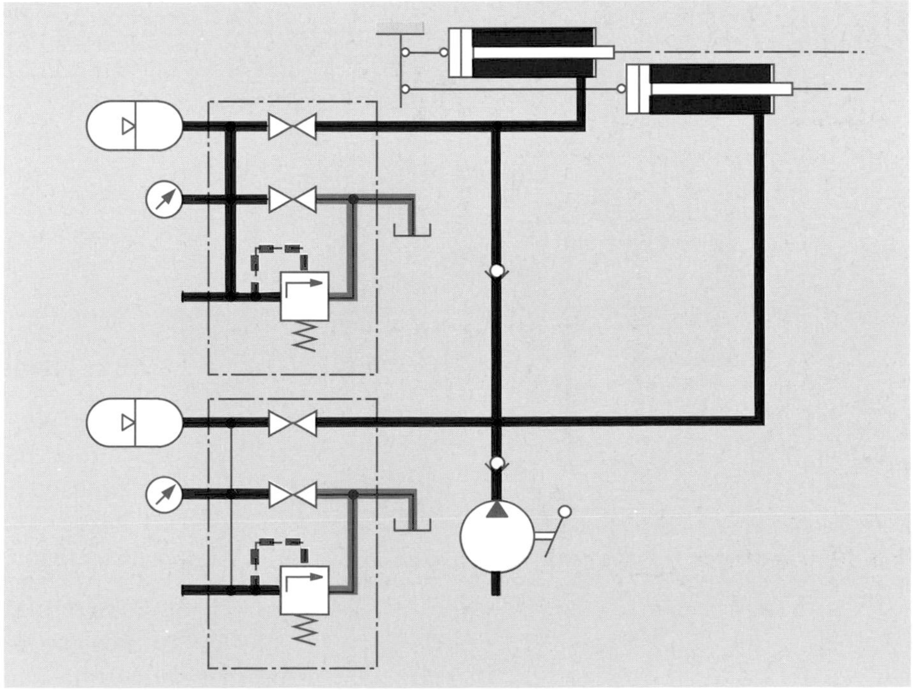

Fig. REF!: *Use of accumulator to tension cable cars*

– Suspension in vehicles (*Fig. 19*)

When driving over uneven roads or tracks mechanical shocks are produced which damage the superstructure and chassis.

By using hydro-pneumatic suspension mechanical shocks are converted into hydraulic shocks through the use of cylinders.

Accumulators absorb these hydraulic shocks.

By using hydro-pneumatic suspension in vehicles this

– reduces the danger of accidents
– increases service life
– enables corners to be taken at higher speeds
– keeps the load in the required position
– reduces material loading and
– decreases operating costs.

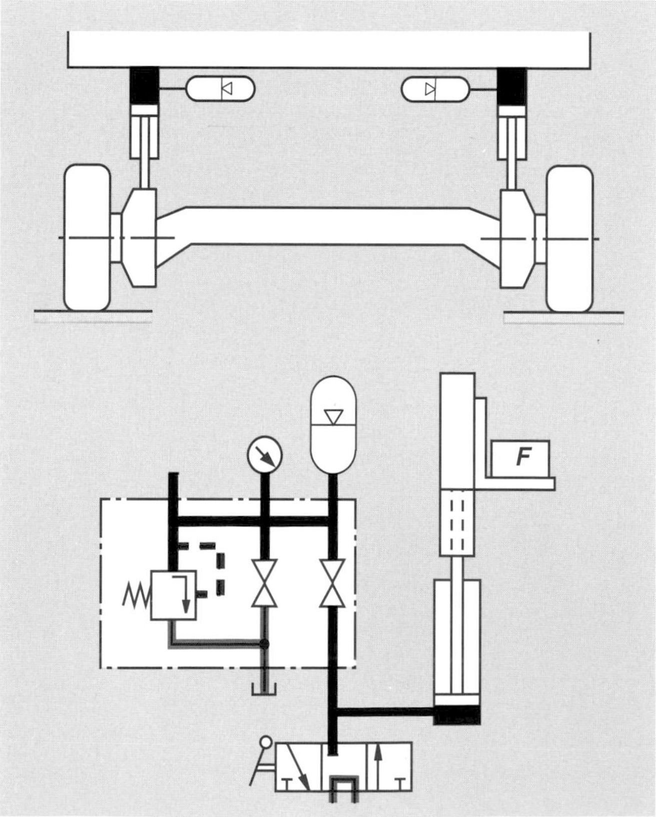

Fig. 19: *Use of accumulators for vehicle suspension*

2.7 Separation of fluids

In systems which require operating fluids to be 100% separated, accumulators are used to separate them. Fluids are separated by the bladder or membrane built into the accumulator.

2.7.1 Separation of liquids and gases

In systems which are primarily pneumatically operated, it is advantageous to hydraulically operate components which need to produce large forces (e.g. compression cylinders).

By using accumulators, hydraulically and pneumatically operated components may be separated. Hence a separate, addition hydraulic power unit does not need to be installed.

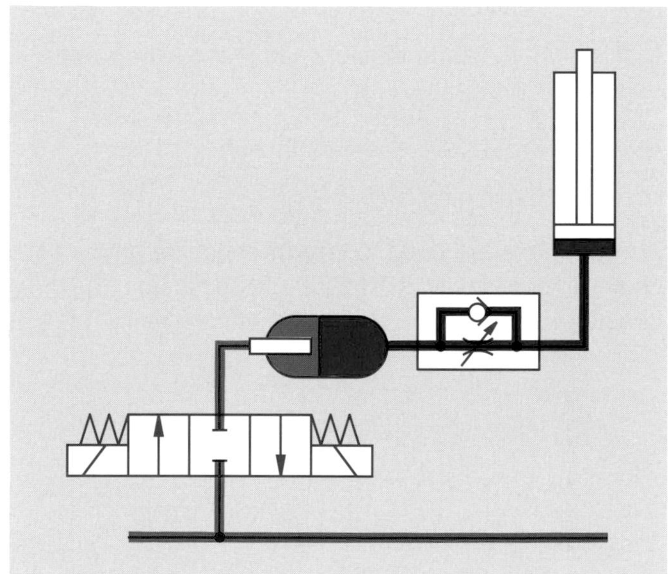

Fig. 20: *Use of accumulators to separate pneumatic part of the system from the hydraulically operated part*

2.7.2 Separation of two fluids

For example, in compressors with floating ring seals which are used in the petrochemical industry, the compressed process gas from the compressor must not be mixed with the isolating fluid for functional and contamination reasons.

In this type of seal an isolating fluid is necessary. The level of pressure of this isolating fluid must lie 0.5 to 1 bar above the level of the gas pressure of the compressor.

Hence a high tank is installed above the compressor in order to ensure that the higher pressure is maintained at the seal.

The fluid in the tank which is neutral to the gas is pressurised with the gas pressure from the compressor.

As, in most cases, the fluid used in this high tank does not possess any lubricating characteristics, the floating ring seals and the shaft bearings must be operated with a lubricating isolating fluid.

The required separation of the two fluids is carried out using accumulators.

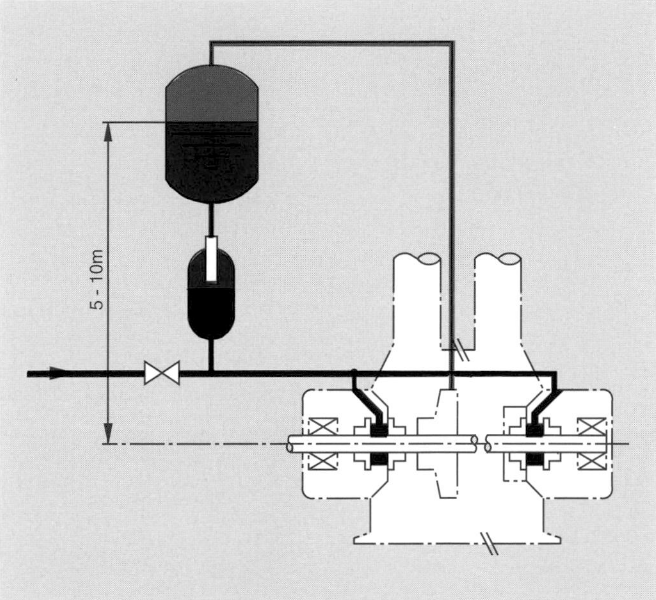

Fig. 21: *Accumulator used to separate fluids*

2.7.3 Separation of two gases

Accumulators are used to balance pressure with atmospheric pressure in systems where there is a danger of external water ingress via tank breathers or in fluid tanks which are filled with nitrogen to avoid condensation forming due to large fluctuations in temperature.

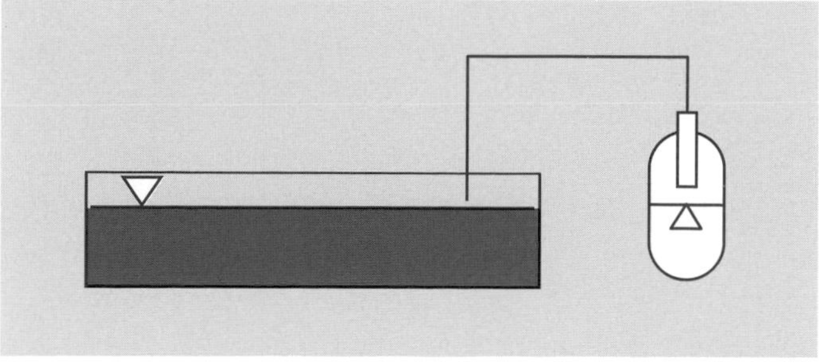

Fig. 22: *Accumulators used as tank breather accumulators*

3 Gas accumulators with separating element

Accumulators basically comprise a fluid compartment and a gas compartment with a gastight separating element. The fluid compartment is connected to the hydraulic circuit. As the pressure is increased, the gas becomes compressed and fluid is fed into the accumulator.

The following types of accumulators with separating elements are used in hydraulic systems:

- bladder accumulator
- membrane accumulator
- piston accumulator

Fig. 23: *Membrane accumulator*

Fig. 24: *Bladder accumulator*

Fig. 25: *Piston accumulator*

3.1 Bladder accumulators

Bladder accumulators comprise a fluid compartment and a gas compartment with a bladder being used as the gastight separating element. The fluid compartment surrounding the bladder is connected to the hydraulic ciruit. Hence as the pressure is increased the bladder accumulator is filled and the gas is compressed. As the pressure is decreased, the compressed gas expands and pushes the stored fluid into the circuit. Bladder accumulators may be installed vertically (preferred position), horizontally or even at an angle (under certain operating conditions). If the accumulator is installed vertically or at an angle the fluid valve must be situated at the bottom.

Bladder accumulators comprise of a welded or forged pressure container (1), accumulator bladder (2), valves for gas input (3) and oil inlet (4). Gas and fluid is separated by the bladder (2).

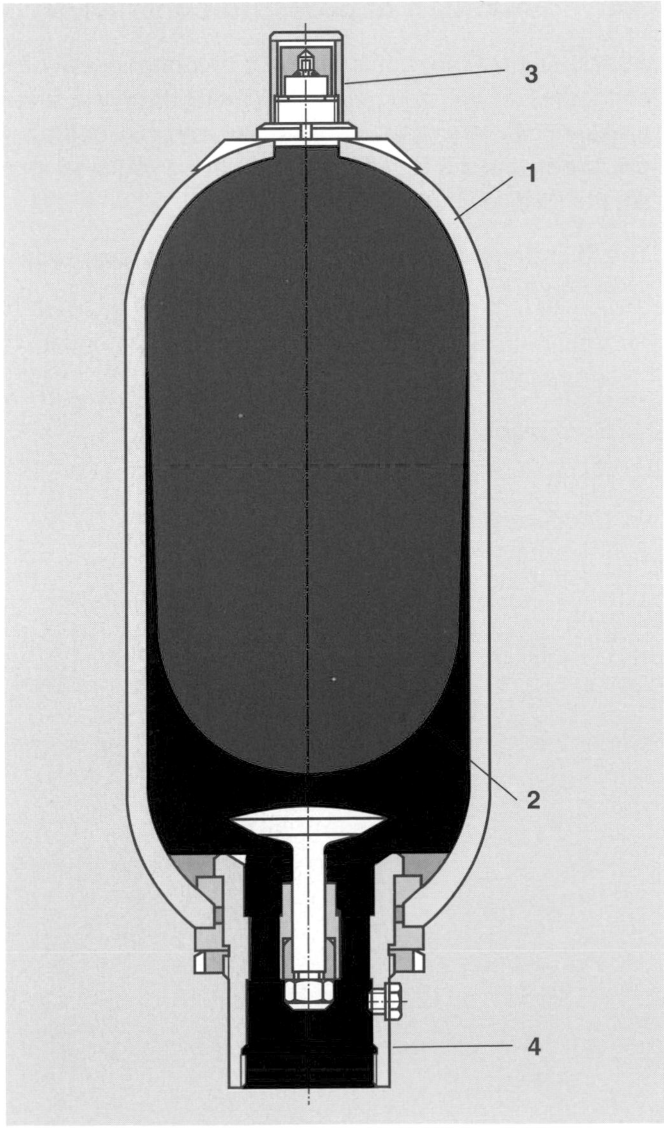

Fig. 26: *Bladder accumulator*

Membrane accumulators

Membrane accumulators comprise a steel container which is resistant to compression and is usually illustrated as either spherical of cylindrical. Inside the accumulator is a membrane made of an elastic material (elastomer) and which is used as the separating element.

There are two types of membrane accumulator available:

- welded construction
- screwed construction

In the welded model the membrane is pressed into the lower part before the circular seam welding is carried out. By using a suitable welding process, e.g. electron beam welding and by situating the membrane correctly, this ensures that the elastomer material is not damaged when the welding is carried out.

In the screwed model the membrane is held in position by screwing the top and bottom part to clamping nuts.

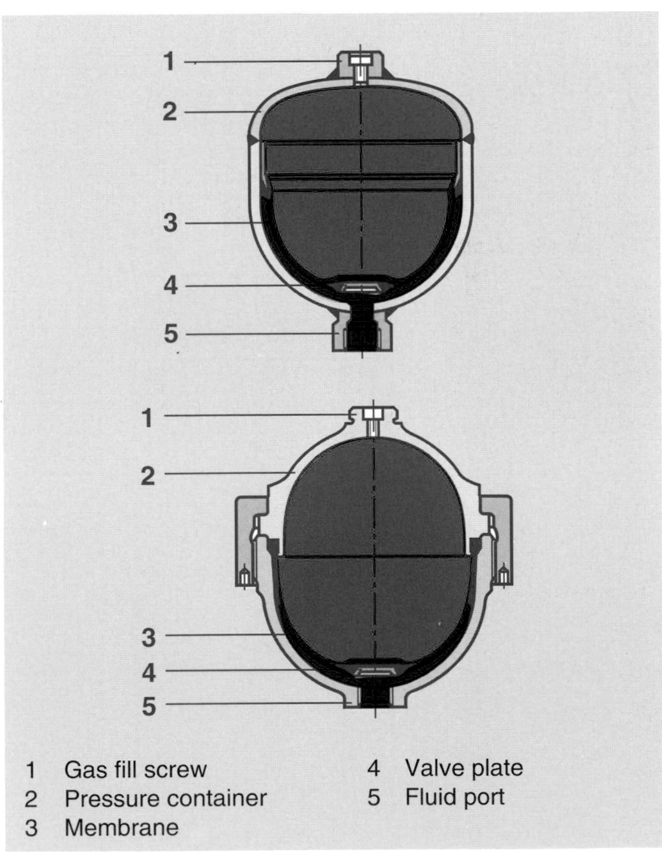

Fig. 27: *Membrane accumulator: top: welded, bottom: screwed construction*

3.3 Piston accumulator

Piston accumulators comprise fluid and gas compartments with a piston being used as the gastight separating element. The gas side is pre-filled with nitrogen.

The fluid part is connected to the hydraulic circuit. Hence as the pressure is increased the piston accumulator is filled and the gas is compressed. As the pressure is dereased, the compressed gas expands and pushes the stored fluid into the circuit. Piston accumulators may be installed in any position. However the preferred position is the vertical one with the gas side at the top, so that deposits of dirt particles from the fluid on the piston seals are avoided.

The design of a piston accumulator is shown in *fig. 28*. The main components comprise external cylinder tube (1), piston (2) with sealing system and also the front covers (3,4) which include the fluid (5) and gas ports (6). The cylinder tube has two tasks. On the one hand it is used to receive the internal pressure and on the other hand it is used to guide the piston, which is used as the separating element between the gas and fluid chambers.

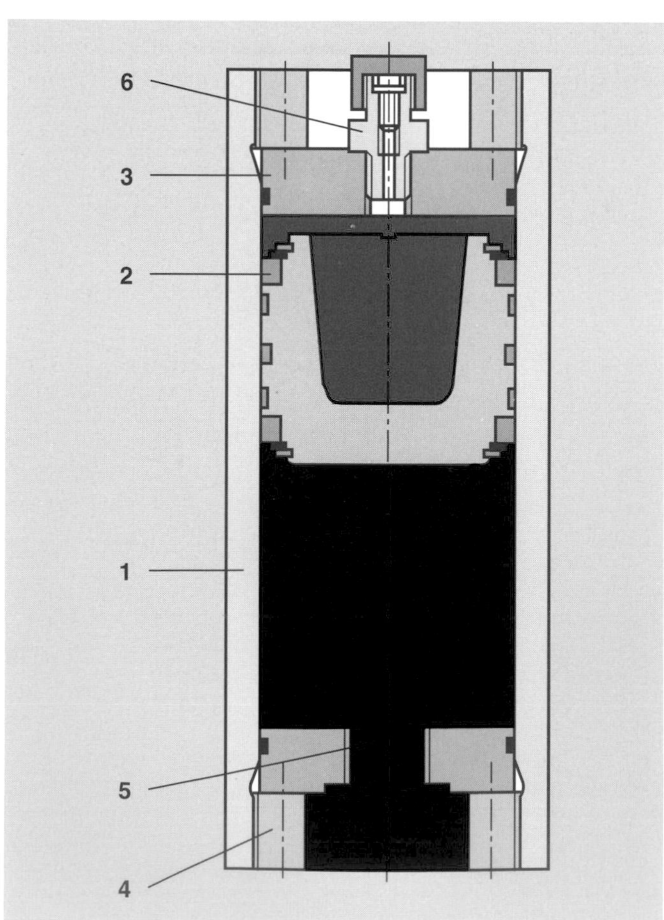

Fig. 28: *Piston accumulator*

A requirement exists for the friction between the piston seal and internal wall to be kept very low during piston movements in order to balance the pressures as much as possible between both pressure chambers. For this reason the surface of the internal wall of the cylinder tube must be finely machined. Due to the friction present between the piston seal and the internal wall, it is not possible to avoid a pressure difference between the fluid and gas chambers. However, by selecting a suitable sealing system it is possible to limit the pressure difference to approx. 1 bar.

It is possible to monitor the position of the piston in piston accumulators. A trigger cam is situated on the protruding piston rod which can be used to operate limit switches. The positon of the piston at any point may be monitored by using this trigger cam. Often the position of the piston is used to control the switching on and off of the hydraulic pump(s).

3.4 Addition of pressure containers

Additional pressure containers are recommended to be connected to the accumulator if there is only a small pressure difference between the max. and min. operating pressures and if a large volume of gas is required for a small effective volume.

The following points need to be taken into account when selecting the size of accumulator required:

- Volume expansion due to fluctuations in ambient temperature
- Permissible pressure and volume ratio $p_2/p_0 = V_0/V_2$
- Effective volume

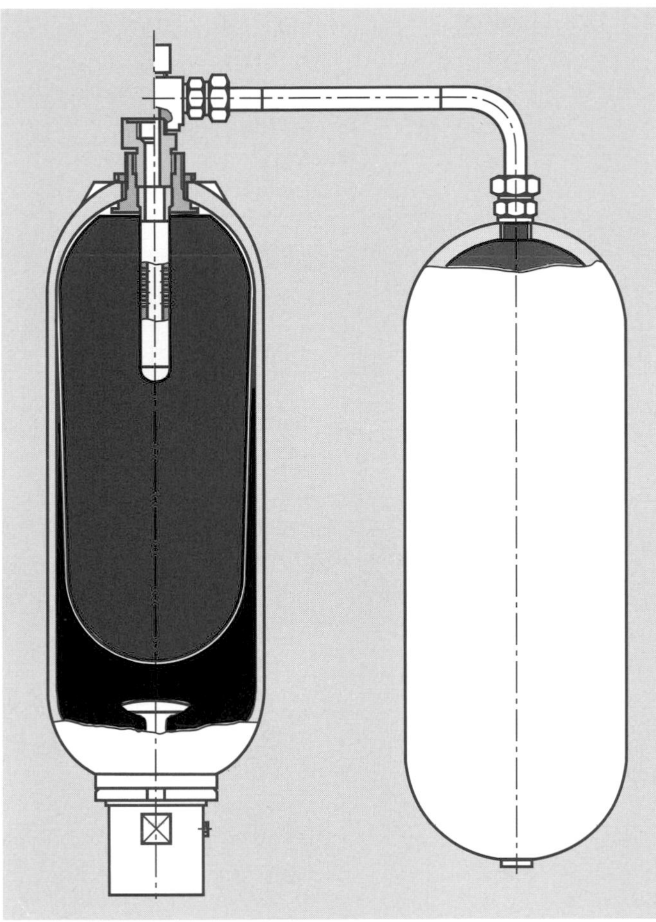

Fig. 29: *Addition of nitrogen bottles*

4 Accessories for hydro-pneumatic accumulators

4.1 Safety and isolating control blocks

Fig. 30: *Bladder accumulator mounted on safety and isolating control block*

The safety and isolating control block is an accessory for protecting, isolating and unloading accumulators or hydraulic actuators. This control block fulfils the safety requirements and acceptance standards in the countries in which it is used. In particular, it passes the pressure container regulations with respect to pressure container equipment in accordance with the points mentioned in the technical regulations on pressure containers.

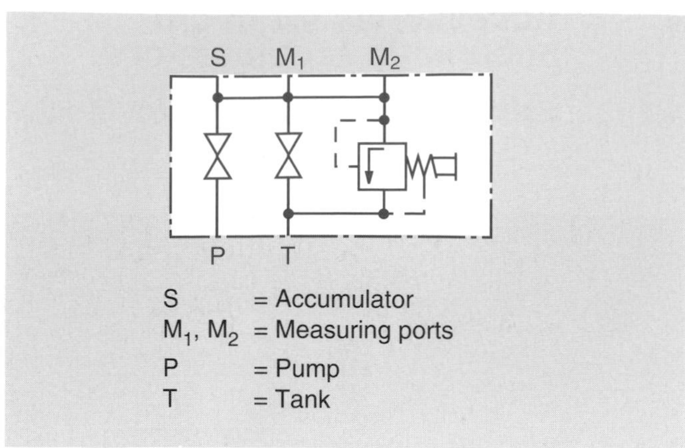

Fig. 31: *Safety and isolating control block with manual unloading*

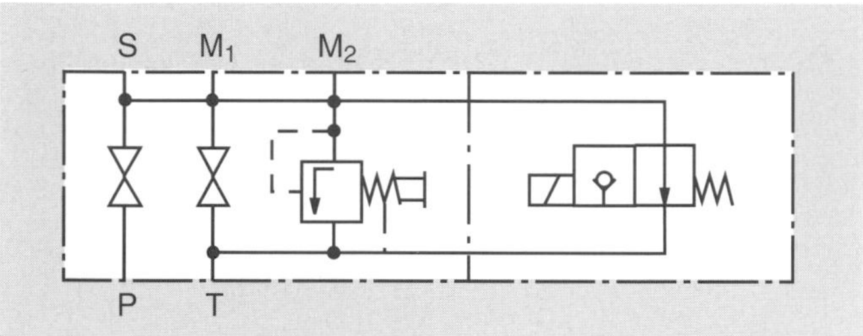

Fig. 32: *Safety and isolating control block with solenoid operated unloading*

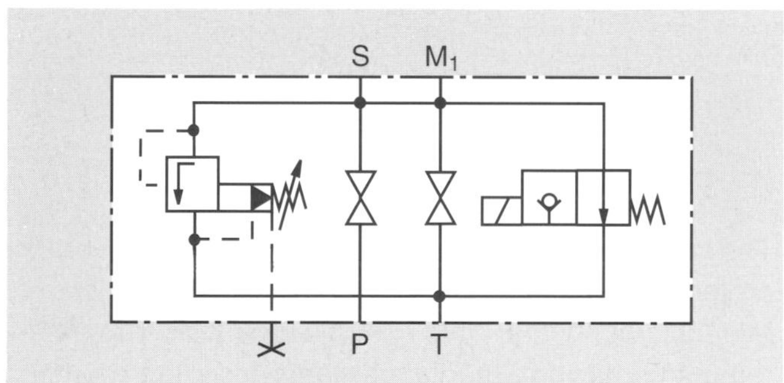

Fig. 33: *Safety and isolating control block with pilot operated pressure relief valve*

4.1.1 Design

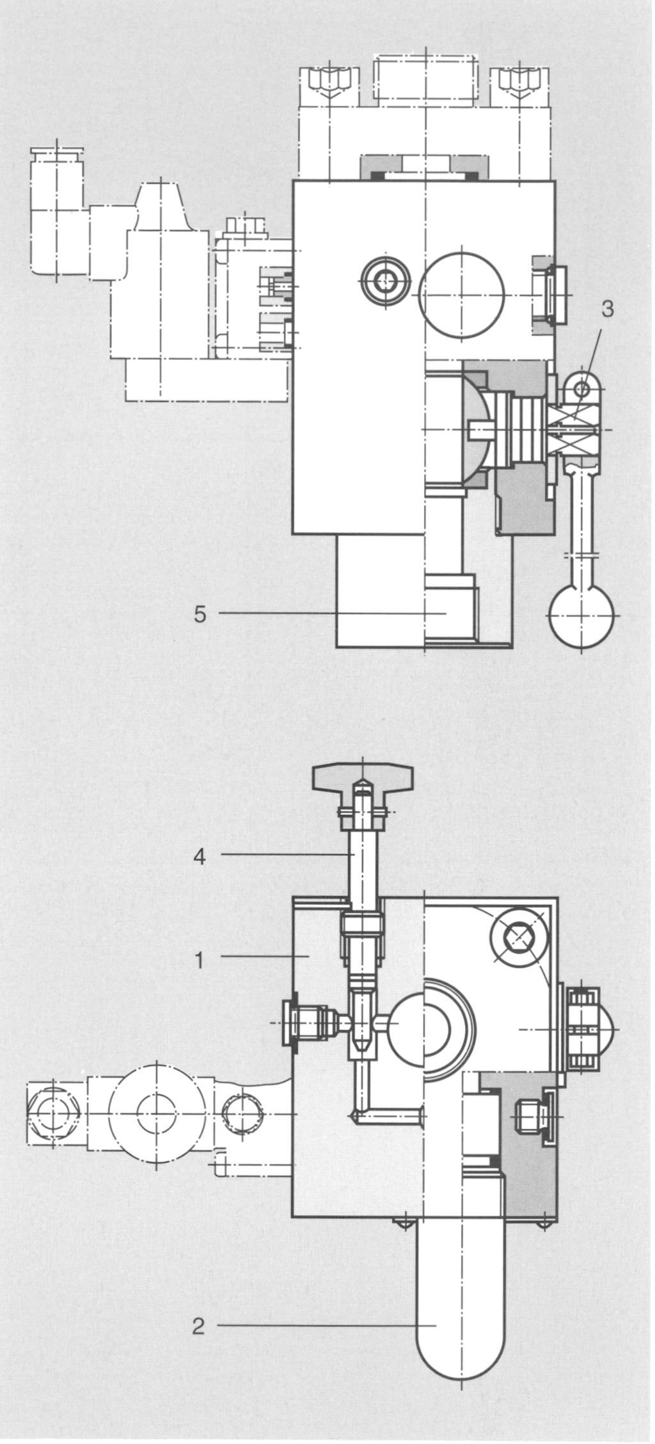

Fig. 34: *Safety and isolating control block*

The safety and isolating block comprises valve block (1), cartridge pressure relief valve (2), main shut-off valve (3), manually operated safety valve (4) and in addition to system port (5) it also comprises the specified pressure gauge ports.

4.2 Filling and testing procedures

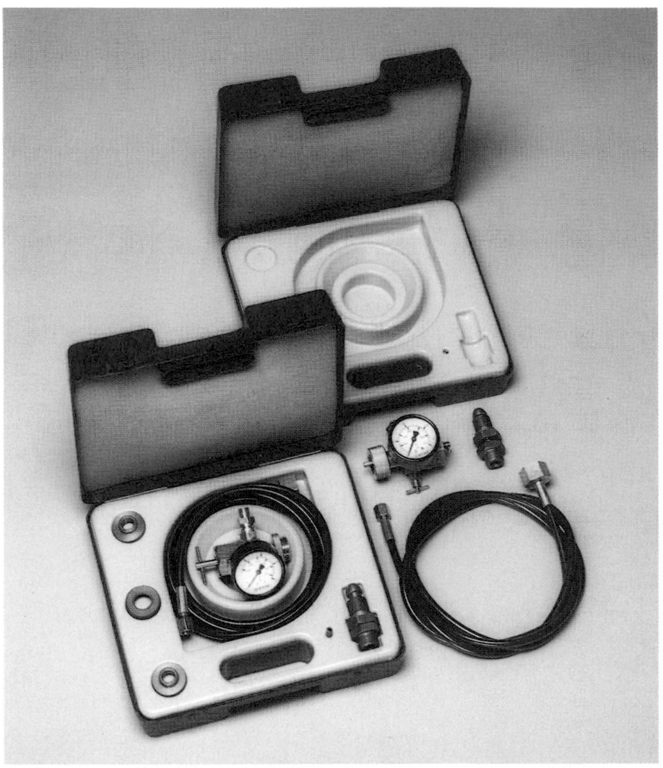

Fig. 35: *Filling and testing unit*

Normally nitrogen losses are very low in hydro-pneumatic accumulators. However, in order to avoid the piston striking the cover and the bladder or membrane becoming too deformed if the initial pressure p_0 decreases, it is recommended that the gas pre-charge pressure is regularly checked.

By using the filling and testing unit, accumulators are filled with nitrogen or the intial nitrogen pressure available is altered. For this purpose, the filling ang testing unit is screwed onto the gas valve of the accumulator and connected to a standard nitrogen bottle via a flexible filling hose. The initial pressure p_0 set at the accumulator must be examined before each new installation and after any repair and then at least once in the week following this initial examination. If no nitrogen losses are detected, then a further examination can take place after four months. If a change in pressure has not occurred during this time, then further examinations need only take place once a year.

4.3 Nitrogen charging devices

Fig. 36: *Portable nitrogen charging device*

Fig. 37: *Mobile nitrogen charging device*

Nitrogen charging devices are used for quickly and economically filling nitrogen into accumulators. They make the most of standard nitrogen bottles up to a residual pressure of 20 bar and a max. accumulator loading pressure of 350 bar.

4.4 Fixing elements

Fig. 38: *Bladder accumulator with fixing element*

Hydro-pneumatic accumulators must be sufficiently protected and secured due to their weight and in addition due to the acceleration forces created by the fluid present in the accumulators. The securing of these accumulators must be such that no additional forces or torques are transferred by the accumulators to the hydraulic circuit.

5 Design of hydro-pneumatic accumulators with separating element

5.1 Definition of operational parameters

The parameters needed to design an accumulator are clarified in the schematic representations shown in *fig.39*.

The parameters which describe the gas state are pressure, temperature and volume.

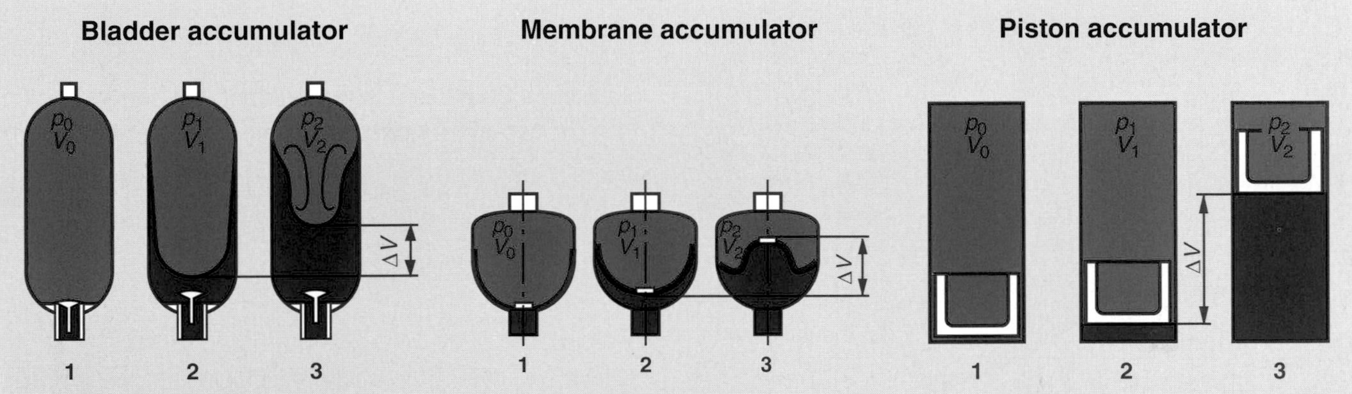

Bladder accumulator

p_0 = gas pre-fill pressure
p_1 = minimum operating pressure
p_2 = maximum operating pressure
V_0 = effective gas volume
V_1 = gas volume at p_1
V_2 = gas volume at p_2
ΔV = useful volume

1 The bladder is pre-filled with nitrogen. The fluid valve is closed and prevents the bladder from discharging.

2 Once the min. operating pressure has been reached, a small amount of fluid should remain between the bladder and the check valve (approx. 10% nominal volume of accumulator), so that the bladder does not strike the valve each time an expansion occurs.

3 Accumulators at max. operating pressure. The change in volume ΔV between the levels at min. and max. operating pressures correspond to the useful fluid volume:

$\Delta V = V_1 - V_2$.

Membrane accumulator

p_0 = gas pre-fill pressure
p_1 = minimum operating pressure
p_2 = maximum operating pressure
V_0 = effective gas volume
V_1 = gas volume at p_1
V_2 = gas volume at p_2
ΔV = useful volume

1 The membrane pressurised by nitrogen assumes the internal contour of the accumulator. The valve plate closes the fluid port and thus prevents the membrane from discharging.

2 Level at min. operating pressure. A small amount of fluid should remain in the accumulator, so that the valve plate does not strike the bottom each time an unloading occurs. p_0 should always be smaller than p_1.

3 Level at max. operating pressure. The change in volume ΔV between the levels at min. and max. operating pressures correspond to the useful fluid volume:

$\Delta V = V_1 - V_2$.

Piston accumulator

p_0 = gas pre-fill pressure
p_1 = minimum operating pressure
p_2 = maximum operating pressure
V_0 = effective gas volume
V_1 = gas volume at p_1
V_2 = gas volume at p_2
ΔV = useful volume

1 The piston accumulator is pre-filled with nitrogen. The piston rests on the cover and thus closes the fluid port.

2 The min. operating pressure should be approx. 5 bar higher than the gas fill pressure. This should prevent the piston from striking the cover during each unloading process and hence causing the fluid pressure in the system to collapse.

3 Once the max. operating pressure has been reached, the useful volume ΔV in the accumulator is available for use:

$\Delta V = V_1 - V_2$.

Fig. 39: *Operating parameters*

5.2 Change of state in a gas

Changes of state may be

- isochoric
- isothermal
- adiabatic or
- polytropic

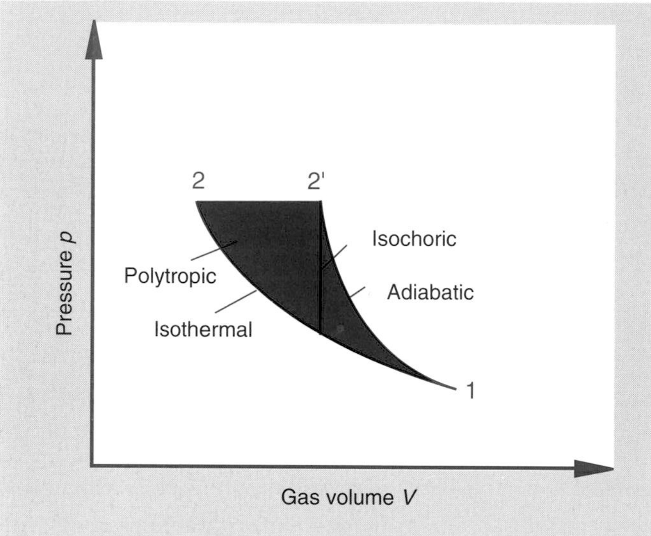

Diagram 2: *Change of state shown in p-V diagram*

5.2.1 Isochoric change of state

In this change of state, a change in volume does not occur, i.e. no work is carried out due to a change in volume. This change of state occurs when a gas chamber is filled at low temperature and the initial pressure changes due to heat exchange with the outside.

Gas law: $p/T = p_1/Y_1 = \text{constant}$ (1)

5.2.2 Isothermal change of state

In this change of state a complete heat exchange occurs with the outside. There is no change in temperature.

This state is found in accumulators when fluid is loaded or unloaded over a long period. Due to the long operation cycles a complete heat exchange can occur between the gas and environment.

Gas law: $p \cdot V = p_1 \cdot V_1 = \text{constant}$ (2)

5.2.3 Adiabatic change of state

In this change of state loading or unloading occurs so quickly that heat exchange with the environment is not possible.

Gas law: $p \cdot V^{\kappa} = p_1 \cdot V_1^{\kappa} = \text{constant}$ (3)

The dependence of temperature on volume and temperature on pressure may also be deduced from the thermal gas law.

$$T \cdot V^{\kappa-1} = T_1 \cdot V_1^{\kappa-1} \text{ and} \quad (4)$$
$$T \cdot p^{(1-\kappa)/\kappa} = T_1 \cdot p_1^{(1-\kappa)/\kappa}$$

In these equations κ is the adiabatic exponent, which is 1.4 for two atom gases such as nitrogen under normal conditions.

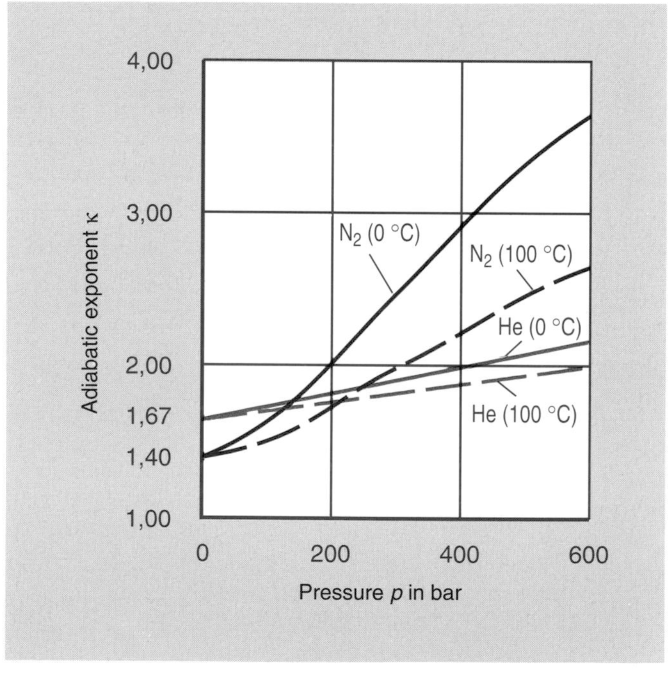

Diagram 3: *Adiabatic exponent for nitrogen and helium dependent on pressure at 0°C and 100°C*

 Accumulators and Accumulator Applications

5.2.4 Polytropic change of state

As the operation of an accumulator never follows the theory with respect to no heat exchange, a change of state occurs which is between that of isothermal and adiabatic. This type of change of state is known as polytropic. The mathematical relationships which are valid are those for analogue adiabatic changes of state, whereby the adiabatic exponent is replaced by a polytropic exponent N.

5.3 Determination of accumulator size

The equations used for the design of an accumulator are dependent on the time required for the loading and unloading processes. As a rule of thumb, the following limits may be used to decide on which equation to use:

Cycle time < 1 minute
→ adiabatic change of state

Cycle time > 3 minutes
→ isothermal change of state

Cycle time between 1 and 3 minutes
→ polytropic change of state

The equations used In design are shown in *table 3*. Furthermore in designing an accumulator certain values found by experience must be adhered to, in order to utilise the accumulator volume to an optimum extent and in order not to reduce the service life of the accumulator.

Experiential values for the various types of accumulator are shown in *table 2*.

5.4 Deviations from ideal gas behaviour

The gas laws are only valid for ideal gas characteristics. However, various gases, such as nitrogen, deviate from the ideal gas laws especially at high pressure. This behaviour is known as real or non-ideal behaviour. The mathematical relationship between the state parameters p, T and V can only be approximated for real gas behaviour. Using such an approximation to a sufficient degree of accuracy in practice requires a lot of effort and is very time-consuming requiring a lot of computer time and is only possible if computers are available. For this reason, it is recommended to use correction factors which take real gas behaviour into account.

Hence the volume produced in an isothermal change of state is given by

$$V_{0\ \text{real}} = C_i \cdot V_{0\ \text{ideal}}$$

and in an adiabatic change of state by

$$V_{0\ \text{real}} = C_a \cdot V_{0\ \text{ideal}}$$

The correction factors C_i and C_a in these equations may be determined from the manufacturer's documentation.

	Bladder accumulator		**Membrane accumulator**		**Piston membrane Low friction model**
	High pressure	**Low pressure**	**Welded model**	**Screwed model**	
Gas fill pressure $p_0 (T_2)$ (at max. operating temperature)	$\leq 0{,}9 \cdot p_1$ (Energy storage) $= 0{,}6$ to $0{,}9 \cdot p_m$ (Shock absorption) $= 0{,}6 \cdot p_m$ (Pulsation damping)		$\leq 0{,}9 \cdot p_1$ (Energy storage) $0{,}6 \cdot p_m$ (Pulsation damping)		$\leq p_1 - 5$ bar < 2 bar (low friction piston model) < 10 bar (normal piston model)
Installation position	Vertical (Horizontal only under certain operating conditions)		Any	Any	Any (Check monitoring device)
Max. pressure ratio p_2/p_0	4 : 1	4 : 1	4 : 1 to 8 : 1	10 : 1	No limitations
Max. operating pressure	550 bar	35 bar	210 bar	400 bar	350 bar
Fluid flow	up to 40 L/s	up to 140 L/s	4 to 6 L/s	4 to 6 L/s	Dependent on piston diameter is the max. permissible piston velocity 3.5 m/s
Accumulator volume	up to 50 L	up to 450 L	up to 3.5 L	up to 10 L	up to 250 L
General	–Replaceable bladder –Monitoring possible under certain conditions	–Replaceable bladder –No monitoring	– Small gas and useful volume –Cheap model – Membrane not replace-able –No monitoring	– Small gas and useful volume – Replaceable membrane –No monitoring	– Monitoring possible – Install in preferred position for model with additional elements – Replaceable piston
p_m = mean operating pressure at free flow Pressures: always absolute pressures					

Table 2: *Installation conditions for standard accumulators*

 Accumulators and Accumulator Applications

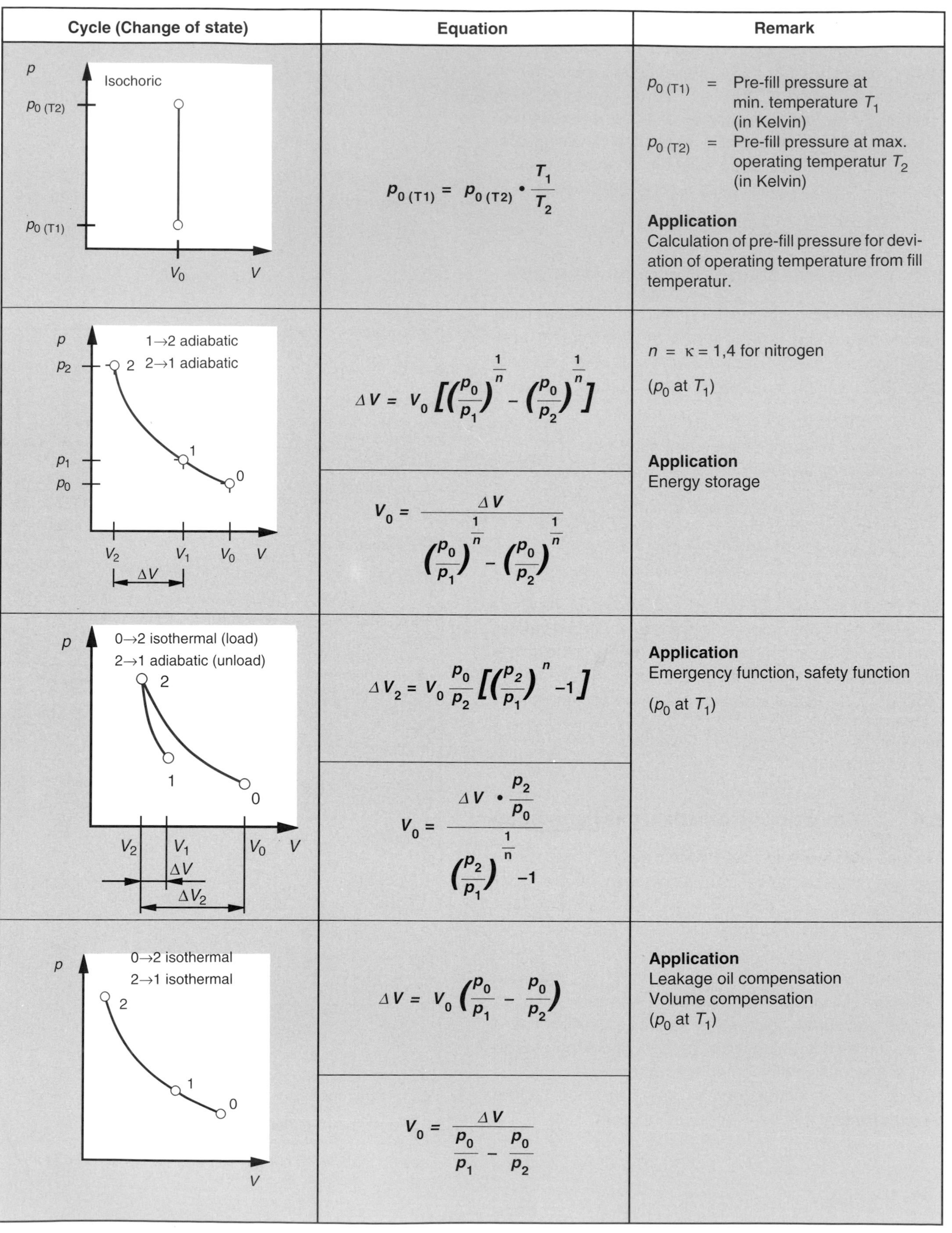

Cycle (Change of state)	Equation	Remark
Isochoric (p; $p_{0\,(T2)}$; $p_{0\,(T1)}$; V_0; V)	$p_{0\,(T1)} = p_{0\,(T2)} \cdot \frac{T_1}{T_2}$	$p_{0\,(T1)}$ = Pre-fill pressure at min. temperature T_1 (in Kelvin) $p_{0\,(T2)}$ = Pre-fill pressure at max. operating temperatur T_2 (in Kelvin) **Application** Calculation of pre-fill pressure for deviation of operating temperature from fill temperatur.
1→2 adiabatic 2→1 adiabatic (p; p_2; p_1; p_0; 2; 1; 0; V_2; V_1; V_0; V; ΔV)	$\Delta V = V_0 \left[\left(\frac{p_0}{p_1}\right)^{\frac{1}{n}} - \left(\frac{p_0}{p_2}\right)^{\frac{1}{n}}\right]$ $V_0 = \frac{\Delta V}{\left(\frac{p_0}{p_1}\right)^{\frac{1}{n}} - \left(\frac{p_0}{p_2}\right)^{\frac{1}{n}}}$	$n = \kappa = 1{,}4$ for nitrogen (p_0 at T_1) **Application** Energy storage
0→2 isothermal (load) 2→1 adiabatic (unload) (p; 2; 1; 0; V_2; V_1; V_0; V; ΔV; ΔV_2)	$\Delta V_2 = V_0 \frac{p_0}{p_2} \left[\left(\frac{p_2}{p_1}\right)^{n} - 1\right]$ $V_0 = \frac{\Delta V \cdot \frac{p_2}{p_0}}{\left(\frac{p_2}{p_1}\right)^{\frac{1}{n}} - 1}$	**Application** Emergency function, safety function (p_0 at T_1)
0→2 isothermal 2→1 isothermal (p; 2; 1; 0; V)	$\Delta V = V_0 \left(\frac{p_0}{p_1} - \frac{p_0}{p_2}\right)$ $V_0 = \frac{\Delta V}{\frac{p_0}{p_1} - \frac{p_0}{p_2}}$	**Application** Leakage oil compensation Volume compensation (p_0 at T_1)

Table 3: *Basic equations for the design of accumulators*

5.5 Design procedure

In order to calculate and determine the relevant accumulator size, it is expected that the volume of fluid ΔV and energy Q required to cover needs are known. Taking into account other conditions such as

- max. operating pressure
- max. and min. operating temperature
- operating pressure difference

an accumulator is designed assuming initially that the change of state between operating pressures p_1 and p_2 is adiabatic. This limiting assumption is permitted, as all the requirements of the other changes of state will be fulfilled if calculations are made on this basis.

By checking the calculation afterwards taking into account the time behaviour and hence the deviation from the given adiabatic change of state, the design may be corrected (correction factors c_a and c_i may be found in the manufacturer's documentation).

The pre-fill pressure (initial gas pressure) of the accumulator should be between 0.7 and 0.9 of the minimum operating pressure (at max. operating temperature).

$$p_{0(T2)} \leq 0.9 \bullet p_1 \qquad (5)$$

By doing this, this avoids the accumulator separating element operating in the range of the fluid valve and hence avoids possible damage being done to it.

5.6 Selection of type of accumulator for typical applications

5.6.1 Membrane accumulator

They are used for small gas volumes. The advantages of a membrane accumulator is a good seal and long service life. They may be installed in any position and they operate without inertia.

5.6.2 Bladder accumulator

Bladder accumulators are used for medium gas volumes and when accumulators need to deliver oil. Having improved the quality of the bladder in recent years, the bladder is now gas-tight and has a long service life.

Bladder accumulators are installed vertically to horizontally with the fluid oulet valve at the bottom or horizontally.

5.6.3 Piston accumulator

Piston accumulators are used for large gas volumes. Piston accumulators are especially useful when adding gas bottles.

The disadvantage of these accumulators is the weight of the separating piston and hence the slower oil delivery of the accumulator, as well as the friction of the seals on the piston. This results in the useful pressure being reduced by as much as 10%. When loading and unloading a piston velocity of 2 m/s should not be exceeded. Piston accumulators may be installed in any position.

6 Safety regulations

Accumulators must only be repaired by the manufacturer. Under no circumstances should welding, soldering or drilling be carried out on the accumulator.

As high pressure gas is dangerous due to the stored energy, the manufacturer's regulations with respect to installation and servicing of accumulators must be adhered to.

The most important servicing task is to periodically monitor the initial pressure p_0.

Accumulators must be installed where access is easy and they must be firmly mounted. Mountings must be able to withstand shocks in case pipes break.

A check valve should be installed in the line between the pump and accumulator, so that no inertia forces effect the pipe lines.

Every pressure container must have a suitable pressure gauge which displays the actual operating pressure. The maximum permissible excess operating pressure must be indicated on the gauge. A suitable safety valve must be present for each pressure container and the setting on this valve must be protected from unauthorised tampering.

Safety valves must not be able to close with respect to the accumulator. Easily accessible shut-off devices must be installed in the pressure lines as close to the pressure containers as possible.

In Germany accumulators as a sub-group of pressure containers must obey the pressure container regulations. Installation, equipment and operation are all regulated by a particular regulation. Accumulator pressure containers are categorised with respect to permissible excess operating pressure p in bar, contents I in litres and pressure contents product $p \bullet I$.

Depending on which group an accumulator belongs to, the tests described in *table 4* must be carried out.

Accumulators which are installed abroad require valid papers for the country in which they are installed to say that they have passed the relevant acceptance standards, as each country has a different set of standards.

Group	Tests before commissioning at the manufacturer's	at the operator's factory	Repeatable tests
II $p > 25$ bar and $p \bullet I \leq 200$	Pressure test. Manufacturer confirms via stamp "HP" or certificate that the manufacture and pressure tests have been carried out in accordance with regulations.	Acceptance tests (Tests on equipment and installation with respect to regulations) by authorised person.	Operator may decide how often tests are to be carried out from experience of operation and fluid.
III $p > 1$ bar, $p \bullet I > 200$ and $p \bullet I \leq 1000$	Pre-test on construction and pressure by relevant authority and certificate from manufacturer or individual acceptance tests relevant to country.	Acceptance tests by authority.	As for group II.
IV $p > 1$ bar and $p \bullet I > 1000$	As for group III.	As for group III.	Internal tests: Every 10 years for non-corrosive fluids, otherwise every 5 years. Pressure test: Every 10 years, tests by relevant authority.

Table 4: *Test groups and tests for accumulators*

Notes

Notes

Chapter 10

Non Return Valves

Dr Harald Geis, Johann Oppolzer

1 General

Non return valves are used in hydraulic systems to stop flow in one direction and to allow free flow in the opposite direction. They are also known as check valves.

non return valves are designed with seats and hence are able to isolate circuits with no leakage. Balls, plates, poppets or poppets with soft seals are used as isolating elements.

The advantage of using a ball as a seal is that it can be produced economically. The disadvantage is that the ball is deformed a little during operation, i.e. the seat presses into the ball. As the seat does not always press onto the same point, this leads to leakages after a while. The ball needs to be additionally controlled, so that the seat is not knocked out of true (e.g. by spring loading and flow forces).

On the other hand poppets always resume the same position due to their control. After a short period of operation the poppet has penetrated the seat and and the valve is completely sealed. Production of poppets is not as easy or cheap as that of balls. Mannesmann Rexroth non return valves primarily contain poppets as the isolating element due to their higher operating safety factor.

Poppets with soft seals are only suitable for use in systems with low operating pressures and low flow velocities. However, they do have the advantage that inaccuracies in manufacturing of poppet seats can be compensated for.

Depending on application, non return valves may be categorised into 3 groups (see *fig. 1*).

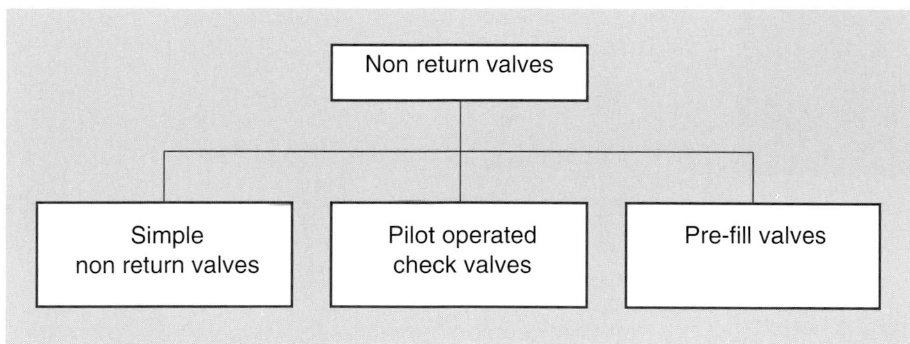

Fig. 1: *Types of non return valves*

2 Simple non return valves

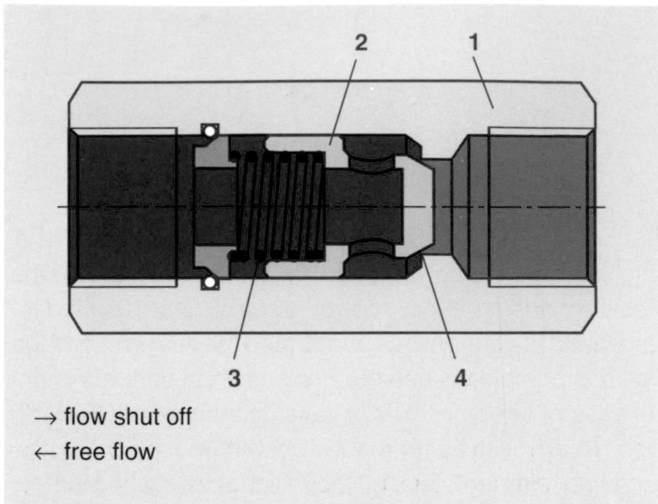

Fig. 2: *Pipe mounted non return valve*

Fig. 2: *Non return valves*

These valves (*figs. 2 and 3*) basically comprise housing (1) and hardened piston (2), which is pushed onto the seal seat (4) by means of spring (3).

When there is flow through the valve in the direction of the arrow, the poppet is lifted from its seat by the fluid pressure and allows free flow. In the opposite direction, the spring and the fluid push the poppet onto the seat and close the connection.

The cracking pressure depends on the spring selected (its compression) and the pressurised poppet surface area, and is generally between 0.5 and 5 bar, depending on the application.

A non return valve without spring must always be fitted vertically. The isolating element then remains on the seat in the no flow condition due to gravity.

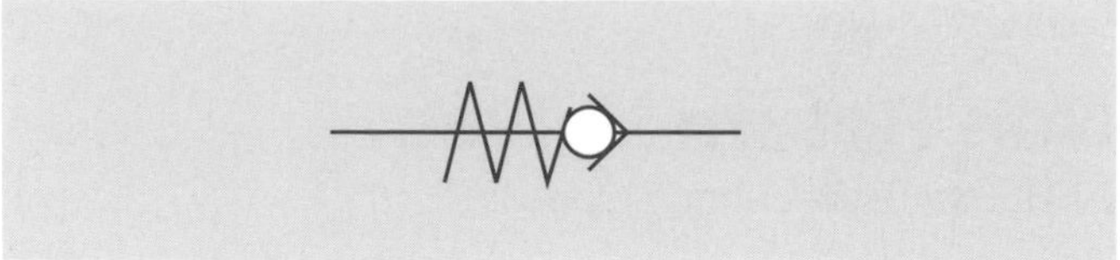

Fig. 4: *Non return valve*

Non return valves are available for

- sub-plate mounting
- pipe mounting (threaded connections)
- pipe mounting (flanged connections)
- as cartridge elements or
- as sandwich plate valves

Important parameters

Sizes:	6 to 150
Flow:	up to 15 000 L/min (at v_{oil} = 6 m/s)
Operating pressure:	up to 315 bar
Cracking pressure:	without spring; 0.5; 1.5; 3 or 5 bar

These valves are used

- For by-passing throttling points
- For shutting off one direction of flow
- As by-pass valves, e.g. for by-passing a return line filter when a particular back-pressure has been reached due to contamination or
- As pre-tensioning valves (holding valves) to create particular backpressures in circuits

The so-called "rectifier circuit" is achieved by connecting four non return valves as shown in the diagram (*fig. 5*). It is used mainly in connection with flow control valves or pressure control valves. With this circuit, the fluid must flow through the valve in the same direction for forward flow (red) and return flow (green) (*figs. 5 and 6*).

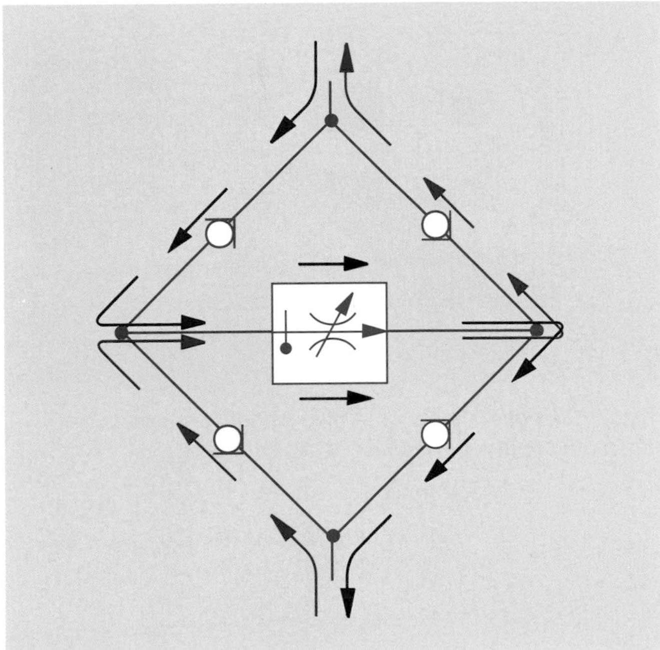

Fig. 5: *Circuit diagram for rectifier circuit*

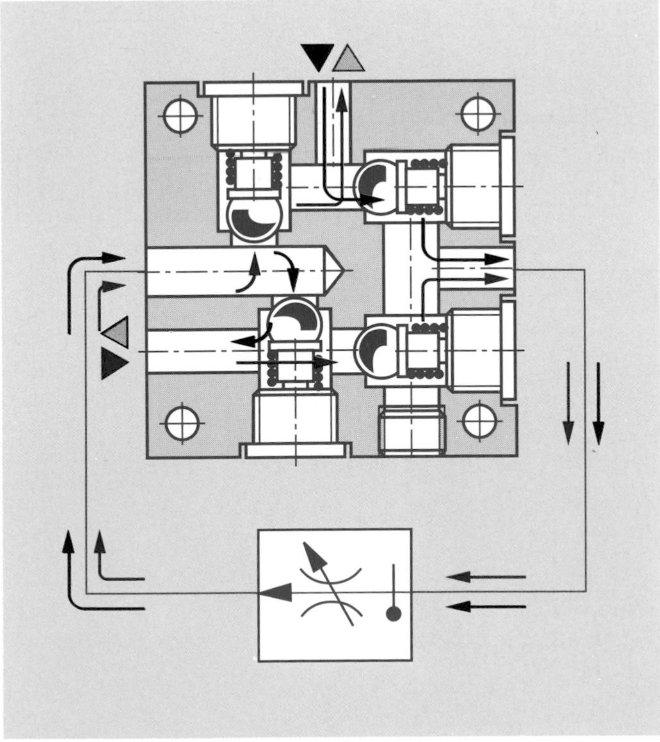

Fig. 6: *Rectifier sandwich plate, type Z4S*

3 Pilot operated check valves

As opposed to the simple non return valves, pilot operated check valves may also be opened in the direction of closure.

These valves are used, for example:

- to isolate working circuits under pressure
- to prevent the load from dropping, if a line should break
- to prevent creep movements of hydraulically loaded actuators

There are two types of pilot operated check valves.

3.1 Model without leakage port (valves, type SV)

Free flow is from A to B in the valve shown in *Fig. 7*.

Fluid pressure acts on area A_1 of the main poppet (1) and lifts this poppet from its seat against spring force (3). No flow is allowed in direction B to A, which corresponds with the function of a normal check valve.

Pilot piston (4) opens the valve. This piston is pushed to the right due to the pilot oil being fed into port X, and thus opens the main poppet (1) once a specified pilot pressure has been reached.

The pilot pressure required corresponds to the ratio of area A_1 to the area of the pilot spool. Usually this ratio is approx. 1:3.

Once the pilot pressure has been reached, the complete area A_1 is abruptly opened. This may result in decompression shocks, especially if large volumes under pressure are freed. These compression shocks not only cause noise, but also stress the complete hydraulic system, especially the screws and moving valve parts.

For applications, where these effects must be avoided, the valve is designed with pre-opening (pilot poppet) (see *fig. 8*).

When pressure is applied to control port X, the pilot spool 4 is pushed to the right. First the pilot poppet (2) and then the main poppet (1) are thus pushed from their seats. When the pilot poppet is opened, only a small area is open to flow. This causes the cylinder to decompress slowly before the complete area is opened by opening the main poppet. Flow is from B to A in the valve. This design allows the fluid under pressure to decompress slowly.

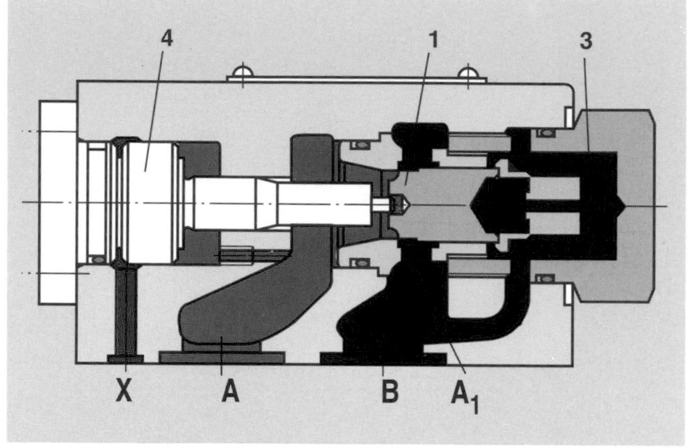

Fig. 7: *Pilot operated check valve without pre-opening of the main poppet and without case drain port*

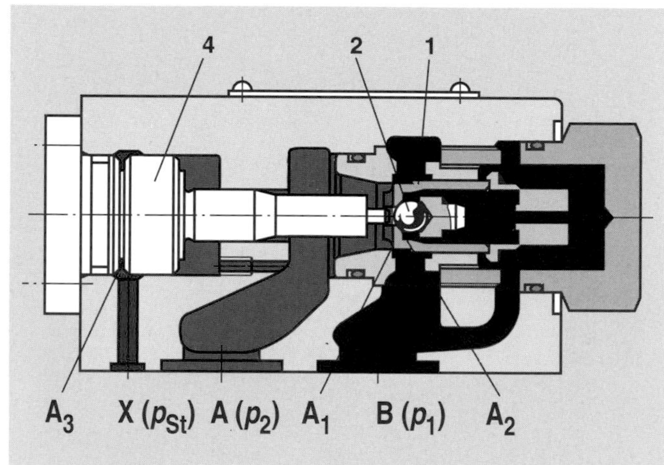

Fig. 8: *Pilot operated check valve with pre-opening of the main poppet and without drain case port*

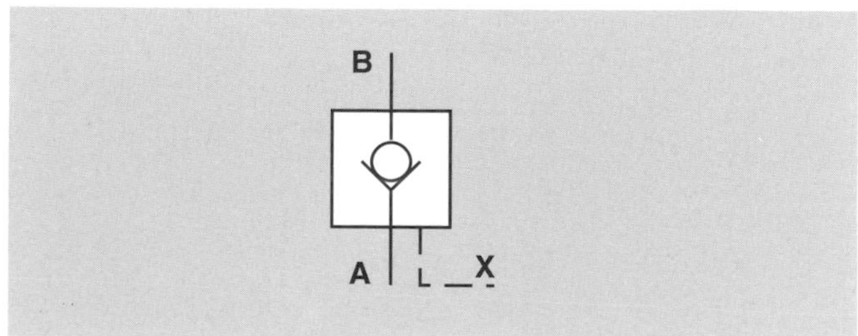

Fig. 9: *Pilot operated check valve without case drain port*

A certain minimum pilot pressure is required, so that the valve can also be reliably controlled by means of the control piston.

Below is shown how the required pilot pressure can be determined. The symbols used in the calculations are as follows:

p_{St} = pilot pressure
p_1 = pressure at port B of the valve
p_2 = pressure at port A of the valve
A_1 = area of main poppet
A_2 = area of pilot poppet
A_3 = area of control spool
A_K = area of cylinder piston
A_R = area of cylinder annulus
F = cylinder load
F_F = spring force with friction

Balance of forces at valve, see *fig. 8*

$$p_{St} \cdot A_3 = p_1 \cdot A_1 + F_F + p_2 \cdot (A_3 - A_1)$$

$$A_3 > A_1 \qquad (1)$$

This calculation is valid for zero pressure at port A ($p_2 \approx 0$ bar). Pressure at port A would act at the control spool in opposition to the pilot pressure.

Balance of forces at cylinder, see *fig. 10*

$$p_1 \cdot A_R = p \cdot A_K + F$$

$$p_1 = p \cdot \frac{A_K}{A_R} + \frac{F}{A_R} \qquad (2)$$

If equation 2 is substituted into equation 1 and solved for p_{St}, the required pilot pressure is produced for port X for the check valve without leakage port.

$$p_{St} \geq \left(p \cdot \frac{A_K}{A_R} + \frac{F}{A_R}\right) \cdot \frac{A_1}{A_3} + \frac{F_F}{A_3} \qquad (3)$$

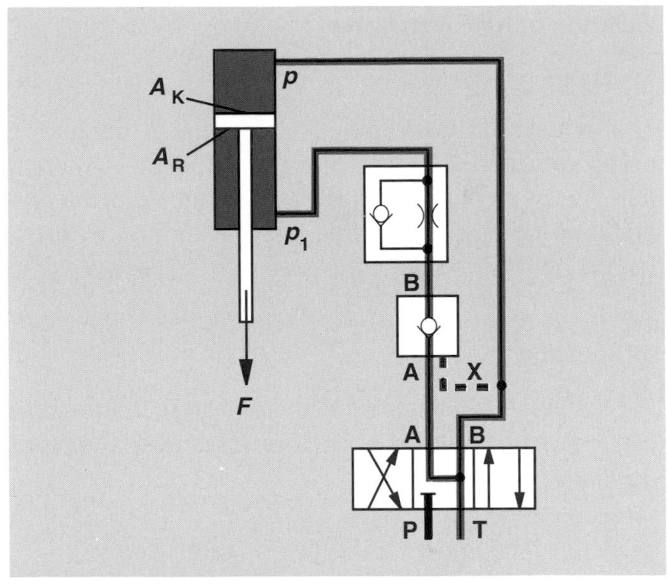

Fig. 10: *Circuit diagram*

3.2 Model with leakage port (Valves, type SL)

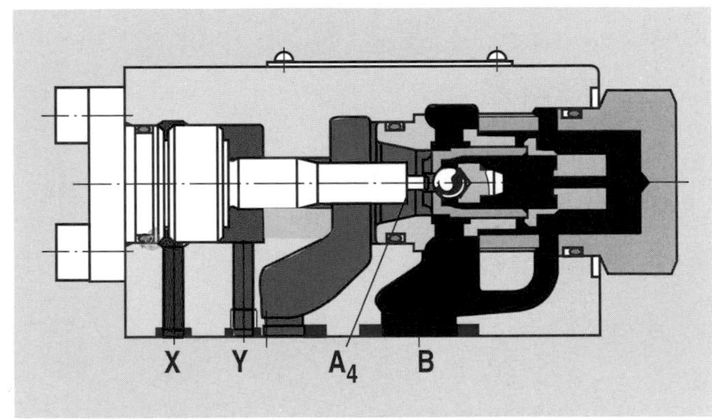

Fig. 11: *Pilot operated check valve with pre-opening of the main poppet and case drain port*

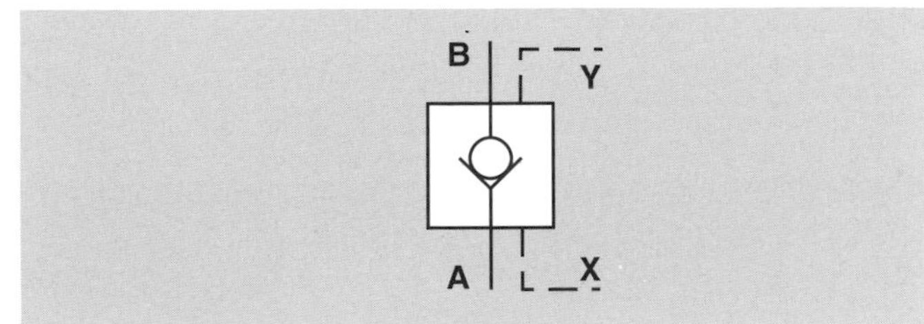

Fig. 12: *Pilot operated check valve with case drain port*

The difference to valve type SV is the additional drain port Y. The annulus area of the control piston is separated from port A. Pressure at port A affects only surface A_4 of the control spool (*fig. 11*).

Balance of forces at valve

$$p_{St} \bullet A_3 = p_2 \bullet (A_4 - A_1) + p_1 \bullet A_1 + F_F \quad (4)$$

The equation shows, that if the valve is opened, a pressure p_2 may be created ($p_2 > 0$). This pressure only acts on the push rod and hence does not effect the pilot pressure greatly. In general, the pressure p_2 supports the pilot pressure due to the area ratio.

The balance of forces at the cylinder (*fig. 10*) is described by equation 2.

If equation 2 is substituted Into equation 4, the required pilot pressure to open the check valve with leakage port is produced.

$$p_{St} \geq p_2 \bullet \frac{A_4 - A_1}{A_3} + \left(p \bullet \frac{A_K}{A_R} + \frac{F}{A_R}\right) \bullet \frac{A_1}{A_3} + \frac{F_F}{A_3} \quad (5)$$

From the theoretical considerations (equations 3 and 5), it can be seen that check valve, type SV (without leakage port) must not be pressurised at port A, but this is permitted in check valve, type SL (with leakage port).

Check valves, types SV and SL are available for

- sub-plate mounting
- pipe mounting (threaded connections) (*fig. 13*)
- pipe mounting (flanged connections)
- as cartridge elements or
- as sandwich plate valves (*fig. 14*)

Important parameters

Sizes:	6 to 150
Flow:	up to 6400 L/min
Operating pressure:	up to 315 bar

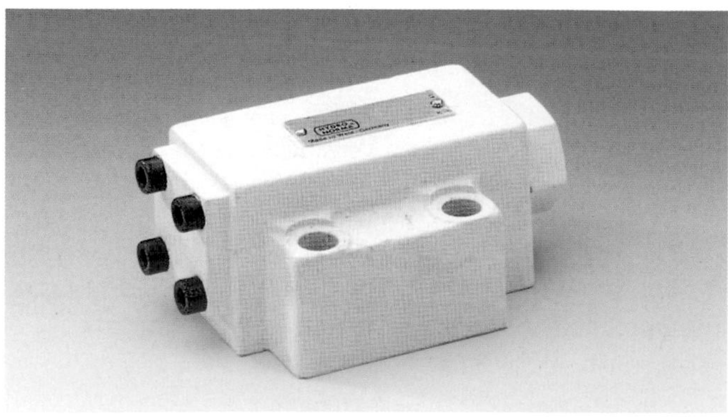

Fig. 13: *Pilot operated check valve*

By fitting two pilot operated check valves (1) and (2) in one housing, a double pilot operated check valve, type Z2S, is obtained (*fig. 14*).

There is free flow in direction A_1 to A_2 or B_1 to B_2, while flow is blocked from A_2 to A_1 or B_2 to B_1. If, for example, there is flow from A_1 to A_2, control spool (3) is pushed to the right and pushes the poppet of the check valve (2) from its seat.

The connection from B_2 to B_1 is now open. The valve therefore operates at flow direction B_1 to B_2.

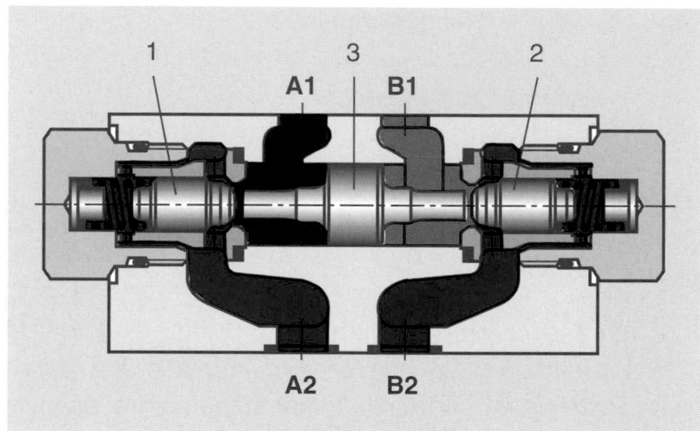

Fig. 14: *Double check valve for sandwich plate mounting, type Z2S*

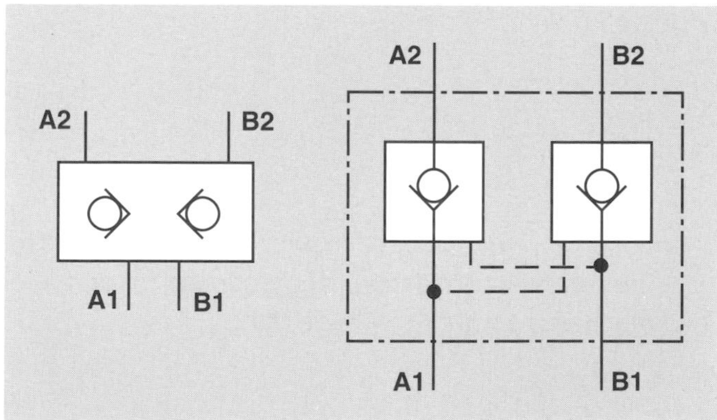

Fig. 15: *Symbols for double check valves (left: simplified symbol, right: detailed symbol)*

The circuit example below shows the task of the double check valve:

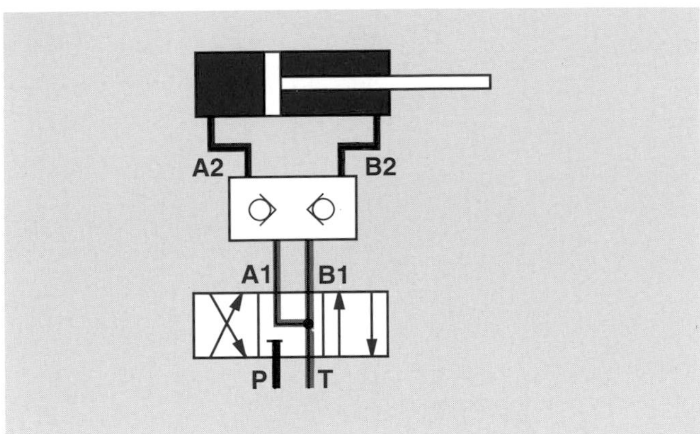

Fig. 16: *Circuit example*

Both parts of the cylinder are closed leakfree. At any desired idle position, the cylinder cannot be moved, even by an external force.

This means, for example, that a cylinder under load will not begin to 'creep', even during a long idle period.

In order to guarantee safe closing of both valve poppets, both actuator ports (A and B) must be unloaded when the directional valve is in its neutral position by connecting these parts to the return line.

A double check valve is generally fitted as a sandwich plate between the directional control valve and the subplate.

Important parameters

Sizes:	6 to 25
Flow:	up to 300 L/min
Operating pressure:	up to 315 bar
Cracking pressure:	1.5; 3; 7.5 and 10 bar (sizes 6 and 10) 2.5; 5; 7.5 and 10 bar (sizes 16 and 25)

3.3 Applcations using pilot operated check valves, types SV and SL

3.3.1 Pilot operated check valve, type SV

These valves may be used, if port A is at zero pressure when the valve is opened.

No additional connection of leakage line Y is necessary.

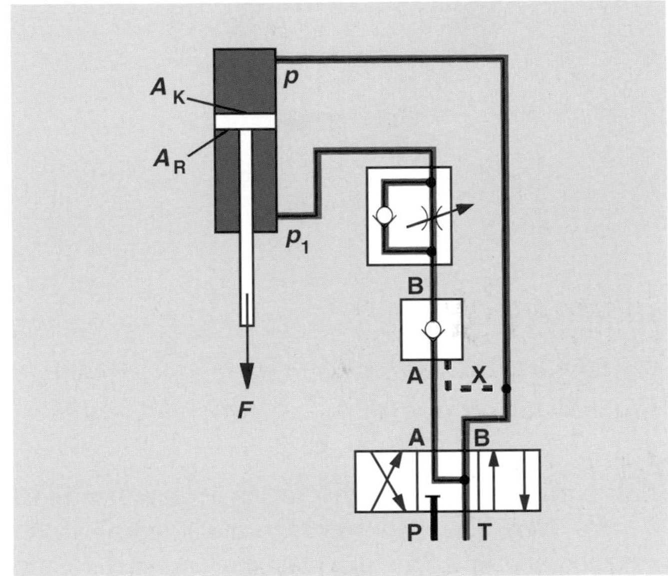

Fig. 17: *Use of pilot operated check valves, type SV*

3.3.2 Pilot operated check valve, type SL

These valves must be used if port A is under pressure when the valve is opened.

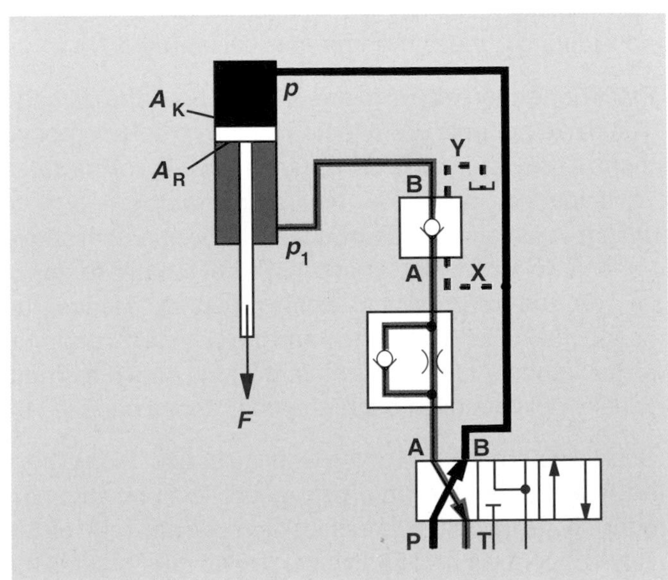

Fig. 18: *Use of pilot operated check valves, type SL, port A (for example) is subject to a back pressure due to the throttle check valve*

3.4 Pre-fill valves

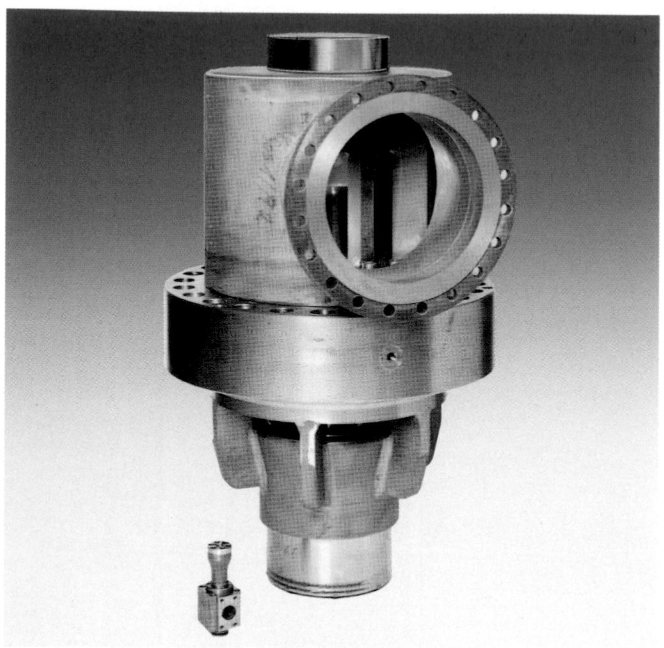

Fig. 19: *Pre-fill valve, type SF, size 500 (p_{max} = 350 bar; Q_{max} = 50 000 L/min) in comparison with a valve, size 40*

Prefill valves are large size hydraulic pilot operated check valves. They are used mainly to prefill large cylinder volumes and to isolate the main working circuit under pressure, for example, in presses.

The valve shown in *fig. 20* comprises pilot poppet (1) and main poppet (2) which are held on their seats by spring (3). The force of this spring only exceeds the weight of the poppet by a small amount. Spring (4) pushes the control piston (5) into start position.

The function will be described in more detail by considering a press cylinder application (*fig. 21*).

Port A is connected with a pre-fill tank above the cylinder. The valve poppets are affected by the oil column above them. If the piston rod side (annulus area A_R) of the press is unloaded, the piston moves downwards due to its weight. A negative pressure occurs in the chamber above surface A_K which also affects port B of the pre-fill valve, i.e. on the rear of the closing poppet. Hence the connection to tank is opened and the cylinder sucks oil in as it extends. At the same time, the high pressure pump usually delivers oil into the chamber above surface A_K.

Shortly before the end of the working stroke, the cylinder is braked to the desired press speed. The pressure now building up (working pressure) affects the rear of the valve poppet via prefill valve port B and thus isolates the working circuit from the tank.

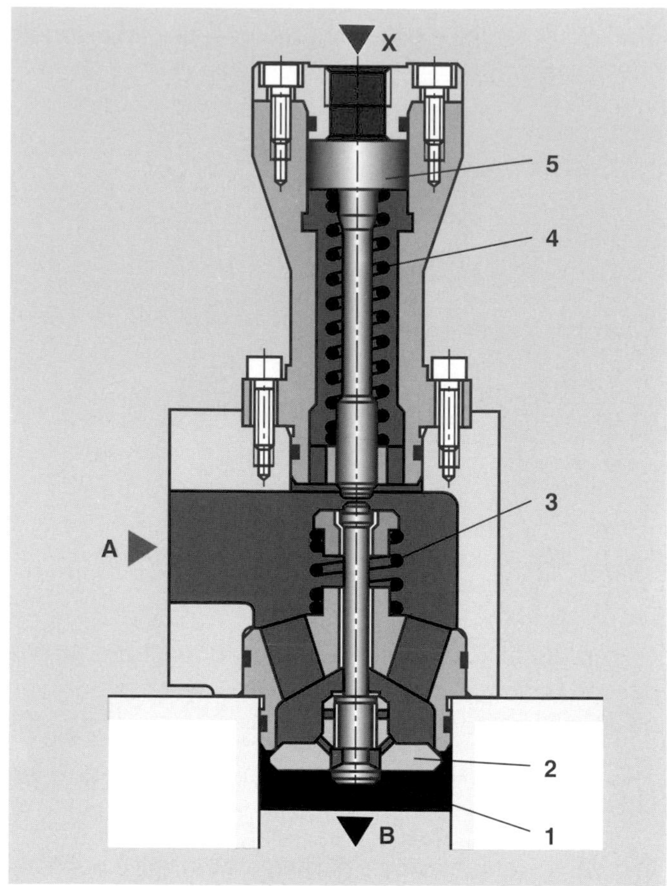

Fig. 20: *Pre-fill valve with pre-opening poppet*

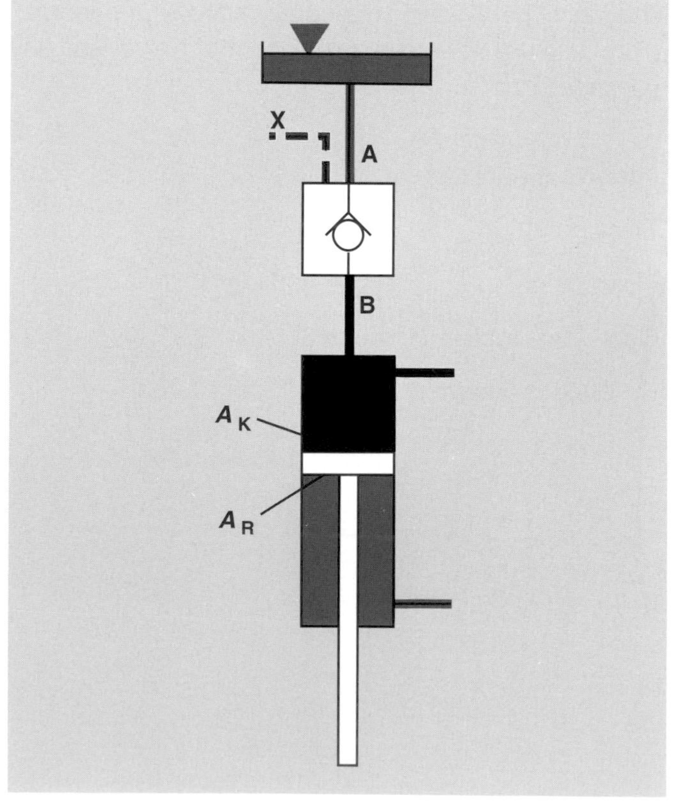

Fig. 21: *Circuit example*

After the working stroke, the press cylinder must retract. By switching over the control elements, pressure affects, for example, the annulus area A_R, and by means of prefill valve control port X, control spool (5). It pushes open the pilot opening poppet (1) and then the main poppet (2). The fluid above the surface A_K can now be pushed back into the pre-fill tank. The cylinder can retract again.

Depending on application, prefill valves can be fitted with or without pilot opening poppets.

The pilot pressure may be calculated in the same way as for the pilot operated check valves mentioned in sections 3.1 and 3.2.

Larger valves are always fitted with pilot opening poppets.

Pre-fill valves are available for

- flanged connections
- tank mounting
- manifold mounting

Important parameters

Sizes:	40 to 500
Flow:	up to 50 000 L/min (at v_{oil} = 6 m/s)
Operating pressure:	up to 350 bar
Cracking pressure:	without spring; 0.5; 1.5 or 3 bar

4 2- way cartridge valves (logic elements)

A special type of non return valve is the 2-way cartridge valve, also known as a logic element. They are described in detail in the manual "The Hydraulics Trainer, Volume.4".

Notes

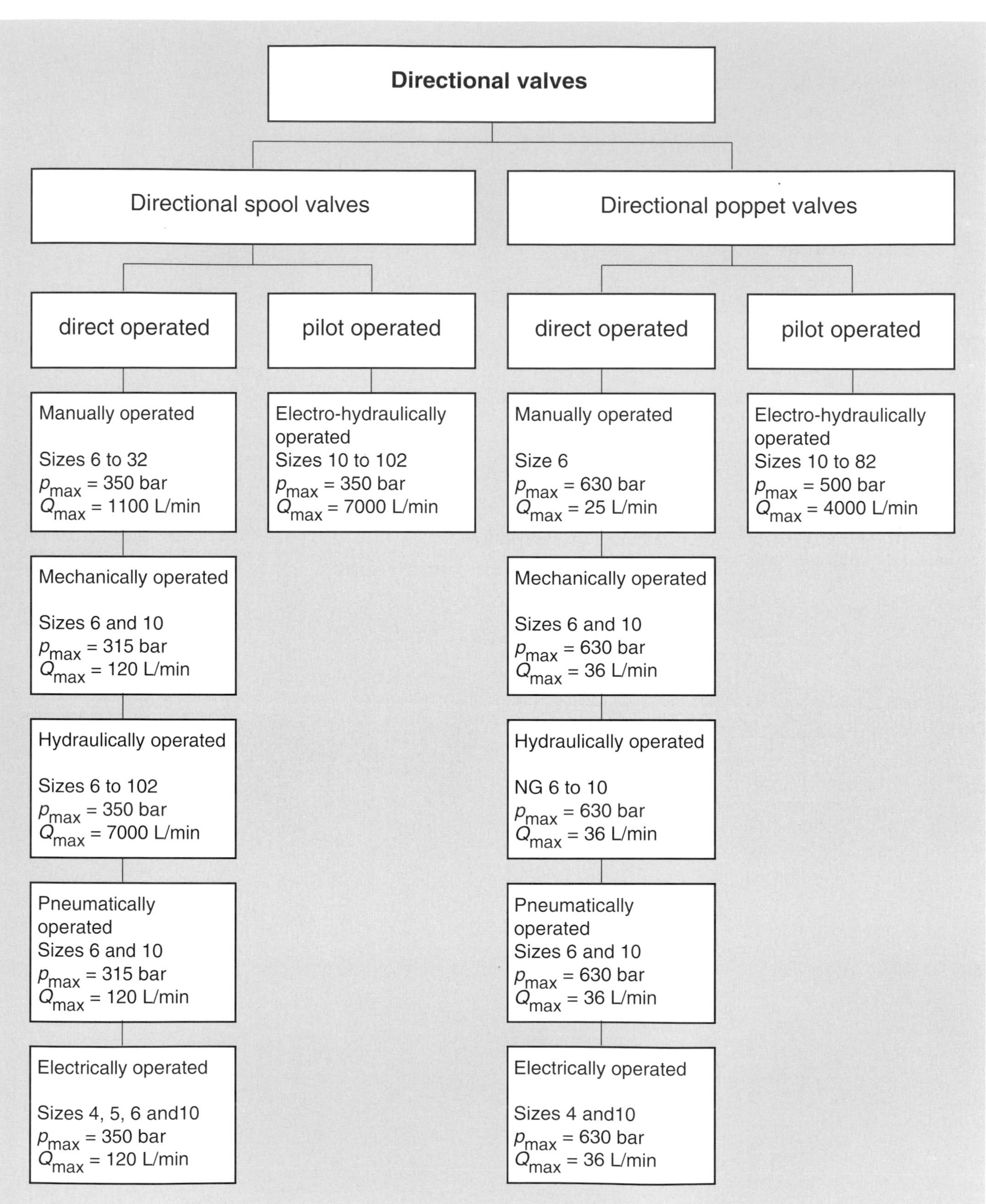
Directional valves
Directional spool valves
Directional poppet valves
direct operated
pilot operated
direct operated
pilot operated
Manually operated
Sizes 6 to 32
p_{max} = 350 bar
Q_{max} = 1100 L/min
Electro-hydraulically operated
Sizes 10 to 102
p_{max} = 350 bar
Q_{max} = 7000 L/min
Manually operated
Size 6
p_{max} = 630 bar
Q_{max} = 25 L/min
Electro-hydraulically operated
Sizes 10 to 82
p_{max} = 500 bar
Q_{max} = 4000 L/min
Mechanically operated
Sizes 6 and 10
p_{max} = 315 bar
Q_{max} = 120 L/min
Mechanically operated
Sizes 6 and 10
p_{max} = 630 bar
Q_{max} = 36 L/min
Hydraulically operated
Sizes 6 to 102
p_{max} = 350 bar
Q_{max} = 7000 L/min
Hydraulically operated
NG 6 to 10
p_{max} = 630 bar
Q_{max} = 36 L/min
Pneumatically operated
Sizes 6 and 10
p_{max} = 315 bar
Q_{max} = 120 L/min
Pneumatically operated
Sizes 6 and 10
p_{max} = 630 bar
Q_{max} = 36 L/min
Electrically operated
Sizes 4, 5, 6 and10
p_{max} = 350 bar
Q_{max} = 120 L/min
Electrically operated
Sizes 4 and10
p_{max} = 630 bar
Q_{max} = 36 L/min

Table 1

Chapter 11

Directional Valves

Dr Harald Geis, Johann Oppolzer

1 General

1.1 Operation and function

All valves which are used to control the start, stop and change in direction of flow of a fluid are called "directional valves".

1.2 Special characteristics

The designation of a directional valve refers to the number of service ports (not including control ports) and the number of spool positions.

A valve with 2 service ports and 2 spool positions is thus designated as a 2/2 way directional valve (*Fig. 1*).

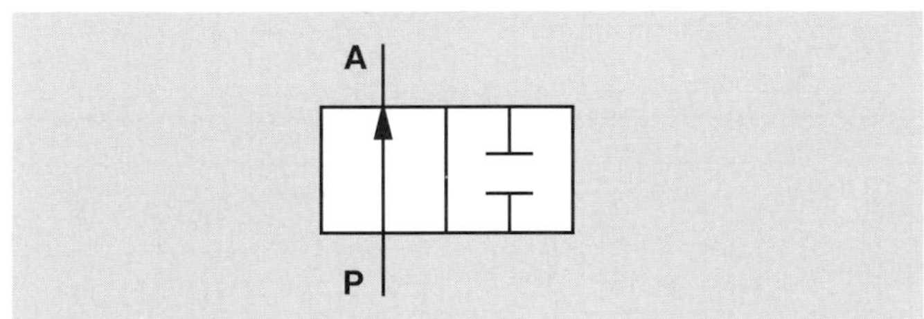

Fig. 1: *2/2 way directional valve*

A directional valve with 4 service ports and 3 spool positions is then a 4/3 way directional valve (*Fig. 2*).

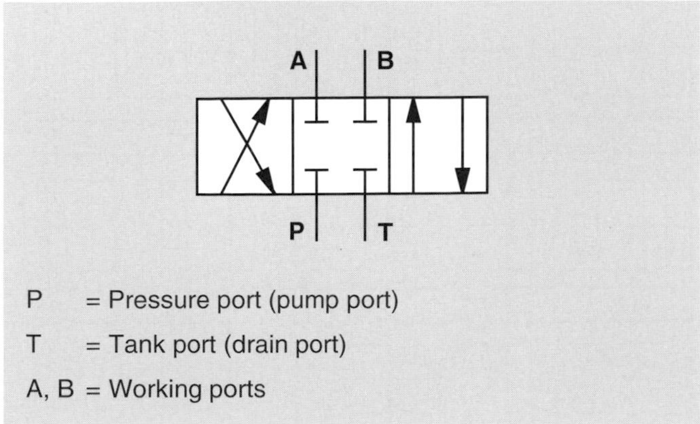

Fig. 2: *4/3 way directional valve with designation of ports*

Spool positions as well as their corresponding operating elements are labelled with little letters "a" and "b". In fig. 3 a valve with 2 spool positions is shown and also a valve with 3 spool positions. In directional valves with 3 spool positions, the central position is the "neutral position (or rest position)".

The rest position is the position which moving parts have assumed when they are not active, but affected by a force (e.g. spring).

This position is designated as "0" in valves with 3 or more spool positions. In valves with 2 spool positions, the rest position is designated either as "a" or "b".

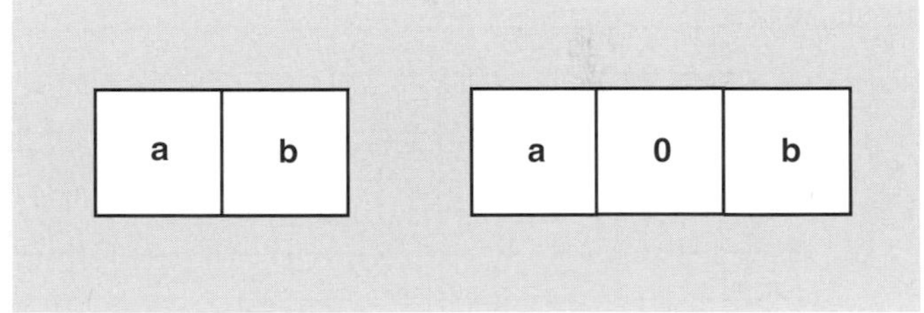

Fig. 3: *Basic symbol for directional valves, left: 2-way valve, right: 3-way valve*

When a valve is shown horizontally (fig. 4), the order of the spool positions a,b,... follows the alphabet from left to right.

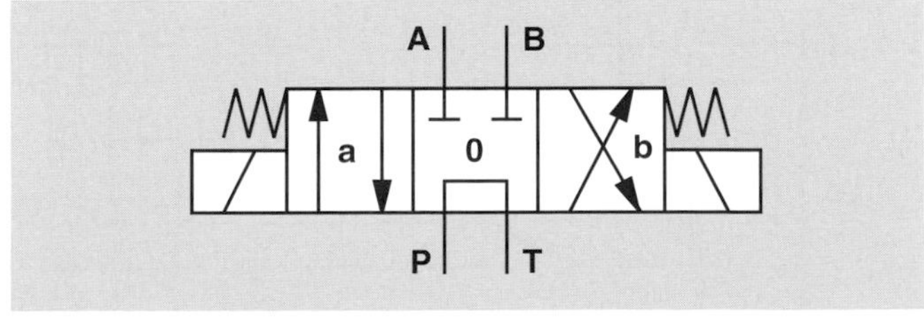

Fig. 4: *4/3 way directional valve with designation of ports, spool positions and operating elements*

In *table 2*, the most common symbols for directional valves are shown, which may be combined with each other to produce a large number of functions. In practice, about 250 spool variations exist.

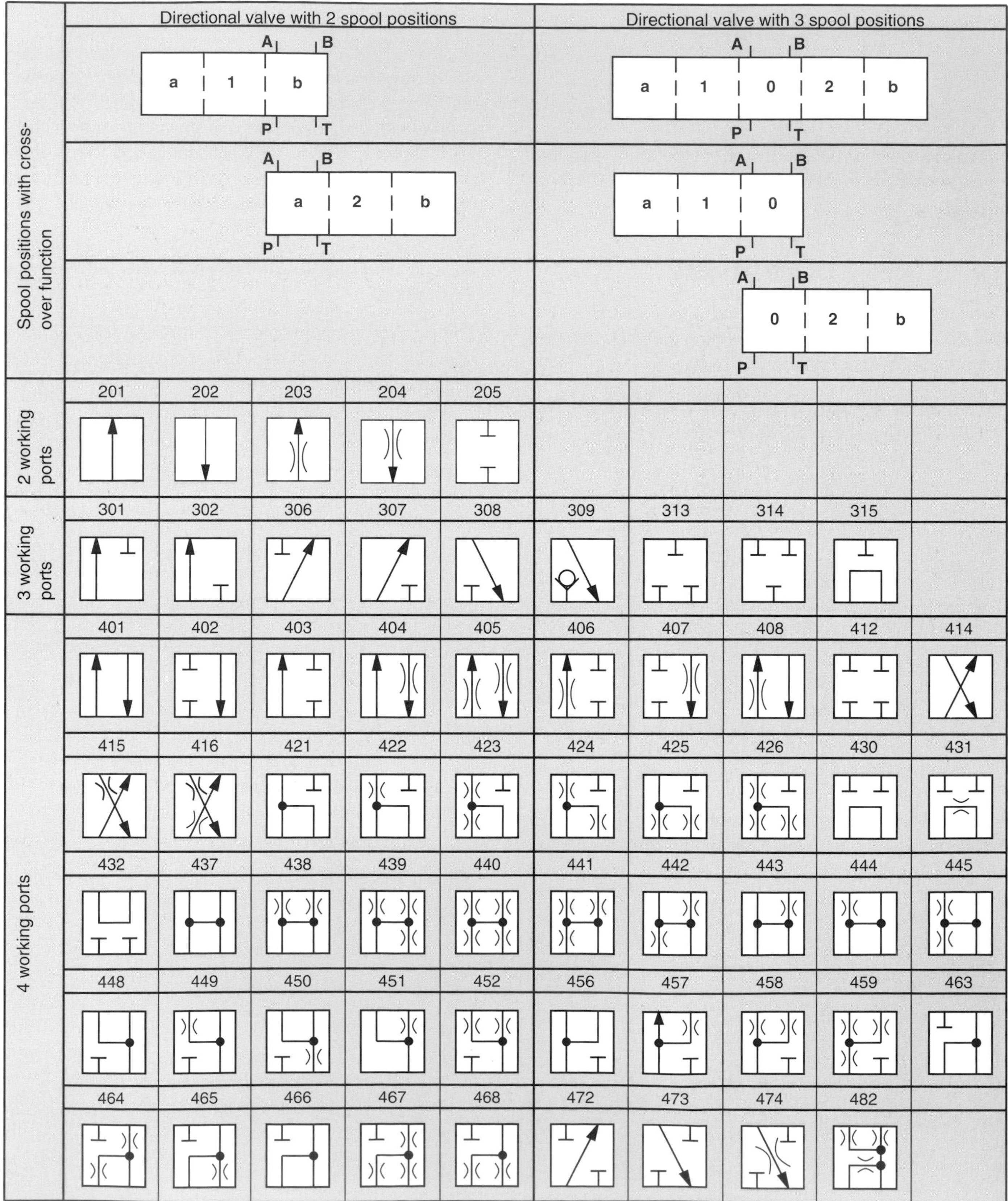

Table 2: *Summary of spool types*

1.3 Directional valve power

The performance and quality of a directional valve is determined on the basis of the following criteria:

- dynamic power limit
- static power limit
- resistance to flow
- leakage (in directional spool valves)
- operation time

1.3.1 Dynamic performance limit

The product of flow and operating pressure is the dynamic power limit of a directional valve (*diagram 1*). Power limits may be a function of the control spring, the solenoid or control pressure. Depending on the type of spool, one of these 3 parameters determines the power limit of the valve. The operating force must be able to overcome the spring force and the axial force existing in the valve. The spring force on its own must be capable of returning the spool against the axial force to its initial position.

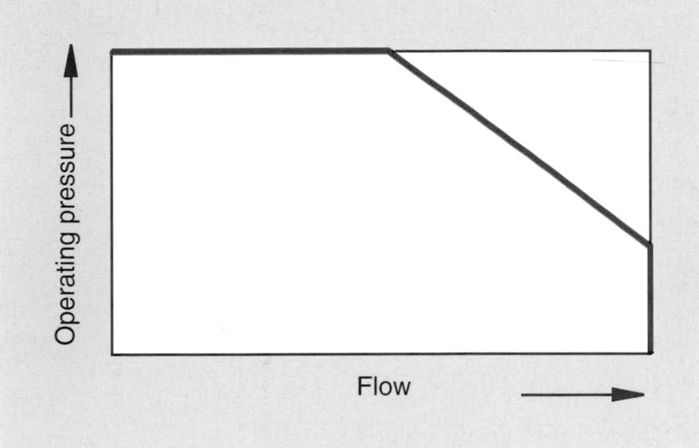

Diagram 1: *Power limit for directional valve*

The axial forces present in a directional valve are not the same in either size or direction for all spool types in one size of valve.

The performance limit which is a measure of the permissible flow at a particular pressure is determined by the axial force, which is produced in a directional valve when the control spool is operated.

It comprises the following parts

- mass force F_m
- stability force F_z
- flow force F_{St}
- resistance force F_w

1.3.2 Static performance limit

The static performance limit of a directional valve is very dependent on the effective time of the operating pressure. Under the influence of pressure, time and other factors, such as dirt, a retaining force is produced between the spool and the housing, which acts in opposition to the movement of the control spool.

If the directional valve is operated frequently, this retaining force is hardly noticeable. It is only after long idle times and at high pressure that this force leads to the spool sticking. This effect is particularly noticeable in direct operated valves, as only low operating forces are available for these valves.

In contrast to dynamic forces, the retaining force is very dependent on the time which the valve spends under pressure in one position.

There are several factors responsible for the creation of this force:

- Level of operating pressure
- Diameter of control spool
- Oil viscosity and temperature
- Quality of the surface finish of the housing bore and the control spool
- Spool clearance
- Filtration
- Overlap length and interruption of this overlap length through unloading grooves.

1.3.3 Pressure difference

The difference between the valve input pressure and the valve output pressure is the pressure difference Δp, i.e. the internal resistance of the directional valve. This pressure difference is produced in the region of laminar flow, mainly through friction with the wall and in the region of turbulent flow, mainly through the loss of kinetic energy due to the flow detaching itself from control lands.

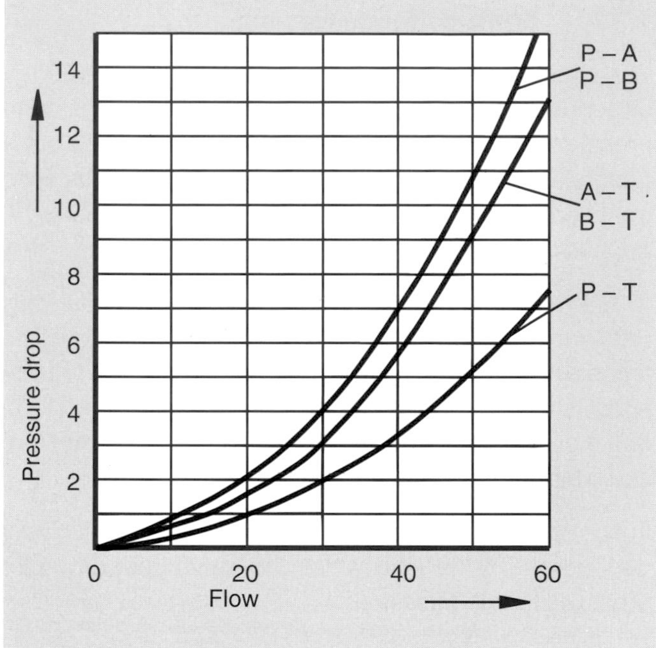

Diagram 2: *Δp-Q operating curve for a 4/3 way directional valve*

As, in practice, the pressure difference cannot be sufficiently accurately calculated, the manufacturers determine the values for individual valve sizes empirically and then show the results in the form of Δp-Q operating curves (*diagram 2*). It has to be made clear in these diagrams which connections (arising from an operation) the curves are referring to (e.g. P to A and B to T or P to B and A to T, etc.).

In order to compare measurements with these values it is necessary to carry out experiments to DIN ISO 4411, whereby the viscosity of the fluid must be kept constant.

1.3.4 Operation times

The operation time of a directional valve is the time required from when the operating force is initially introduced to when the control element completes its stroke. Its determination is in accordance with ISO 6403. Experiments on electrically operated directional valves have shown that the operating time comprises 4 phases (*diagram 3*).

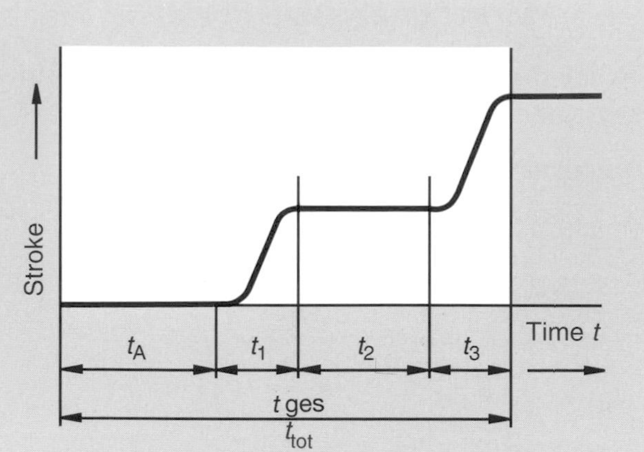

t_A: Response delay time, is the time it takes for the solenoid armature to move after the energizing voltage has been switched on. During this time the solenoid force required to overcome the spring pre-tension and the holding forces (stick-slip) is built up.

t_1: Time for flow force to become effective at the main control land (start-up range).

t_2: Time for solenoid force to build up, which is required to overcome maximum flow force. It is dependent on the amount of flow force and effects the operating time t_{tot} (flow force range).

t_3: Time for control spool to cross-over and up to end of valve stroke (cross-over range).

Diagram 3: *Stroke-time diagram (spool operation phases)*

1.4 Types of directional valve

There are three types of directional valve, which vary in how they are constructed:

- Directional spool valves
- Directional poppet valves
- Rotary directional valves

The directional spool valve is the most common one used due to its many advantages, such as

- Simple construction
- Good pressure compensation, hence low operating forces
- High operating power
- Low losses
- Variety of control functions

2 Directional spool valves

Directional spool valves in which a moving spool is situated in the valve housing.

Depending on the number of flow paths to be controlled, two or more annular channels are formed or cast into a housing made of hydraulic cast iron, spherical graphite cast iron, steel or other suitable materials. These channels run either concentrically or eccentrically around a bore. Hence control lands are formed in the housing, which act together with the control spool lands.

When the control spool is moved, it connects or separates the annular channels in the housing.

Directional spool valves are sealed along the clearance between the moving spool and the housing. The degree of sealing depends on the clearance, the viscosity of the fluid and especially on the level of pressure. Especially at high pressures (up to 350 bar) leakages occur to such an extent that they have to be taken into account when determining system efficiency. From reference material, it is known that the amount of leakage is primarily dependent on the clearance between spool and housing. Hence in theory, the clearance must be reduced or the length of overlap increased as the operating pressure increases.

However, this is not done for several reasons:

- As the pressure increases, the spool bends by a large amount in the axial direction and this leads to the clearance decreasing in the direction of the high pressure side. This must be taken into account when selecting a clearance, in order to prevent the spool from sticking.
- As the operating pressure increases, the required tensioning force needed to press the directional valve on the sub-plate also increases. The higher screw tensioning force which results causes the housing bore to deform by a large amount. This is a particular effect, which acts in opposition to the requirement for a smaller clearance, as the deformation of the bore must be compensated for by a larger clearance.
- Smaller clearances are more difficult to manufacture. In order to find a technical and economic solution, compromises need to be made between the various requirements.

Care must be taken in choosing the materials for the valve housing and control spool, so that materials have more or less the same expansion coefficient.

Temperature affects the fluid. As the temperature rises, viscosity falls and the density of the fluid (*diagrams 4 and 5*) and the leakage increase.

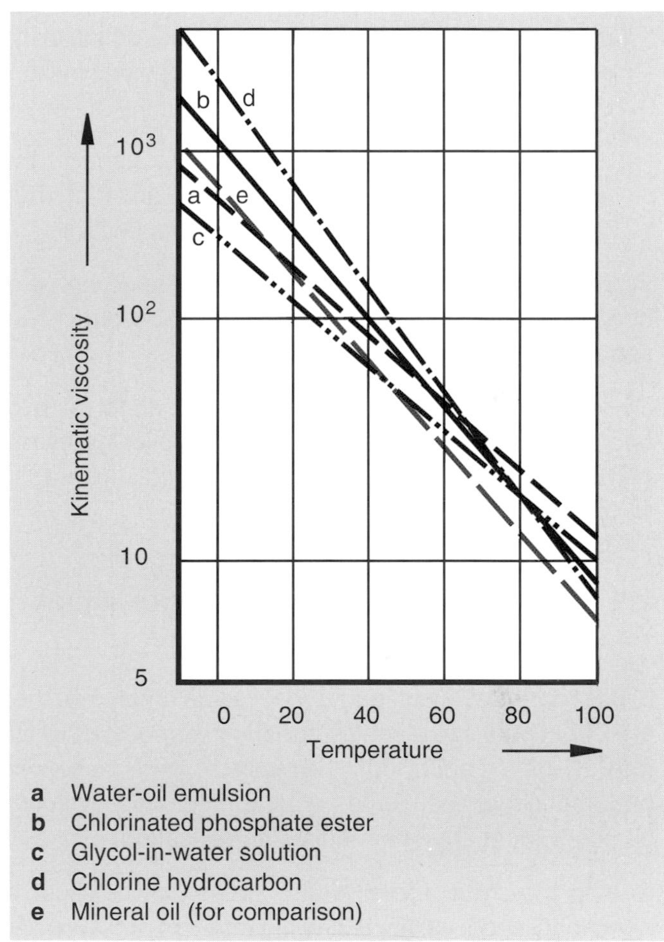

Diagram 4: *Viscosity of fluids dependent on temperature*

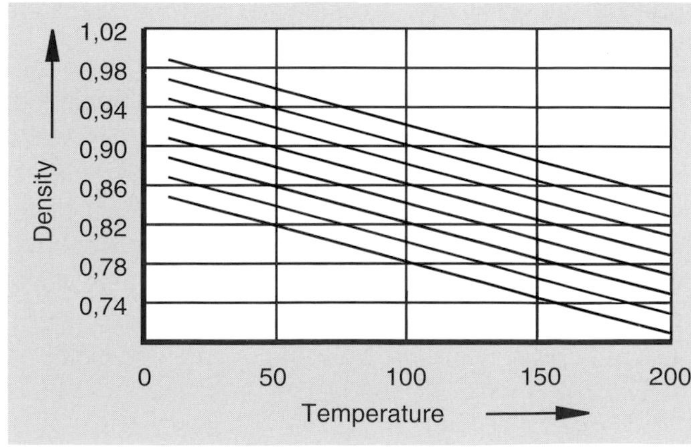

Diagram 5: *Density of fluids dependent on temperature*

The leakage losses from spool valves affect the volumetric efficiency of hydraulic systems and hence must be taken into account when designing a system.

Effects of leakage losses on hydraulic control are:

- Actuators, e.g. cylinders which are under a load pressure, may move in the effective direction of the load pressure due to the leakage losses.
- Actuators with a varying area ratio (single rod cylinders) may wander in the effective direction of the larger piston area, when using control valves with a closed central position.
- If accumulators are used in hydraulic circuits, the leakage of the spool must be taken into account when calculating the size of accumulator required.

In order to avoid losses due to leakages, a special type of directional spool valve (see "Leakage free directional spool valves", *section 2.3*) may be used.

Directional spool valves may be either direct or pilot operated. Whether a valve is direct or pilot operated, primarily depends on the required operating force and hence the size of the valve.

2.1 Direct operated directional spool valves

"Direct operated directional spool valves" imply that they are directional spool valves the control spools of which may be operated directly by solenoid, pneumatic/hydraulic forces or by a mechanically acting device without any intermediate amplification.

Due to the static and dynamic forces, which occur in directional spool valves due to the effect of pressure and flow, direct operated directional spool valves are usually only available up to a size 10. This limit corresponds to a power of about 120 L/min at an operating pressure of 350 bar and is mainly valid for solenoid operated directional spool valves.

Of course direct operated valves with solenoid operation could be produced for sizes larger than size 10. However considering the required operating forces, e.g for the size of solenoid required, for reasons of safety, idle times and due to the pressure shocks (which are difficult to control), it is not normally sensible to have direct operated valves of sizes above size 10.

The various types of operation are described below.

2.1.1 Electrical operation
Various types of solenoid operation

This type of operation is the most common, due to the automatic processes required in industry.

Usually one of four basic types of stroke solenoid is used:

- DC air gap solenoids.
- DC wet pin solenoids.
  These are also known as "pressure tight" solenoids. The solenoid armature runs in oil and the armature chamber is connected to the T port.
- AC air gap solenoid.
- AC wet pin solenoid.

The DC solenoid has a high degree of reliability and provides smooth operation. It does not burn out, if it stops during a stroke, for example, due to a sticking spool. It is suitable for a high frequency of operations.

A characteristic of the AC solenoid is its short operation times. If the solenoid armature cannot switch through to its end position, the AC solenoid will burn out after a certain time (approx. 1 to 1.5 hours for wet pin solenoids).

Mannesmann Rexroth mainly use wet pin solenoids in directional spool valves. This type is particularly advantageous for equipment in the open air or in a humid conditions (no corrosion of the internal parts). As the armature runs in oil, there is less wear, cushioned armature stroke and good heat transfer.

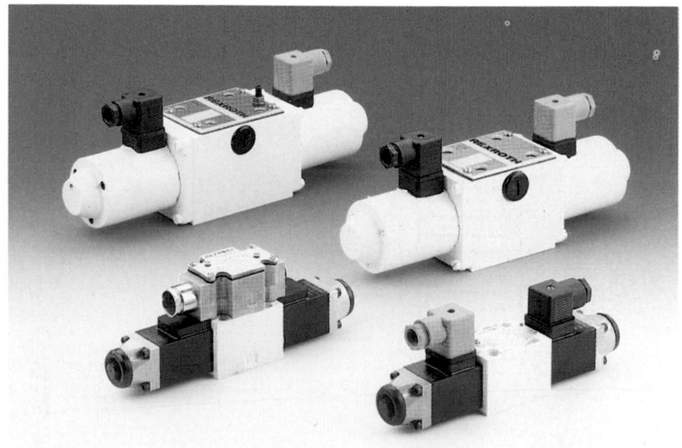

Fig. 5: *Electrically operated directional spool valve*

In fig. 6 is a directional spool valve with three spool positions. On the left hand side is an wet pin DC solenoid (4) and on the right hand side is an wet pin AC solenoid (5). (This model with " mixed" solenoids is only shown here for demonstration purposes.) The armature chamber of each solenoid is connected to the tank chamber of the valve housing. Hence these valves are known as three chamber valves.

The springs (6) are supported on the solenoid housings and centre the spool in neutral position by means of spring pad (8).

The solenoids shown are fitted with hand emergency operators (7). The control spool may thus be operated manually from outside. It is thus easy to check the operation of a solenoid.

Channels P, A and B are separated by lands in the housing. The T channel is not blocked, but connected to both tank chambers via a bypass channel within the valve. These chambers are sealed from the outside by the operating element or by a cover.

In a 5-chamber valve the T channel forms a chamber on both sides by means of lands (1) within the housing, in the same way as P, A and B have formed chambers (*fig. 7*).

The two end chambers (2) are connected together via a bore. If the control spool is moved, fluid is displaced from one end chamber into the other. By fitting a orifice or adjustable throttle (3) into this connection bore the operating time may be altered dependent on the diameter of the jet or the throttle setting.

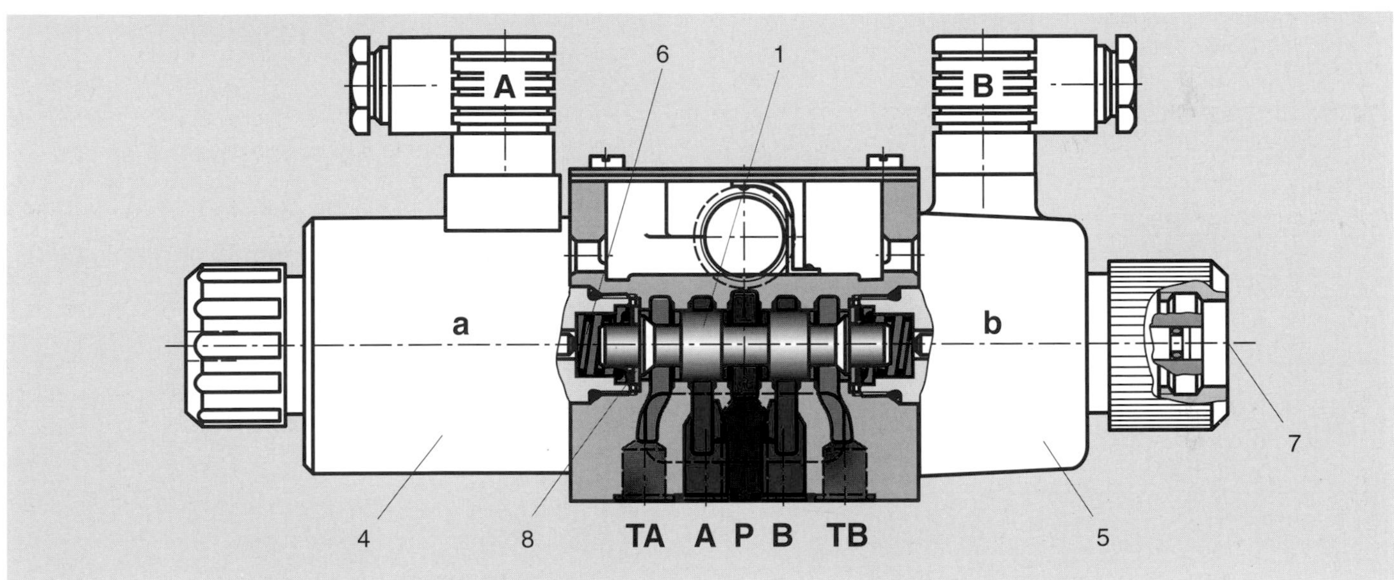

Fig. 6: *Directional spool valve with 3 chambers*

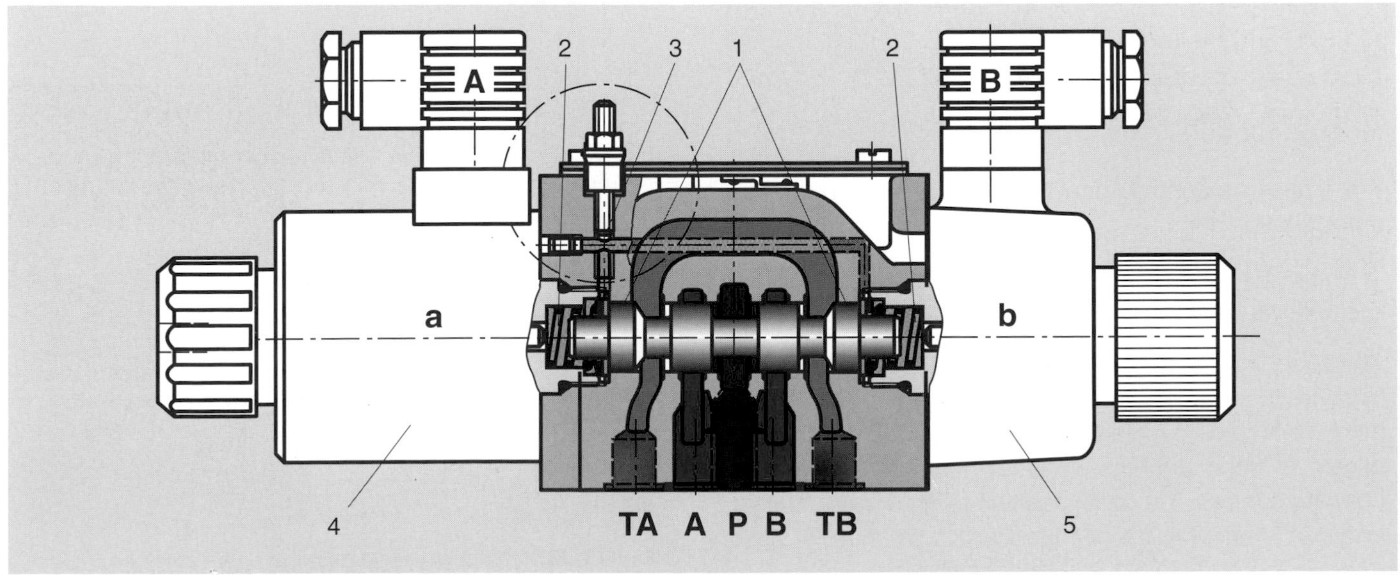

Fig. 7: *Directional spool valve with 5 chambers*

2.1.2 Mechanical manual operation

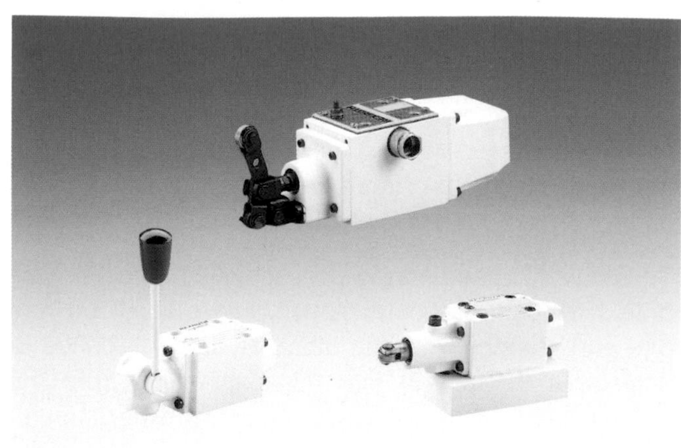

Fig. 8: *Directional valve with mechanical/manual operation*
Left: Roller shaft operation, type WMR
Centre: Roller shaft operation, type WMH
Right: Hand lever operation, type WMM

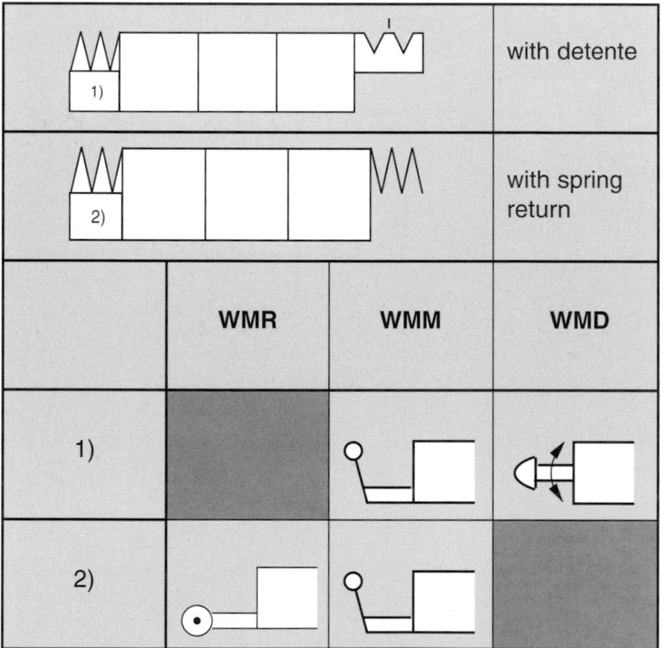

1)			with detente
2)			with spring return
	WMR	WMM	WMD
1)			
2)			

Table 3: *Manual and mechanical operating elements*

Fig. 9 shows a control spool being operated by means of a hand lever (1).

The spool is fixed rigidly to the operating mechanism (2) and follows its movement.

The spool is returned by springs (3), which push the spool back to its initial position once the operating force has been removed (e.g. letting go of the hand lever). If a detent is fitted and the spool cannot be returned by centring springs, the spool position is fixed by the detent and can then only be changed again by means of an operation (not possible in roller operation).

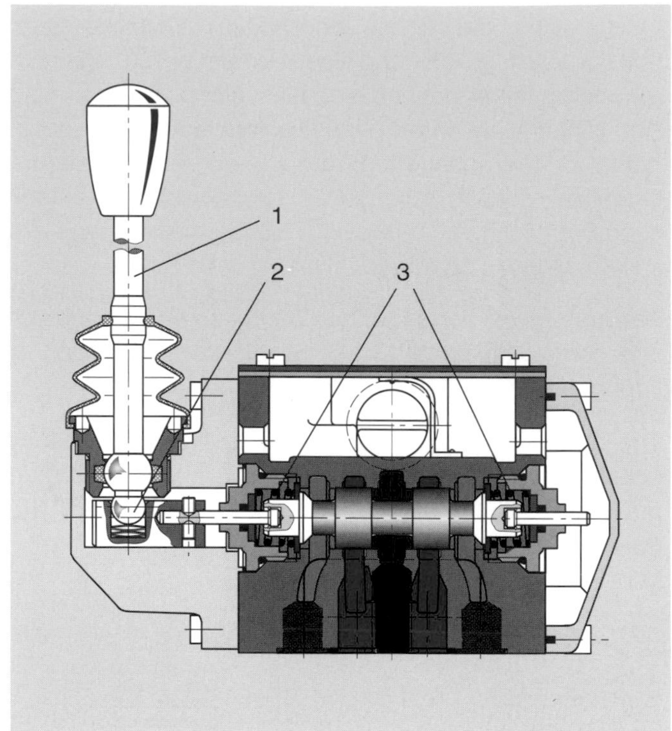

Fig. 9: *Manually operated directional valve, size 10, type WMM*

2.1.3 Fluid operation (hydraulic or pneumatic)

Fig. 10: *Directional valve with fluid operation; left: hydraulic operation, type WHD; right: pneumatic operation, type WP*

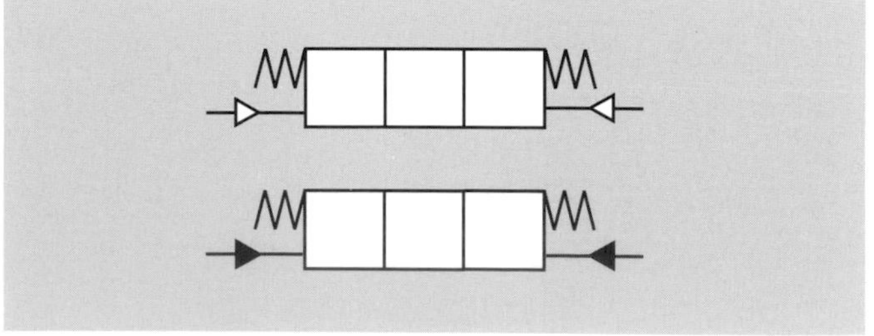

Fig. 11: *Directional valve with spring centering; pneumatic operation (top), hydraulic (bottom)*

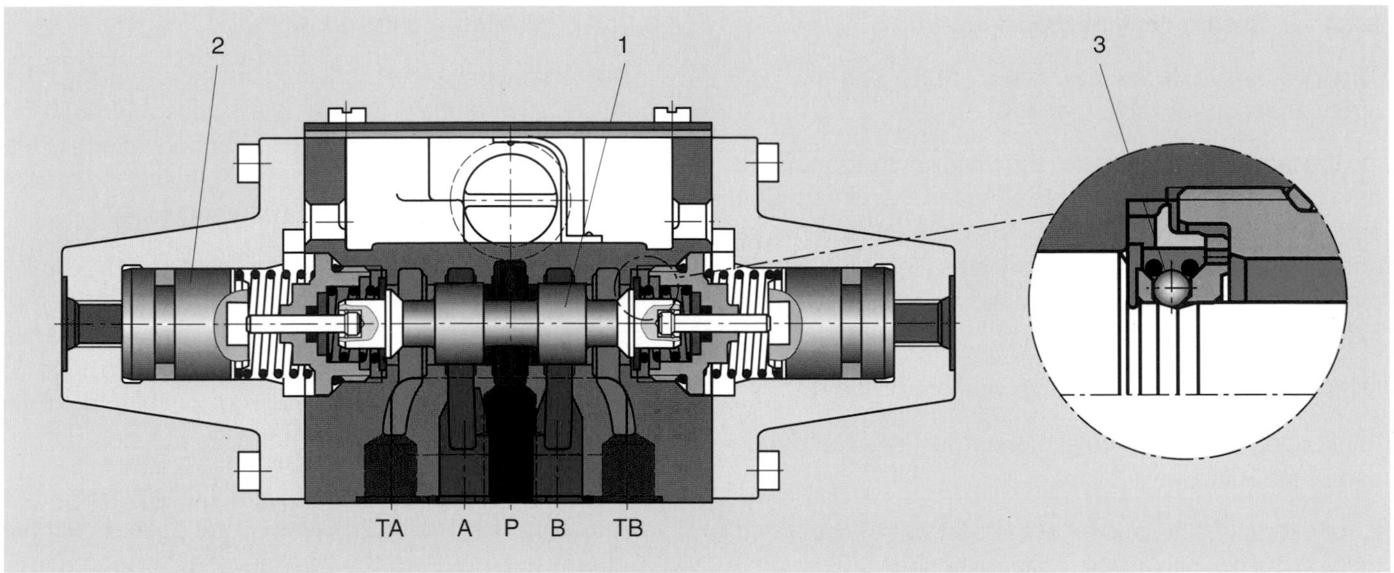

Fig. REF!: *Pneumatically operated directional valve with 2 spool positions and detent*

Spool (1) is in the right hand spool position. This was achieved by pressurising the opposite operating cylinder (2). The spool position is fixed by means of the detent (3).

The control spool is not connected to the operating cylinder. Two operating cylinders are always required if using 2 spool positions with detent or without spring return; or if using 3 spool positions.

An operating cylinder is added, if spool return is by means of a spring in a two spool position valve.

2.2 Pilot operated directional spool valves

For the control of large hydraulic powers, pilot operated directional spool valves are used.

The reason for this is the large operating force required to move the control spool.

For this reason, directional spool valves up to size 10 are usually direct operated and over size 10 pilot operated. Exceptions to this are directional spool valves with hand levers up to size 32.

A pilot operated directional spool valve comprises the main valve (1) and the pilot valve (2) (*fig. 15*).

The pilot valve is generally direct operated electrically (solenoids). When the pilot valve is operated, the control signal from it is amplified hydraulically and used to move the main control spool.

On size 102 (up to 7000 L/min) the pilot valve is itself a pilot operated directional spool valve (*fig. 14*).

Fig. 13: *Electro-hydraulically operated directional spool valves for sandwich plate mounting*

Fig. 14: *Electro-hydraulically operated directional spool valves for flanged connections*

2.2.1 Spring centred model

The pilot valve is an electrically direct operated 4/3 directional control valve (*fig. 15*).

On the spring centred model, the main control spool (3) is held in centre position by the springs (4.1 and 4.2). Both spring chambers (yellow) are thus connected in neutral position via the pilot valve with the tank (light blue) at zero pressure. Thus the centre position for the pilot valve is fixed (symbol J).

Oil is supplied to the pilot valve via control line (5).

Pilot supply is either internal or external (for exact details see *page 200a*).

If, for example, solenoid "a" at the pilot valve is operated, this moves the pilot valve spool to the left.

The left- hand spring chamber (6) is thus subjected to pilot pressure, the right-hand spring chamber (7) remains unloaded to tank.

Pilot pressure acts on the left end of the main spool and pushes it to the right against spring (4.2) until it reaches the cover. Hence port P is connected to port B and A to T in the main valve. When the solenoid is de-energised, the pilot valve returns to the centre position and spring chamber (6) is unloaded to tank again. Spring (4.2) can now push the main spool to the left, until it touches the spring plate of spring (4.1). The spool is once again in the centre position (neutral position).

The control oil from spring chamber (6) is pushed into channel Y via the pilot valve.

The operating process for solenoid "b" is similar.

A certain minimum pilot pressure is necessary to operate the main control spool, which depends on the symbol and valve type.

2.2.2 Pressure centred model

In the centre position of pressure centred valves (fig. 16), both control chambers (6) and (7) are connected with the control pressure. The main control spool is held in the centre position by the effect of the pressurised surfaces of spool (3), centring bush (8) and centring pin (9).

If solenoid "a" at the pilot valve is operated, this moves the pilot spool to the left. Control chamber (6) therefore remains connected with the control pressure, while control chamber (7) is unloaded to tank. Centring bush (8) touches the housing. Centring pin (9) pushes the main control spool to the right unit it reaches the stop.

The springs in chambers (6) and (7) are used, for example, to hold the spool in the centre position without pilot pressure, even with a vertical valve arrangement.

When solenoid "a" is de-energised, the pilot spool returns to the centre position and control chamber (7) is connected with the control pressure once again.

The end surface of spool (3) is larger than the end surface of centring pin (9). The main spool moves to the left until the spool end touches the centring bush. The surfaces of the centring bush and pin are larger than that of spool (3). The spool remains in the centre position.

If solenoid "b" is operated, then the pilot spool moves to the right. Control chamber (7) remains connected with the control pressure, while control chamber (6) is unloaded to tank. The surface of spool (3) is under pressure, causing the main control spool to move to the left, until centring pin (9) touches the cover. Centring bush (8) is also moved.

The desired spool position in the main valve is reached. When solenoid "b" is de-energised, the pilot spool returns to the centre position and control chamber (6) is connected with the control pressure once again.

The surfaces of centring bush (8) and pin (9) under pressure are larger than that of spool (3). The main spool moves to the right until the centring bush touches the housing. The surface of spool (3) acting on the right side is now greater than the surface of centring pin (9) acting on the left side, and the spool remains in the centre position.

A case drain port (violet) is necessary to unload pressure in the chamber between the main spool and the centring bush.

Directional Valves

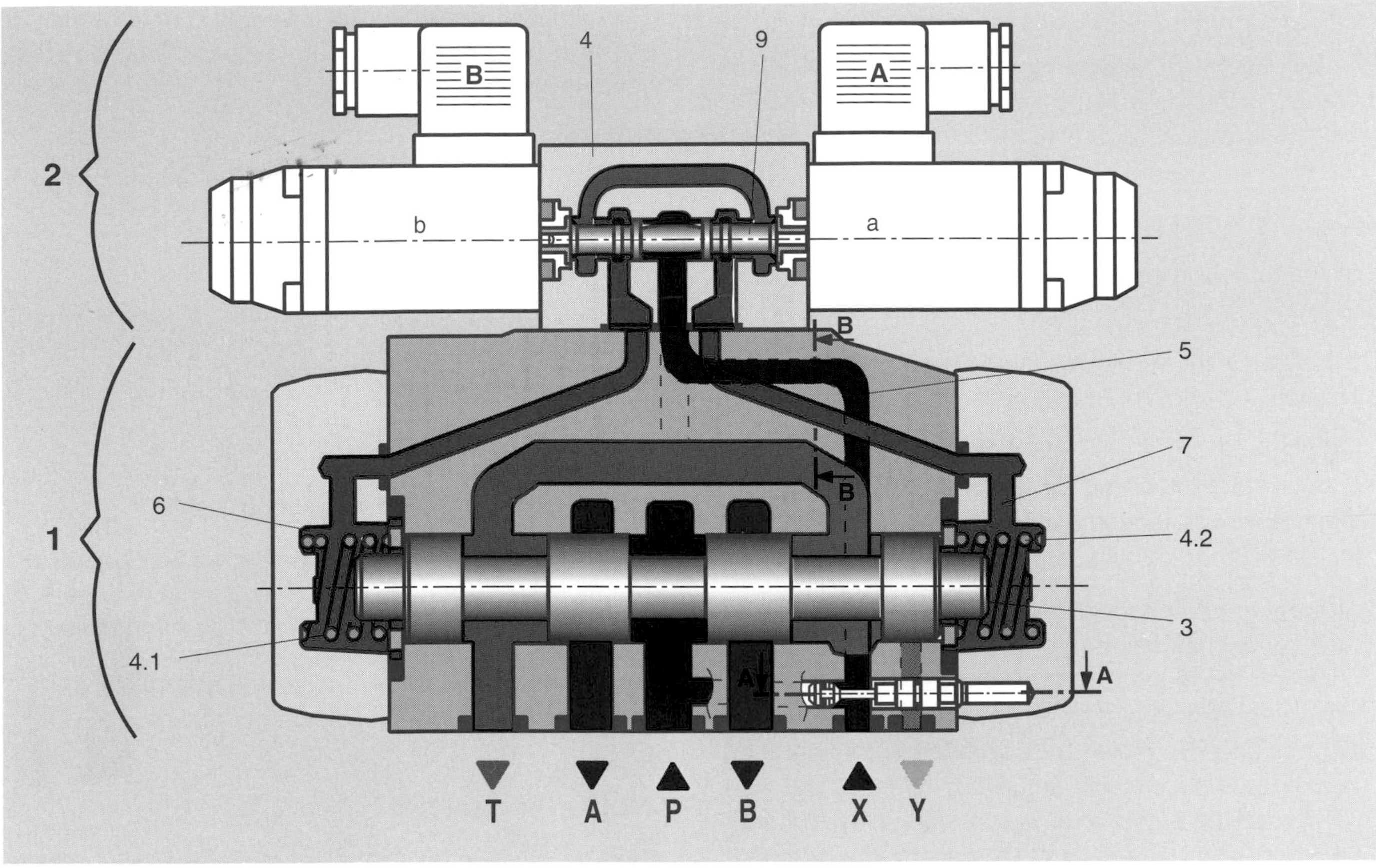

Fig. 15: *Electro-hydraulically operated directional spool valve, spring centred, for sandwich plate*

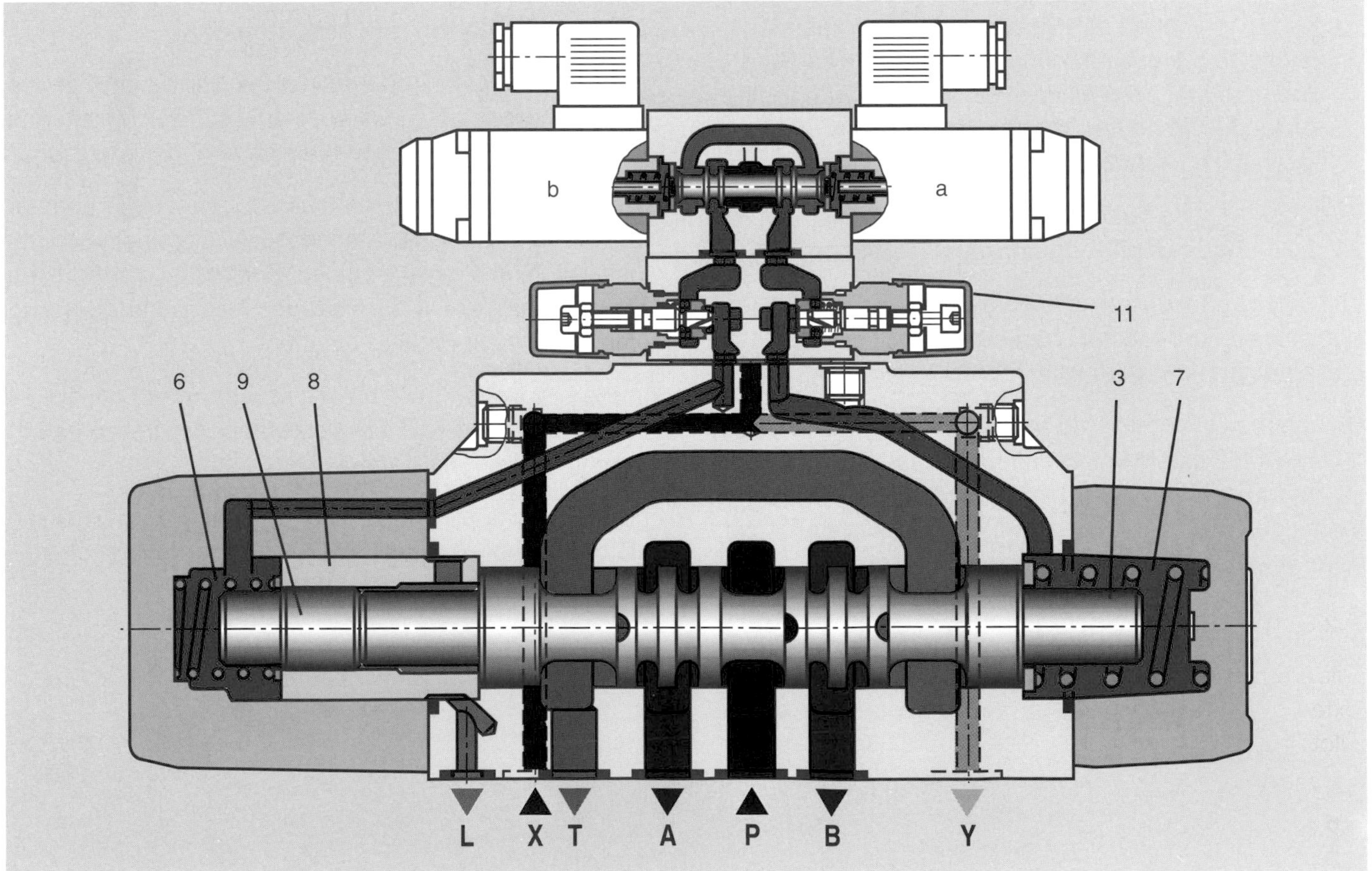

Fig. 16: *Electro-hydraulically operated directional spool valve, pressure centered, for sandwich plate*

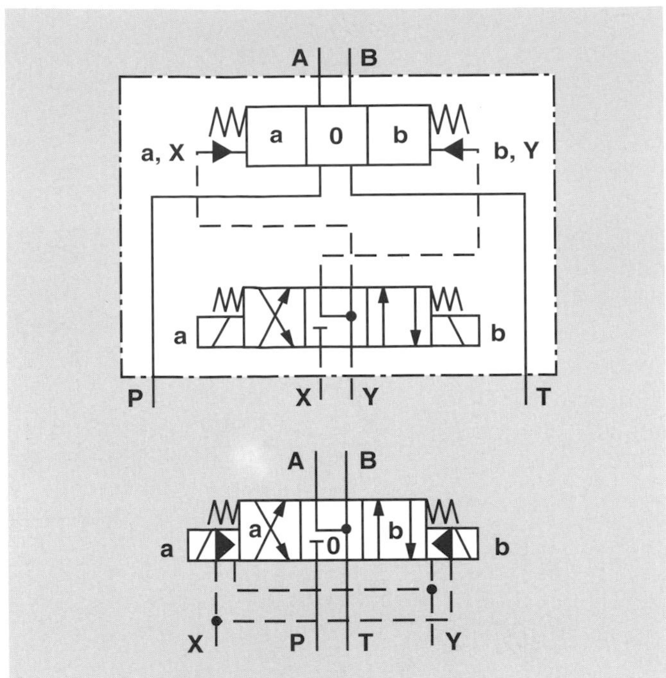

Fig. 17: *Symbol for electro-hydraulically operated directional valve - spring centred; top detailed, bottom simplified*

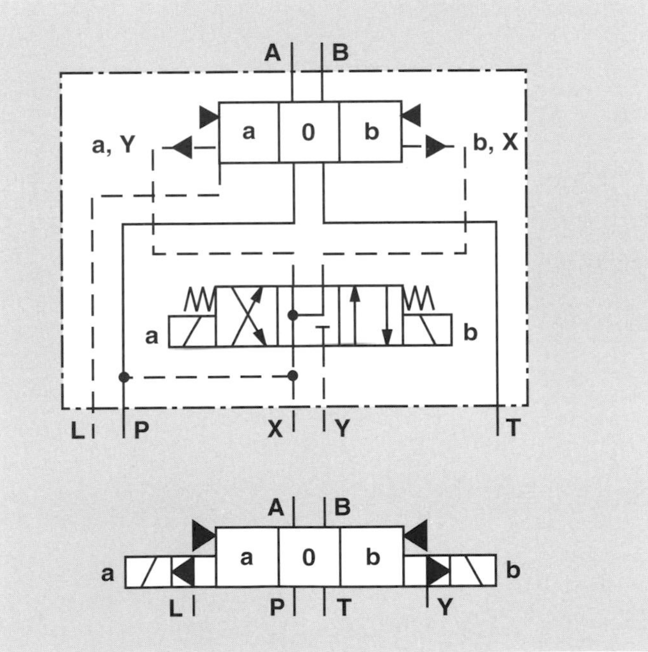

Fig. 18: *Symbol for electro-hydraulically operated directional valve - pressure centred; top detailed, bottom simplified*

Directional Valves

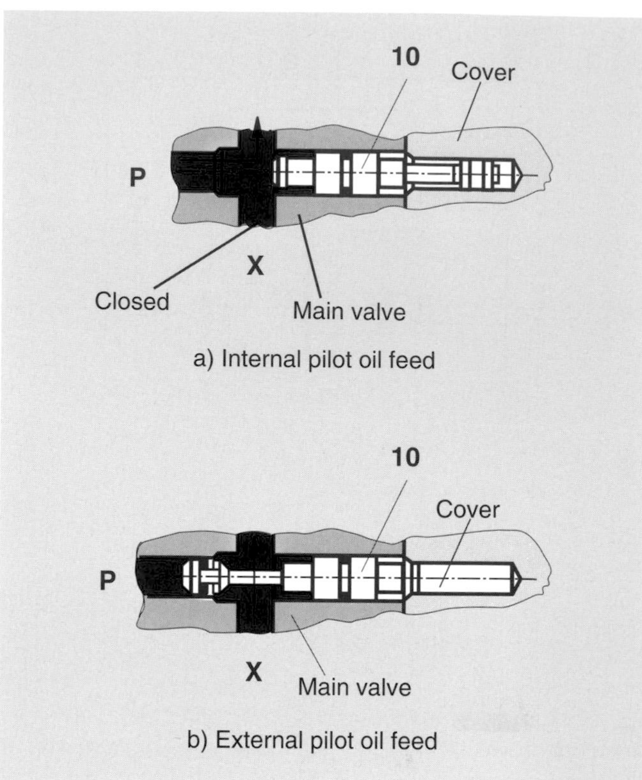

Fig. 19: *Possible pilot oil feed (Section A-A from fig. 15)*

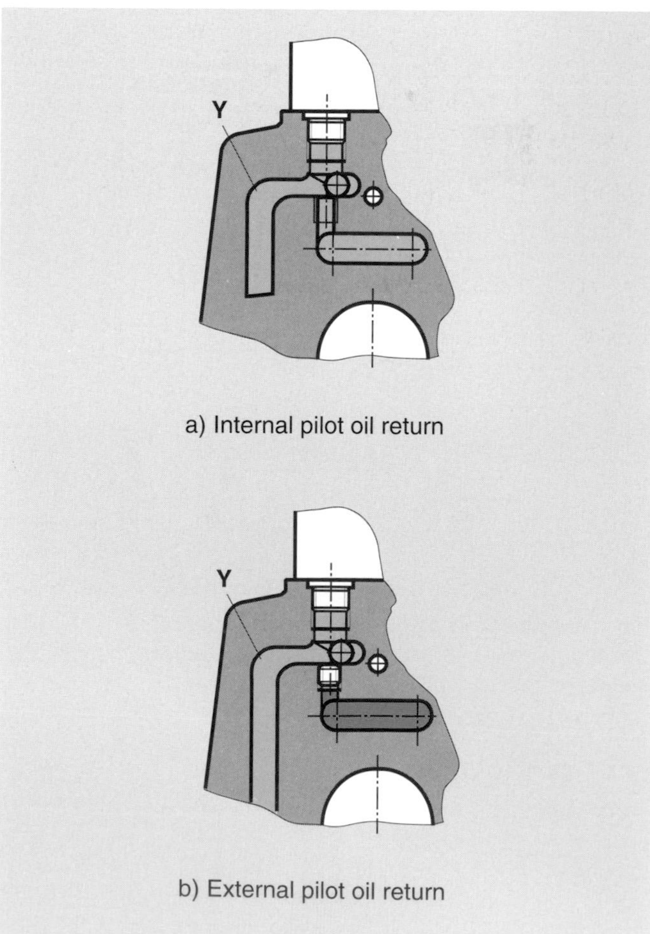

Fig. 20: *Possible pilot oil return (Section B-B from fig. 15)*

2.2.3 Pilot oil supply

Pilot oil supply and/or return may be carried out either externally or internally. In the pressure centred model, the pilot oil return must be carried out externally.

2.2.3.1 Internal pilot oil supply (*Fig. 19a*)

The control fluid in the main valve is taken from channel P and fed to the pilot valve via the control line (red).

Control port X must be closed and the pin (10) mounted as shown. Alternatively it may be in the form of threaded plugs.

No separate pilot circuit is required for internal pilot supply. However, a couple of points must be taken into consideration for practical applications:

- If the main control spool has negative overlap (all ports are connected together) or bypass flow in the centre position, the required pilot pressure does not build up or else breaks down during an operation.
  A preload valve must hence be fitted in channel P in order to produce the minimum control pressure.
  The cracking pressure of the preload valve (approx. 4.5 bar) and the pressure difference of the pilot and main valves may be used as the control pressure.
- Care must also be taken that the operating pressure does not exceed the maximum control pressure, otherwise a pressure reducing valve must be fitted. It brings about a reduction of the pilot pressure; for the valves described this is in the ration 1 : 0.66.
  The same applies for the required minimum pressure.

2.2.3.2 External pilot oil supply (*fig. 19b*)

The pilot oil is taken from a separate control circuit, which in any case can be better adapted to the requirements of pressure and flow, than with internal supply.

On the valve shown (*fig. 15*), it is easy to change "internal" to "external" or vice versa, by changing the mounting position of pin (10) or threaded plug. To modify the model shown, it is necessary only to dismantle the cover and turn pin (10).

The correct mounting position for external pilot supply is shown in *fig. 19*. The pin separates the connection of the control line from channel P.

2.2.3.3 Internal pilot oil drain (*fig. 20a*)

Oil flowing back from the pilot valve is fed direct into channel T of the main valve. Control port Y is closed.

It must also be borne in mind that pressure surges occurring in channel T when operating the main control spool affect the unloaded control chamber as well as the pilot valve.

2.2.3.4 External pilot oil drain (*fig. 20b*)

Oil flowing back from the pilot valve is not fed into channel T of the main valve, but instead fed separately back to tank via port Y.

Fig. 20 shows internal pilot drain and external pilot drain at the same time for comparison purposes.

2.2.4 Accessories

By using accessories, the valves described may be made to match the requirements of particular applications.

2.2.4.1 Operation time adjustment

Fig. 16 shows the operation time adjustment device (damping block). It is designed as a sandwich plate and may be mounted between the pilot and main valves.

This device is a double throttle check valve (see chapter on flow control valves, section 2.1.4). Depending on the installation position, the fluid flowing either to or from the control chambers is throttled and hence the operating time of the main spool is affected.

In the installation position shown, the return control oil flow is throttled. The check valve is open to the control oil supply.

For simple applications, the operating time may be altered by means of orifices in the control channel.

2.2.4.2 Stroke adjustment

By adjusting the stroke, it is possible to roughly throttle the main flow for the current direction of flow.

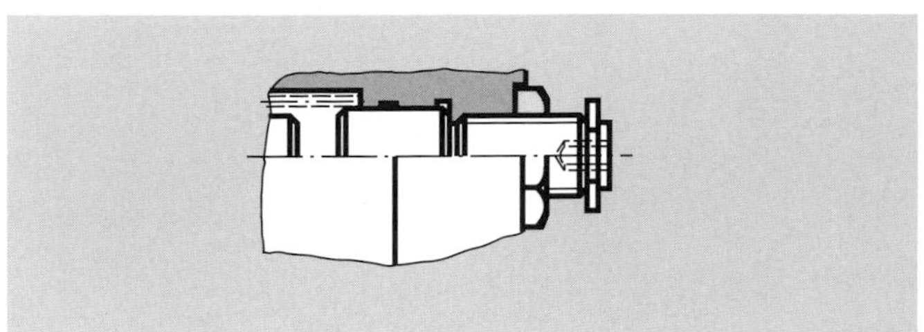

Fig. 21: *Stroke adjustment*

2.2.4.3 End position control

In safety circuits it is essential that the exact spool position of the spool is known. In this case, limit switches are used to monitor the end positions of the main spool. The switches may be operated either mechanically (contact) or inductively (proximity) (*Fig. 22*).

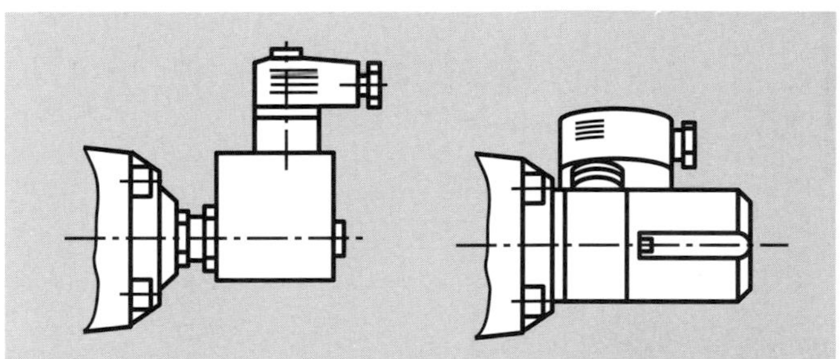

Fig. 22: *Electronic end position control; left: inductive (no movement), right: mechanical (contact)*

In simple terms, in end position control, the position of the main spool may be monitored by means of visual windows. Visual control is carried out via the visual window in the casing.

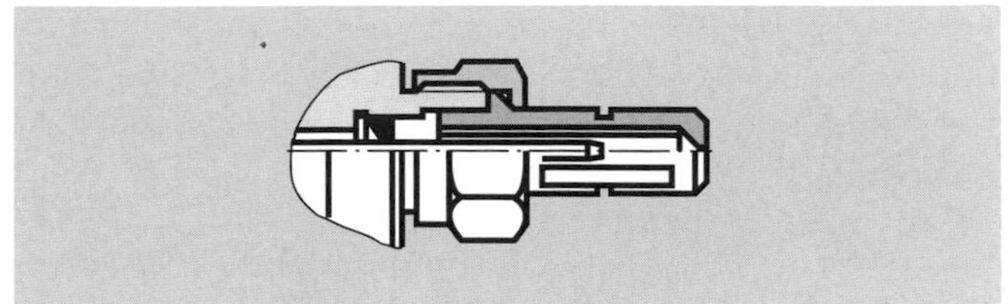

Fig. 24: *End position control via visual window*

2.3 Leak free directional spool valves

The main feature of this special type of valve is that additional sealing elements are arranged between the spool and the spool bore. The additional frictional forces which result must be overcome by higher operating forces.

In principle, this model may be either direct operated (usually manually) or pilot operated (*fig. 23*). Either a standard directional spool valve or a leak free directional poppet valve (section 4) may be used as a pilot valve.

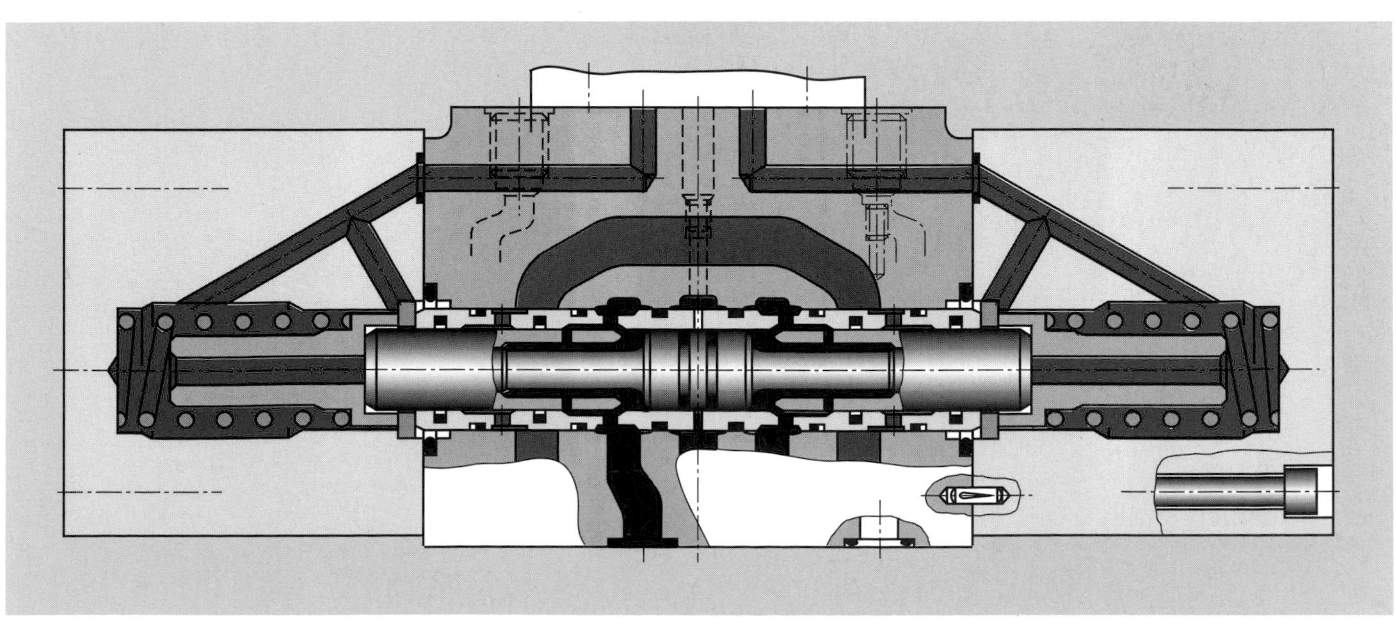

Fig. 23: *Leakage free directional spool valve*

3 Rotary directional spool valves

Rotary spools (*fig. 25*) were often used in the early days of oil hydraulics for operating pressures of up to 70 bar. Due to the development of applications using higher operating pressures, this type of valve is becoming less and less common. This is due to the large operating forces required due to the pressures not being completely balanced.

In addition, electro-magnetic operation of rotary spools is only possible with extensive complications in the mechanical design.

Apart from a few special models and special applications, the rotary directional spool valve is of little importance in oil hydraulics nowadays.

Fig. 25 shows a 3/2 way rotary spool valve. In this valve the various ports are connected together via longitudinal bores by means of rotating the control shaft. It is easy to understand that the control shaft will be pressed onto the housing wall on one side due to the varying pressures in the ports.

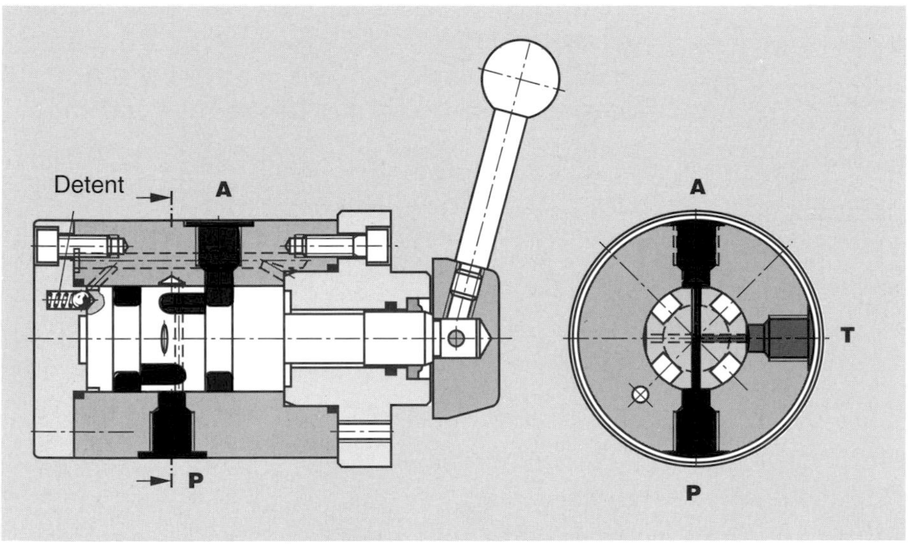

Fig. 25: *Rotary spool valve with detent*

4 Directional poppet valves

Directional poppet valves are directional valves in housing bore(s) of which one or more suitably formed seating elements (moveable) in the form of balls, poppets or plates are situated (*fig. 26*). With this design as the operating pressure increases, the valve becomes more tightly sealed.

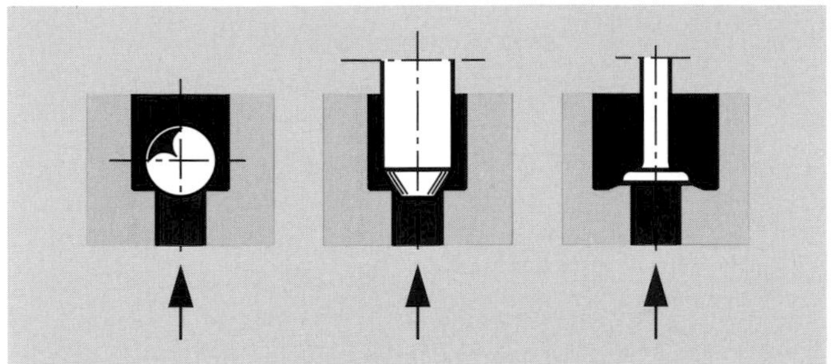

Fig. 26: *Principle of ball (left), poppet (centre) adn plate seat (right)*

The main features of directional poppet valves are:

- No leakage
- Long idle times possible, as their are no leakage oil flows and throttle clearances which could float
- Isolating function without additional isolating elements
- May be used with even the highest pressures, as no hydraulic sticking (pressure dependent deformation) and leakages occur in the valve
- Large pressure losses due to short strokes
- Pressure collapse during operational phase due to negative overlap (connection of pump, actuator and tank channels at the same time). In section 4.1, a way is described, whereby this connection may be bypassed.
- Loss of performance due to incomplete balancing of pressures on the valve axis.

Directional poppet valves may be either direct or pilot operated. Whether a valve is direct or pilot operated depends mainly on the size of the operating force required and on the size of the valve.

4.1 Direct operated directional poppet valves

These are valves with control elements directly operated by a mechanically acting device.

Due to the static and dynamic forces which occur in the directional poppet valve as a result of pressure and flow, direct operated directional poppet valves are usually only available up to a size 10. This limit corresponds to power of approx. 36 L/min at an operating pressure fo 630 bar and is primarily valid for solenoid operated directional poppet valves.

Of course, direct operated directional poppet valves of sizes larger than size 10 could be made available. However considering the required operating forces, e.g for the size of solenoid required, for reasons of operation reliability and due to the pressure shocks (which are difficult to control), it is not normally sensible to have direct operated valves of sizes above size 10.

The function of the most commonly used electrically operated model is described below.

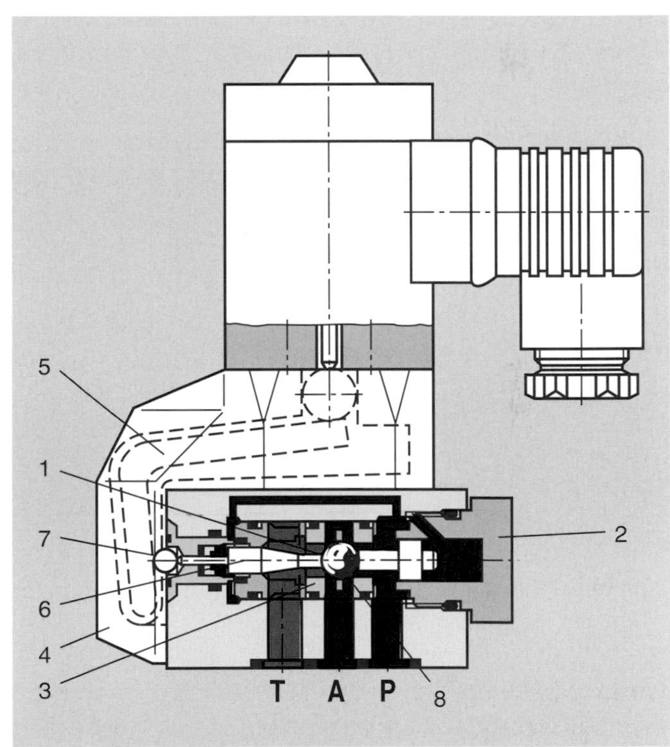

Fig. 27: *Electrically operated 3/2 way poppet valve as a single ball valve*

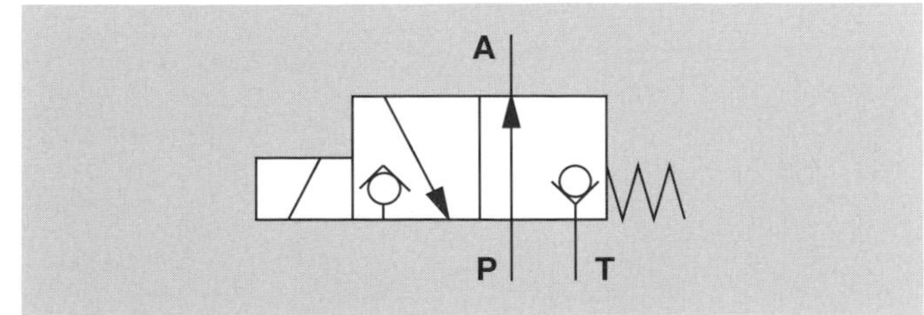

Fig. 28: *Single ball valve*

In the initial position, the seating element which is a ball (1) is pushed to the left onto seat (3) (*fig. 27*) by spring (2).

In the initial position, the connection from P to A is opened, port T is closed. The spool position of the valve is changed by solenoid force. The force affects the seat element (1) by means of a lever (5) supported by bearings, ball (7) and operating plunger (6) in the housing (4). The ball is pushed to the right against spring (2) and pushed on its seat (8). Port P is now closed and the connection from A to T opened. Operating plunger (6) is sealed in both directions. The chamber between the two seals is connected to channel P. Pressure balance is thus achieved on the valve axis, i.e. no pressure force acts on the seat area. This results in only low operating forces being required.

During the operation process, the ports are connected to each other for a short period (see negative overlap).

The variety of spool positions available for directional spool valves are not available for directional poppet valves. This is because of the special design of these valves.

If you wish to exchange the two spool positions shown on the ball valve, a two ball valve design must be used (*figs. 29 and 30*).

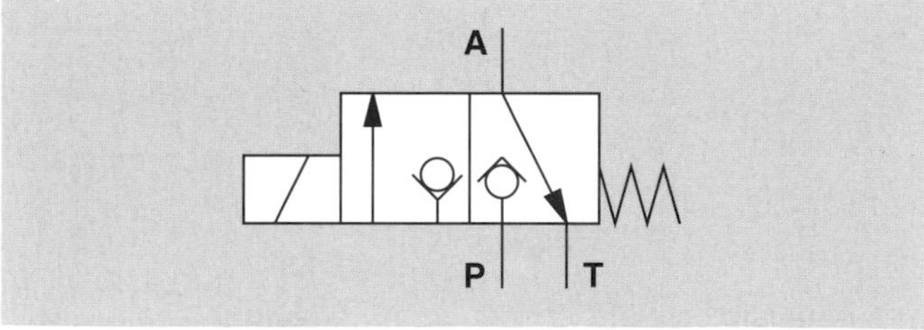

Fig. 29: *2 ball valve*

On a two ball valve, the connection A to T is open and port P closed initially. The spring pushes the ball in channel P onto its seat. In the spool position, the right ball is lifted from its seat, while the left ball is pushed onto its seat.

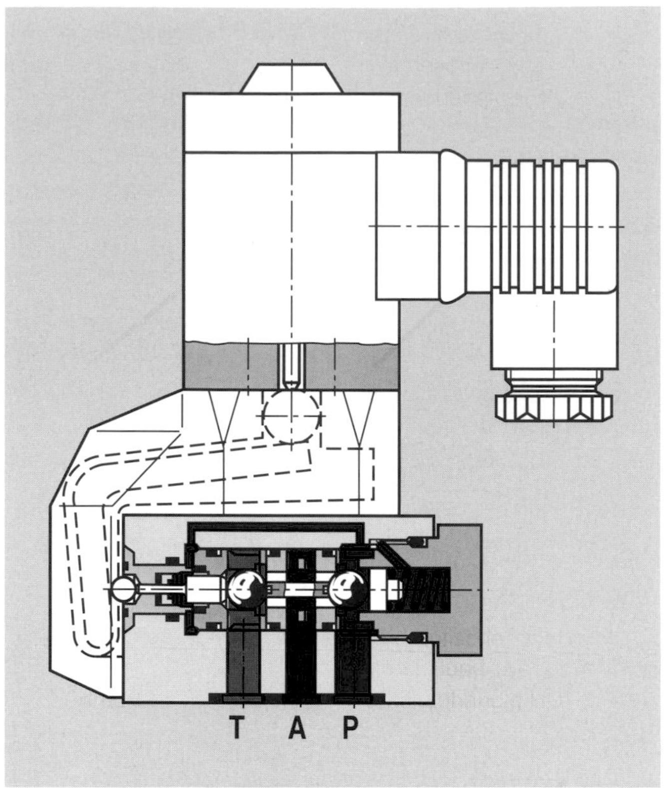

Fig. 30: *Electrically operated 3/2 way poppet valve as a 2 ball valve*

Using a sandwich plate under a 3/2 way directional poppet valve, the function of a 4/2 way valve can be obtained. The schematic diagram below shows the method of operation (*figs. 31 and 32*).

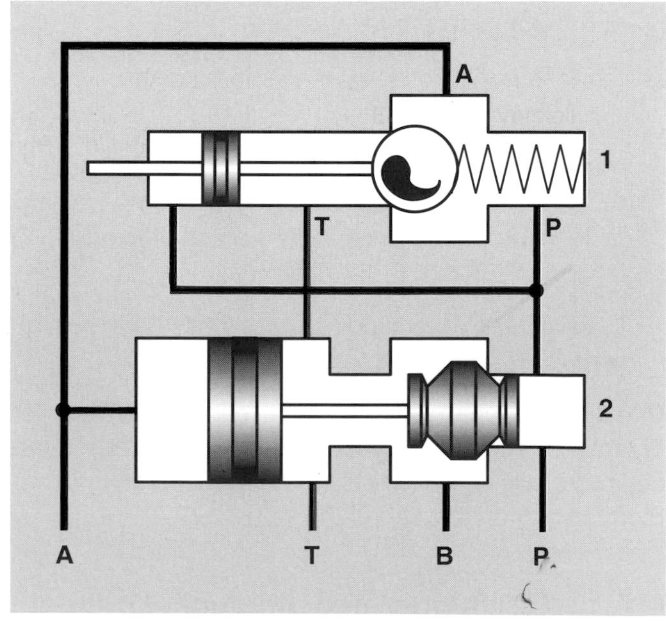

Fig. 31: *Principle of 4/2 way poppet valve in rest position*

The upper part (1) represents the 3/2 way directional poppet valve, the lower part (2) the sandwich plate. Initially the ball of (1) is on its seat. The connection from P to A is opened. A control line runs from A to the spool of valve (2). This surface is greater than that of the right seat element, which is therefore pushed to the right onto the seat. Port B in the sandwich plate is connected to T and port P is closed.

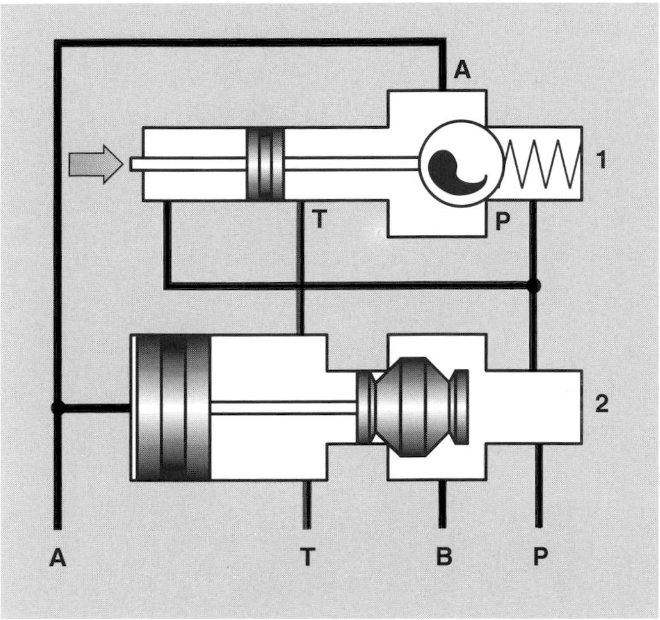

Fig. 32: *Principle of 4/2 way poppet valve in spool position*

When opening a 3/2 way directional poppet valve (1), port P is closed. The connection from A to T is hence opened. At the same time, the large spool in the sandwich plate is unloaded.

Pressure at P pushes the spool with seat element to the left and closes the connection from B to T. Port P is now connected to B and port A to T.

The operating element in the sandwich plate has "positive overlap".

In order to avoid pressure being intensified when single rod cylinders are used, the annulus area of the cylinder must be closed at A.

4.2 Pilot operated directional poppet valves

Direct operated (solenoid operated) directional poppet valves of a smaller size are used for the pilot operation of larger directional poppet valves.

4.2.1 Pilot operated 3/2 way directional poppet valves

A pilot operated 3/2 way directional poppet valve is shown in *fig. 33* the function of which is shown in *fig. 34*.

At rest, control spool (2) is pressurised with pump pressure by pilot valve (1). The pressurised surface of control spool (2) is larger that of the seating element (3). Hence the seating element is pressed onto its seat and port P is closed, whilst port A is connected to T.

If the pilot valve (1) is operated (solenoid energised), control chamber (4) is then connected to port T. The pump pressure lifts the seating element from its seat, port T is closed and port A is connected to P.

The main stage of the valve has a positive overlap (sleeve 5) and therefore during a cross-over, ports P, A and T are closed.

As control of the pilot valve is internal, a minimum pump pressure is required for the operations to be reliable.

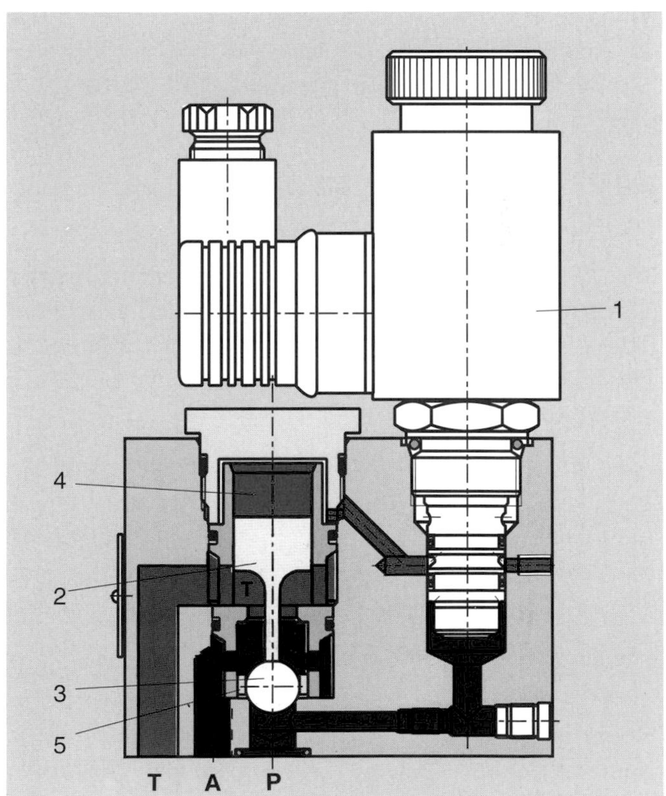

Fig. 33: *Electro-hydraulically operated 3/2 directional poppet valve*

The function of a 4/2 way directional poppet valve may also be obtained by means of a pilot operated 3/2 way directional poppet valve and sandwich plate (see *section 4.1*).

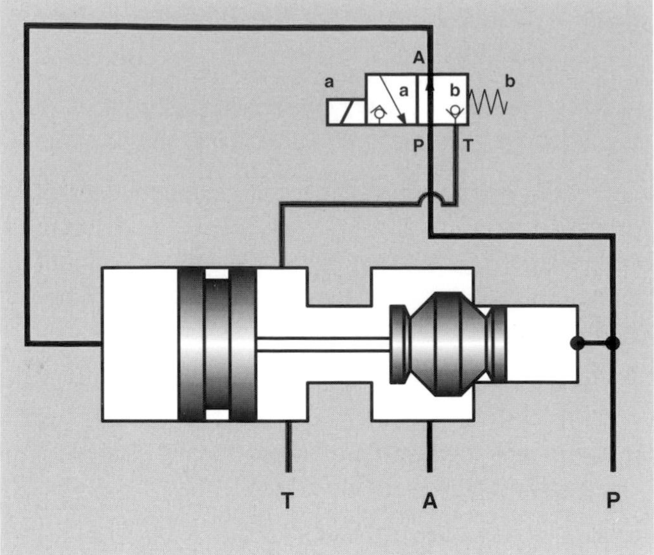

Fig. 34: *Principle of electro-hydraulically operated 3/2 way poppet valve*

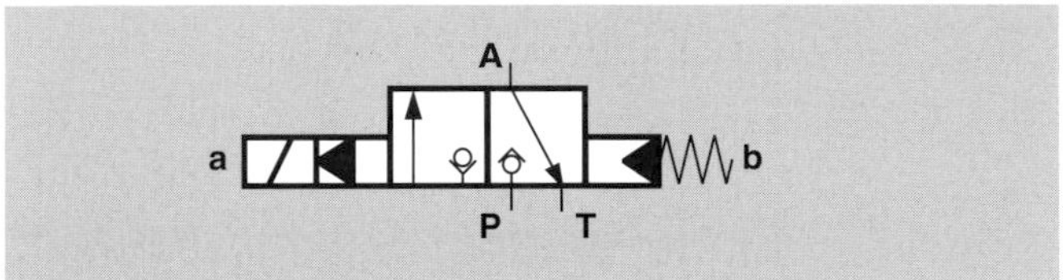

Fig. 35: *Electro-hydraulically operated 3/2 way poppet valve*

4.2.2 Pilot operated 4/3 way directional poppet valves

Fig. 37 shows a pilot operated 4/3 way directional poppet valve in its initial or zero position (see *fig. 36* for function). The 2-way cartridge elements (1,2,3 and 4) are held in closed positions by springs as a result of the balance in pressures.

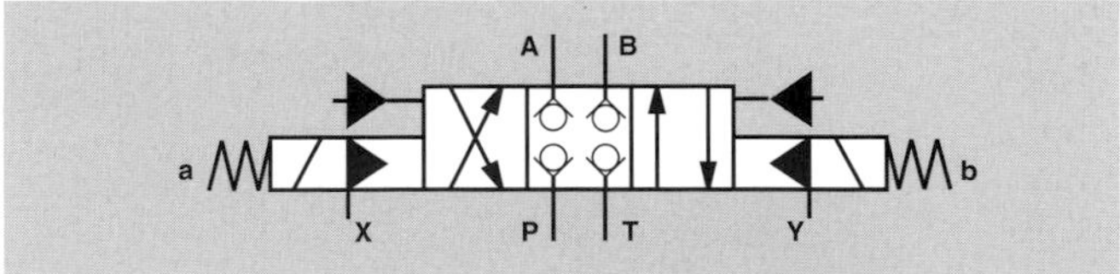

Fig. 36: *Electro-hydraulic 4/3 way poppet valve*

Spool position "b" (P to A and B to T) is achieved by operating control valve "I". The control chambers of cartridge valves (1) and (3) are unloaded and hence opened. The remaining cartridge valves stay closed. By de-energising control valve "I", the zero position is once again assumed.

The same applies for spool position "a" (P to B and A to T). However, now cartridge valves (2) and (4) and control valve "II" are considered.

Pilot valves I and II are supplied via control line (5) with fluid. This supply may be obtained either externally or internally from the pump circuit.

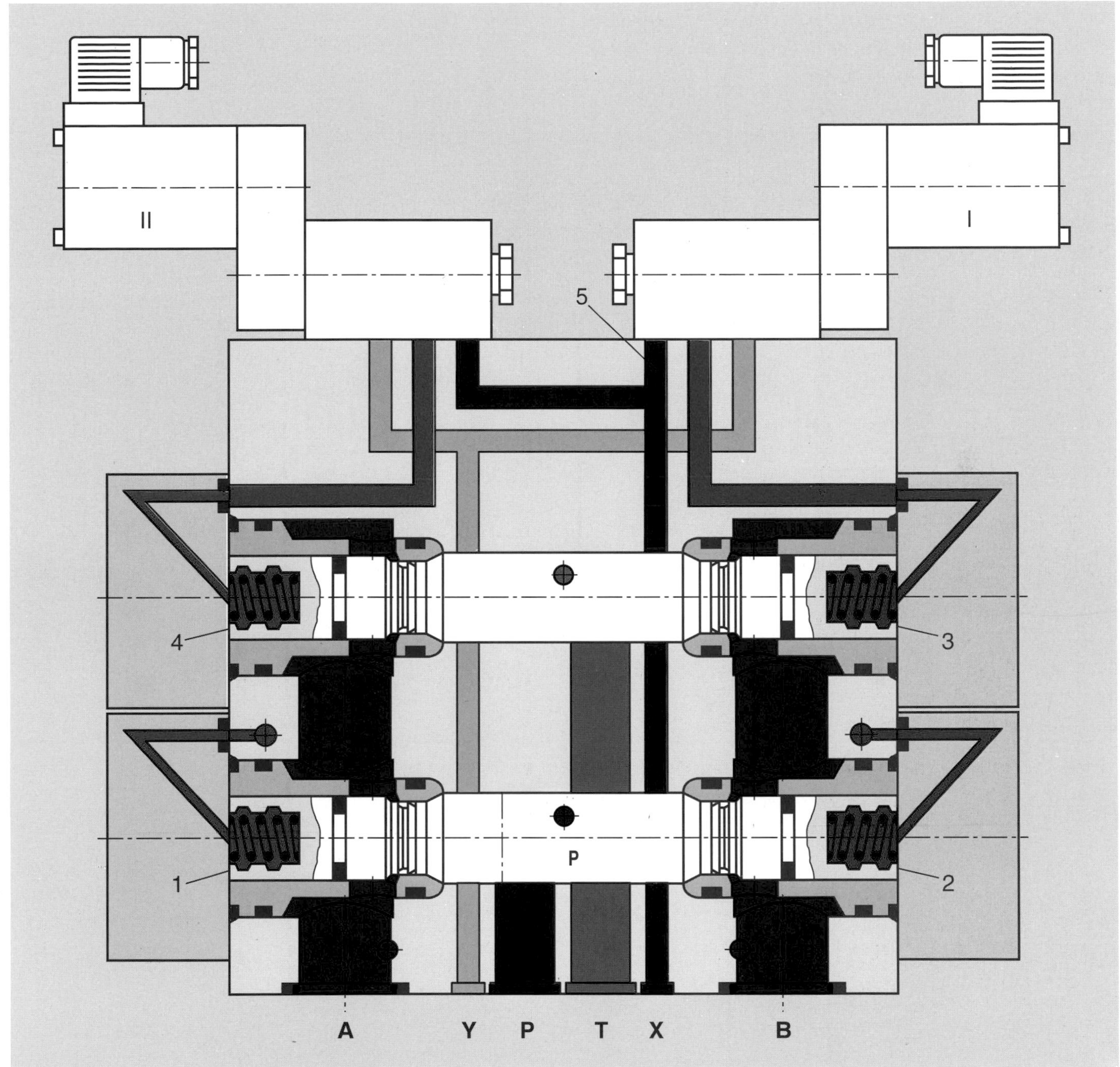

Fig. 37: *Electro-hydraulically operated 4/3 way poppet valve*

4.3 Symbols

There is no distinction made between the symbols for directional spool and directional poppet valves according to DIN ISO 1219. However, in practice it has been found useful to make a distinction between the two. As shown in *table 4*, the seat elements of directional poppet valves are represented by check valves.

2 spool positions, 2 working ports	2 spool positions, 3 working ports	2 spool positions, 4 working ports	3 spool positions, 3 working ports	3 spool positions, 4 working ports
U (B, A)	U (A, P, T)	D (A, B, P, T)	E (A, P, T)	E (A, B, P, T)
C (B, A)	C (A, P, T)	Y (A, B, P, T)	H (A, P, T)	J (A, B, P, T)
				M (A, B, P, T)
				H (A, B, P, T)

Table 4: *Symbols for directional poppet valves*

5. Comparison of directional spool valves with directional poppet valves

	Directional spool valves	Directional poppet valves
Function	In a housing with a central axial bore, radial channels fixed distances apart merge. These channels are fed to the outside as line ports. In the main axial bore, a spool with turned control grooves (annular grooves) is set at a pre-defined position with respect to the housing bore by means of the operating element (e.g. solenoid). This is so that the channels may be isolated from or connected to each other via the annular grooves.	In a housing there are one or more valve seats with balls or poppets as the closing elements. These elements are automatically pushed on the seats via springs and then lifted off the seats by means of pins. Flow always in the direction which would tend to close the valve, as only then is the flow controllable (closed or free flow). In the opposite direction a check valve effect would be present and flow independent of the operating position would always be present.
Design notes	Very simple design. Particularly advantageous especially for complex formations of flow. Clear function. Low surface forces due to complete balancing of pressures, long service life. With respect to the dimensions of the spool large flow openings exist, hence in comparison to size low resis-tances to flow exist. Direction of flow may usually be chosen and is not limited to the symbolic flow.	Easier and clearer design in 2/2 and 3/2 way directional poppet valves. Flow formation, e.g. in 4/3 way model is only possible if a complex design is carried out and a lot of effort put into it. Directions of flow are fixed. Pump and actuator must be connected to specific ports, or else the control behaviour will be changed.
Density	Due to the annular clearance present between the housing bore and spool, a leakage flow is continually present between the high pressure and the low pressure sides. Hermetically sealed closure only possible by means of additional devices (isolating valves) or special designs *(see section 2.3)*. Disadvantageous for clamping hydraulics.	The points of contact between the seat and closing piece are ground and lapped, so a hermetic seal is produced, which is required in the pre-installation for clamping hydraulics.
Sensitivity to contamination	Not very sensitive to large dirt particles due to the large openings to flow. Sensitive to microscopic flowing dirt, which is squeezed together with the leakage oil in the annular clearance and which may lead to sticking of the spool, especially at high pressures.	Not very sensitive to microscopic flowing dirt. However with larger dirt particles the danger does exist that such particles might become stuck between the closing piece and seat. Such contamination is caused when the pipes are installed without thoroughly cleaning and flushing the system. As fixed clearances do not exist, rigid sticking as in spool valves will not occur.
Permissible operating pressures	Depending on the design and housing material up to 350 bar. Use of smaller spool sizes for high pressures and small pump flows in jig and tool design are not very advantageous, as due to the leakage flow the fraction of the flow loss may be relatively high.	Depending on design up to 1000 bar.

Table 5

6 Design notes for the selection of a valve size

The parameters required by the project engineer to determine which directional valve to use are shown in catalogue sheets.

6.1 Dynamic performance limit

The operation performance limits shown in catalogue sheets are valid for 2 directions of flow, e.g. from P to A and at the same time from B to T.

By changing the direction of flow or by closing working ports, large drops in performance are obtained due to the flow forces acting in the valves.

In such applications the valve manufacturer must be consulted.

The direction of flow cannot be changed in directional poppet valves.

Performace limits are measured to the international standard ISO DIS 6403.

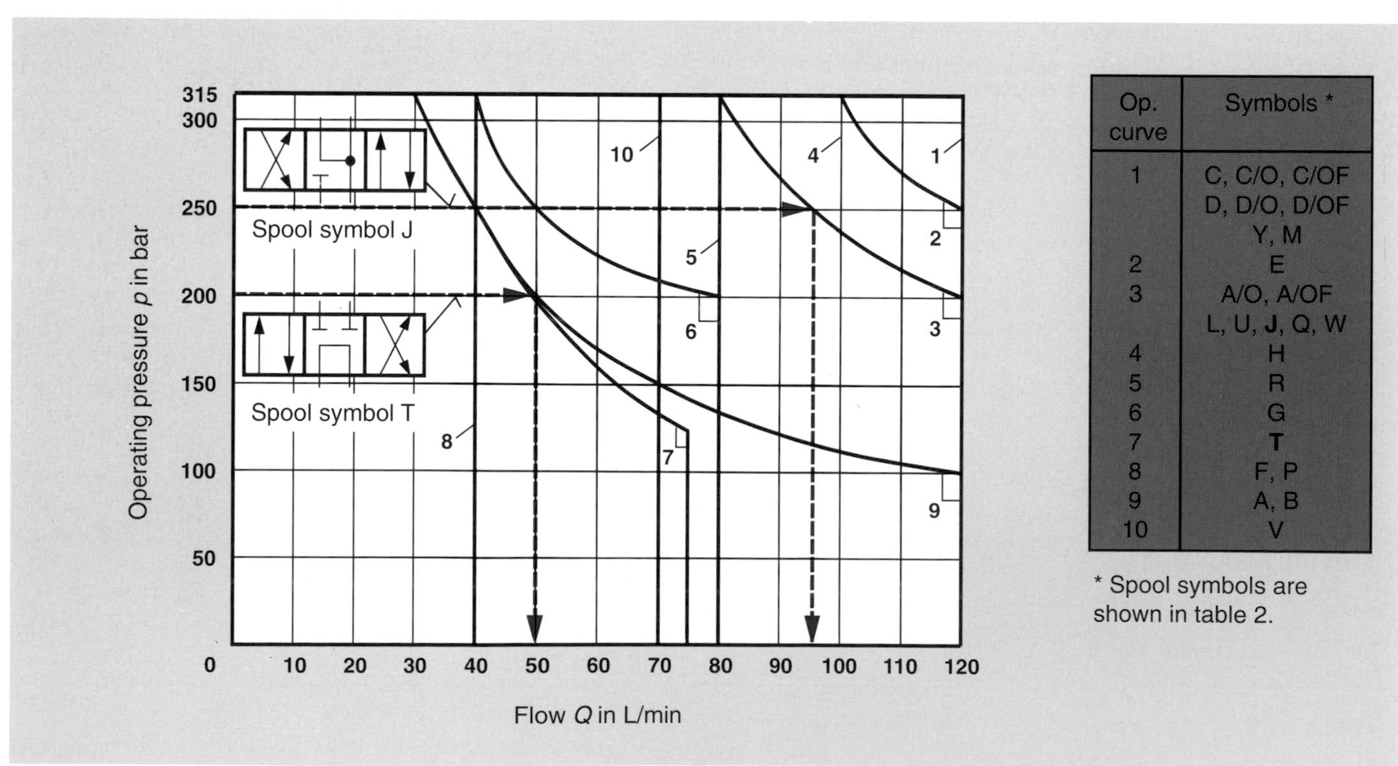

Op. curve	Symbols *
1	C, C/O, C/OF D, D/O, D/OF Y, M
2	E
3	A/O, A/OF L, U, **J**, Q, W
4	H
5	R
6	G
7	**T**
8	F, P
9	A, B
10	V

* Spool symbols are shown in table 2.

Diagram 6: *p-Q operating curves for directional spool valves, 3 chamber model, size 10, with DC solenoids*
Examples: *Spool symbol J: at an operating pressure of p = 250 bar, an controllable flow of up to 95 L/min is possible*
Spool symbol T: at an operating pressure of p = 200 bar, an controllable flow of up to 50 L/min is possible

6.2 Pressure difference in directional valves

The operating curves in catalogue sheets (see *diagram 7*) only consider the pressure differences in directional valves. The pressure drops in the sandwich plate and connecting lines must be added to the pressure difference for the valve.

The pressure difference Δp of a directional valve for spool type J is 3.8 bar from P to A and 4.6 bar from B to T at a flow of $Q = 95$ L/min. Pressure differences of the same magnitude occur in the directions of flow from P to B and A to T. In spool type T, the pressure difference is 1 bar from P to A and P to B, 1.5 bar from A to T and 1.8 bar from B to T at a flow of $Q = 50$ L/min

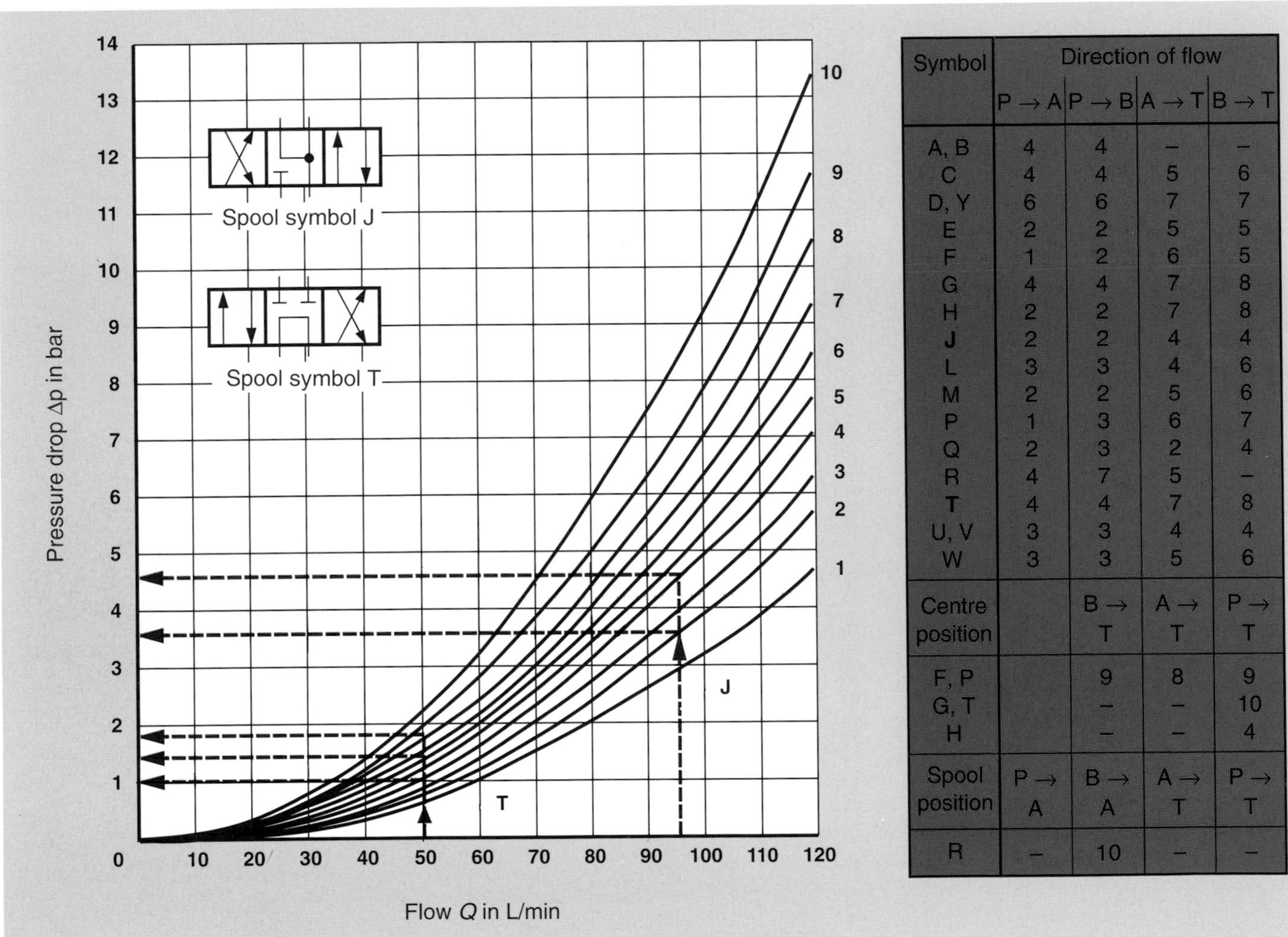

Symbol	Direction of flow			
	P → A	P → B	A → T	B → T
A, B	4	4	–	–
C	4	4	5	6
D, Y	6	6	7	7
E	2	2	5	5
F	1	2	6	5
G	4	4	7	8
H	2	2	7	8
J	2	2	4	4
L	3	3	4	6
M	2	2	5	6
P	1	3	6	7
Q	2	3	2	4
R	4	7	5	–
T	4	4	7	8
U, V	3	3	4	4
W	3	3	5	6
Centre position		B → T	A → T	P → T
F, P		9	8	9
G, T		–	–	10
H		–	–	4
Spool position	P → A	B → A	A → T	P → T
R	–	10	–	–

Diagram 7: *Δp-Q operating curve for directional spool valves, 3 chamber model, size 10*

Notes

Chapter 12

Pressure Control Valves

Dr Harald Geis, Johan Oppolzer

1 Introduction

Pressure control valves are valves which influence the system pressure in a system or part of a system in a particular way. This is achieved by changing the size of throttle openings, which may be done by the use of mechanical, hydraulic, pneumatic or electrically operated adjustment elements.

Depending on how the throttle opening is sealed, pressure control valves may be either spool or poppet valves.

With respect to function, these valves may be put into four groups:

- Pressure relief valves
- Pressure sequence valves
- Pressure shut-off valves and
- Pressure reducing valves

The valves may be either direct operated or pilot operated.

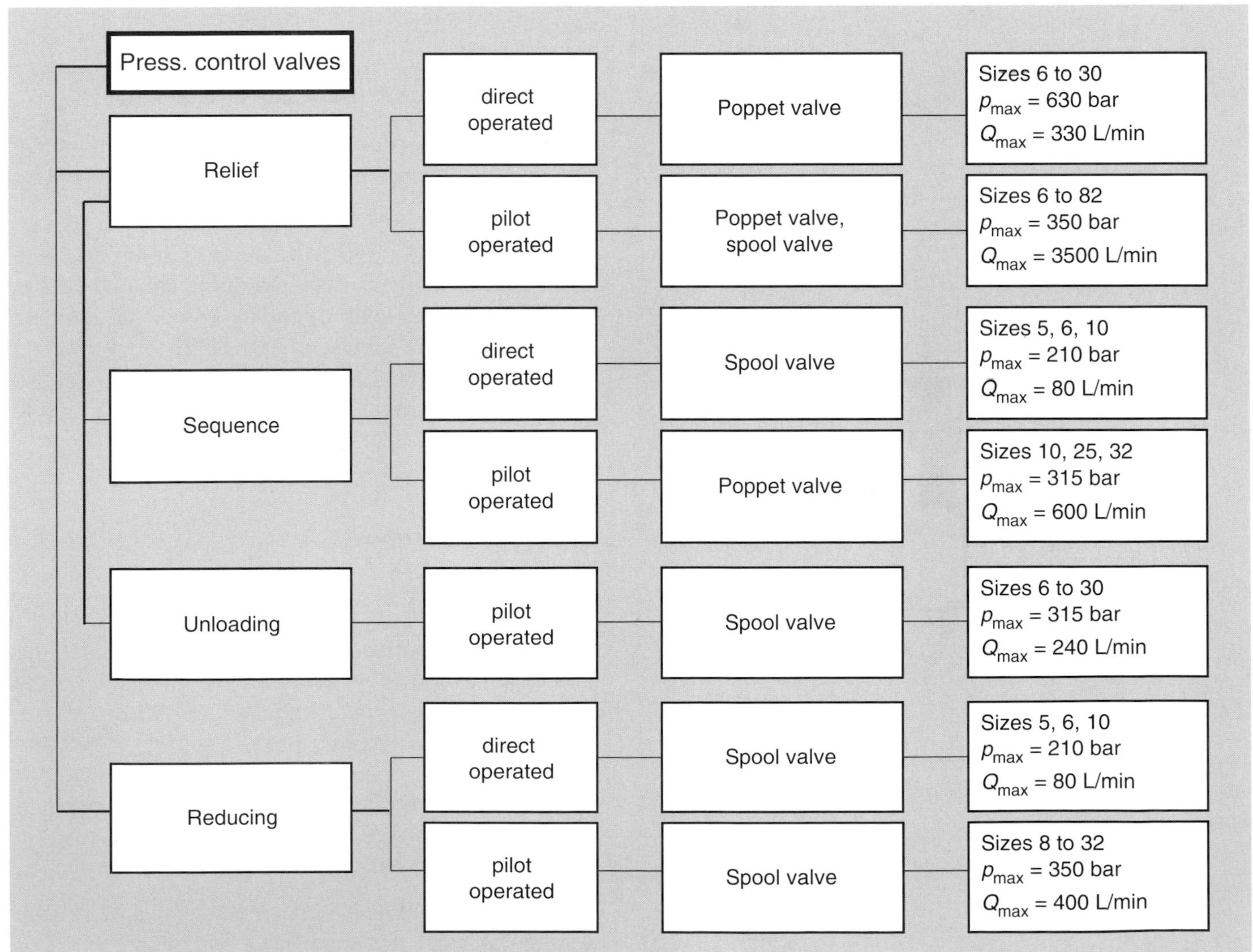

Fig. 1: *Functions, features and power datas of pressure control valves*

2 Pressure relief valves

2.1 Task

Pressure relief valves are used in hydraulic systems to limit the system pressure to a specific set level. If this set level is reached, the pressure relief valve is activated and feeds the excess flow (difference between pump and actuator flow) from the system back to the tank.

Fig. 2 shows a circuit with a pressure relief valve. This valve is always arranged as a bypass valve. Because of its task, the pressure relief valve is also known as a safety valve.

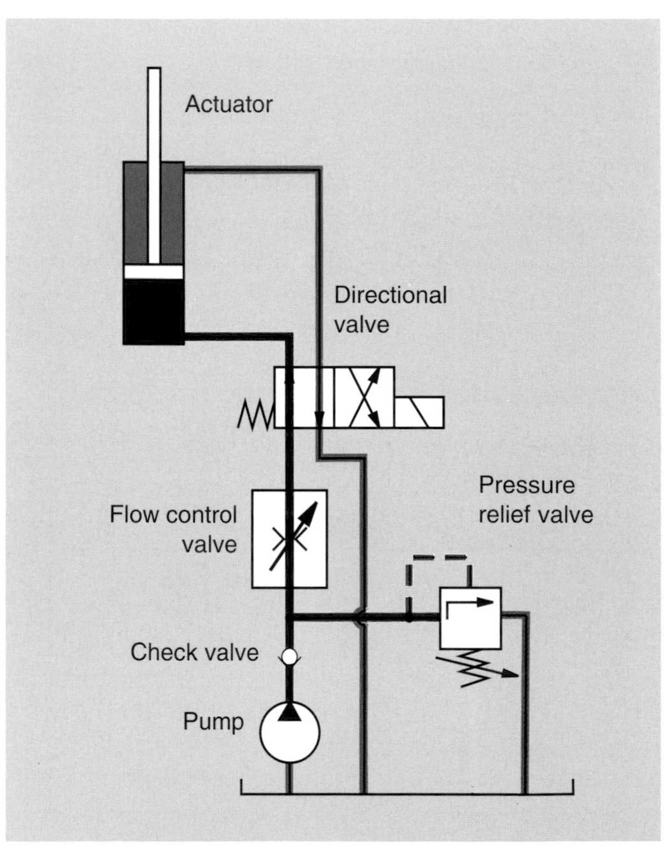

Fig. 2: Typical arrangement for a pressure relief valve

2.2 Function

The basic principle of all pressure relief valves, is that the inlet pressure is fed to a measuring surface, which is acted on by a force (*fig. 3*).

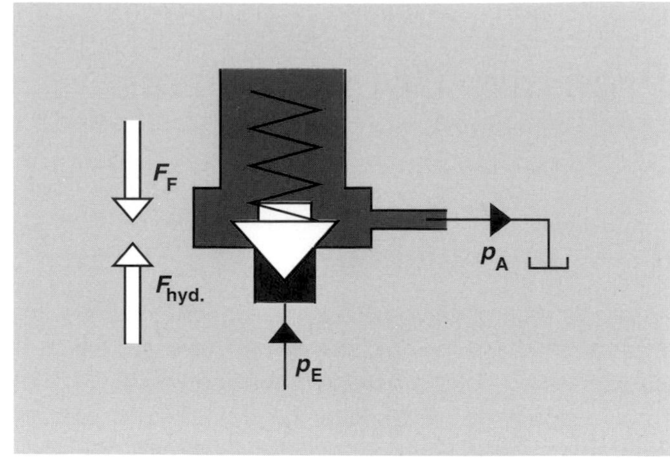

Fig. 3: *Principle of poppet valve used as a pressure relief valve*

The inlet pressure loads the poppet or lower side of the control spool with a hydraulic force.

$$F_{hyd} = p_E \bullet A = F_F + p_A \bullet A \quad (1)$$

p_E = inlet pressure

p_A = output pressure (also tank pressure when unloading)

A = seat surface or lower side of control spool

The force of the pre-tensioned spring F_F acts in the direction of closure. The spring chamber is unloaded to tank.

As long as the spring force is larger than the pressure force, the seating element stays on its seat. If the pressure force exceeds the spring force, the element pushes against the spring and opens the connection. The excess fluid returns to tank. As the fluid flows away via the pressure control valve, hydraulic energy is converted into heat.

$$W = \Delta p \bullet Q \bullet t \quad (2)$$

Δp = pressure difference
Q = flow
t = time

If, for example, no fluid is taken from the actuator, the complete flow must flow away via the valve. Hence the valve opens as much as is required for a balance to be produced between the pressure and spring forces at the seat element. The opening stroke continuously changes with the rate of flow, until the maximum opening stroke is reached (power limit). The set pressure corresponding to the spring force is not exceeded.

As far as the function is concerned, it does not matter whether the valve is a spool valve or a poppet valve.

In addition to providing leak-free sealing, the poppet valve shown in *fig. 3* has the advantage of a quick response time. This is because relatively large flows may be removed even with fairly small valve movements.

On the other hand, the spool valve (*fig. 4*) offers fine control small flows by means of grooves in the spool.

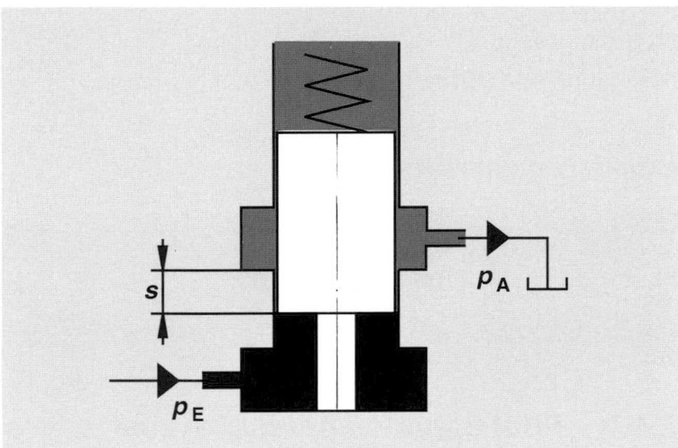

Fig. 4: *Principle of spool valve used as a pressure relief valve*

The control spool here is a measuring element (end area) and control element (control land). In the closed position, leakage oil flows continuously from the inlet of the valve via the clearance between spool and housing to the outlet (pressure free). With respect to response times, the poppet valve is far superior to the spool valve. In a spool valve, as the inlet pressure rapidly rises, the control spool must first traverse the overlap distance *s* (idle stroke) before oil is able to flow via the control lands. During the overlap phase, pressure increases at the inlet of the valve until it reaches the set opening pressure again. The overlap distance is a compromise between response time and leakage.

As may be seen from *fig. 1*, there are two types of pressure relief valves: direct and pilot operated valves.

2.3 Direct operated pressure relief valves, type DBD

Fig. 3 shows a direct operated pressure relief valve. The function considered so far was only with respect to the static forced in the valve.

From the dynamic point of view, we have a spring-mass system, which causes oscillations when it moves. These oscillations affect the pressure and must be eliminated by damping.

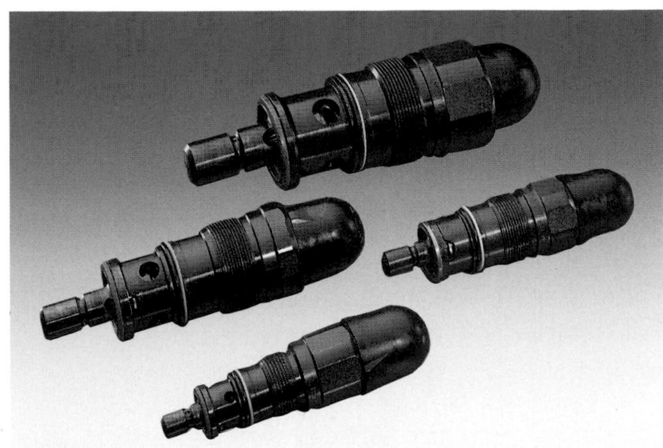

Fig. 5: *Direct operated pressure relief valve*

Possible ways in which damping can be achieved (*fig. 6*) are, for example:

- damping spool and orifice (1) to the spool chamber
- damping spool with one surface (2) or
- damping spool with correspondingly large tolerance play (3) (damping groove).

The spool is fixed rigidly to the closing element. When the spool moves, the fluid must be fed via the orifice or damping groove. A damping force occurs opposite to the direction of movement.

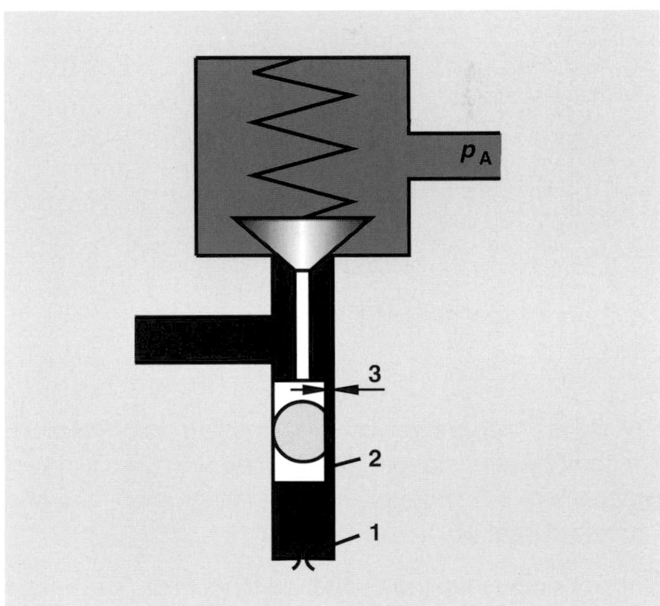

Fig. 6: *Cushioning possibilities for direct operated pressure relief valves*

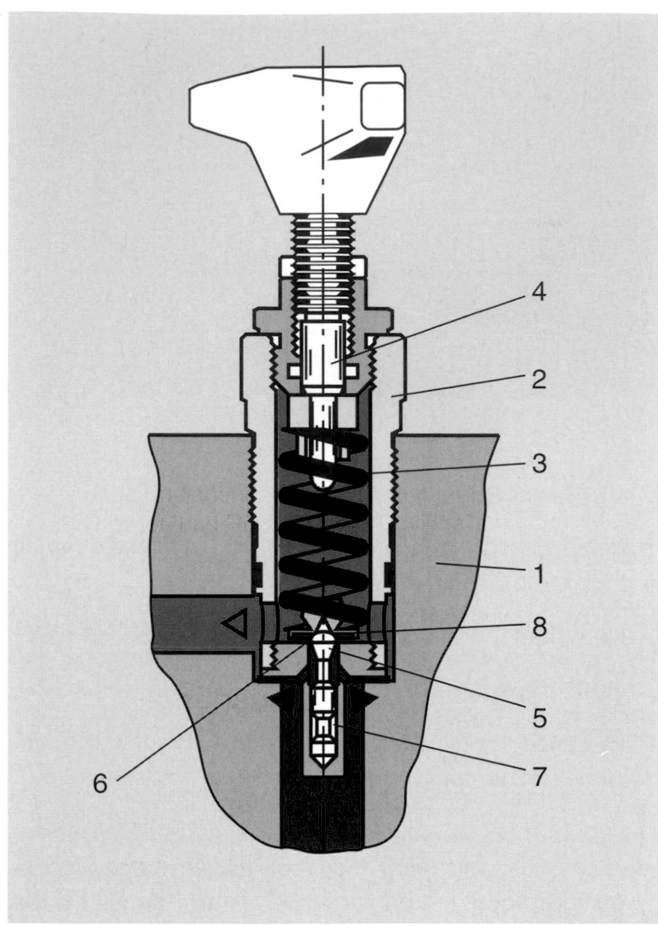

Fig. 7: *Screw-in pressure relief valve*

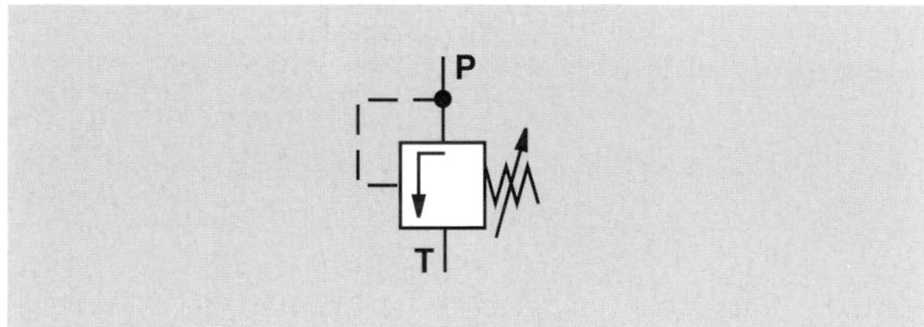

Fig. 8: *Direct operated pressure relief valve*

The valve which is screwed into a housing or control block (1) comprises sleeve (2), spring (3), adjustment mechanism (4), poppet with damping spool (5) and hardened seat (6).

The spring pushes the poppet on to its seat. The spring force can be steplessly adjusted by means of the rotary knob. The pressure is thus also set accordingly. Port P (red) is connected to the system. Pressure in the system acts on the poppet surface. If pressure lifts the poppet from its seat, the connection to port T (blue) is opened. The poppet stroke is limited by a pin in the damping bore (7).

As the spring force also increases with respect to the spring constant as the stroke increases, the underside of the spring retainer is a special shape. The flow forces of the oil flow are used in such a way that the increase in spring force is almost balance out.

In order to maintain a good pressure setting and a flat Δp-Q curve over the complete pressure range (lowest pressure increase possible with increasing flow), the total pressure range is sub-divided into stages. One pressure stage corresponds to a certain spring for a certain maximum set operating pressure.

Important parameters

Sizes	6 to 30
Flow	up to 330 L/min
Pressure stages	25, 50, 100, 200, 315, 400 and 630 bar

2.4 Pilot operated pressure relief valves

Direct operated valves are limited as the flow increases due to the space required for the control spring (see *section 2.5.2*). A larger flow requires a larger poppet or spool diameter. The area and hence the spring force increase proportionally to the diameter squared.

In order to keep the space required for these valves down to a sensible level, pilot operated valves are used for larger flows. They are used to limit the operating pressure(DB) or limit and unload the operating pressure by means of solenoid operation (DBW) (*fig. 9*).

Fig. 9: *Pilot operated pressure relief valves; right without and left with directional valve unloading*

2.4.1 Pressure relief valve, type DB

Pressure relief valve, type DB basically comprises a main valve (1) with main spool cartridge (3) and pilot valve (2) with pressure setting element. The pilot valve is a direct operated pressure relief valve.

The pressure present in channel A acts on main spool (3). At the same time, the pressure is fed to the spring-loaded side of the main spool (3) via control lines (6) and (7) containing orifices (4, 5 and 11) and also to the ball (8) in the pilot valve (2). If the pressure increases in channel A to a level above that set by spring (9), ball (8) opens against spring (9).

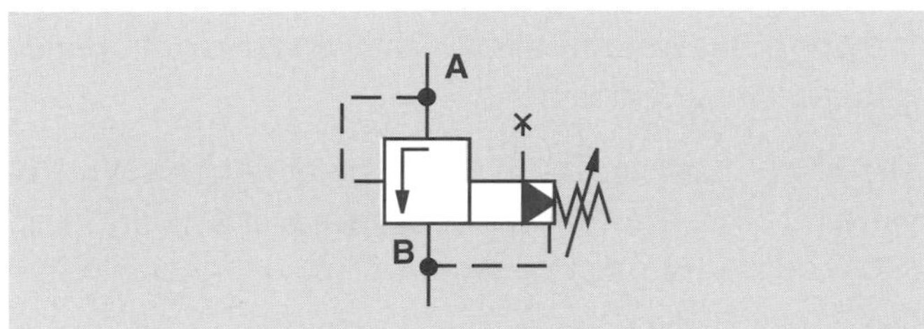

Fig. 10: *Pilot operated pressure relief valve*

The pilot oil flow on the spring-loaded side of the main spool (3) now flows via control line (7), orifice (11) and ball (8) into the spring chamber (12). From here, the flow is fed internally via control line (13) or externally via control line (14) without pressure to tank. Dependent on orifices (4) and (5) a pressure drop exists at main spool (3). Hence the connection from channel A to channel B is opened. Now fluid flows from channel A to channel B maintaining the set operating pressure .

The pressure relief valve may be unloaded via port "X" (15) or by connecting it to a lower pressure (two pressure stages).

The pilot oil may be returned separately (externally) to tank via port (14) (with closed bore (16)). By doing this the effects of backpressures from channel B on the set pressure are avoided.

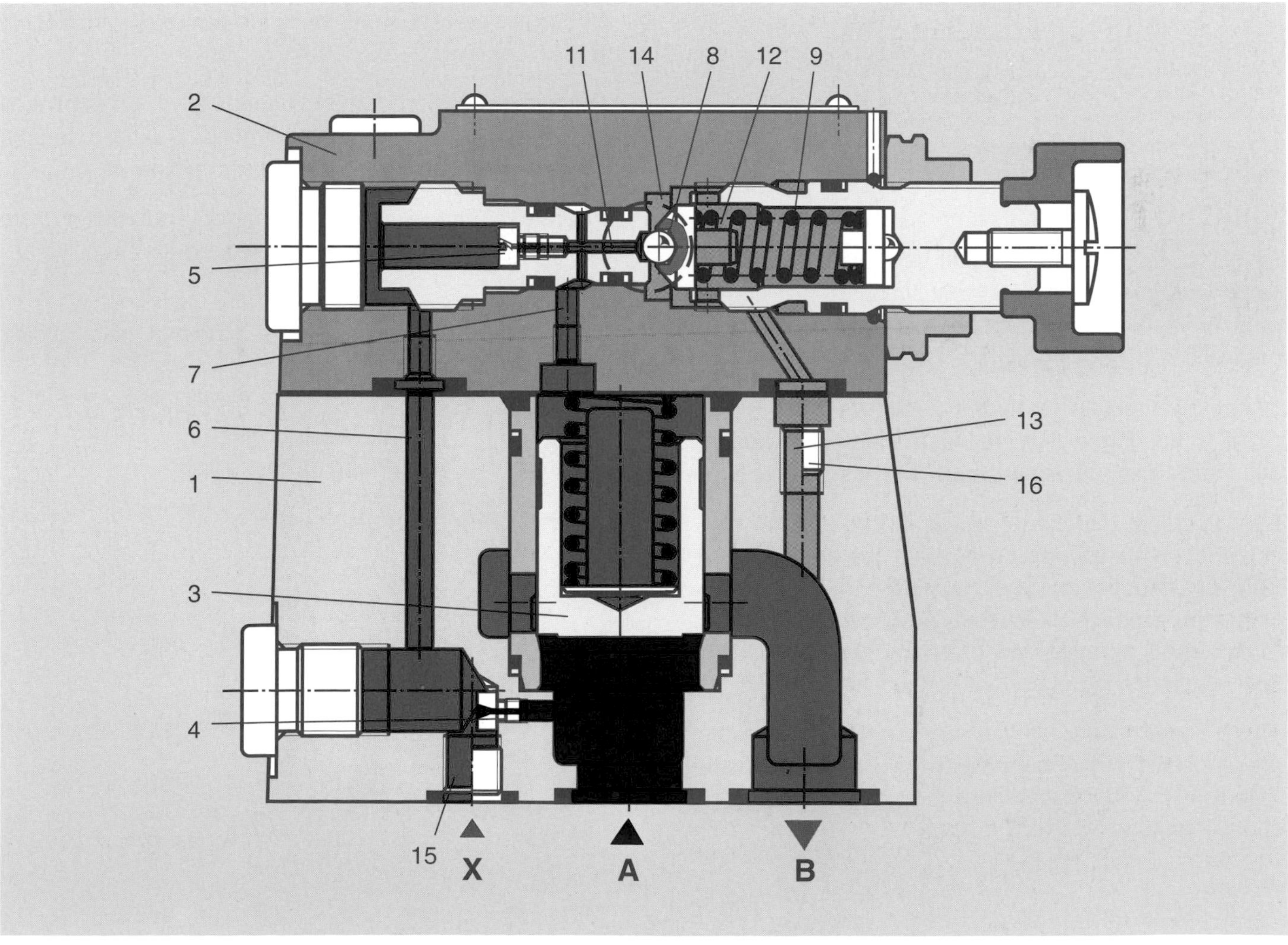

Fig. 11: *Pilot operated pressure relief valve, type DB*

2.4.2 Pressure relief valve, type DBW

The function of this valve corresponds in principle to that of valve, type DB (*fig. 11*). However, the main spool (5) is unloaded by means of integral 3/2 way directional valve (3) (*fig. 13*).

A typical application of this valve is when it is used to run a pump up to speed at no pressure.

Important parameters

Sizes	6 to 82
Operating pressure	up to 350 bar
Flow	up to 3500 L/min

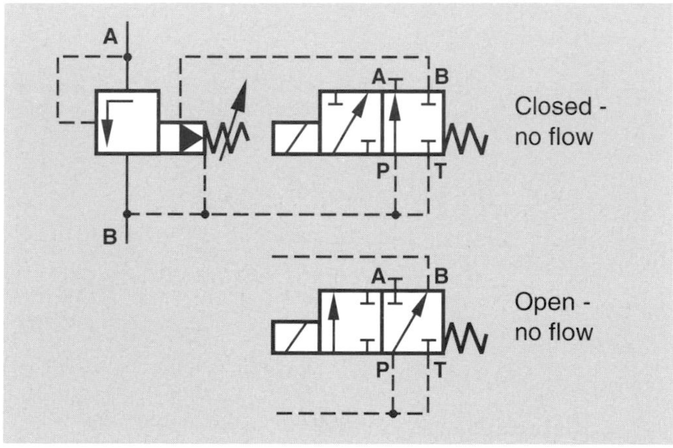

Fig. 12: *Pilot operated pressure relief valve with directional valve unloading*

By combining a pressure relief valve with a directional valve, it is possible to relatively simply switch from the pressure relief function to pressure free operation by means of a control signal (*fig. 13*).

When the directional valve is closed (no flow) (*fig. 12*) there is no connection between the spring side and channel B. The valve operates as a pressure relief valve.

By operating directional valve (3), the main spool chamber on the spring side (1) is connected to channel T (2) of the directional valve. Hence the main spool (5) is lifted from its seat (4). Fluid may now flow from channel A to channel B at a very low pressure (bypass operation; flow resistance is dependent on the system).

This process occurs within a very short time. The system pressure falls rapidly to the much lower bypass pressure. This results in high pressure peaks and considerable acoustic unloading shocks.

In order to solve this problem, various models are used with varying degrees of success, such as

- the use of a spool main spool instead of a poppet main spool
- active piloting
- attenuators or
- shock damping plates.

Shock damping plate

The operation time of a pressure relief valve may be influenced using an shock damping plate and hence the switching process may be carried out more softly. The function of this plate is basically that of a flow control valve with a downstream orifice.

The shock damping plate (6) is situated between pilot valve (7) of the pressure relief valve and directional valve (3). A orifice (8) must be inserted into channel B of the directional valve.

When the directional valve is closed (pressure relief function) (*fig. 14*) spool (9) is pushed against spring (10) by the pilot pressure and hence the connection from B2 to B1 is closed.

When the directional valve is open (*fig. 15*) (the pilot oil may flow via channel B of the directional valve to tank) a constant pressure drop is present at orifice (8).

After a delay, spring force (10) opens the connection from B2 to B1 and hence pressure peaks in the return line are avoided.

The following advantages are obtained when using shock damping plates:

- no dependence on viscosity
- no acoustic unloading shocks and
- much smaller pressure peaks.

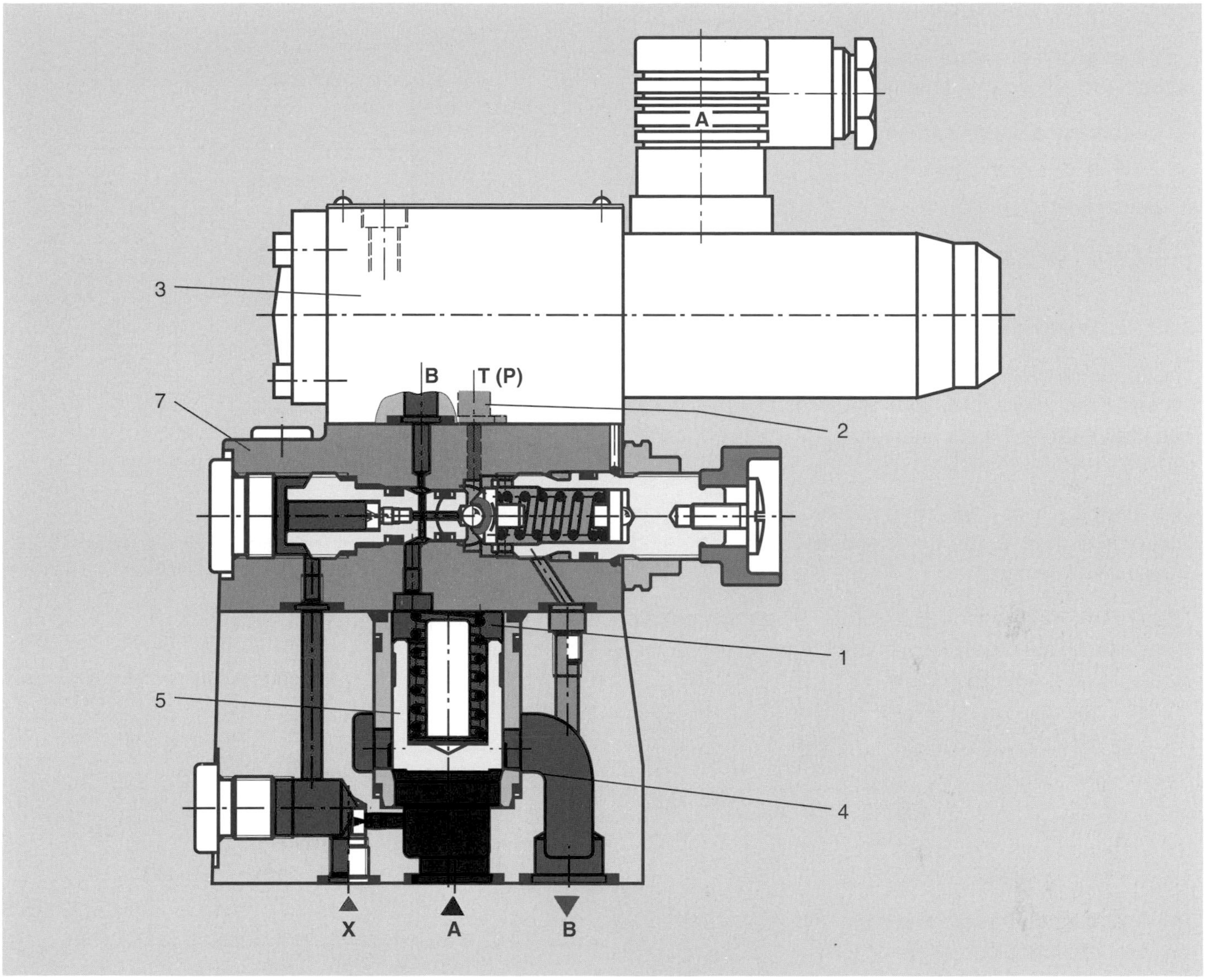

Fig. 13: *Pilot operated pressure relief valve with solenoid operated unloading, type DBW*

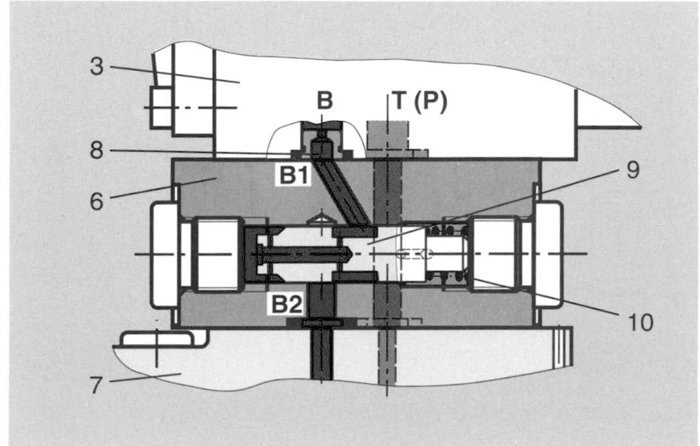

Fig. 14: *Shock damping plate, directional valve closed*

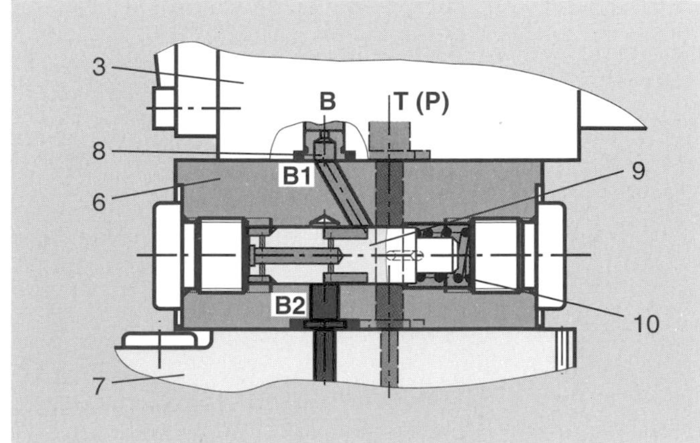

Fig. 15: *Shock damping plate, directional valve open*

2.5 Technical data

The quality of a pressure relief valve is determined with respect to the following criteria:

- dependence of pressure on flow (p-Q operating curve)
- power limit
- dynamic response

2.5.1 Dependence of pressure on flow

The dependence of pressure on flow may be used to view the entire range of applications of a pressure relief valve. The parameter is the set pressure p_E at start of opening ($Q > 0$).

The characteristic operating curves are shown in diagrams 1 and 2 for the direct and pilot operated pressure relief valves.

The control deviation of the valves R represents the change in the set pressure with an increase in flow or the gradient of the operating curve.

$$R = \frac{\Delta p_{Ei}}{\Delta Q} \qquad (3)$$

$$R = \frac{p_{EiQ} - p_{Ei\,(Q=0)}}{\Delta Q} \qquad (3)$$

The operating curve with $R = 0$ is the ideal operating curve.

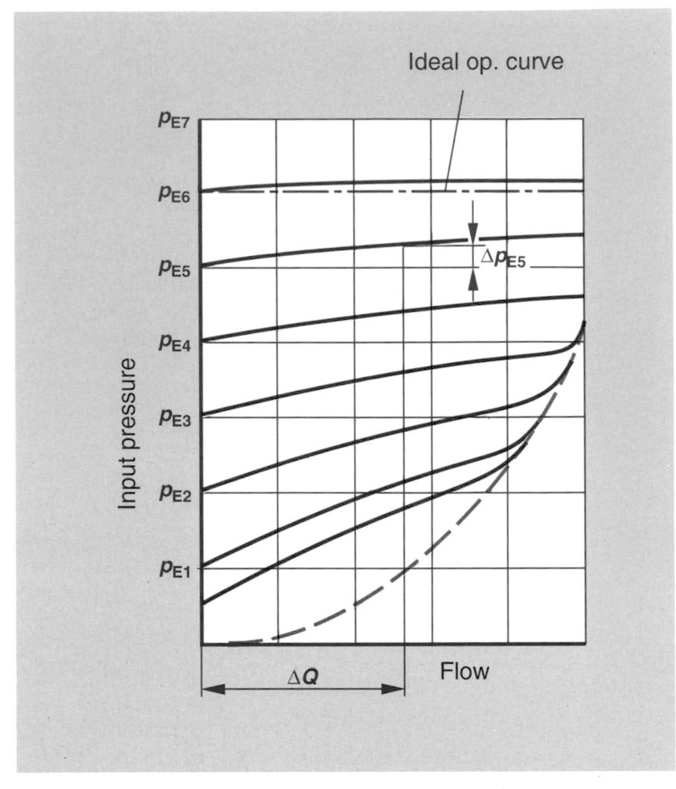

Diagram 1: *Characteristic operating curves of direct operated pressure relief valves*

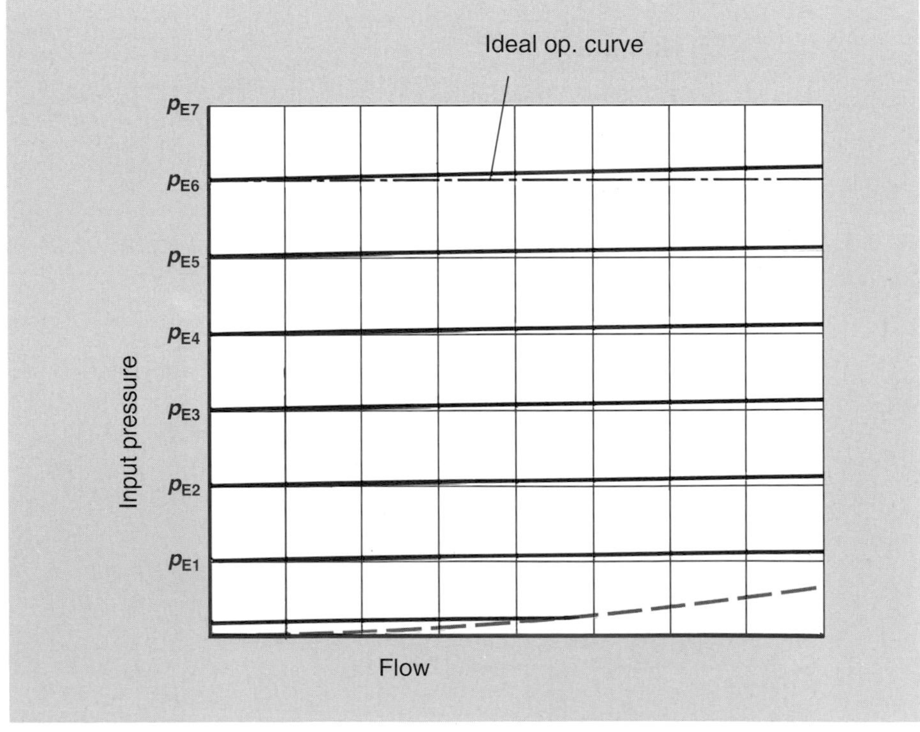

Diagram 2: *Characteristic operating curves of pilot operated pressure relief valves*

The following reasons cause the gradient to deviate from the ideal operating curve.

2.5.1.1 In direct operated pressure relief valves (*fig. 7*)

By increasing the flow, the stroke of the valve poppet increases. Hence the spring is increasingly compressed. The spring force is increased by a considerable amount (*diagram 1*). In addition the pressure loss and flow force increase.

It is possible to flatten the gradient of the operating curve in direct operated pressure relief valves by using a spring retainer shaped in a special way (*fig. 7* (8)). The flow forces from the outlet flow are used on the underside of the spring pad to compensate for the increase in the spring force and to compensate for the flow force acting on the valve poppet.

By matching the spring force to the current setting range (divided into pressure stages) a "practical pressure-flow relationship" is achieved (*diagrams 3 and 4*).

The operating curve with the lowest gradient is attained at the value corresponding to the pressure stage.

Legend to *diagrams 3 and 4*

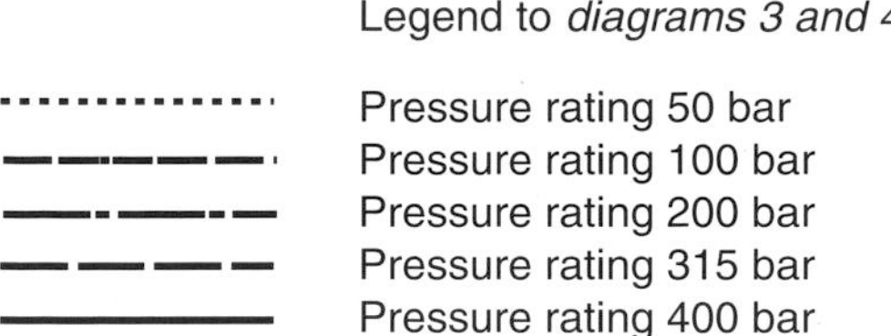

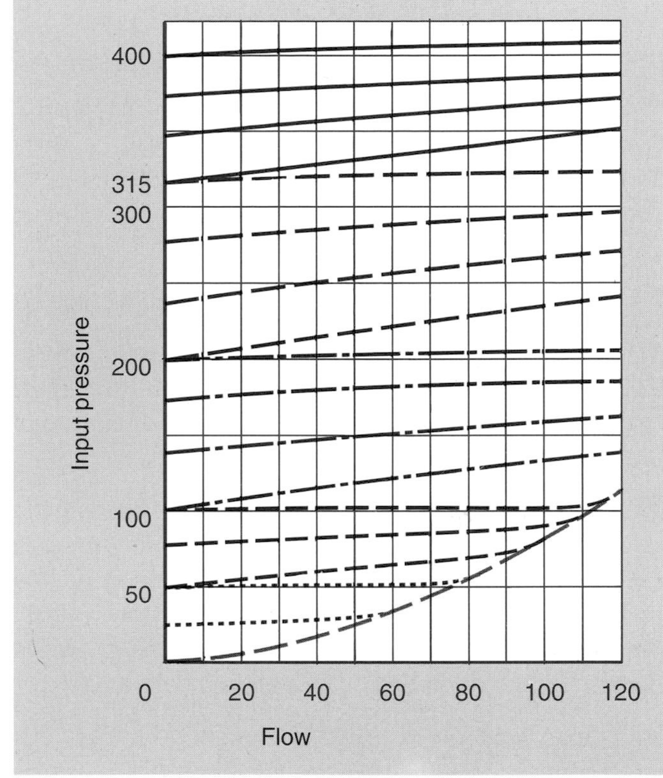

Diagram 4: *p_E-Q operating curves for direct operated pressure relief valves, sizes 8 and 10*

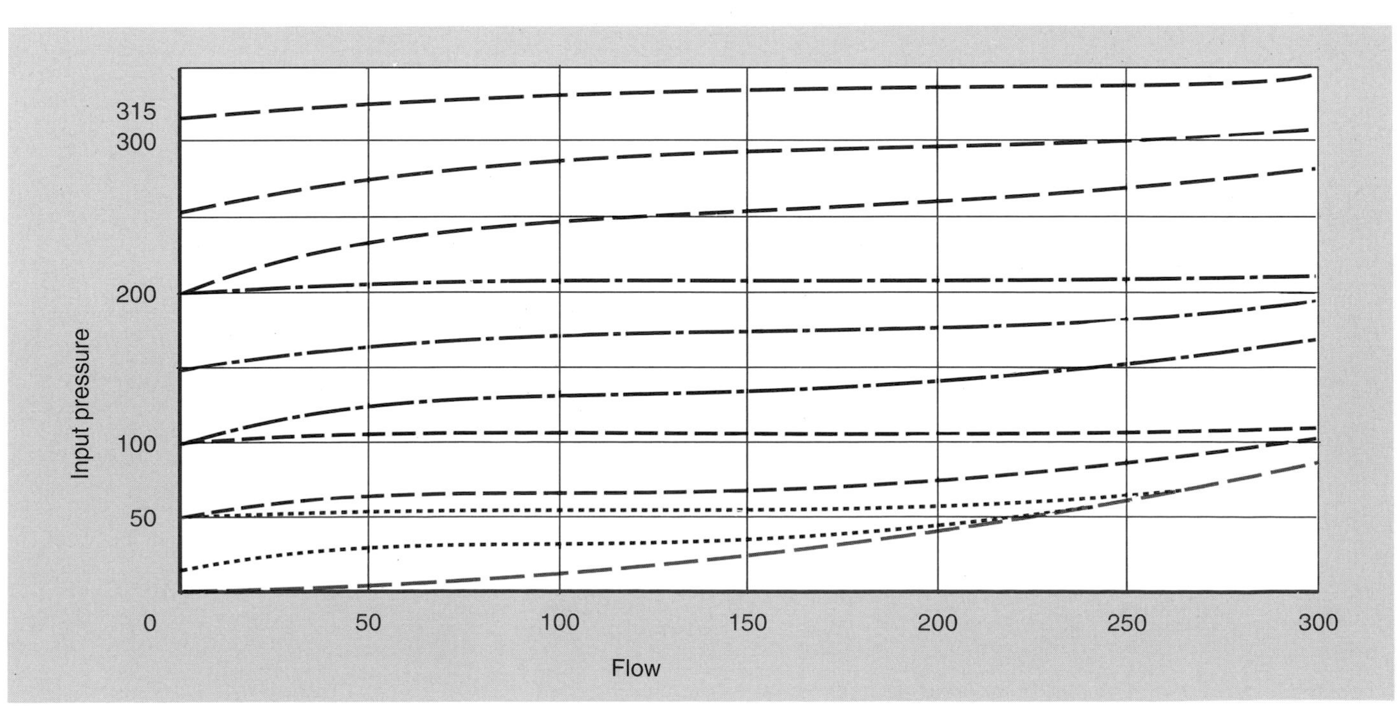

Diagram 3: *p_E-Qoperating curves for direct operated pressure relief valves, sizes 25 and 30*

Direct operated pressure relief valves are usually only used in the recommended pressure setting range.

For example: Pressure rating 200 bar
Setting range 100 to 200 bar or

Pressure rating 300 bar
Setting range 200 to 300 bar.

Pressures may also be set which are below the recommended setting range, theoretically down to p_E = 0 (complete unloading of the spring). However, a large control deviation then needs to be taken into consideration (*diagrams 3 and 4*).

2.5.1.2 Pilot operated pressure relief valves (*fig. 11*)

The gradient of the operating curve for pressure relief valves as the flow increases (diagram 5) is due to the flow force ($F_S \approx Q \bullet \sqrt{\Delta p}$) acting in the direction of closing of the main spool (3).

As the main spool spring only has the task of keeping the main spool (3) in a certain position, its spring force is relatively low. Hence the effect of the spring on the operating curve is negligibly small in comparison to that of the direct operated pressure relief valve. As shown in diagram 5, the operating curves are almost parallel.

By having models for particular pressure stages, this leads to an improvement in the "sensitivity" of pressure setting.

For very small flows (Q < 0.5 to 1 L/min) the pressure-flow curve forms a hysteresis curve. This means that as a valve is closed (decreasing flow) a smaller pressure pS is produced than on opening p_O (increasing flow) (*diagram 6*).

This difference between the opening and closing characteristics is due to the mechanical and hydraulic frictional forces at the control elements (main spool (3) pilot ball (8)) as well as to the contamination in the fluid.

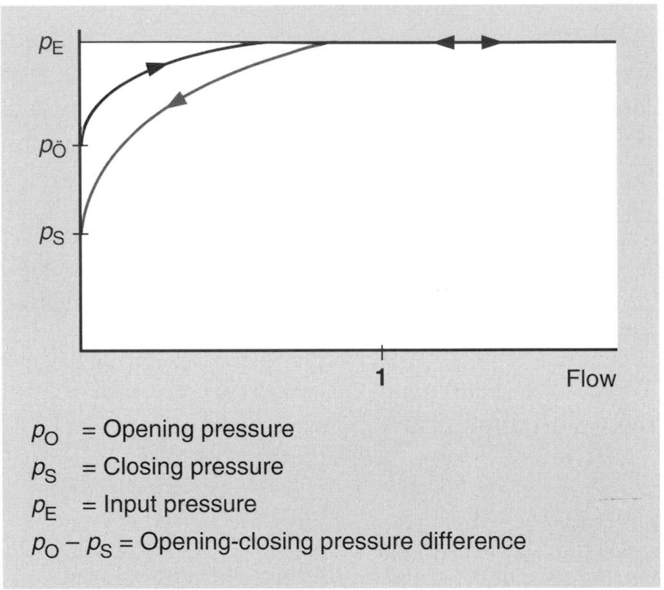

Diagram 6: *Opening and closing characteristics at very small flows*

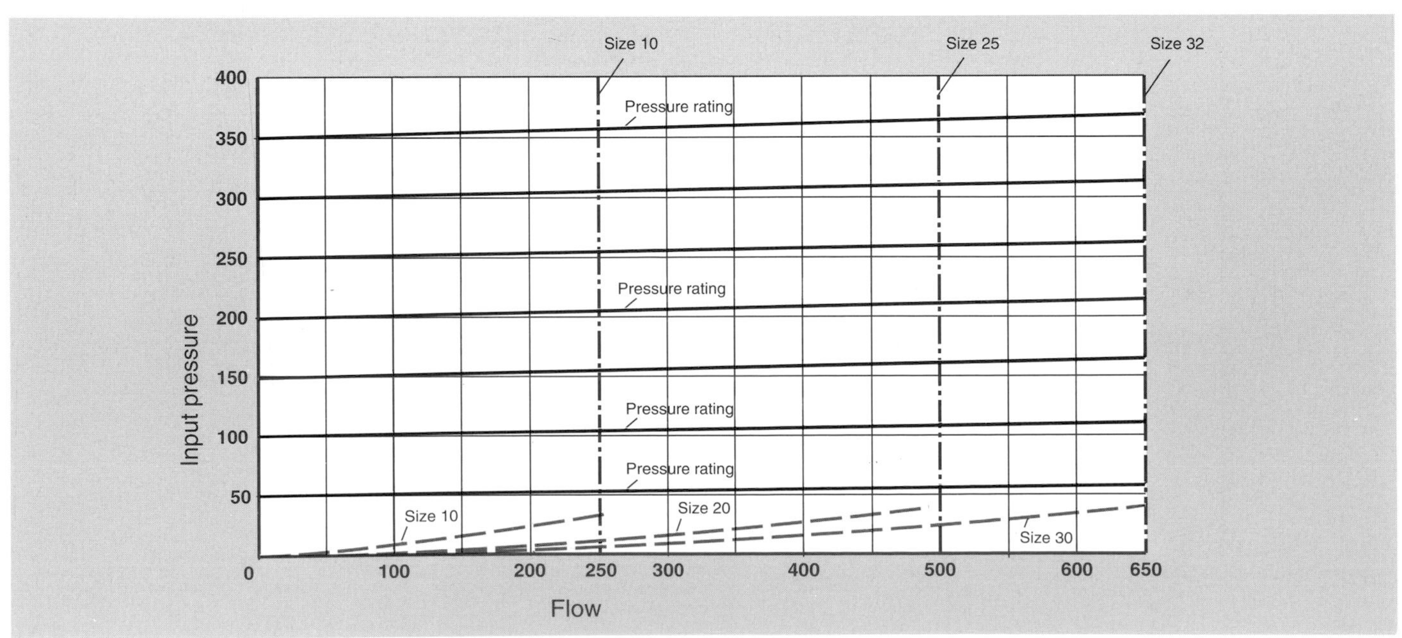

Diagram 5: p_E-*Q operating curves for pressure relief valves*

2.5.2 Power limit

In pressure relief valves there are two power limits: upper and lower limits (*diagrams 7 and 8*).

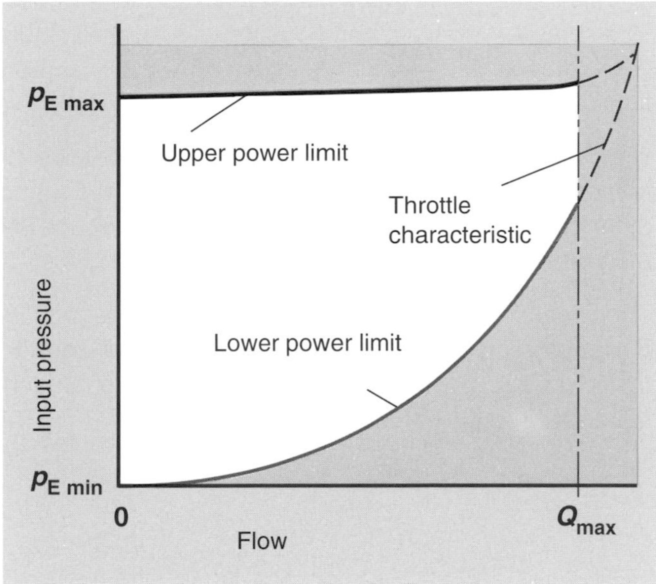

Diagram 7: *Operating range for a direct operated pressure relief valve*

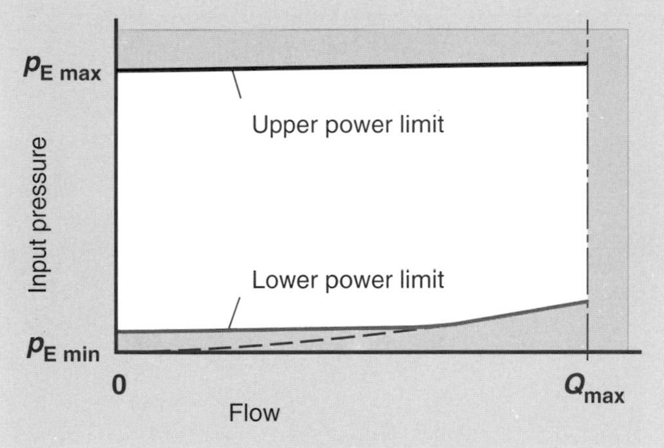

Diagram 8: *Operating range for a pilot operated pressure relief valve*

2.5.2.1 Upper power limit (highest set pressure and max. flow)

The pressure setting p_E determines the upper working range of the pressure relief valve. This pressure is formed from the maximum spring force F_F and the corresponding seat opening A_V of the pilot valve (*fig. 14*).

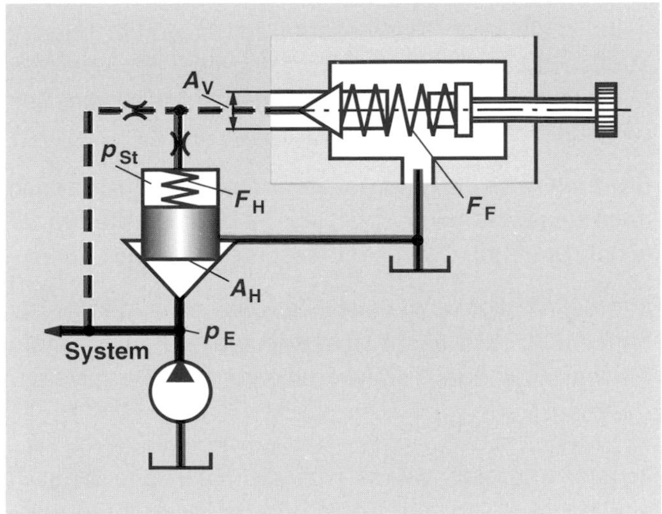

Fig. 16: *Principle of a pilot operated pressure relief valve*

Higher flows require larger seat openings and hence according to $p_E = F_F/A$ larger spring or setting forces. Hence direct operated pressure relief valves are soon in the range where a manual adjustment of p_E is no longer possible.

Therefore pilot operated pressure relief valves are used in for higher pressures, as larger seat diameters A_H in the main stage are easily achieved. The small force of the main spool spring F_H is increased by pilot pressure p_{St}. Pilot pressures due to the low pilot flow may be easily set by direct operated pressure relief valves (no adjustment forces).

2.5.2.2 Lower power limit

a) Direct operated pressure relief valves

In direct operated valves the lower power limit is reached, when the valve poppet has carried out its maximum opening stroke. The max. opening pressure corresponds to the throttling characteristic shown in *diagram 7*.

At any setting the *p*-*Q* operating curve may cut the throttling characteristic and the this determines the power limit of the valve (fully open control opening). This means that if the flow is increased further, pressure increases in accordance with the throttling characteristic.

b) Pilot operated pressure relief valves

In pilot operated valves the lowest pressure setting at the start of opening is determined by the force of the main spool spring and the pilot pressure. This value is usually between 1.5 and 4.5 bar for standard valves.

If the main spool has reached its maximum opening stroke as a result of the increasing flow, the operating curve cuts the throttle characteristic at the lowest set pressure (*diagram 8* – dotted line).

Dependent on the much larger opening area of the valve main stage, the lower power limit for pilot operated valves is only attained at low set pressures.

In order to avoid flow velocities which are too large and hence to avoid pressure losses in the hydraulic system, the maximum flow is limited dependent on the valve size (*diagram 8*, Q_{max}).

In pilot operated valves with electrical unloading via directional valve, type DBW, the lower power limit is equal to the "bypass" pressure. This is determined by the pre-tensioning force of the main spool spring and the pilot pressure of the pilot fluid which flows via the directional valve to tank.

2.5.3 Dynamic behaviour

The dynamic behaviour of a pressure relief valve is characterised by its response to a sudden change in the flow or pressure.

The valve should be able to react quickly, that is with as little delay as possible, compensate for pressure peaks which appear and reach the set pressure within a short time.

In order to avoid pressure peaks, damping needs to be incorporated. However this together with friction and moment of inertia of the moving parts tends to reduce the response of the valve.

The dynamic behaviour of the valve is dependent on its design, the operating state of the main spool and the hydraulic system itself. The static behaviour is only dependent on the valve design.

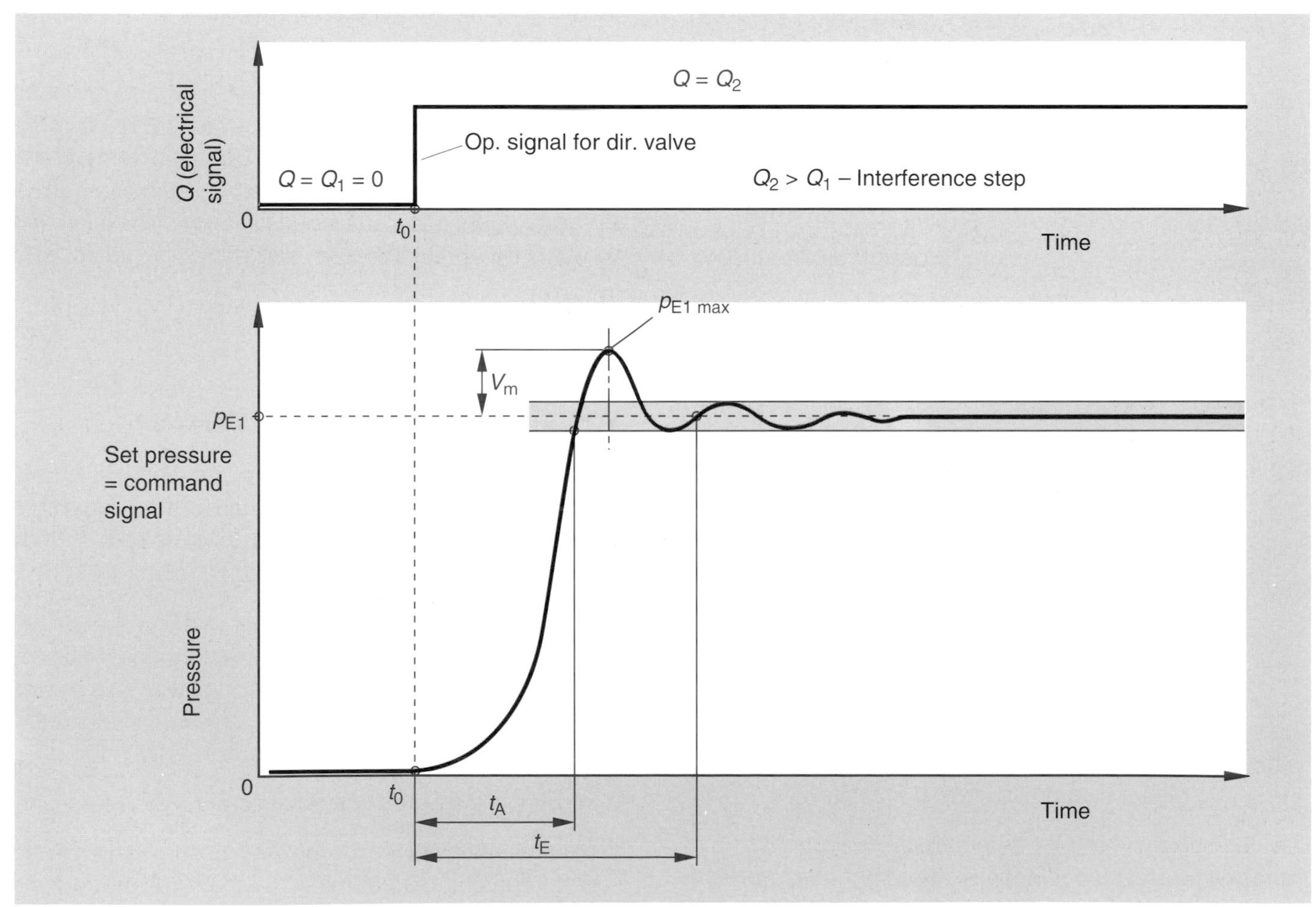

Diagram 9: *Response behaviour of a pilot operated pressure relief valve on opening*

There are two types of operating states (movement phases) for the main spool:

2.5.3.1 Movement of the main spool in another stroke position, e.g. when opening

The following reasons may cause the main spool to change its position:

a) A sudden jump or drop in pressure in the hydraulic system, due to a sudden change in the flow.

b) A sudden change in the pilot pressure due to the operation of directional valve (type DBW).

The dynamic behaviour may be examined on the basis of the response operating curve (*diagram 9*).

The operating curve is almost independent of the type of energizing.

The following parameters are used for the determination of the response:

- Build-up period t_A
  is the time which lapses from time t_0 until the pressure reaches the lower limit of the transient tolerance.
- Transient period t_E
  is the time which lapses from time t_0 until the transient tolerance is reached for the last time and then not exceeded any more.
- Pressure peak p_{Emax}
  $p_{Emax} = V_m / p_E \bullet 100$ in %

The maximum overshoot V_m is the largest deviation of the response from the set command value after the transient tolerance has been overshot for the first time.

2.5.3.2 Movement of the main spool within a controlled position due to pressure oscillations in the hydraulic system

In practice, flows in a hydraulic system due to pressure pulses from the hydraulic pump amongst other things are not free of oscillations.

Pressure relief valves may be encouraged to oscillate creating noise due to these pressure pulses. Depending on the frequency of this noise, the valve noise is known as "chatter, buzzing, whistling or screaming".

The cause of this is the spring-mass system, which consists of the moving valve parts of mechanical spring and oil column acting as a spring.

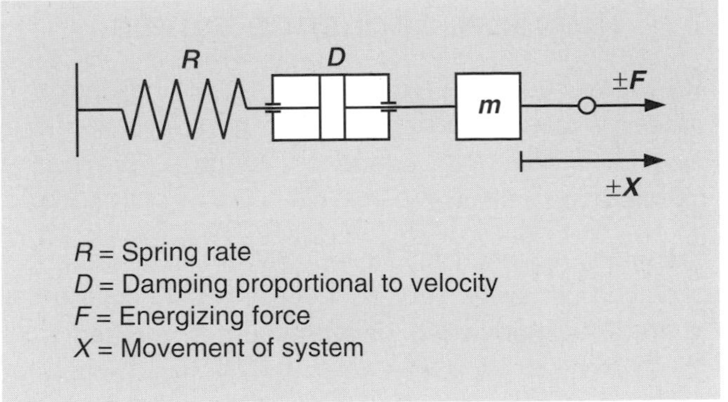

Fig. 17: Principle of spring-mass system

The relationship between force *F* and movement *x* of the mechanical system is described by equation 4.

$$m \bullet x = F - D \bullet x - R \bullet x \qquad (4)$$

The oscillations which appear may be removed by suitable damping measures. See *fig. 6* (damping spool in direct operated valves).

Pilot operated valves are hydraulically cushioned (*fig. 14*). Orifices between the main stage and the pilot valve limit the pilot flow and hence the movement of the main spool.

It is important for undisturbed hydraulic system operation that the pressure relief valve compensates for any oscillations which occur and hence enables the operational behaviour to be stable.

If this is not done, high frequency oscillations as well as noise will lead to an increase in wear (cavitational erosion).

This results in as shorter service life for the valves and a lower hydraulic system availability.

2.5.3.3 Influence of valve design

In spool valves a certain length of overlap must always exist, in order to limit the internal leakage. Due to this idle stroke, this results in a dead period, e.g. when the valve is opened, where the inlet pressure continues to rise. This results in pressure peaks.

On the other hand in poppet valves, the valve poppet opens immediately on the inlet pressure reaching the set command level. As expected the pressure peaks are considerably lower.

3 Pressure sequence valves

Pressure sequence valves are similar in design to pressure relief valves. Depending on application, they may be divided into sequence, by-pass, pre-load or deceleration valves.

Pressure sequence valves are arranged in the main flow of a hydraulic system and connect or disconnect a further hydraulic system when a set pressure is reached.

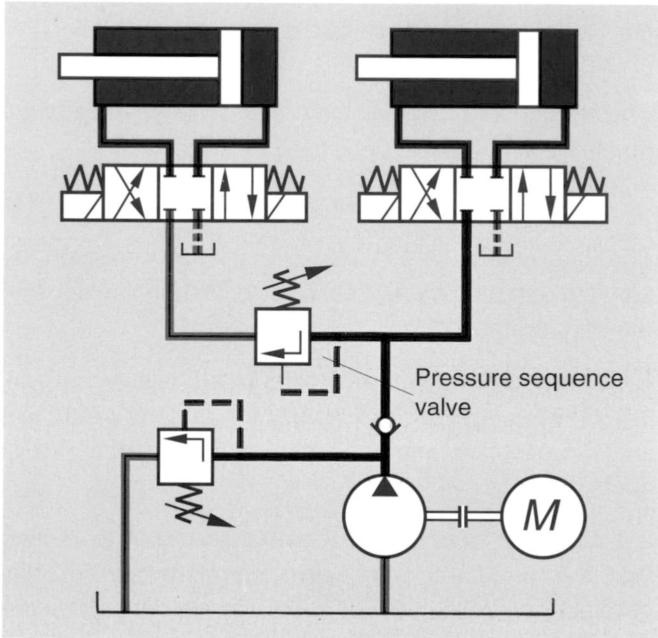

Fig. 18: *Control with pressure isolating valve*

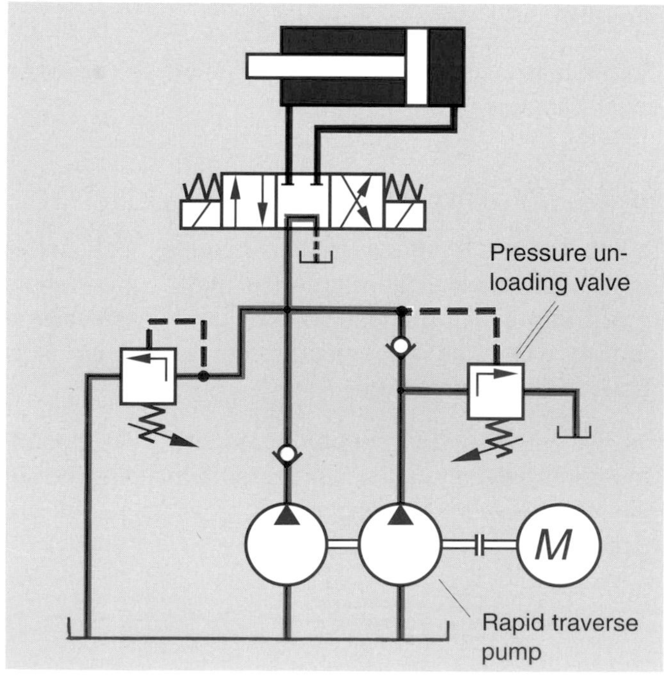

Fig. 19: *Control with shut-off rapid traverse pump*

3.1 Sequence valves

Basically pressure relief valves may be used as sequence valves. The pre-requisite for this is that the pressure in channel T (in direct operated pressure relief valves) or in channel B (in pilot operated pressure relief valves) cannot change the set pressure. This is achieved by feeding the leakage oil in direct operated pressure relief valves and the pilot oil in pilot operated pressure relief valves externally and pressure free to tank.

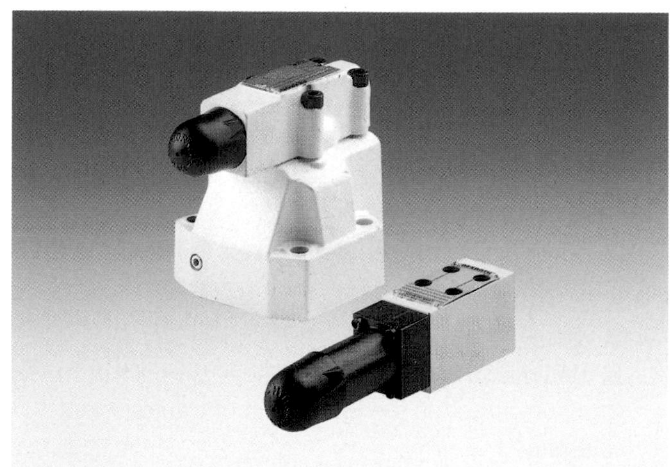

Fig. 20: *Direct and pilot operated pressure isolating valve*

3.1.1 Direct operated sequence valve, type DZ.D (*fig. 21*)

The adjustment element (4) is used for setting the sequence pressure. The compression spring (3) keeps the control spool (2) in its initial position. The valve is closed.

Pressure in channel P acts on surface (8) of the control spool (2) via control line (6) and hence acts against the force of spring (3). If the pressure in channel P exceeds the value set at spring (3), control spool (2) is pushed against compression spring (3). The connection from channel P to channel A is opened. The system attached to channel A is connected without the pressure in channel P falling.

The control signal is fed either internally via control line (6) and orifice (7) from channel P or externally via port B (X).

Depending on the application, leakage oil is returned externally via port T (Y) or internally via port A.

A check valve may be optionally built into the system to allow free return flow of the fluid from channel A to channel P. Pressure gauge port (1) is fitted so that the sequence pressure may be monitored.

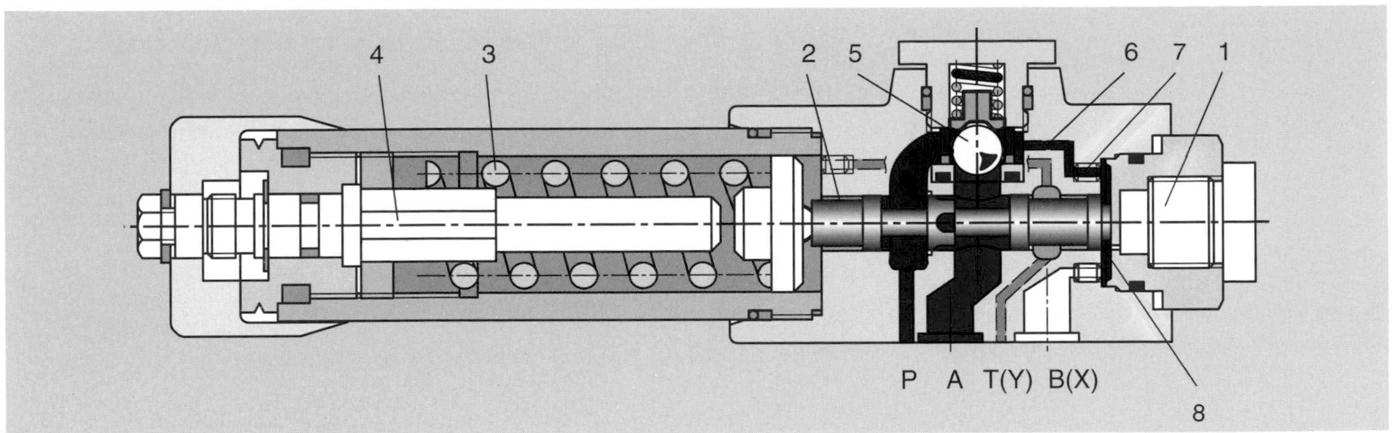

Fig. 21: *Direct operated pressure sequence valve*

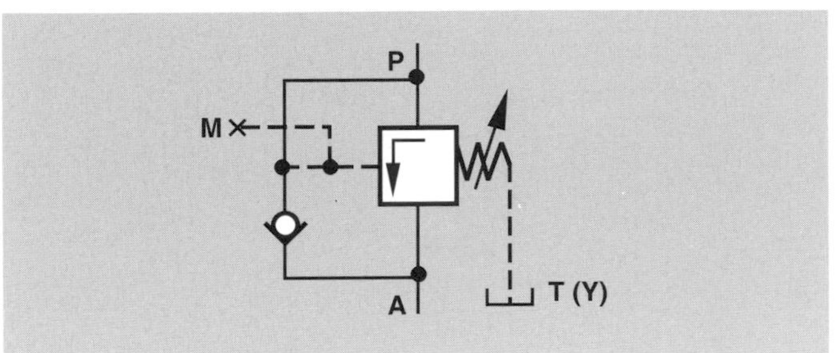

Fig. 22: *Direct operated pressure sequence valve; internal pilot oil feed, external pilot oil return*

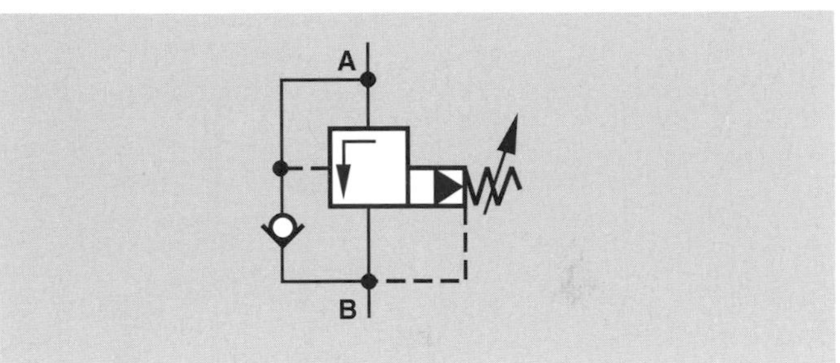

Fig. 23: *Pilot operated pressure sequence valve; internal pilot oil feed, internal pilot oil return*

Important parameters:

Sizes	5, 6 and 10
Flow	up to 80 L/min
Max. input pressure	315 bar
Max. set sequence pressure	210 bar

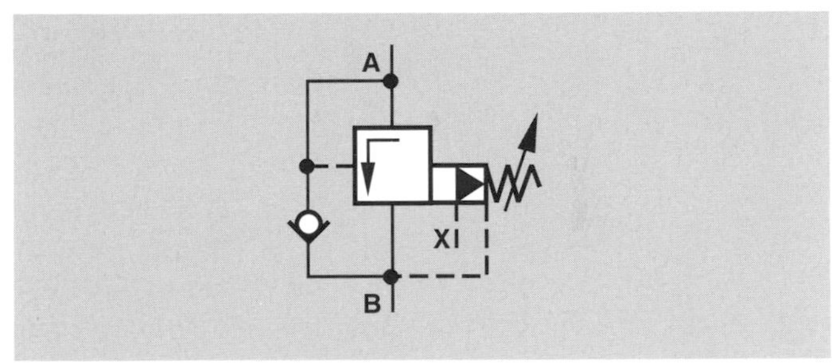

Fig. 24: *Pilot operated pressure sequence valve; external pilot oil feed, internal pilot oil return*

3.1.2 Pilot operated sequence valve, type DZ (*fig. 27*)

Pilot operated sequence valves basically comprise main valve (1) with main spool insert (2) and pilot valve (3) with adjustment element (11).

A check valve (4) may be optionally built into the system to allow free return flow of the fluid from channel A to channel B.

Dependent on the application (pre-load, sequence or by-pass) pilot oil is fed and/or returned either internally or externally.

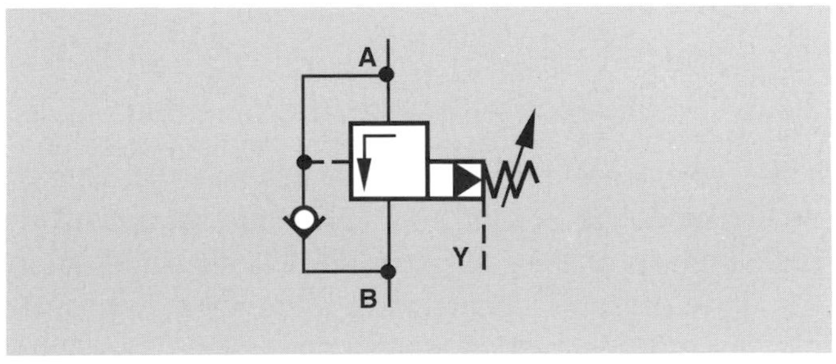

Fig. 25: *Pilot operated pressure sequence valve; internal pilot oil feed, external pilot oil return*

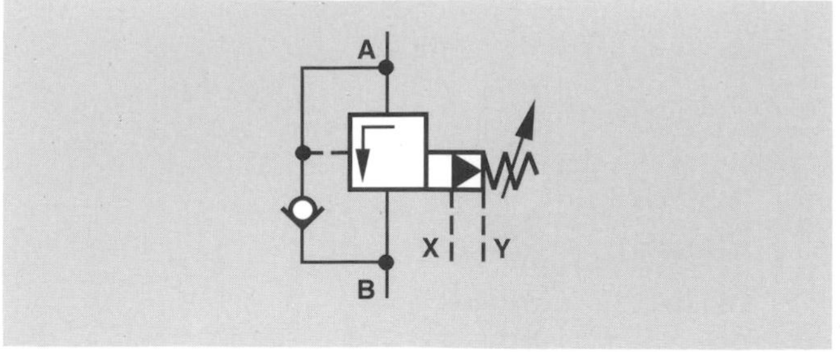

Fig. 26: *Pilot operated pressure sequence valve; external pilot oil feed, external pilot oil return*

3.1.4 Sequence valve with external drain

In comparison to the sequence valve with internal drain. here the leakage oil arising at the pilot spool is fed externally and pressure free to tank via port Y.

The pilot oil is fed internally via line (9) into channel B.

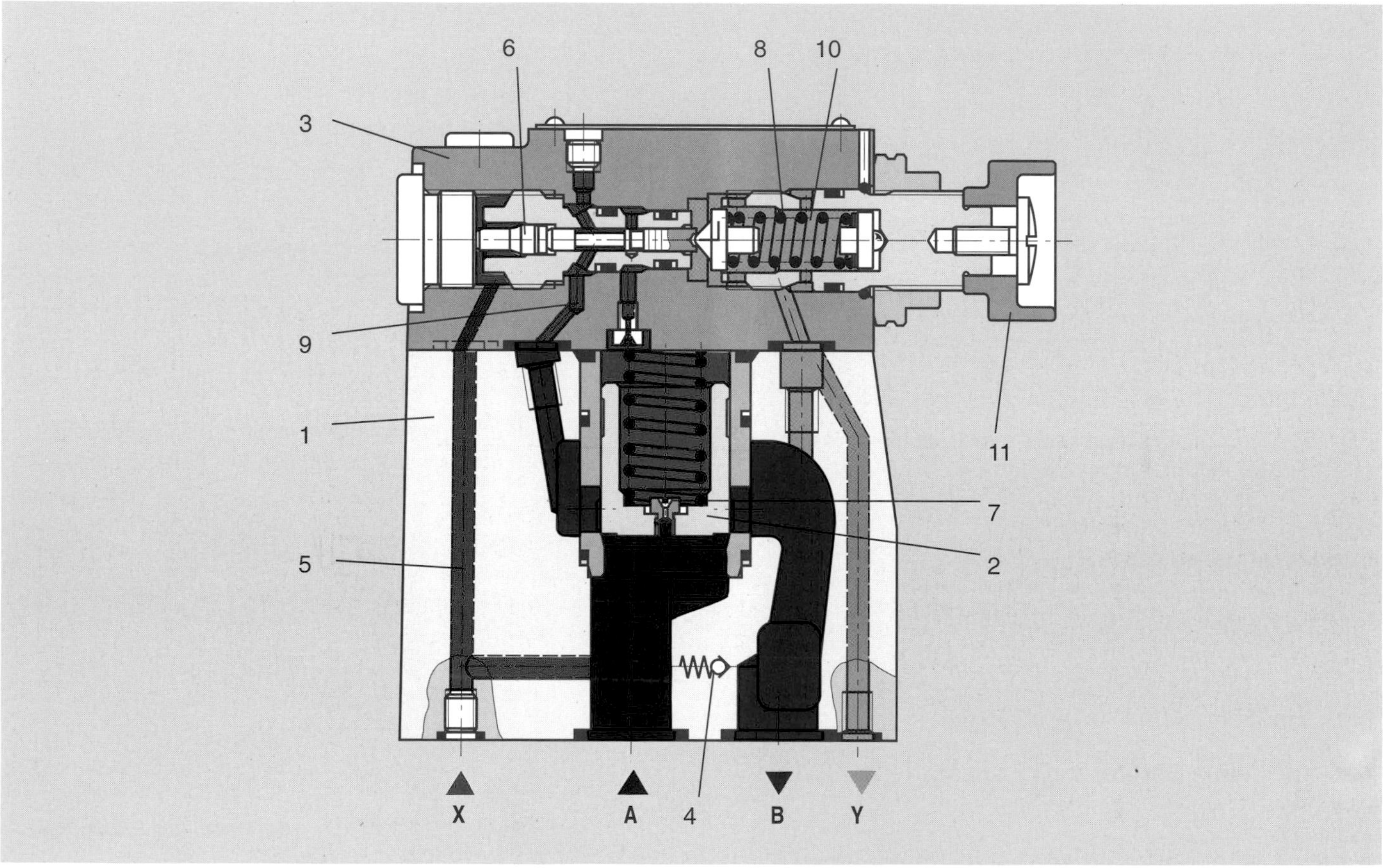

Fig. 27: *Pilot operated pressure sequence valve; internal pilot oil feed, internal pilot oil return*

3.1.3 Sequence valve with internal drain *(fig. 27)*

The pressure present in channel A acts via control line (5) on pilot spool (6) in pilot valve (3). At the same time the pressure acts on the spring loaded side of the main spool (2). If the pressure exceeds the value set at spring (8), pilot spool (6) is pushed against spring (8). The control signal for this is fed internally via control line (5) from channel A. The fluid on the spring loaded side of main spool (2) now flows via control line (9) into channel B. A pressure drop is produced across main spool (2). The connection from channel A to channel B is free whilst the pressure set at spring (8) is maintained. The leakage arising at pilot spool (6) is fed internally into channel B.

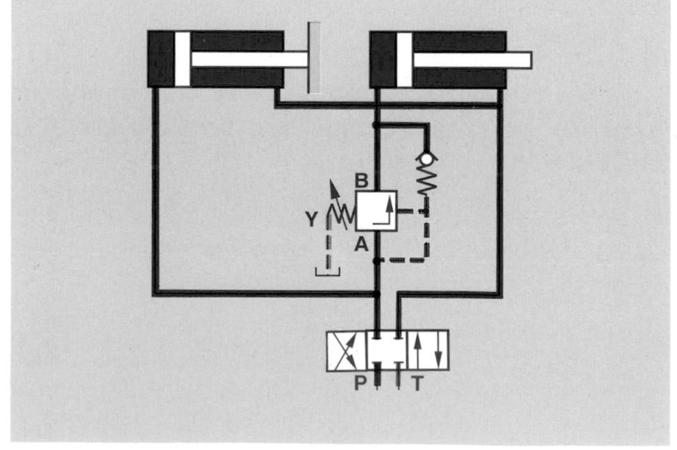

Fig. 28: *Pressure sequence valve*

3.1.4.1 Use as bypass valve (*fig. 29*)

The pressure present in channel X acts via control line (5) on pilot spool (6) in pilot valve (3). At the same time pressure in channel A acts on the spring loaded side of the main spool (2) via orifices (7). If the pressure in channel X exceeds the value set at spring (8), pilot spool (6) is pushed against spring (8). Now fluid flows from the spring loaded side of the main spool (2) to spring chamber (10) of the pilot valve via the bore in the pilot spool. The pressure on the spring loaded side of main spool (2) falls. Main spool (2) is lifted off its seat and channel A is connected to channel B. Fluid now flows at almost zero pressure from channel A to channel B.

In this model, pilot oil from spring chamber (10) is returned pressure free via port Y.

Important parameters

Sizes	10, 25 and 32
Flow	up to 450 L/min
Max. operating pressure	315 bar
Max. set sequence pressure	315 bar

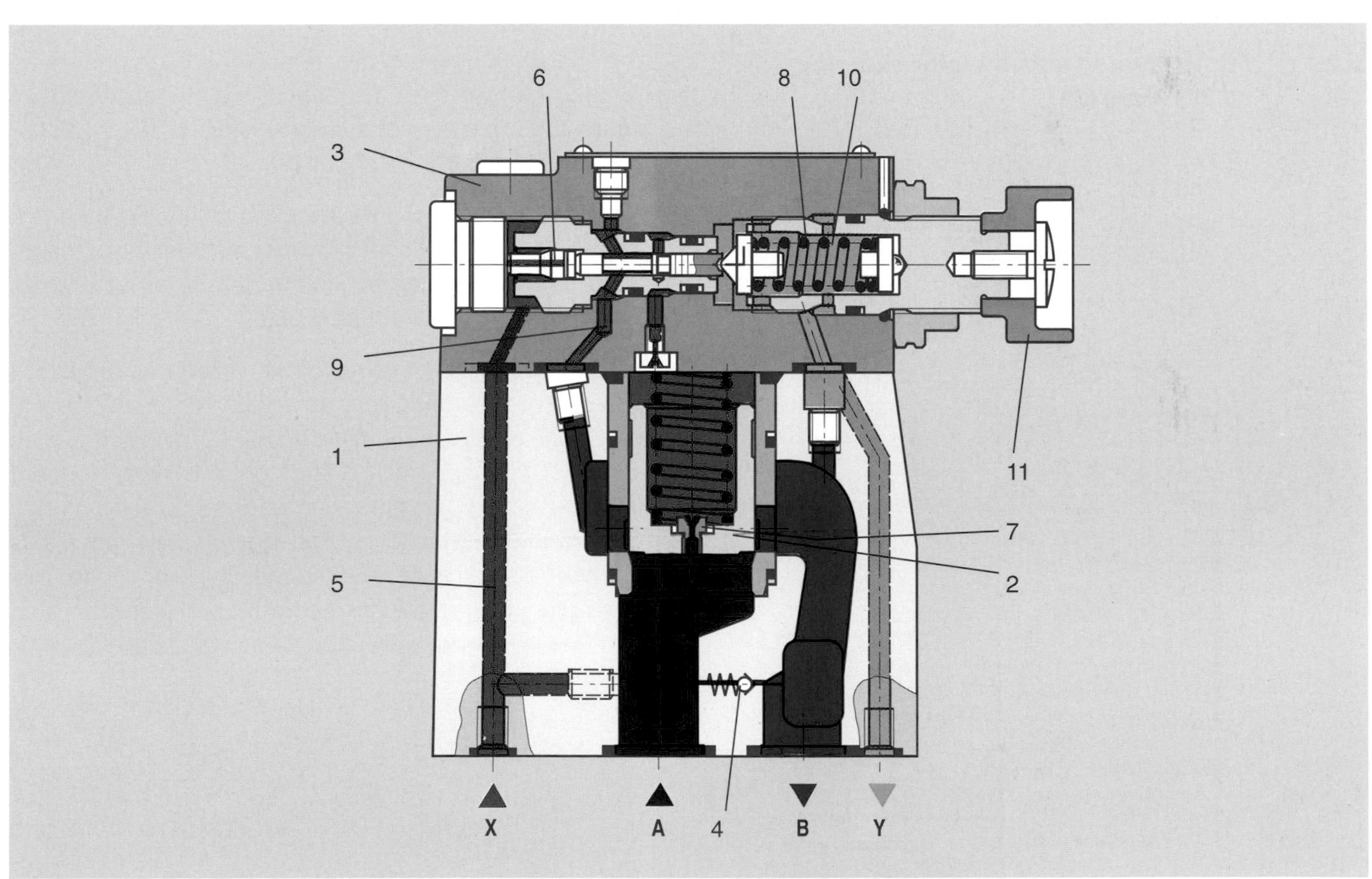

Fig. 29: *Pilot operated pressure sequence valve; external pilot oil feed, external pilot oil return*

3.2 Accumulator charging valves

Accumulator charging valves, also known as pressure unloading valves, are mainly used in hydraulic systems with accumulators. Their main task is to switch pump flow to pressure free flow once the accumulator has been charged.

Accumulator charging valves are also used in hydraulic systems with high and low pressure pumps (dual circuit systems). In these cases, the low pressure pump is switched to pressure free flow as soon as the set high pressure has been reached.

Accumulator charging valves (*fig. 31*) basically comprise main valve (1) with main valve insert (3), pilot valve (2) with pressure setting element (16) and check valve (4). The check valve is built into the main valve in valves of size 10, but is built into a separate plate arranged below the main valve for valve sizes 25 and 32.

3.2.1 Pilot operated accumulator charging valves, type DA

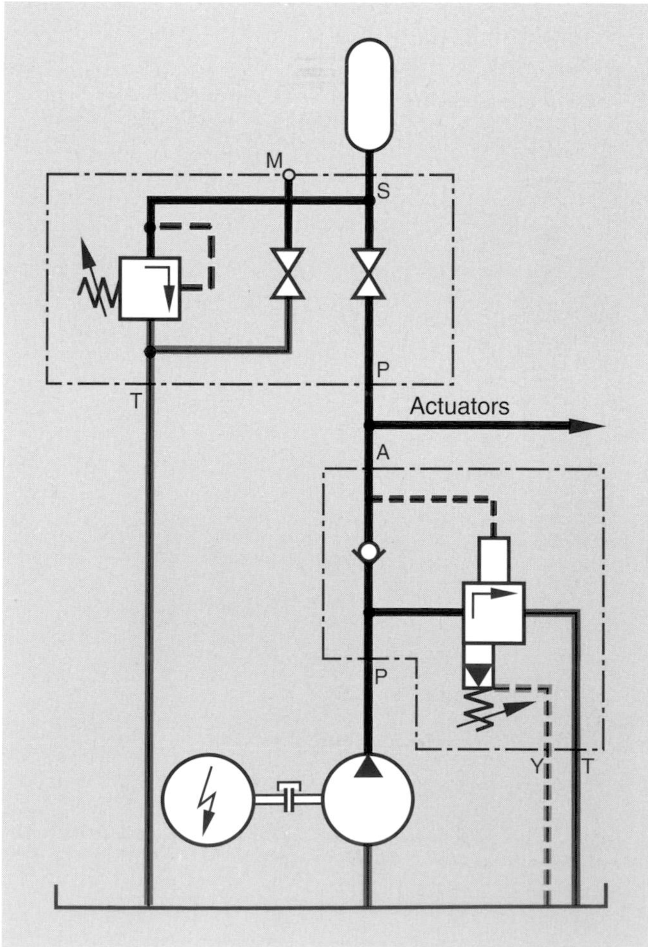

Fig. 30: *Hydraulic system with accumulator and pressure unloading valve*

3.2.1.1 Change of pump flow from P to A into P to T

The hydraulic pump delivers fluid to the system via check valve (4). The pressure present in channel A acts on pilot spool (6) via control line (5). At the same time pressure in channel P acts on the spring loaded side of main spool (3) and ball (9) in pilot valve (2) via orifices (7) and (8). As soon as the shut-off pressure for the hydraulic system set at pilot valve (2) is reached, ball (9) opens against spring (10). Fluid now flows via orifices (7) and (8) into spring chamber (11). From here, fluid is fed internally or externally via control line (12) and channel T into the tank.

Dependent on orifices (7) and (8) a pressure drop exists across main spool (3). Due to this, main spool (3) is lifted from its seat and the connection from P to T is opened. Check valve (4) now closes the connection from A to P. Ball (9) is now held open by the pressure in channel P.

3.2.1.2 Change of pump flow from P to T into P to A

The end surface area of pilot spool (6) is 10 % (may even be 17 %) larger than the effective surface at ball (9). Hence the force at pilot spool (6) is 10 % (17 %) larger than the effective force at ball (9).

Pilot spool (6) is pressure balanced until the set pressure is reached. If the pilot control is opened, then the pressure at pilot spool (6) is larger than at ball (9) and the spool position of pilot spool (6) changes.

If the pressure at pilot spool (6) has fallen with respect to the set shut-off pressure by an amount corresponding to the switching pressure difference (10 or 17 %), then spring (10) pushes ball (9) back onto its seat. Hence a pressure builds up on the spring loaded side of main valve (3). Together with the force of spring (14) main spool (3) is pushed onto its seat. The connection from P to T is interrupted. Once again the hydraulic pump delivers fluid from P to A into the hydraulic system via check valve (4).

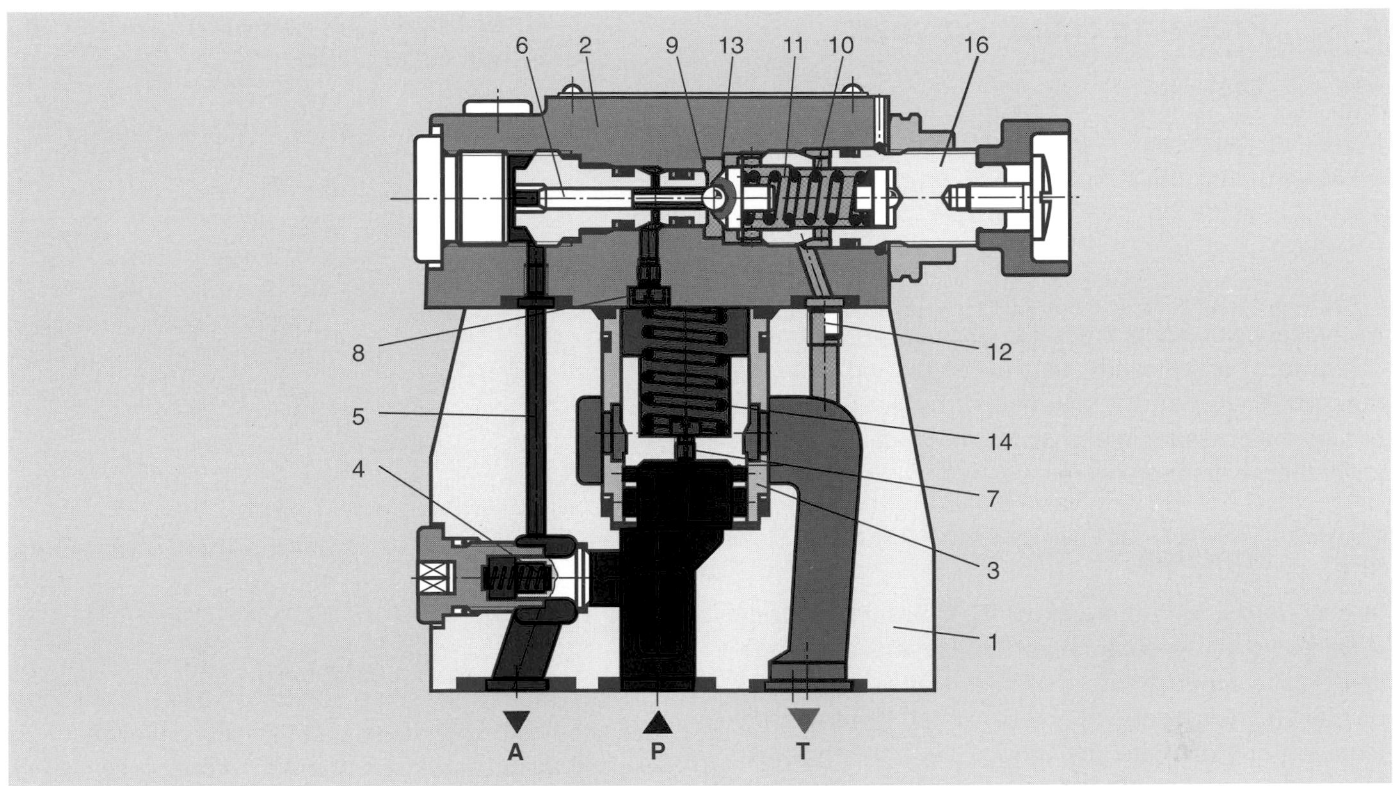

Fig. 31: *Pilot operated pressure shut-off valve, type DA*

3.2.2 Pilot operated accumulator charging valve, type DAW

The function of this valve is the same as the function for valve, type DA.

However, by operating directional valve (15) pressure below the shut-off pressure set at pilot valve (2) may be switched at random from P to T and P to A.

Important parameters

Sizes	10, 20 and 30
Flow	up to 250 L/min
Operating pressure	up to 315 bar

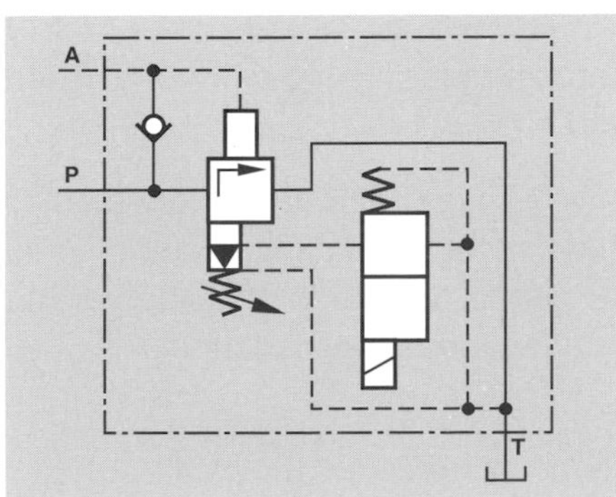

Fig. 32: *Pilot operated shut-off valve, type DAW*

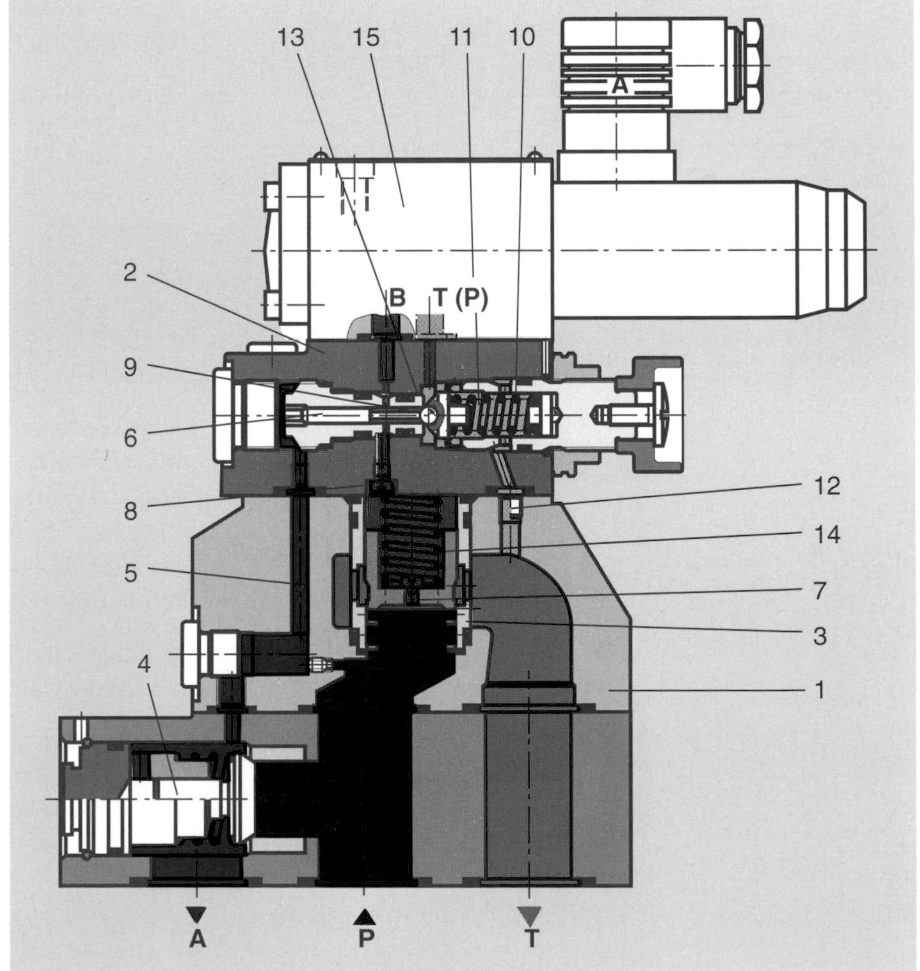

Fig. 33: *Pilot operated pressure shut-off valve, type DAW*

4 Pressure reducing valve

4.1 Task

In contrast to pressure relief valves which affect the input pressure (pump pressure), pressure reducing valves are used to influence the output pressure (actuator pressure).

The reduction of input pressure (primary pressure) or the maintenance of output pressure (secondary pressure) is achieved at a set value, which is below the charging pressure available in the main circuit. It is thus possible to reduce the pressure in one part of the system to a level lower than system pressure.

4.2 Function

In accordance with the task of the pressure reducing valve not to let the output pressure rise above a certain level, this output pressure is fed to the end control element (spool or poppet) and compared there with the force set at the control spring (*fig. 34*). If the hydraulic force $p_A \cdot A_K$ exceeds the set spring force, the spool moves upwards in the closing direction of the control lands. In the control position the spool is force balanced ($F_F = p_A \cdot A_K$). At the control land, dependent on flow Q and input pressure p_E, an opening is produced which is required to keep p_A constant.

In principle there are two types of pressure reducing valve: direct and pilot operated.

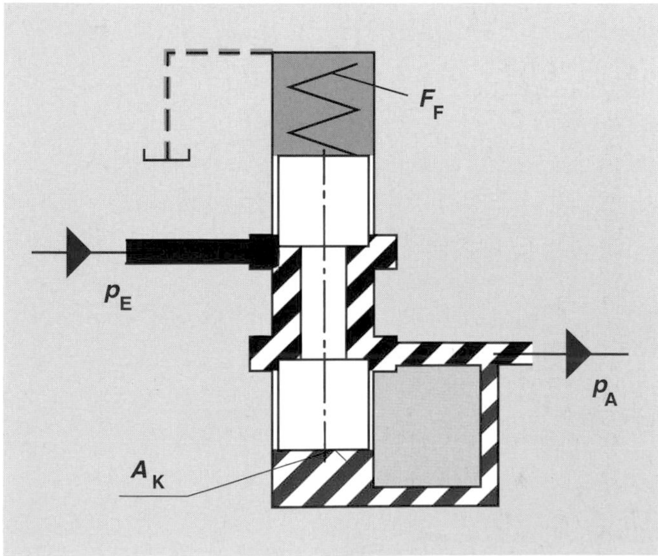

Fig. 34: *Principle of 2-way pressure reducing valve*

4.3 Direct operated pressure reducing valve, type DR.D

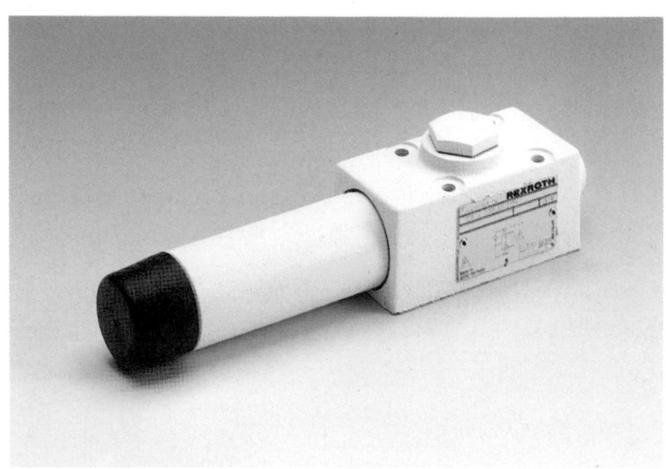

Fig. 35: *Direct operated pressure reducing valve, type DR6DP*

Direct operated pressure reducing valves are mainly designed as 3-way models, i.e. adjustment element (1) ensures the pressure safety of the secondary circuit (*fig. 36*). Whether the adjustment is made by rotary knob as shown or by simple screw with protective cap or lockable rotary knob with scale, is only dependent on the individual case and the requirements of the user.

Initially the valves are open, i.e. there is free flow from channel P to channel A. At the same time pressure in channel A acts via control line (2) on the spool surface opposite to compression spring (3). If the pressure in channel A exceeds the value set at compression spring (3), control spool (4) moves to the control position and keeps the pressure set in channel A constant. Signal and pilot oil flows are taken internally from channel A via control line (2).

If the pressure in channel A continues to increase due to the effects of external forces on the actuator, control spool (4) is pushed further against compression spring (3). Hence channel A is connected to tank via control land (5) at control spool (4). As much fluid flows to tank as is required to prevent the pressure rising any further.

Leakages from spring chamber (6) are always returned externally via channel T (Y).

An optional check valve (7) may be built into the system to allow free return flow of the fluid from channel A to channel P. Pressure gauge port (8) is available for the monitoring of the reduced pressure in channel A.

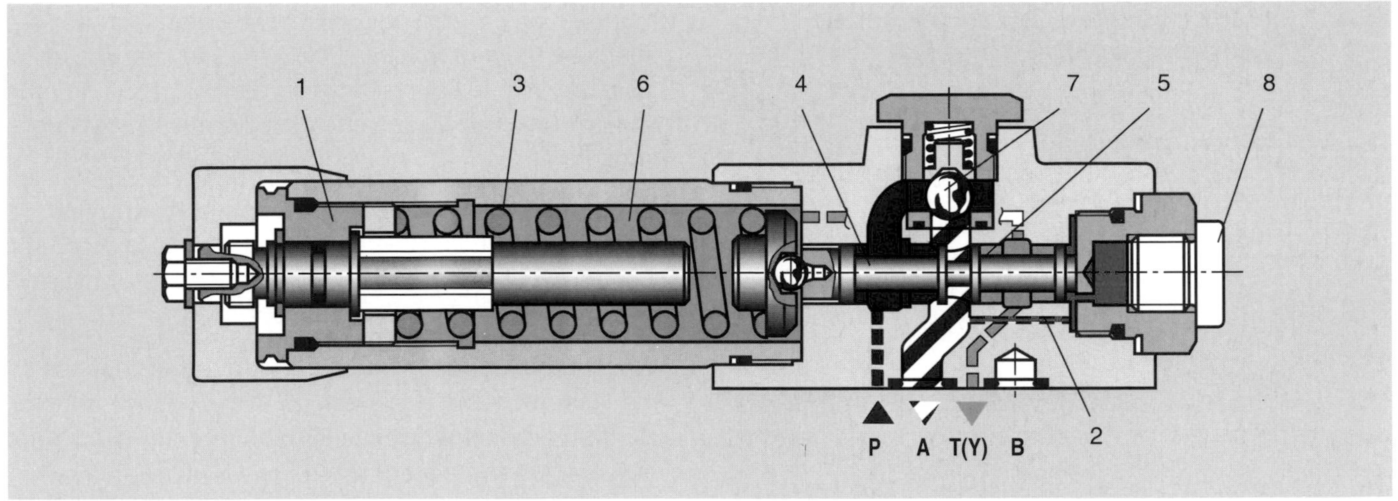

Fig. 36: *Direct operated pressure reducing valve*

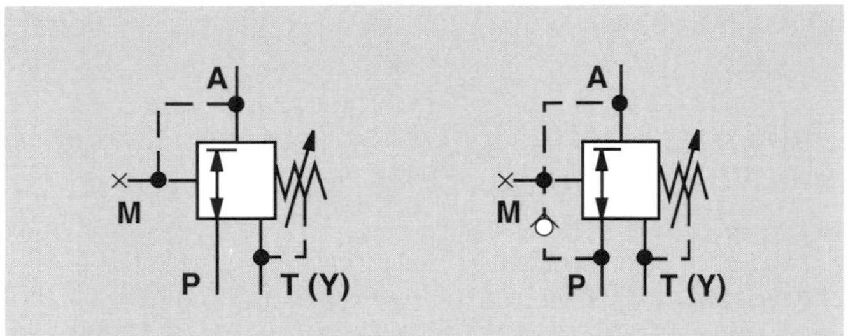

Fig. 37: *Direct operated pressure reducing valves; left without, right with check valve*

Important parameters

Sizes	5, 6 and 10
Max. input pressure	315 bar
Max. output pressure	210 bar (315 bar)
Flow	up to 80 L/min

4.4 Pilot operated 2-way pressure reducing valves, type DR

In order to reduce pressures at larger flows, pilot operated pressure reducing valves are used.

As with the pilot operated pressure relief valve, a direct operated pressure relief valve is connected to the spring side of the control spool (*fig. 39*)

The pilot operated valve is the measuring element of the system.

The desired output pressure is set at spring (1) of the pilot valve.

At rest, the valve is open, i.e. fluid may freely flow from channel B via main spool insert (2) to channel A.

The pressure to be controlled present in channel A acts on the bottom of the main spool. At the same time, pressure acts on the spring loaded side of main spool (4) via orifice (3) and on ball (6) in pilot valve (7) via channel (5). The pressure also acts on ball (6) via orifice (8), control line (9), check valve (10) and orifice (11). Depending on the setting of spring (1) a pressure builds up in front of ball (6), in channel (5) and in spring chamber (12). This pressure keeps the control spool (13) in its open position. If p_A reaches the pressure set at spring (1), the pilot valve reacts (ball (6) lifts off its seat).

Hence pilot oil flows from the valve output via orifices (8) and (5) to the pilot valve. The pressure drop existing at the orifices acts on the control spool in the main stage and moves the main spool against the spring. The desired reduced pressure is attained, once a balance is present between the pressure in channel A and the pressure set at spring (1).

Pilot oil is returned from spring chamber (14) always externally via control line (15) to tank.

In the pressure reducing valve, two control circuits are effective: control circuit 1 for the compensation of instability due to small flows and control circuit 2 for the compensation of closing effect on the main spool due to large flows.

Control circuit 1 is effective from channel A via orifice (8), control line (9), ball (10) and orifice (11) to the pilot control. Control circuit 2 is effective from channel A via orifice (3) and control line (5) to the pilot control.

Whether control circuit (1) or (2) is effective depends on the local pressure relationships at orifices (3) and (8). During most operating conditions both control circuits are active at the same time.

At very high flow velocities, a lower pressure drop exists at orifice (8) than at orifice (3). In order to avoid the direction of flow changing from orifice (3) to orifice (8), check valve (10) isolates control circuit 1 from control circuit 2.

An optional check valve (16) may be built into the system to allow free return flow of the fluid from channel A to channel B.

Pressure gauge port (17) is available for the monitoring of the reduced pressure in channel A.

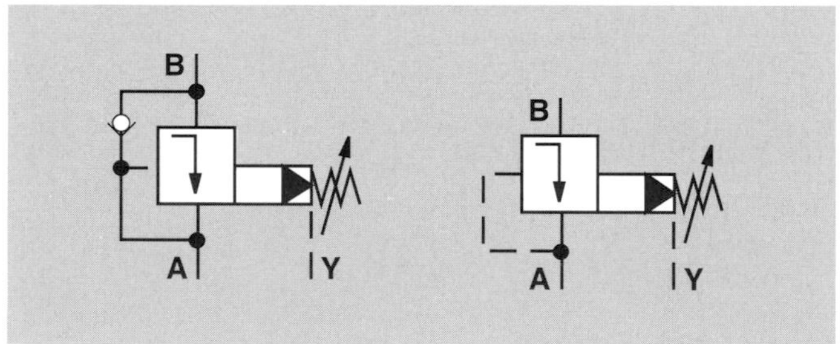

Fig. 38: *Pilot operated pressure reducing valve; left with, right without check valve*

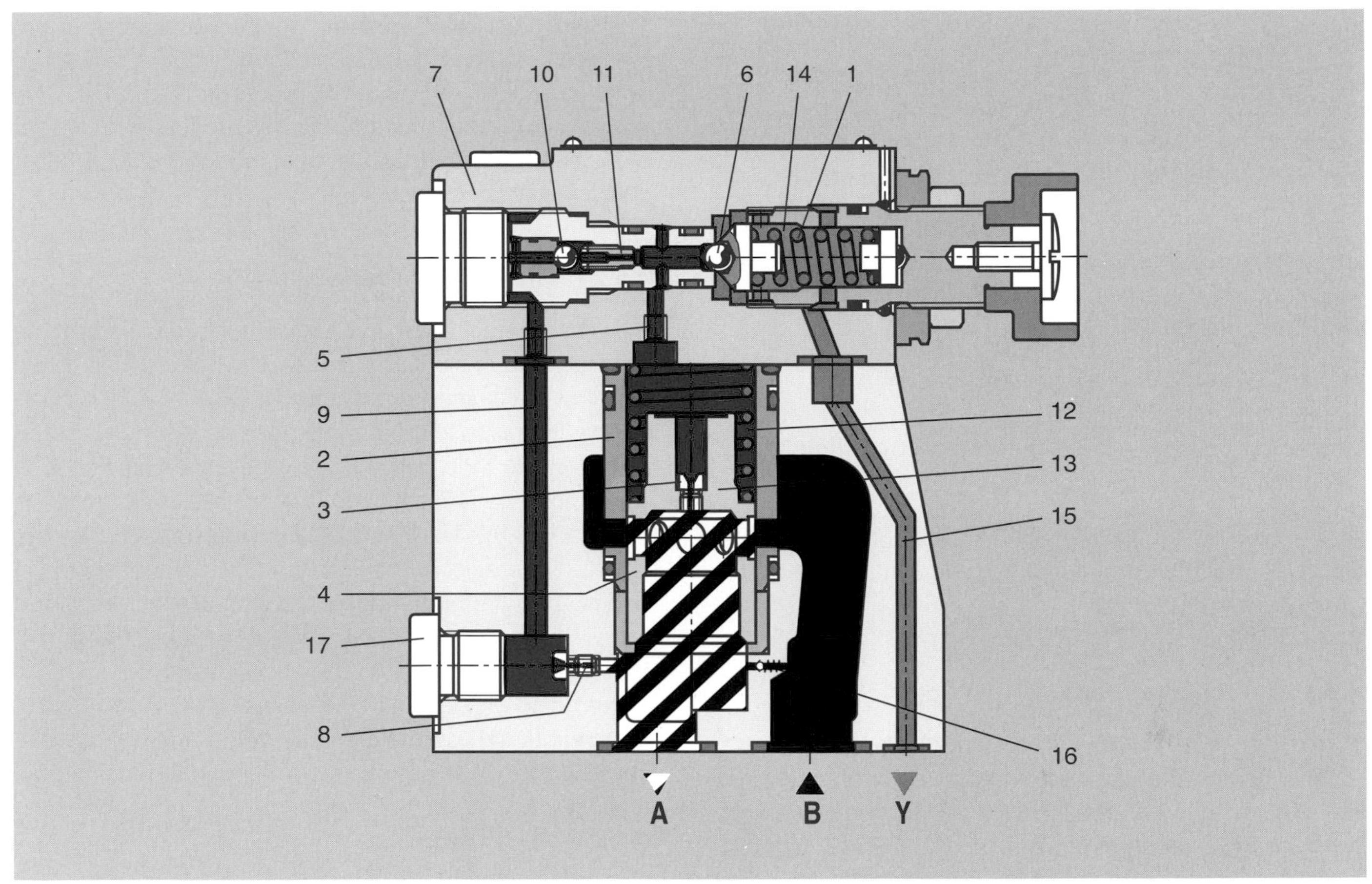

Fig. 39: *Pilot operated pressure reducing valve*

Important parameters

Sizes	10, 25 and 32
Operating pressure	up to 315 (350) bar
Flow	up to 400 L/min

4.5 Pilot operated 3-way pressure reducing valve, type 3DR

3-way pressure reducing valves (*fig. 40*) basically comprise main valve (1) with control spool (2) and direct operated pressure reducing valve (3) used as the pilot valve.

Initially control spool (2) is held at rest against spring (6) via spring (5) and spring pad (4). Connections P to A and A to T are closed.

Spring (5) is slightly more pre-tensioned than spring (6), so that the rest position of main spool (2) is precisely defined by the apring pad (4) as a stop in the housing of main valve (1).

Pilot spool (7) is held by spring (8) in an open initial position. 3 pressure functions (diagram 10) may be carried out with this valve.

4.5.1 Pressure reducing function

Pilot oil flow is fed from port P via control line (9) to the pilot valve. This flow then proceeds via the open connection in the pilot valve to control line (10) of the main valve and further on to the spring chambers (11) and (12) of main spool (2) as well as to port A via control line (13).

If the pilot flow at port P is sufficient, a pressure builds up at port A as a result of the actuator resistance. This pressure acts via control line (13), main spool orifices (14 and 15), lines (10 and 16) on pilot spool (7) and pushes this spool against spring (8). At the variable opening between bore (17) and control land (18) of the pilot spool (7) the input pressure (port P) is reduced to the pilot pressure set at spring (8). (Pilot oil flow proceeds from the pilot valve output into control line (10), spring chamber (11) and from here via main spool orifices (14 and 15) onto spring chamber (12) and further via control line (13) onto port A). A pressure drop is present at orifices (14 and 15). When the required actuator flow in A becomes larger than the available pilot oil flow, the pressure drop at orifices (14 and 15) increases and pushes the main spool to the left against spring (5). Connection P to A is opened and the actuator is supplied with the required flow.

The new position of the main spool corresponds to the balance between pressure and spring forces (pressure drop at orifices (14 and 15), springs (5 and 6)). The pressure in A is held constant with respect to the value set at pilot spring (8) and whilst obeying the pressure- flow characteristic of the valve.

4.5.2 Pressure holding function

If no flow is required at port A (cylinder or motor idle), the pressure drop at orifices (14 and 15) decreases. Main spool (2) is pushed via spring (5) to the right against spring (6) and so to the closing position. As the pressure in P is greater than that in A, leakage flows from P to A as well as via line (13), orifices (14, 15) and via line (10) to pilot valve (3). The increase in pressure due to the leakage flow acts via control line (16) on pilot spool (7) and pushes this further against spring (8) until its control land (19) opens the connection to pressure free port Y (tank). The pressure in A is still kept constant in accordance with the value set at spring (8). As a result of the low leakage flow the pressure drop at main spool orifices (14 and 15) is not sufficient to push the main spool against spring (6). Main spool (2) remains in the closed position.

4.5.3 Pressure limiting function

If the pressure increases in A due to the influence of external forces on the set value, a larger amount of pilot oil flows via line (13), orifices (14 and 15), line (10) and control land (19) of pilot spool (7) and then via Y to tank. The direction of pilot oil flow is now in the opposite direction to that occurring in the pressure reduction function. If the pressure drop at orifices (14 and 15) exceeds the value which corresponds to the force of spring (6), main spool (2) is pushed to the right against spring (6) and the connection of A to T is opened. The new position of the main spool corresponds to the balance of pressure and spring forces (pressure drop at orifices (14 and 15), spring (6)). The pressure in A is held constant with respect to the value set at pilot spring (8) and whilst obeying the pressure- flow characteristic of the valve.

Pilot flow is always externally returned, as pressure free as possible, via line (20) to port Y.

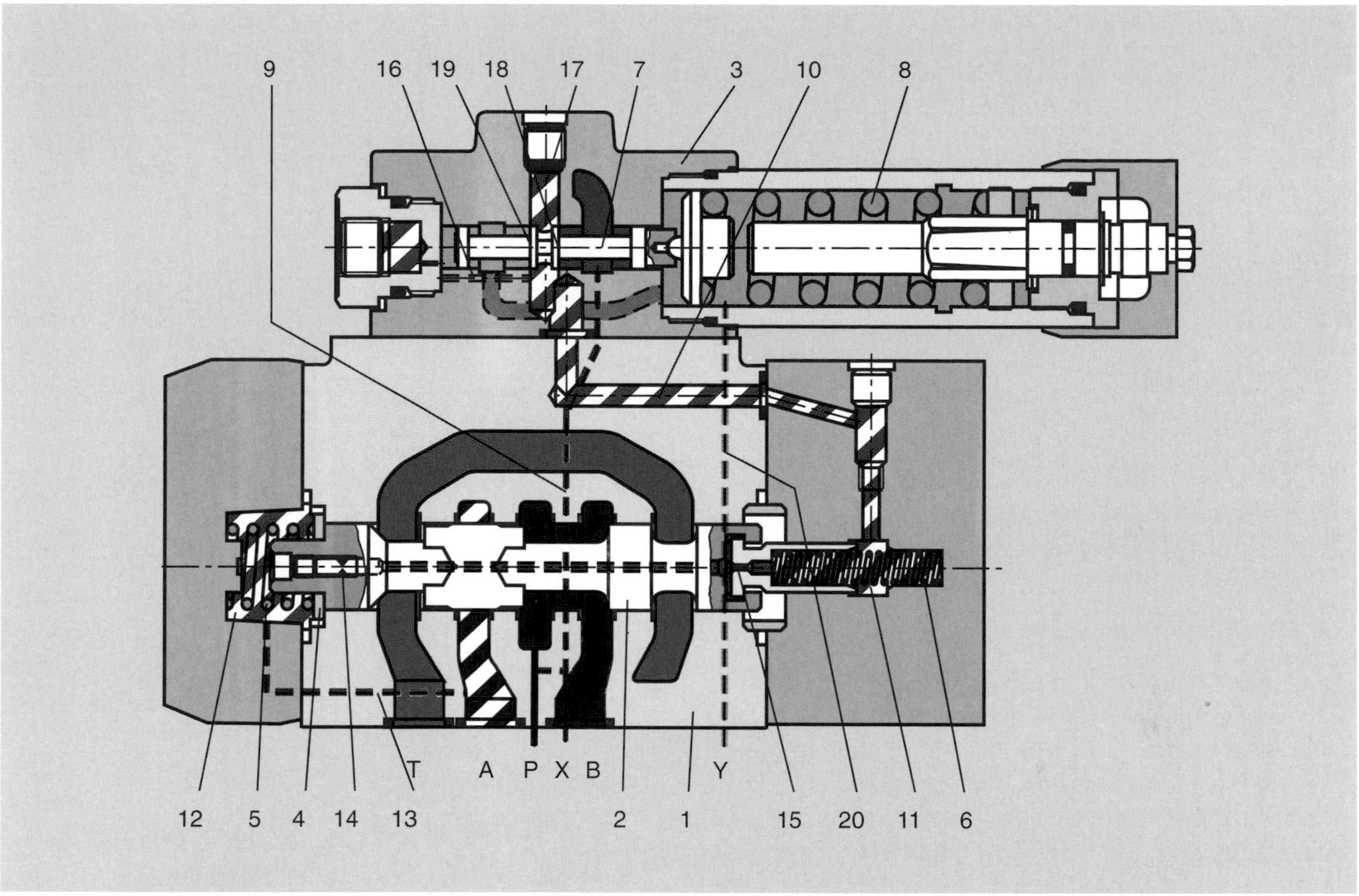

Fig. 40: *Pilot operated 3-way pressure reducing valve*

Important parameters

Sizes	10, 25 and 32
Operating pressure	up to 210 (350 bar)
Flow	up to 400 L/min

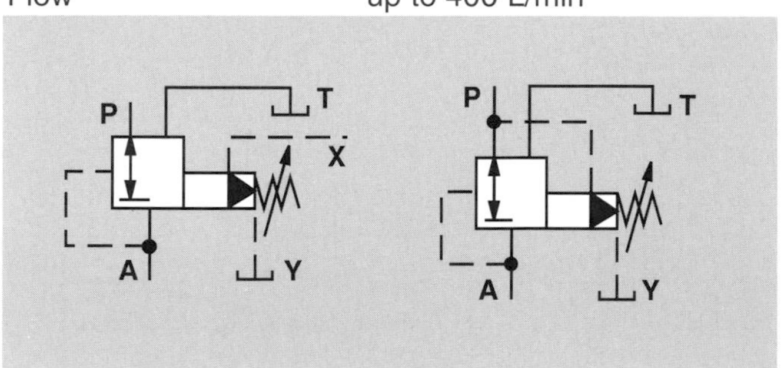

Fig. 41: *3-way pressure reducing valve; left external, right internal pilot oil feed*

4.6 Technical Data

4.6.1 Stationary operating curves

The same operating curves apply to the pressure reducing valve as to a pressure relief valve, though there are some exceptions. The flow described is the flow to the actuator and the setting pressure is the output pressure p_A.

The operating curve field (diagram 10) shows the change in output pressure p_A with respect to the flow at a constant input pressure p_E. In pressure reducing functions, the dotted line represents the lowest actuator resistance dependent on flow. This operating curve is used when considering the application limit for the valve in the hydraulic system.

When considering the pressure relief function (only 3-way pressure reducing function) the characteristic of the return resistance (tank line) is also shown as a dotted line. This represents the limit of application for a controlled pressure limiting function and is dependent on the hydraulic system used.

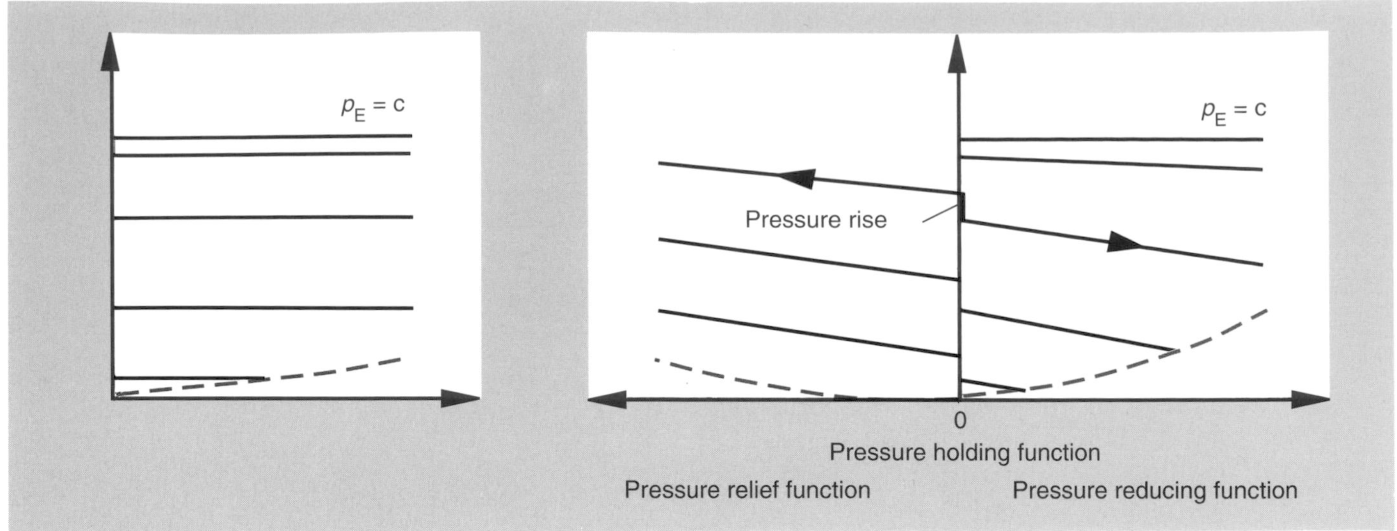

Diagram 10: p_A-Q *operating curves for pilot operated pressure reducing valves, left: 2-way model, right: 3-way model*

4.6.1.1 Control deviation

The control deviation is the change in the set pressure with respect to the flow. There is a considerable difference in the gradients of the operating curves (control deviation) between pilot operated and direct operated pressure reducing valves. The control deviation in direct operated valves is larger than in pilot operated valves, as the change in spring force with respect to the stroke of the main spool is larger. On the operating curve field of the 3-way model (*diagram 10*), there is a clear pressure increase set during the pressure holding function in the cross-over from pressure reducing function to pressure relief function. This pressure increase is produced as a result of the positive overlap of the control lands of pilot spool (7) and main spool (2). During the cross-over, pilot spool (7) carries out an "idle stroke", during which both pilot ports are closed. Accordingly the force of the pre-tensioning spring is increased and hence the pressure at valve output A is increased.

This increase in pressure may be avoided by using a negative overlap in the pilot spool. However, an increase in the leakage flow must then be reckoned with.

4.6.1.2 Pilot oil flow

In 3-way pressure reducing valves, the pilot oil always flows to the actuator during the pressure reducing function. In the pressure holding function the leakage drains away via port Y. In pilot operated 2-way pressure reducing valves the complete pilot oil always drains away via port Y. This is dependent on the actuator flow, the pressure difference between valve input and output and the level of the set pressure.

The pilot oil flow curve as a parameter for the pressure reducing valve, size 10 (2-way pressure reducing valve) is shown in diagram 11 with respect to the pressure difference ($\Delta p = p_E - p_A$).

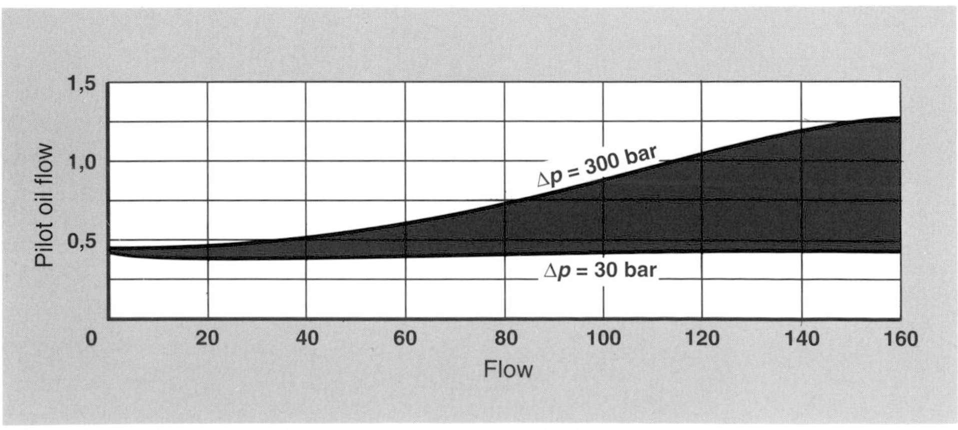

Diagram 11: Q_{St}-Q *operating curve at* Δp ($p_E = p_A$) *of 30 and 300 bar*

4.6.1.3 Lowest pressure setting and maximum actuator flow

Both of these parameters may only be considered in conjunction with each other. Basically the valve is set at a flow of zero. The dotted operating curve of the actuator resistance dependent on flow represents the lowest pressure at the valve output (*diagram 10*, pressure reducing function). Each point on this operating curve represents a specific setting value for the valve. At the same time this is the lowest pressure which may be set for the particular application being considered.

If a lower value is set, the desired flow may no longer be obtained. In theory, in direct operated pressure reducing valves the lowest pressure of $p_A = 0$ may be set. However, no actuator flow is available then, as the origin of the operating curve for the actuator resistance is also at zero (*diagram 10*). In pilot operated pressure reducing valves, the lowest pressure set is determined by the force of the main spool spring in addition to the backpressure of the pilot flow acting on the main spool. This pressure is generally in the region of 3 to 7 bar when the flow is zero.

An exception to this is the 3-way pressure reducing valve, as here the pilot oil flow is fed from a direct operated pilot operated pressure reducing valve directly to the actuator.

A further application limit in pressure reducing valves is found in the minimum pressure difference required between input and output. If the selected value is too low, the control spool reaches its max. stroke before the desired actuator flow is available. A further pressure reduction is then not possible in such cases.

For these reasons, the operating curves supplied by the manufacturer for the minimum pressure difference dependent on flow must be taken into account (*diagram 12*).

In summary, the lowest set pressure is attained, when the appropriate control operating curve cuts the actuator resistance curve at the desired flow.

4.6.2 Dynamic characteristics

In practical applications, good dynamic characteristics are demanded of pressure reducing valves. The pressure peaks which occur when the actuator (cylinder of motor) is suddenly idle should be kept as low as possible. The pressure drops which occur when the machine is restarted after an idle period should also be kept low.

With the exception of pilot-operated 3-way pressure reducing valve, the main spool in pressure reducing valves is open initially. If the actuator flow is suddenly decreased, the control spool must close against the spring as quickly as possible. The delay which occurs due to the frictional and flow forces leads to an undesirable increase in pressure (pressure peak) in the actuator circuit.

On the other hand, if the flow suddenly increases the main spool must open as quickly as possible, in order to avoid the actuator pressure sinking by a large amount over a short time. The size of pressure peaks and pressure drops are dependent on the dynamic characteristics of the valve (type, pilot circuit), actuator (cylinder or motor), parameters (p_E, p_A, Q), as well as to a large extent on the actuator flow (e.g. cylinder and pipe volume).

4.6.2 Notes on applications

A critical application is that of pressure holding, if no flow is required on the actuator side. The control spools working in the range of the overlap are prone to being contaminated (dirt particles entering the control clearance) due to the continuous and considerable flow of pilot oil. This leads to pressure oscillations on the actuator side.

In order to avoid this, it is sensible to add a by-pass line for a small flows (0.5 to 1.5 L/mm). In addition, it is especially important to filter the fluid really well.

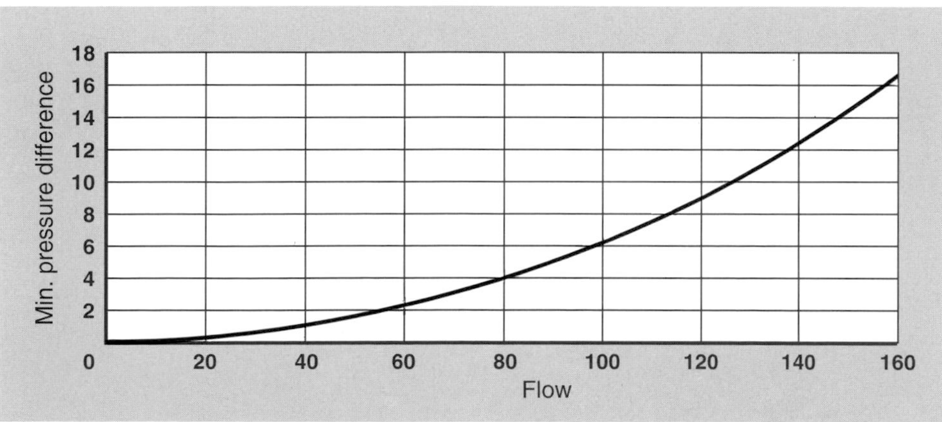

Diagram 12: Δp_{min}-*Q operating curve*

Notes

Chapter 13

Flow Control Valves

Dr Harald Geis, Johann Oppolzer

1 General

Flow control valves are used to influence the speed of movement of actuators by changing the opening to flow (decreasing or increasing) at a throttling point.

A special flow control valve is a flow divider which divides a flow into two or more flows.

Dependent on their behaviour flow control valves may be divided into 4 groups (see *table 1*).

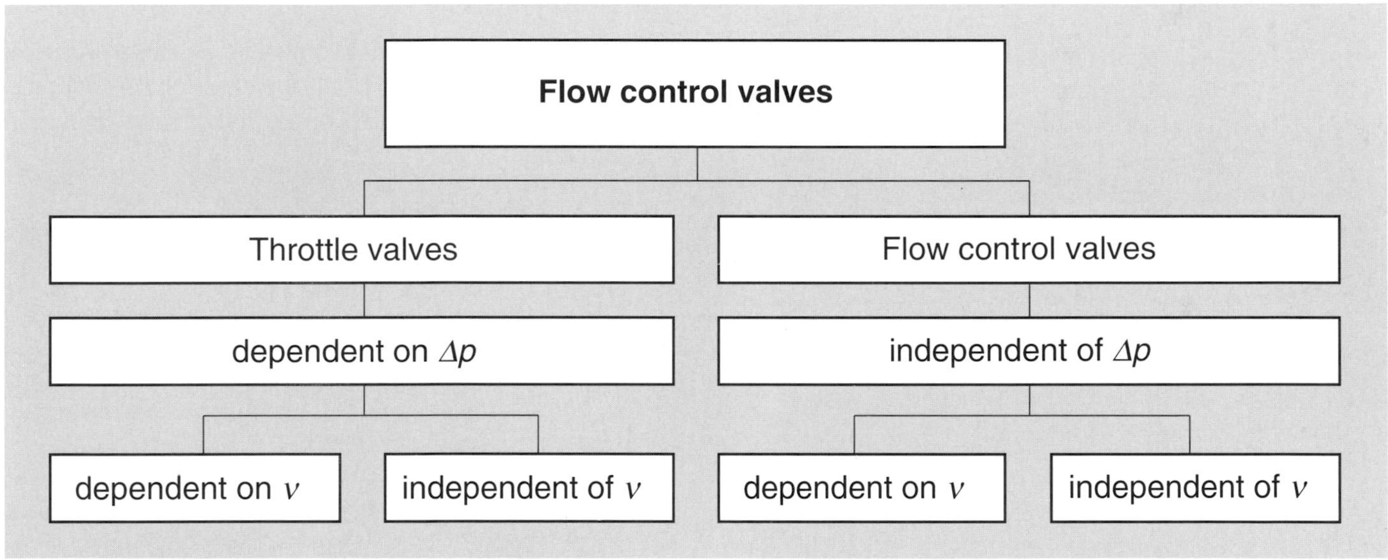

Table 1: *Summary of types of flow control valves*

Fig. 1: *Throttle valves*

Fig. 2: *Flow control valves*

The flow is adjusted in flow control valves by means of throttles. The flow at a throttling point may be calculated according to DIN 1952:

$$Q = \alpha \cdot A \cdot \sqrt{\frac{\Delta p \cdot 2}{\rho}} \qquad (1)$$

Where

Q	= flow	in	m^3/s
A	= throttle opening	in	cm^2
Δp	= pressure loss	in	N/m^2
ρ	= density	in	Ns^2/m^4
α	= flow coefficient dependent on throttle type 0.6 to 0.9		

The flow coefficient considers several influences, such as contraction, friction, viscosity and the type of throttling point and may be used for jets and orifices.

$$\alpha = \sqrt{\frac{1}{\xi}} \qquad (2)$$

The resistance coefficient may be calculated as follows for laminar flow:

$$\xi = \frac{l \cdot 64 \cdot \nu}{v \cdot d_H{}^2} \qquad (3)$$

l	= throttle range	in	m
ν	= kinematic viscosity	in	m^2/s
v	= flow velocity	in	m/s
d_H	= hydraulic diameter	in	m

$$d_H = \frac{4 \cdot A}{U} \qquad (4)$$

A = throttle opening

U = flow path

From equation 1, it is clear that the throttle area may be made larger for smaller pressure differences (constant flow). This prevents the valve from becoming "clogged".

Throttling is very dependent on the type of throttling point (see *table 2*). This is especially the case for the change in opening with respect to the throttle path (possible resolution).

Name/form	Diagram	Throttle opening A in cm^2	Remark
Throttle	d	$\frac{d^2 \cdot \pi}{4}$	Good throttle opening due to small wetted contact area, but dependent on viscosity due to long throttling path.
Orifice	d	$\frac{d^2 \cdot \pi}{4}$	Good throttle opening due to small wetted contact area. The throttling path is almost zero and hence nearly independent of viscosity.

Table 2: *Throttle openings for constant throttles*

Name/Form	Diagram	Throttle opening A in cm^2	Remark
Needle throttle	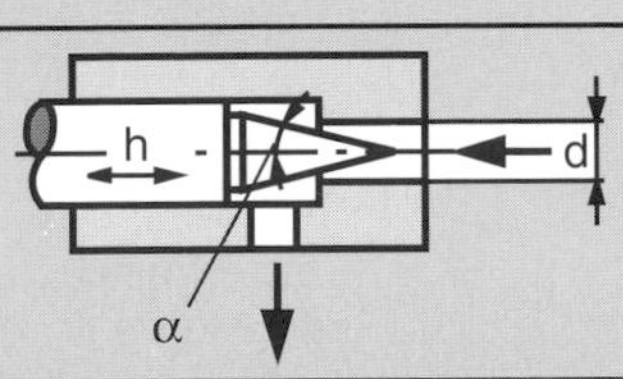 h, d, α	$(d - h \cdot tg\alpha) \cdot h \cdot tg\alpha \cdot \pi$	The throttle path is short, the wetted contact area small and the influence of viscosity low. Danger of clogging for small flows, as they require a very small annular opening. Poor resolution.
Longitudinal slot (triangle)	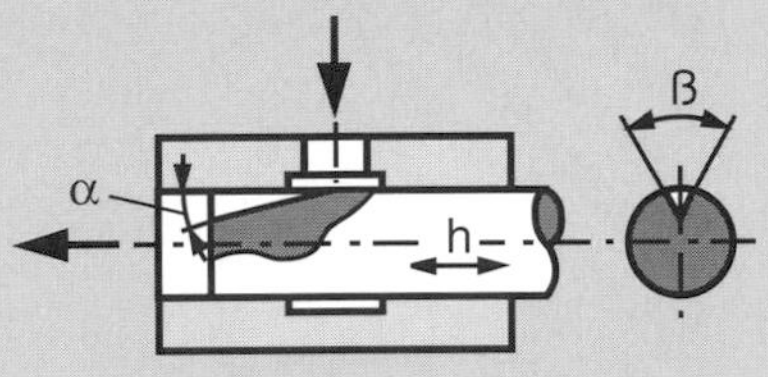 α, h, β	$\frac{h^2}{\sin^2 \alpha} \cdot tg\beta / 2$	The throttle path is relatively short and the wetted contact area relatively small. The influence of viscosity and the danger of clogging is small. Good resolution for the adjustment path for changing the opening to flow. Suitable for small flows.
Longitudinal slot (rectangle)	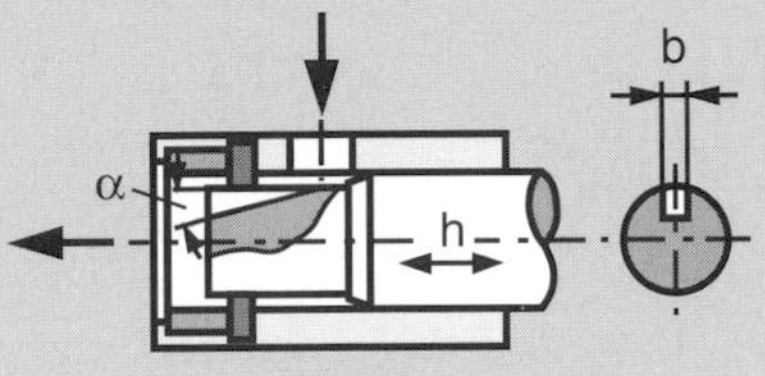 α, h, b	$tg\ \alpha \cdot h \cdot b$	Throttle path is relatively short and the wetted contact area is relatively small. Influence of viscosity and danger of clogging low. Good resolution of adjustment path with respect to the changing of the opening to flow. Suitable for small flows.
Clearance throttle	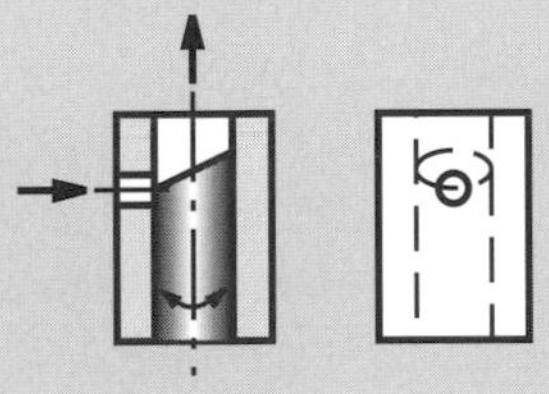		Short throttle path, but large wetted contact area Influence of viscosity still relatively low. Not so suitable for small flows as the throttling point is a small clearance and hence the danger of clogging is high. Poor resolution.
Circumference throttle Triangular form	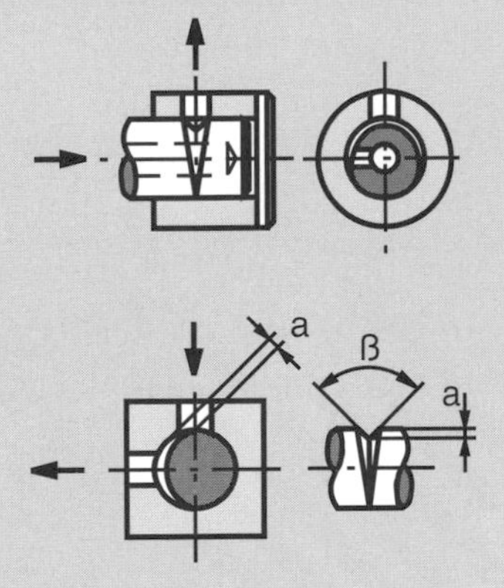 a, β, a	$\frac{tg\ \beta}{2} \cdot a^2$ (circular section ignored)	Throttle path is long, hence dependent on viscosity. The resolution (adjustment path with respect to changes in the opening to flow) is not very good, as usually it is only possible to turn through 90 to 180°.

Table 3: *Throttle openings for variable throttles*

From *diagram 1*, it is clear that the triangular shape is the best one with respect to the resolution of the adjustment path.

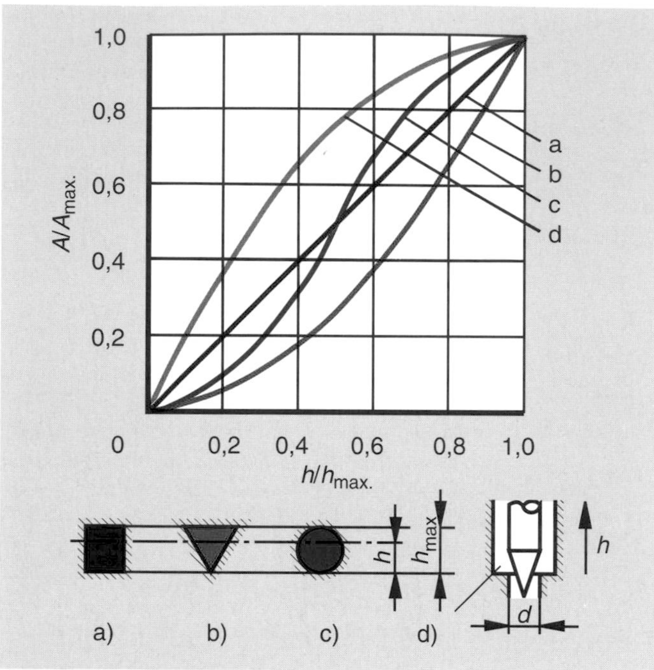

Diagram 1: *Resolutions for different types of throttle*

2 Throttle valves

The flow of throttle valves is related to the pressure drop at the throttle position, i.e. a larger pressure drop results in a larger flow.

In many controls where a constant flow is not essential, throttle valves are often used on their own as flow control valves are too expensive for this purpose.

Throttle valves are used, when

- there is constant working resistance or
- a change in speed is irrelevant or even desirable with changing load.

Equation 3 for the resistance coefficient shows the relationship to the viscosity. The shorter the throttle length l, the less noticeable is a change in viscosity. It should also be noted that the flow increases as the fluid becomes thinner.

Whether a valve is dependent on or is practically independent of the viscosity, depends on the throttle design.

2.1 Viscosity dependent throttle valves

2.1.1 Pipe mounted throttle valves

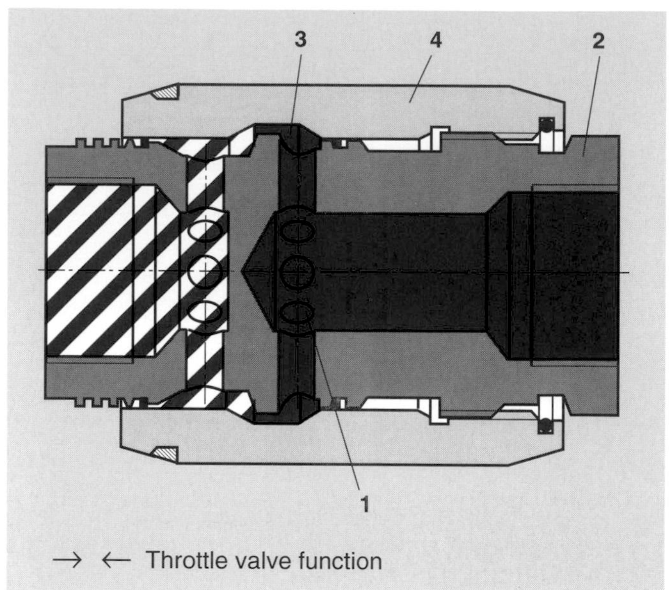

Fig. 3: *Throttle valve, type MG*

Fluid reaches throttle position (3) by means of side bores (1) in housing (2). This throttle is formed between the housing and adjustable sleeve (4). By turning the sleeve, the annular opening at the throttle position may be altered steplessly. Throttling occurs in both directions (*fig. 3*).

If throttling is required in one direction only, and additional check valve is necessary.

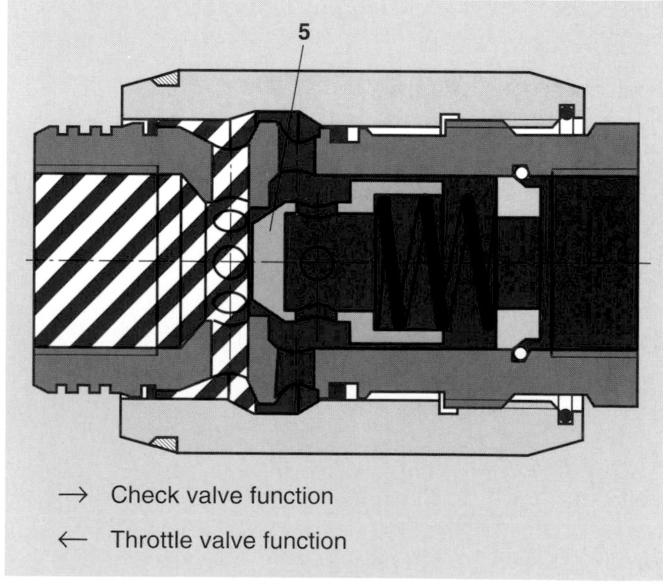

Fig. 4: *Throttle check valve, type MK*

In the throttling direction, fluid reaches the rear side of valve poppet (5). The poppet of the check valve is pushed on its seat. The throttling procedure is as for valve type MG (*fig. 3*).

In the opposite direction (from right to left) the flow acts on the face surface of the check valve. The poppet is lifted from its seat. Fluid flows unthrottled through the valve. At the same time, part of the fluid passes over the annular clearance and thus the desired self-cleaning process is achieved.

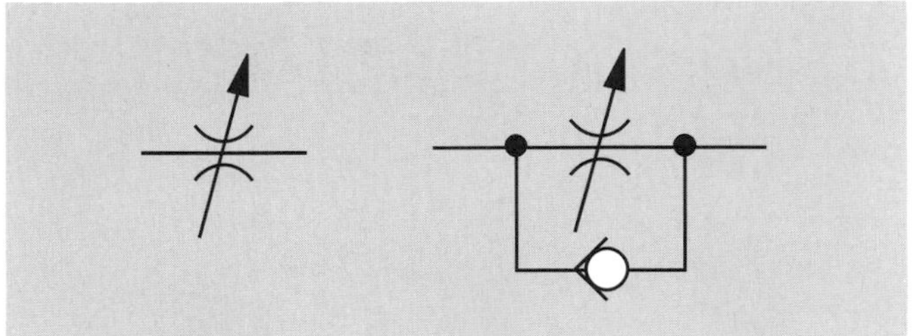

Fig. 5: *Left: throttle valve, right: throttle check valve*

Fig. 6: *Pipe mounted throttle and throttle check valves*

Important parameters

Sizes:	6 to 30
Flow:	up to 400 L/min
Operating pressure:	up to 315 bar

2.1.2 Throttle valves for sub-plate mounting and flange connection (may also be installed directly into pipes)

This model is suitable for larger flows of up to 3000 L/min at a pressure of 315 bar. The large displacement forces which are produced may be easily controlled by the square ended adjustment screw (1).

Fig. 7: *Throttle valve for subplate mounting, type MG*

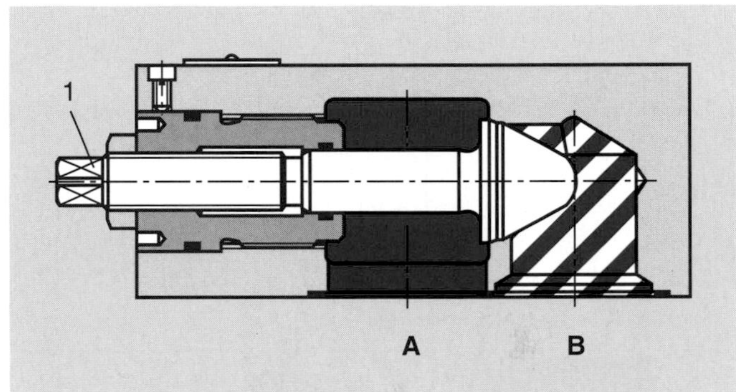

Fig. 8: *Throttle valve for subplate mounting, type MG*

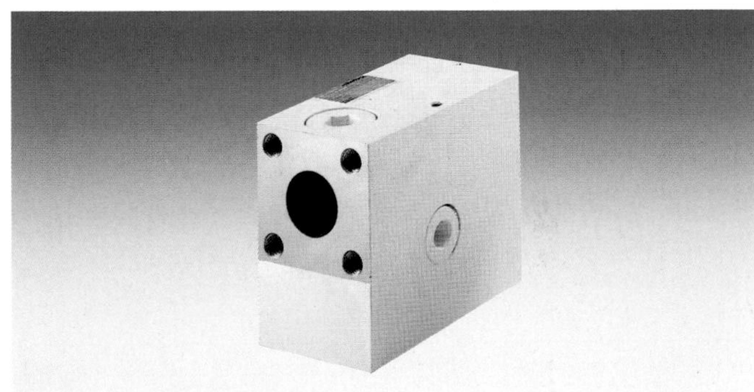

Fig. 9: *Throttle check valve for flange mounting, type MK*

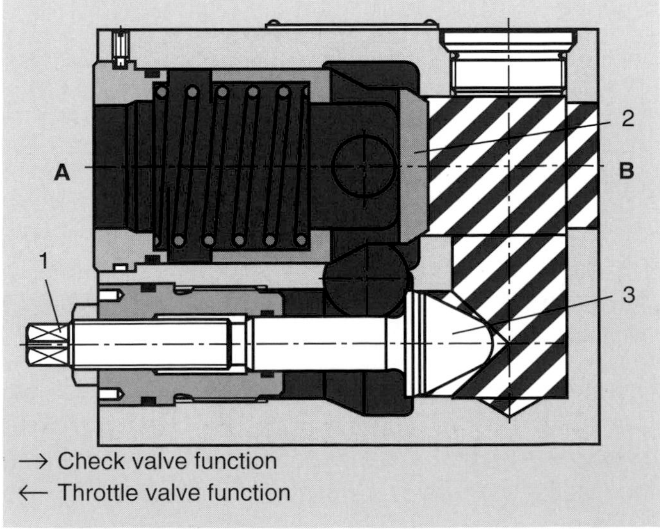

Fig. 10: *Throttle check valve for flange mounting, type MK*

2.1.3 Throttles and throttle check valves for manifold mounting

This valve is designed to be inserted into a manifold and therefore does not have its own housing. The valve is inserted or screwed into the installation cavity.

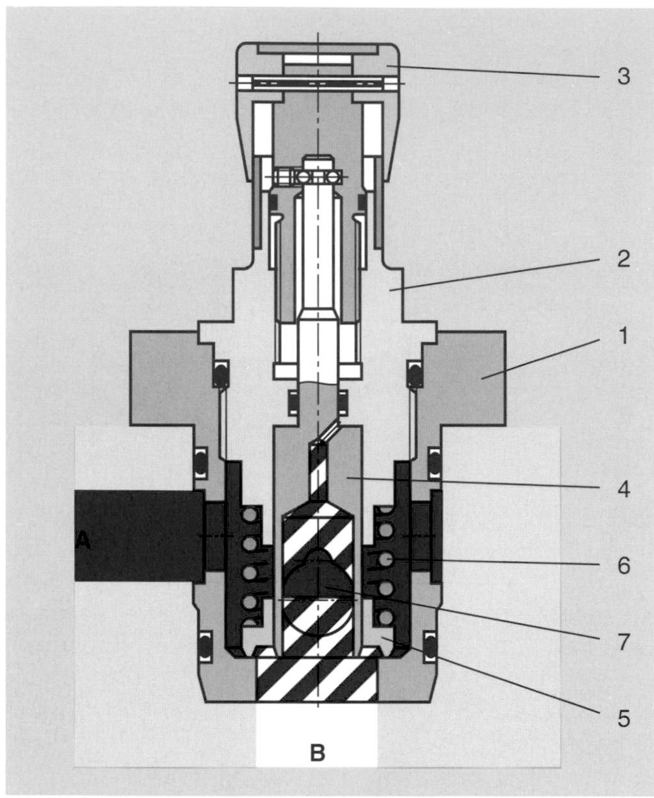

Fig. 11: *Cartridge throttle check valve, type FK*

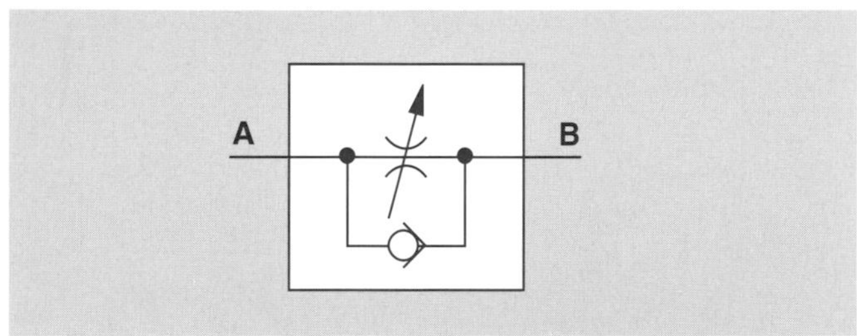

Fig. 12: *Throttle check valve for manifold mounting, type FK*

The throttle/check valve comprises a cartridge bush (1), valve body (2) with adjustment head (3) and throttle pin (4) and also a check valve (5) with spring (6).

The throttle direction is from A to B. The throttle opening is formed by the throttle pin with throttle opening (7) and check valve ring (5). When the adjustment knob is turned, the throttle pin moves vertically and alters the throttle opening.

When there is flow from B to A the check valve ring is pushed upwards. Fluid flows without throttling to port A.

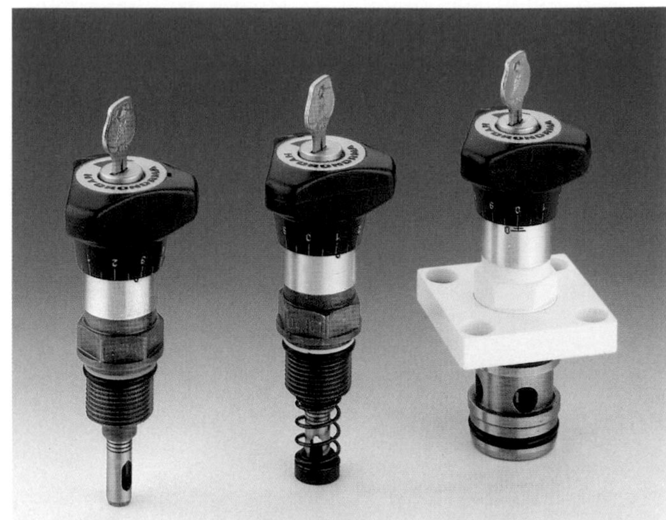

Fig. 13: *Throttle and throttle check valves for manifold mounting, left and centre: screwed in, right: inserted*

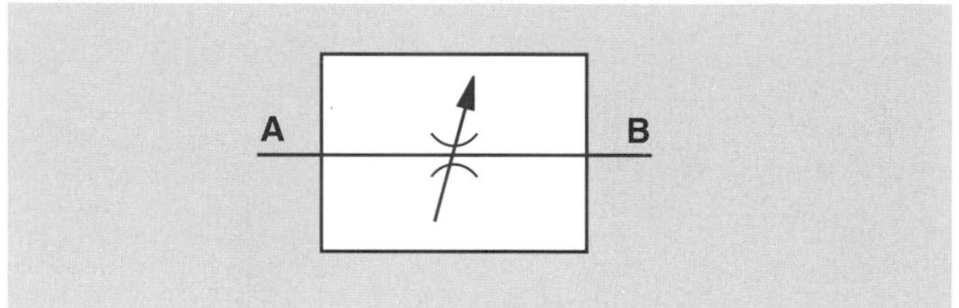

Fig. 14: *Throttle valve for manifold mounting, type FG*

Important parameters

Sizes:	16, 25 and 32
Flow:	up to 400 L/min
Operating pressure:	up to 315 bar
3 adjustment elements:	– rotary knob
	– lockable rotary knob with scale or
	– rotary knob with scale

Various cracking pressures

2.1.4 Throttle check valves for sandwich plate mounting

These valves may be used for limiting either main or pilot flow in one or two actuator ports. In type Z2FS (*fig. 15*), two symmetrically arranged throttle check valves are mounted in a sub-plate, which limit flow in one direction and allow free flow in the opposite direction.

2.1.4.2 Limiting of pilot flow

The twin throttle check valve may be used to set the operation times (pilot flow limitation) in pilot operated directional valves. The valve is then placed between the pilot valve and the main valve.

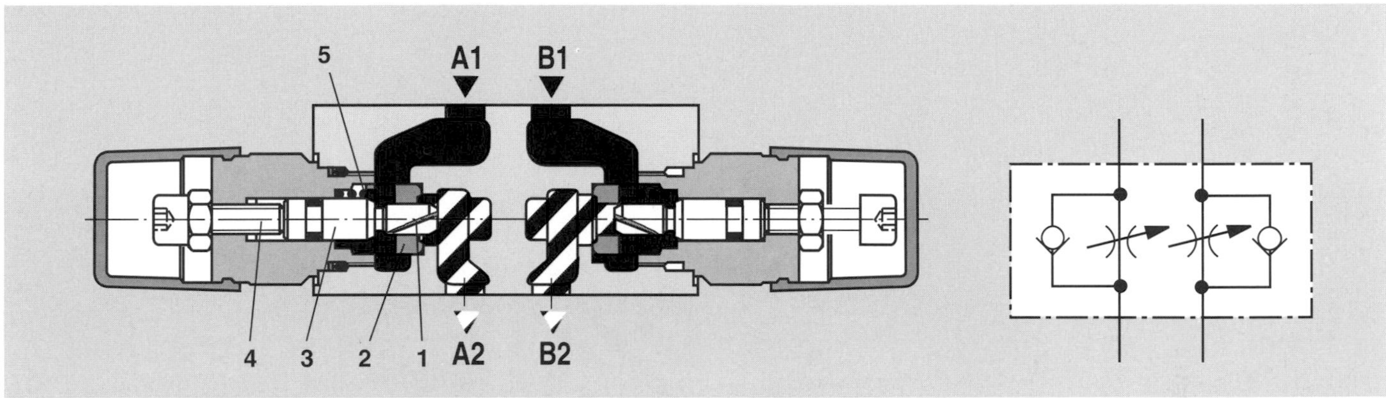

Fig. 15: *Twin throttle check valve, type Z2FS*

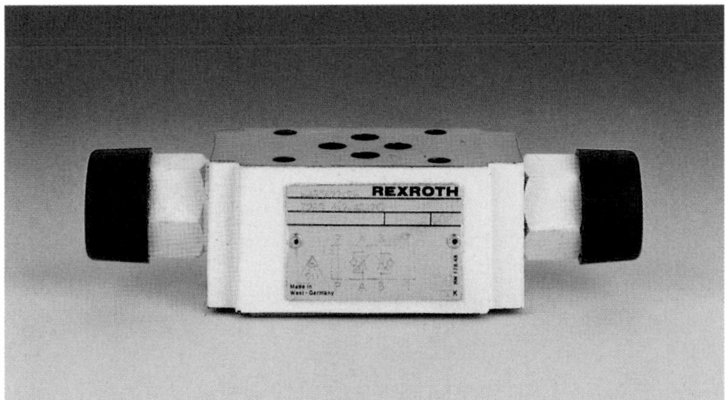

Fig. 16: *Twin throttle check valve, type Z2FS*

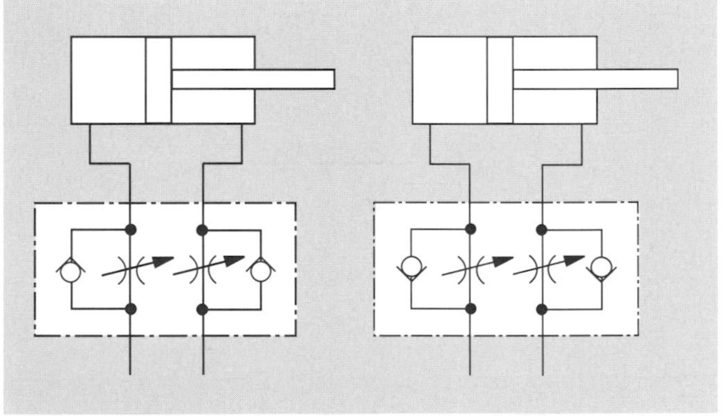

Fig. 18: *Circuit example, left: feed circuit, right: return circuit*

Fluid in channel A1 reached actuator A2 via throttling point (1) which is formed by the valve seat (2) and throttle spool (3). Throttle spool (3) may be axially adjusted by means of setting screw (4) and hence throttle opening (1) is adjusted.

The fluid returning from actuator B2 pushes valve seat (2) against spring (5) in the direction of throttle spool (3) and hence allows free return flow. Depending on the installation, throttling may take place either in the feed or return lines (meter-in or meter-out).

2.1.4.1 Limiting of main flow

In order to change the velocity of an actuator (main flow limitation), the twin throttle check valve is fitted between the directional valve and subplate.

Important parameters

Sizes:	6, 10, 16 and 22
Flow:	up to 350 L/min
Operating pressure:	up to 350 bar
4 adjustment elements:	Screw with lock nut and protective cap, lockable rotary knob with scale, screw with scale or rotary knob with scale.

2.1.5 Deceleration valves

Deceleration valves are used to smoothly decelerate or accelerate hydraulically moved loads. Deceleration/ acceleration is related to the movement of the load.

In fig. 19 a model is shown with a normally open main flow throttle (2), with secondary fixed flow throttle (7) and check valve (6).

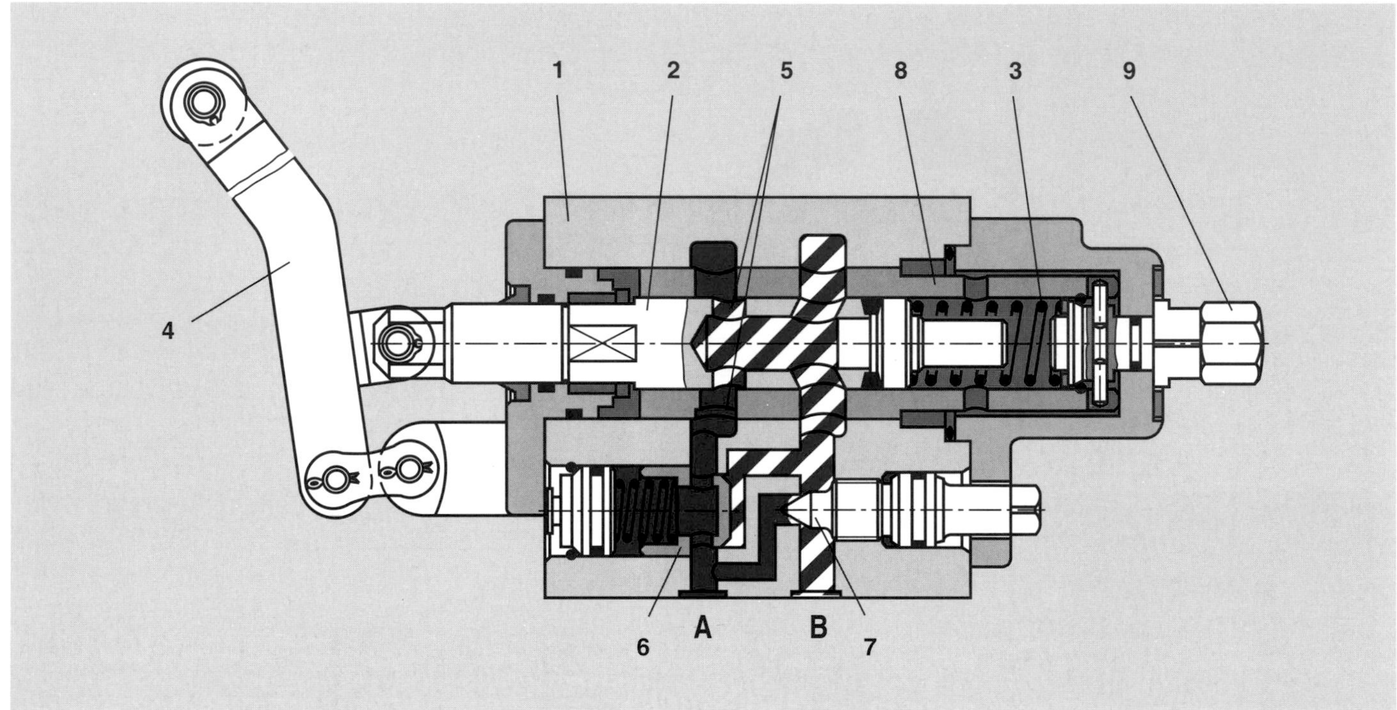

Fig. 19: *Deceleration valve with roller lever operation*

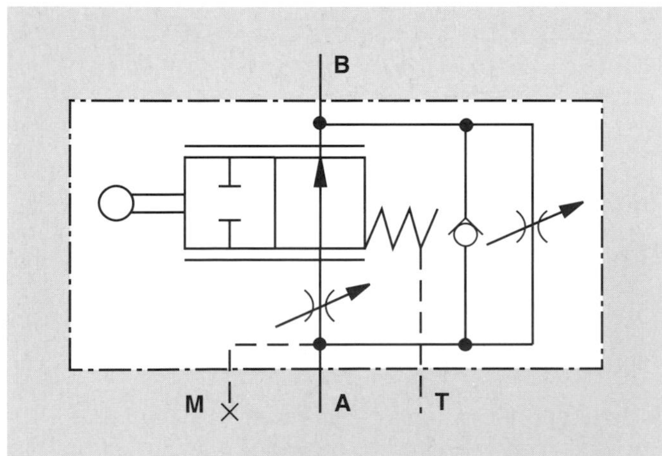

Fig. 20: *Symbol for a deceleration valve*

The main throttle spool (2) is pushed to the left into its rest position by spring (3) in housing (1).

Depending on the spool type, the connection A to B is open in the rest position (as shown in *fig. 20*) or closed. *Fig. 21* shows the arrangement.

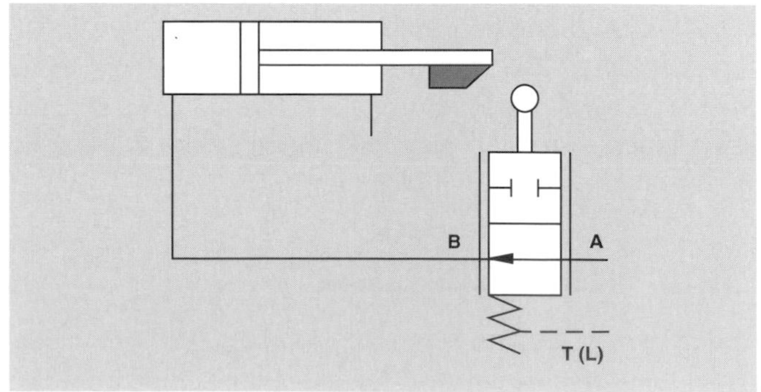

Fig. 21: *Circuit example using a deceleration valve*

The cylinder the velocity of which is to be changed, operates the roller lever (4) of the deceleration valve via a cam. *Fig. 21* shows the relevant arrangement.

The throttle spool is pushed back against the spring. Flow opening (5) therefore decreases as the piston moves. The cylinder speed decreases and hence the cylinder decelerates.

If the connection A to B is completely closed, the cylinder remains stationaryl. It has interrupted the oil supply (not completely leakfree).

The deceleration is dependent on the cam form employed.

In order to allow the cylinder to travel out of the closed position, a check valve (6) can be arranged in parallel to the throttle spool. It ensures free flow from B to A. The cylinder then travels unthrottled from its position. If a check valve is not present, an acceleration occurs when travelling out of the end position.

A smaller flow may be set on secondary flow throttle (7) if main flow throttle (2) is closed (rapid traverse/feed).

Important parameters

Sizes:	6 to 32
Flow:	up to 700 L/min
Operating pressure:	up to 315 bar

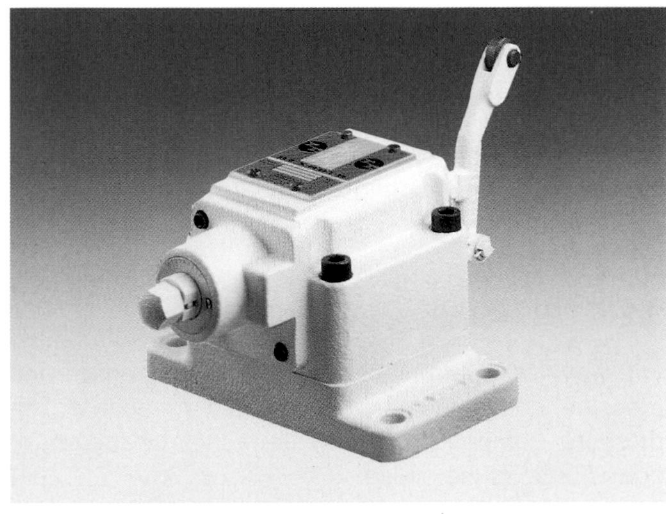

Fig. 22: *Deceleration valves operated by roller lever*

2.2 Throttle valves independent of viscosity

These valves (*fig. 23*) also known as fine throttles are designed with orifice type throttles. They basically comprise housing (1), setting element (2) and orifice (3).

Flow from A to B is throttled at orifice window (4). The throttle opening is adjusted by a pin (5) the lower end of which is a lip in the form of a helix. The low dependence on temperature is due to the throttle being a sharp edged orifice.

The preferred direction of flow is from A to B. By means of an adjustment screw (6) the orifice revealed by the centre pin can be opened and closed. Hence the adjustment is matched to the adjustment scale (little deviation). During operation, the orifice with adjustment screw is supported on the valve mounting face.

A pin (8) is fitted to ensure that the orifice cannot turn.

Depending on the type of orifice a linear or progressive flow curve over the adjustment angle (300°) may be selected (see *diagram 1*).

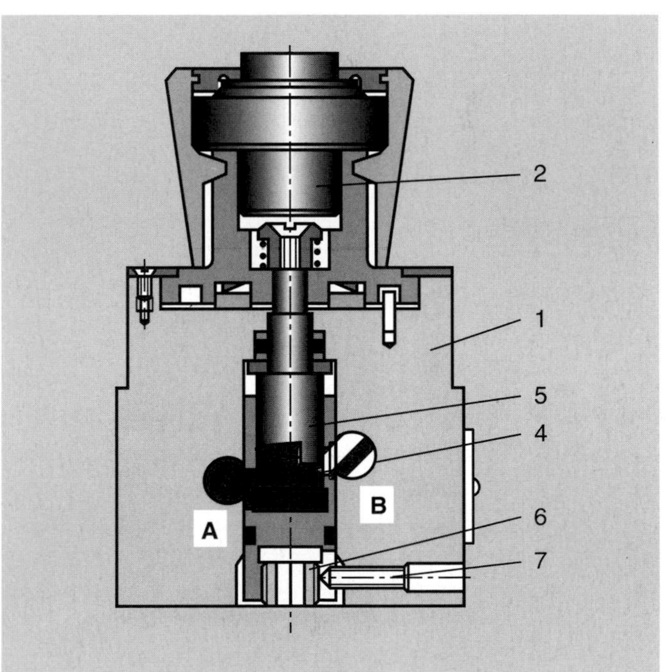

Fig. 23: *Fine throttle valve, type F*

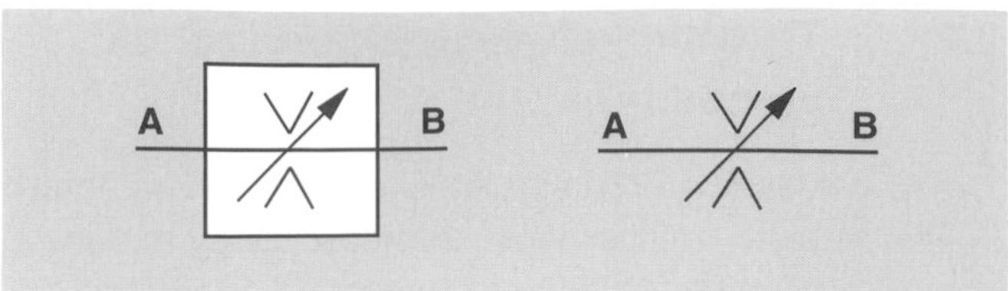

Fig. 24: *Fine throttle valves; left for subplate mounting, right: for manifold mounting*

Fig. 25: *Fine throttle valves; left for sub-plate mounting, type F...P, right for manifold mounting, type F...K*

Important parameters

Sizes:	5 and 10
Flow:	up to 50 L/min
Operating pressure:	up to 210 bar

3 Flow control valves

3.1 General

Flow control valves are used to keep a set flow constant regardless of pressure variations. This is achieved in that in addition to adjustable throttle (1) (measuring throttle) an additional moving throttle (2) is built into the system, which operates as a control throttle (pressure compensator) and at the same time as a comparison element in the closed loop control circuit (*fig. 26*).

Due to the two throttles working together, the changing pressure difference p_1 - p_3 due to the load pressure is divided into two parts:

- the internal and constant pressure difference p_1 -p_2 at the adjustable measuring throttle and
- the external and variable pressure difference p_1 - p_3.

The flow control valve is a controller comprising the following main elements (*fig. 26*):

- measuring throttle (1) and
- pressure compensator (2) with spring (3).

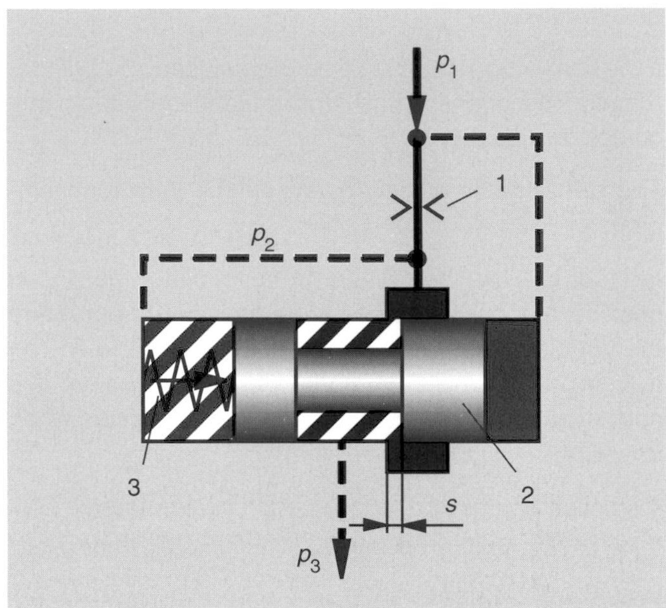

Fig. 26: *Principle of flow control valves*

The adjustable measuring throttle (1) changes the pressure difference p_1 - p_2 when a change in the temperature or viscosity of the fluid occurs. This effect may be negated by suitable design of the throttle.

The arrangement of the pressure compensator determines the type of flow control valve. If the compensator is arranged in series with the measuring throttle, the device is then known as a 2-way flow control valve. If on the other hand the compensator is arranged in parallel with the measuring throttle, the device is then a 3-way flow control valve.

3.2 2-way flow control valves

In 2-way flow control valves the measuring orifice and pressure compensator are arranged in series. The pressure compensator may be either upstream or downstream of the orifice.

3.2.1 Upstream pressure compensator

Fig. 27 shows a 2-way flow control valve with an upstream pressure compensator.

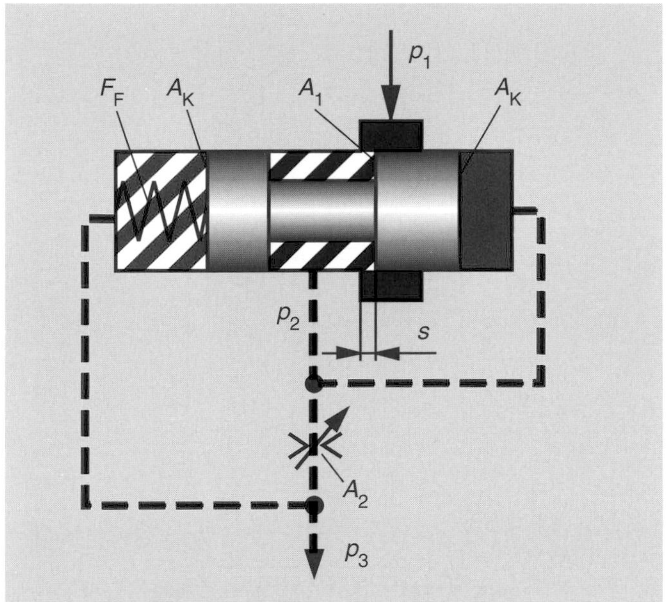

Fig. 27: *Principle of 2-way flow control valve with upstream pressure compensator*

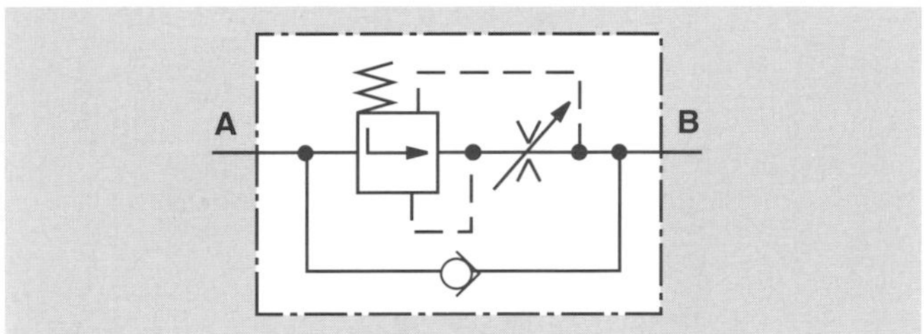

Fig. 28: *2-way flow control valve with upstream pressure compensator*

Control orifice A_1 and measuring orifice A_2 are connected in series. The control spool is pressurised on the right by p_2 and on the left by p_3 and F_F.

Ignoring the flow forces the following is true for the balance at the control spool:

$$p_2 \cdot A_K = p_3 \cdot A_K + F_F \tag{5}$$

The pressure drop at the measuring orifice is given by

$$\Delta p = p_2 - p_3 = F_F / A_K = \text{constant} \tag{6}$$

As the stroke of the control spool is about 1 mm or less and the spring rate is low, the change in spring force with respect to spool stroke may be neglected and hence Δp and Q are constant. As a spring pre-tension is present, the valve cannot operate until the external pressure difference p_1 - p_3 is greater than $\Delta p = F_F / A_K$.

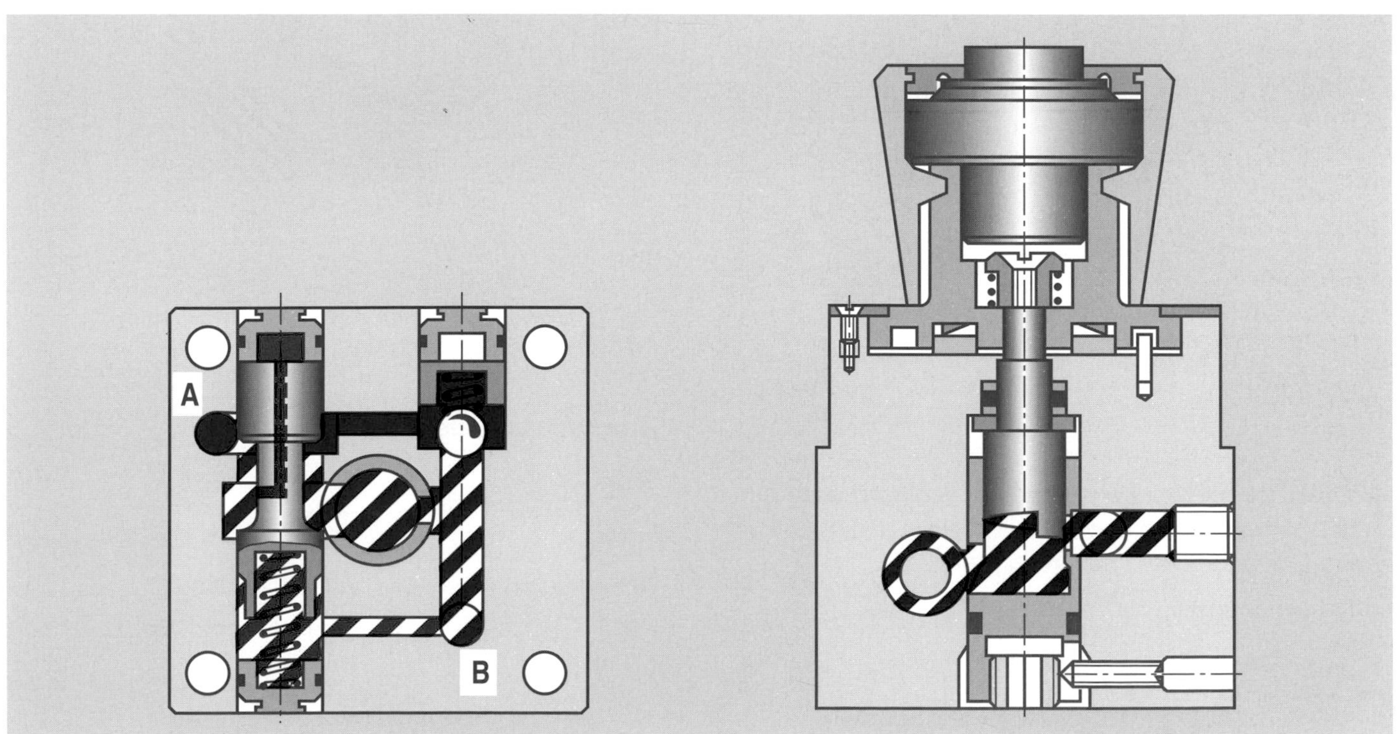

Fig. 29: *2-way flow control valve with upstream pressure compensator*

3.2.2 Downstream pressure compensator

Fig. 30 shows a 2-way flow controller with a down-stream pressure compensator. If the flow and friction forces are once again ignored, the balance at the pressure compensator is given by

$$p_1 \cdot A_K = p_2 \cdot A_K + F_F \qquad (7)$$

$$\Delta p = p_1 - p_2 = F_F / A_K = \text{constant} \qquad (8)$$

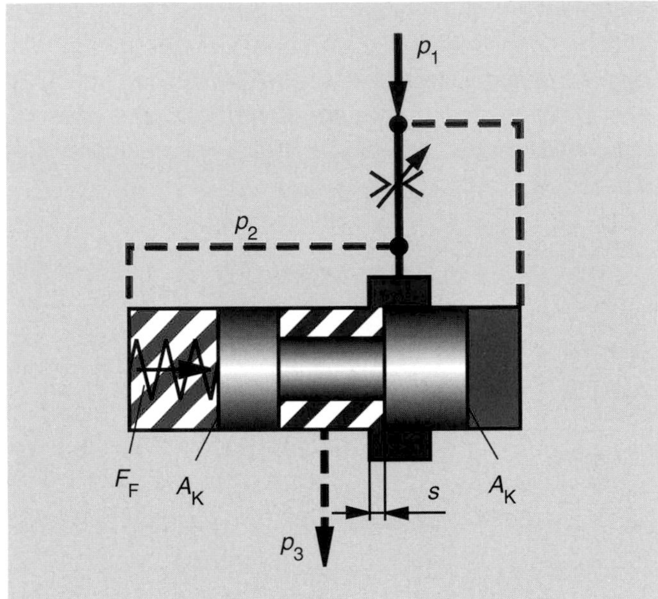

Fig. 30: *Principle of 2-way flow control valve with down-stream pressure compensaotor*

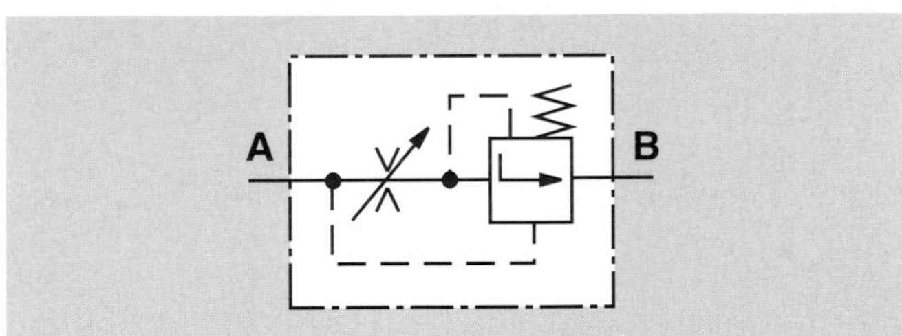

Fig. 31: *2-way flow control valve with downstream pressure compensator*

Whether the pressure compensator is placed upstream or downstream in the flow control valve is dependent on the design and is not relevant in practice.

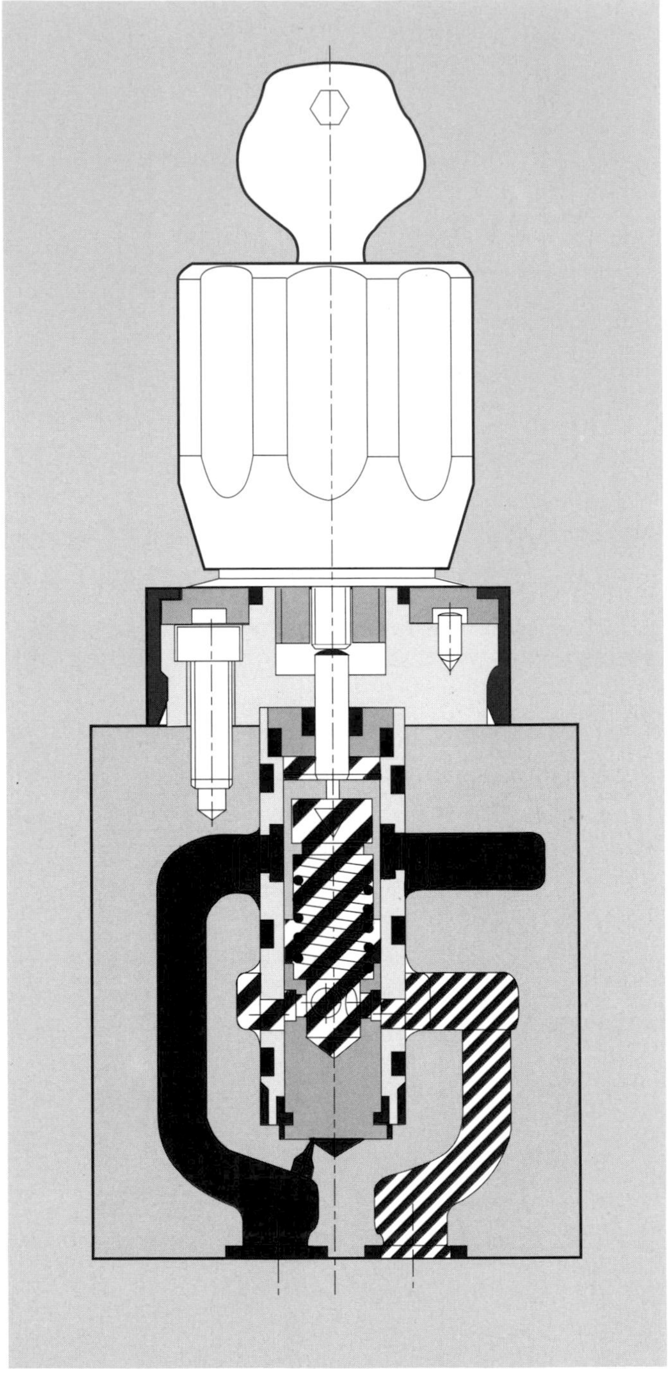

Fig. 32: *2-way flow control valve with downstream pressure compensator*

Important parameters

Sizes:	5, 6, 10 and 16
Flow:	up to 160 L/min
Operating pressure:	up to 315 bar

3.2.3 Application of 2-way flow control valves

There are basically three areas of application:

- Meter-in (primary control)
- Meter-out (secondary control)
- Feed secondary flow control (by-pass)

3.2.3.1 Meter-in

Here the flow control valve is placed in the pressure line between the hydraulic pump and the actuator (*fig. 33*).

This type of control is recommended for hydraulic systems in which the actuator acts against a positive resistance (opposing force) to the controlled flow.

An advantage of this circuit is that the pressure present between the flow control valve (1) and working cylinder (2) only amounts to the working resistance of the cylinder. As there is less pressure on the cylinder seals, there is also lower friction from the sealing ring in the cylinder.

A disadvantage is that because the pressure relief valve (3) is upstream of the flow control valve it is set to the highest actuator pressure. Due to this the hydraulic pump (4) delivers the maximum set pressure even when the actuator only requires a low force.

In addition the heat from the throttle is fed to the actuator.

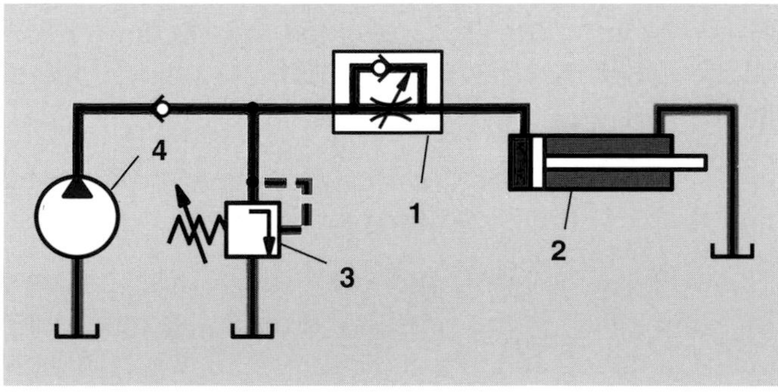

Fig. 33: *Meter in*

3.2.3.2 Meter out

Here the flow control valve (1) is situated in the line between actuator (2) and tank (*fig. 34*).

This type of control is recommended for hydraulic systems with negative or pulling working loads, which tend to cause the cylinder piston (2) to move more quickly than the speed which corresponds to the delivery flow of the pump (4).

The advantage of this is that no counterbalance valve is required. In addition the heat from the throttle is led to tank.

A disadvantage of this type of control is that the pressure relief valve (3) here also needs to be set to the maximum actuator pressure (heat creation).

Even in idle operation several elements of the cylinder are under maximum operating pressure (higher friction).

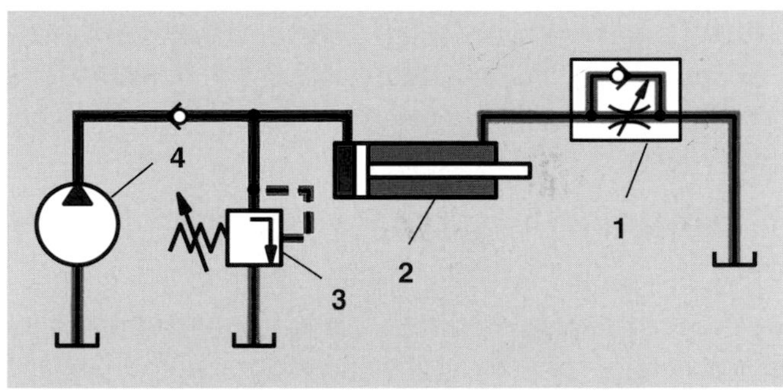

Fig. 34: *Meter out*

3.2.3.3 By-pass control

Here the flow control valve (1) is arranged in parallel to the actuator (2) (*fig. 35*).

The flow control valve only controls the flow being fed to the actuator to a limited extent, as a set portion of the pump delivery flow is returned to tank.

However an advantage of this type of control is that during a working stroke only the pressure required for the load is built up.

Hence less power is converted to heat. It is not until the cylinder runs against the stop that the pressure set on the pressure relief valve (3) is reached.

In this control the throttle heat is also led back to tank.

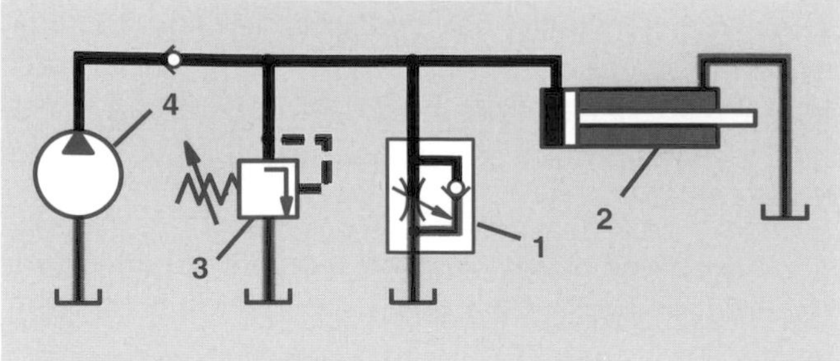

Fig. 35: *Feed by-pass control*

3.2.3.4 Avoidance of jumps when starting

At rest, there is no flow through the flow control valve and the pressure compensator is completely open.

As flow starts the spool of the pressure compensator moves to its control position. However in the time it takes the spool to reach its control position it is possible for a large volume of fluid to briefly flow through the orifice before control is established.

In practice this behaviour causes the cylinder to jump as it starts.

In order to avoid this effect, the spool of the pressure compensator may be kept close to the control position mechanically by a stroke limiter (1) (*fig. 36*).

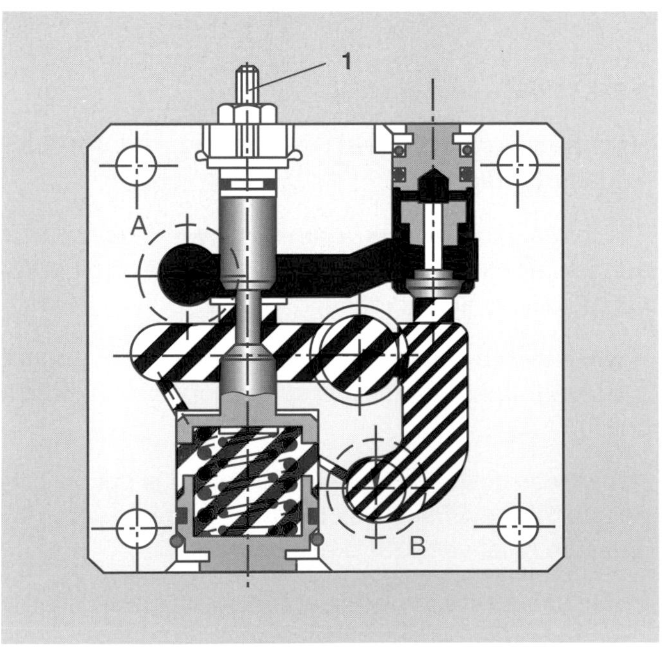

Fig. 36: *Flow control valve with mechanical stroke limiting to prevent jumps on start-up*

Another possible way of avoiding this starting jump is by means of a special circuit which hydraulically keeps the spool of the pressure compensator at a closed initial position. (*fig. 37*).

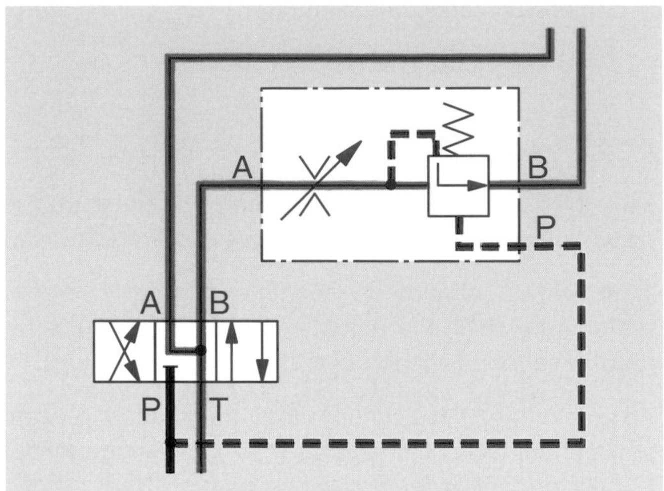

Fig. 37: *Pressure compensator kept closed by hydraulic means*

3.3 3-way flow control valves

In contrast to 2-way flow control valves, the measuring orifice A_2 and the control orifice A_1 are not connected in series but in parallel in 3-way flow control valves.

The pressure compensator controls the excess flow via an additional line to tank. A pressure relief valve must be included in the hydraulic circuit to protect the maximum pressure. Usually this pressure relief valve is integrated into the 3-way flow control valve.

As the excess flow Q_R is returned to tank, 3-way flow control valves may only be placed in the feed lines to actuators (meter-in).

In this type of valve it is also possible to have an unloading port X which enables flow to be almost free.

The hydraulic pump need only supply an operating pressure which is the pressure drop at the measuring orifice greater than the actuator pressure, whereas in 2-way flow control valves the hydraulic pump must always create the pressure set at the pressure relief valve.

Hence a 3-way flow control valve has smaller power losses, a better degree of efficiency in the system and less heat is created.

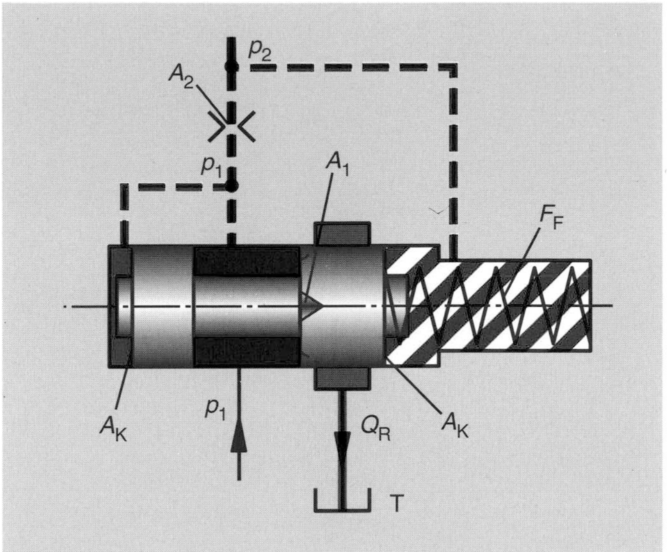

Fig. 38: *3-way flow control valve*

The following is true for the balance of forces:

$$p_1 \bullet A_K = p_2 \bullet A_K + F_F \qquad (9)$$

Hence

$$\Delta p = p_1 - p_2 = \frac{F_F}{A_K} = \text{constant} \qquad (10)$$

If Δp is constant, then Q is also constant.

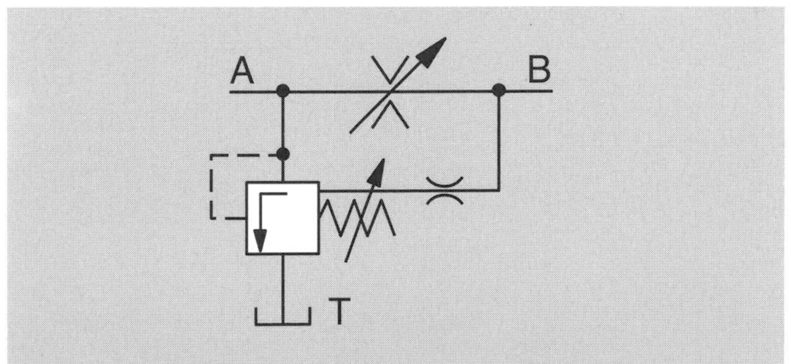

Fig. 39: *3-way flow control valve with downstream pressure compensator*

Important parameters

Sizes:	10 and 16
Flow:	up to 160 L/min
Operating pressure :	up to 315 bar

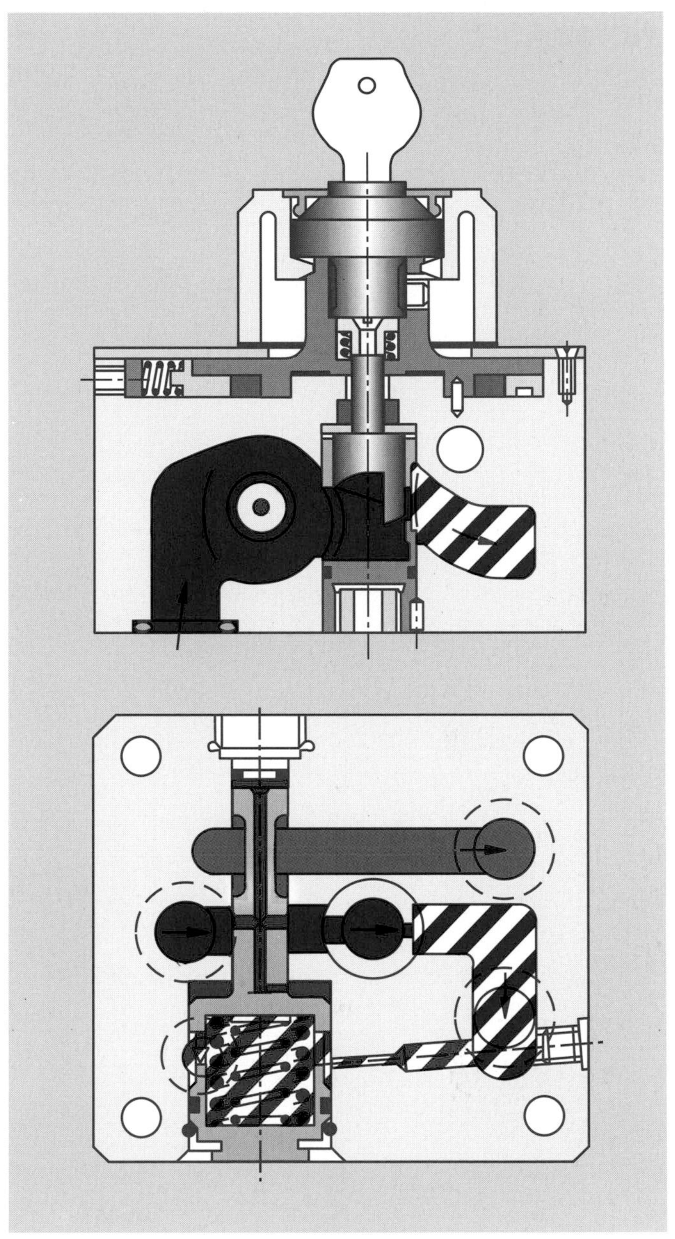

Fig. 40: *3-way flow control valve*

Notes

Chapter 14

Filters and Filtration Technology

Martin Reik

1 Basics

Filters are devices which separate solid particles from fluids. The filters used to filter solid particles from fluids or to separate dust from gas are made out of fibre or granules.

The filtered fluid is known as the filtrate (this expression is not used in hydraulics).

The process is known as filtration. The size of particles present in fluids are shown in *table 1*.

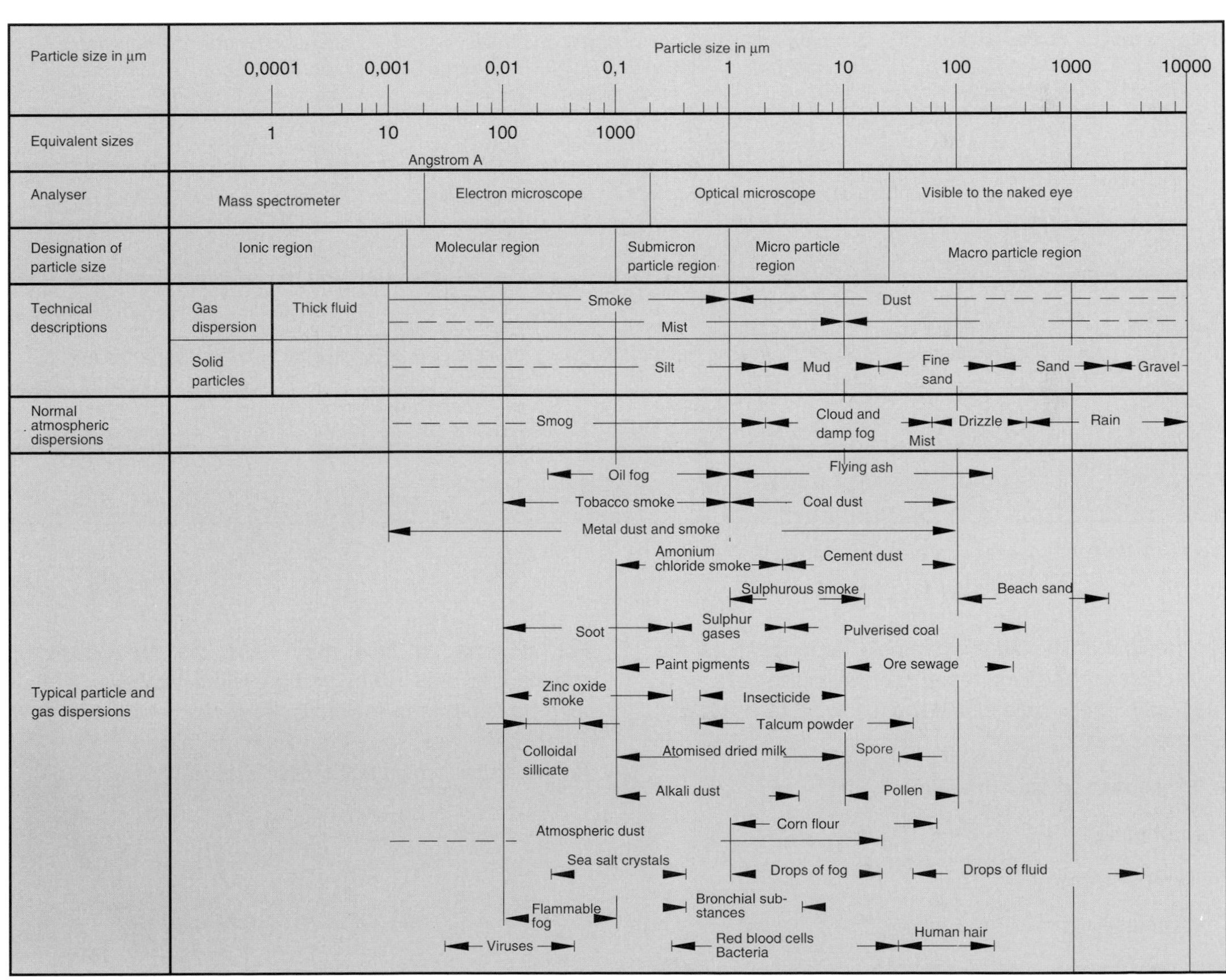

Table 1: *Sizes of particles for various substances*

Various filtration processes are used to filter particles. The choice of process is dependent on the required filter pore size.

The features of individual filtration processes are shown in *table 2*.

Medium to be filtered	**Fluid**				**Gas**	
Filtration process	**RO** Reverse osmosis	**UF** Ultra-filtration	**MF** Micro filtration Membrane filtration	**FF** to **GF** Fine filtration to rough filtration	**MFG** Micro filtration	**FFG** Fine filtration to rough filtration
Filterfeinheit	0 to 0.001 µm	0.001 to 0.1 µm	0.1 to 3.0 µm	3 to 1 000 µm	0.1 to 3.0 µm	3 to 1 000 µm
Molecular weight	up to approx. 1000	up to 1 000 000	—	—	—	—
Use	Removal of soluble substances (e.g. salt) from fluid.	Removal of smallest particles and colloids from fluids	Removal of particles from fluids.	Removal of particles from fluids.	Removal of particles from gases.	Removal of particles from gases.
Application	Desalination of salt water. Removal of heavy metals.	Environmental, separation of macro molecules and emulsions, e.g. oil-water separation	Semi-conductor technology, pharmaceutical industry, food industry	Water preparation, hydraulics, lubrication technology, split into safety and working filtration	Semi-conductor technology, pharmaceutical industry, sterile ventilation of chambers	Ventilation of chambers, ventilation of hydr. tanks, ventilation of computers, ventilation, vehicles
Filter medium	Membrane	Membrane	Membrane	Depth filter, surface filter	Membrane	Depth filter, surface filter
Types	Pipe membrane, flat membrane	Pipe membrane, flat membrane, capillary mem-brane	Pipe membrane, flat membrane	Elements with organic and innorganic fibre, wire mesh, split pipe, centrifuge, cyclone	Pipe membrane, flat membrane	Elements with organic and innorganic fibre, steel mesh, cyclone

Table 2: *Filtration processes for gases and fluids*

The design of the filter system is dependent on the characteristics and requirements of the fluid to be filtered. The fluid must be able to fulfil the following tasks as well as some others:

- Pressure and force transfer
- Lubrication
- Temper transfer
- Cleaning

However, it must be pointed out that the fluid must be capable of fulfilling several tasks at the same time.

For example, a fluid may have the main task of transferring force in a hydraulic system. However, it must also be capable of lowering the friction resistance and wear, as well as the high localised operating temperatures which occur (see *table 3*).

Medium to be filtered	Fluid					
Main task of medium	Transfer of forces		Reduction of frictional resistance		Temperature transfer	Cleaning of components
Type of medium	– Hydraulic oil – Fire resistant fluids – Water		– Hydraulic oil – Lubicating oil – Fat		– Thermal oil – Cooling machine oil – Water – Hydraulic oil	– Operating oils – Water-oil emulsions – Cold cleaner
Types of system	Hydraulic systems Stationary systems	Mobile systems	Lubricating systems Circulation lubrication	Losses lubrication	– Cooling systems – Heat transfer	– Cleaning systems
Examples	– Machine tools – Founderies – Heavy industry	– Construction machines – Communal devices – Ship-building	– Gear boxes – Sealers – Loaders	– Single line systems – Multi-line systems – Machine tools	– Plastic smelting – Calenders	– Test rigs – Cooling of workpieces – Cleaning of worked parts
Criteria for the filter	– Narrow clearances between moving parts – Large tank volume – Good filtration required	– Narrow clearances between moving parts – Small tank volume – Average filtration required	– High wear – Rough filtration usually sufficient	– Narrow clearances between moving parts – Average filtration required	– Removal of carbon residue – Good filtration required	– Prevent contamination of newly processed components – Rough filtration sufficient
Required filter pore size	3 to 20 µm	6 to 30 µm	10 to 100 µm	10 to 30 µm	3 to 20 µm	3 to 100 µm

Medium to be filtered	Gas	
Main task of medium	Processing	Ventilation
Type of medium	Air	Air
Types of systems	– Suction air – Systems to remove dust	– Clean room technology – Air-conditioning
Examples	– Suction air from int. combustion engs., sealers and hydr. systems – Exhaust air from power stations	– High quality manufacturing plants – Buildings
Criteria for the filter	– Protection of pistons in internal combustion engines – Environment protection – Good filtration necessary	– Sterile ventilation – High quality filtration required
Required filter pore size	1 to 10 µm	0.1 to 30 µm

Table 3: *Tasks of the medium to be filtered*

In hydraulic systems filtration is in the range of fine

filtration to coarse filtration.

The following sections only deal with this filtration process.

2 Notes on design and servicing

In order for the hydraulic system to operate without problems, certain pre-requisites must be taken into account during design and operation of the system:

- Clear definition of task for the system and the components used in the system. So that no mistakes are made in the design phase for a system, a specification must be written.
- Determination of which components are to be used and their quality rating.
- Consideration of sensitivity to contamination of the components, ambient contamination and possibility of dirt ingress into the hydraulic system.
- Determination of realistic periods between servicing.
- Amount that system is used.
  Period of operation of the system per day (one or more shifts).

The factors which must be taken into account for disturbance free operation of a hydraulic system are shown in *table 4*.

One of the pre-requisites for disturbance free operation of a hydraulic system is the filtration of the fluid and the ambient air which comes into contact with the tank.

The contamination which is to be removed by filters comes from the environment into the hydraulic system via filler caps and seals.

This type of contamination is known as external contamination or contamination entering from outside the system.

The expected rate of contamination ingress is only dependent on the ambient contamination and the system and component formation.

The moving parts in the hydraulic system, e.g pumps, pistons and valves also create particles (dust). This type of contamination creation is known as internal dirt production.

Above all, the danger exists, that due to solid particles entering the system whilst the system is being assembled, individual components may be damaged or destroyed on commissioning.

Many of the malfunctions occurring in hydraulic systems are due to heavily contaminated fluids. When a new fluid is filled into a hydraulic system, it is often contaminated to an impermissible high degree.

Fig. 1 shows some of the sources of contamination in hydraulic systems.

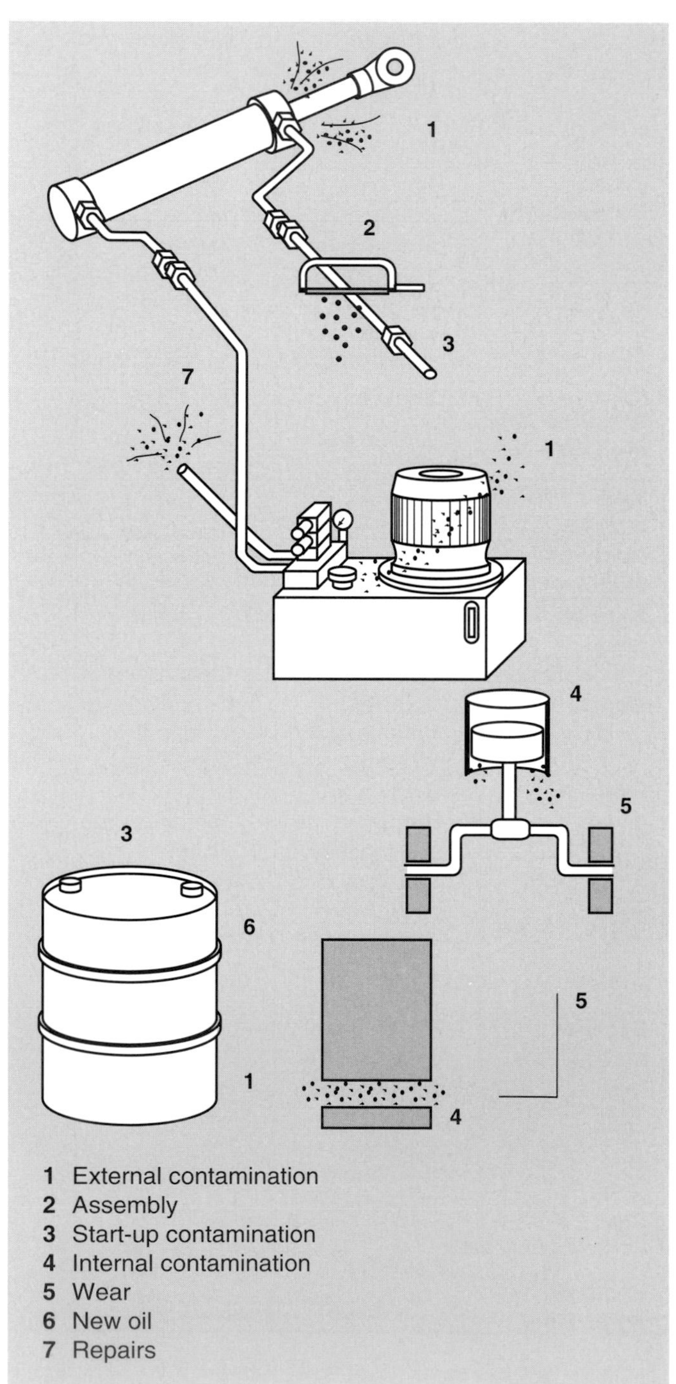

Fig. 1: *Sources of contamination*

Definition of task	System design	Contamination control
– Determination of task by user taking into account market requirements – Design of circuit by system manufacturer – Achieving advertised advantages whilst maintaining high technological standard – Disturbance free system model – Low servicing and energy costs – Economic cost/power ratio – Specification written for complete system	– Taking into account acceptance regulations – Design of switching logic – Selection of components e.g. pumps, cylinders, motors, valves and accessories – Matching components to each other – Determination of operating fluid – Determination of conditions for use for the complete system – Amount of use for the system – Determination of operating time for the system (one, two or three shift operation)	The functionality and hence the cost of the hydraulic system are effected by: – Installation contamination, – Fluid contamination on delivery, – Ambient contamination and dirt ingress, – Servicing of the system, – Ambient system conditions, – Production of wear in components, – Use of highly effective filters, – Determination of system specific filter power, – Correct filter arrangement and – Careful sealing of hydraulic system.
Responsibility System operator System manufacturer	*Responsibility* System operator System manufacturer Component supplier	*Responsibility* System operator Installation engineer Component supplier

Table 4: *Criteria for satisfactory operation of a hydraulic system*

2.1 Causes of contamination

2.1.1 Contamination in the manufacture of components (component contamination)

As a result of the extremely complex internal contours of housings and internal parts of components, these can often not be cleaned properly. When the hydraulic system is flushed, this contamination is passed into the fluid.

Components are usually preserved when they are stored. Preservatives fuse dirt and dust. This dirt also finds its way into the fluid when the system is commissioned.

Typical contamination is:
Swarf, sand, dust, fibres, paint, water or preservatives.

2.1.2 Contamination during assembly (assembly contamination)

As the individual components are put together, e.g. in the installation of screws, solid particles may be produced.

Typical contamination is
Sealing material, scale, weld spatter, pieces of rubber from hoses, residue of pickling and flushing fluid, separating and grinding dust.

2.1.3 Contamination during operation of the system (production contamination)

Due to abrasion in components, particles are produced. Particles smaller than 15 μm are particularly guilty of causing wear.

Ageing processes in fluids usually initiated at high operating temperatures, cause the lubricity of the fluid to change.

Contamination entering the hydraulic system from outside causes disturbances in operation and wear.

2.1.4 Critical clearances in hydraulic components

In order to ensure that the hydraulic components function correctly a clearance must be left between the moving parts.

Particles which become trapped in these clearances lead to malfunctions and also to wear. The critical clearances for various hydraulic components are shown in *table 5*.

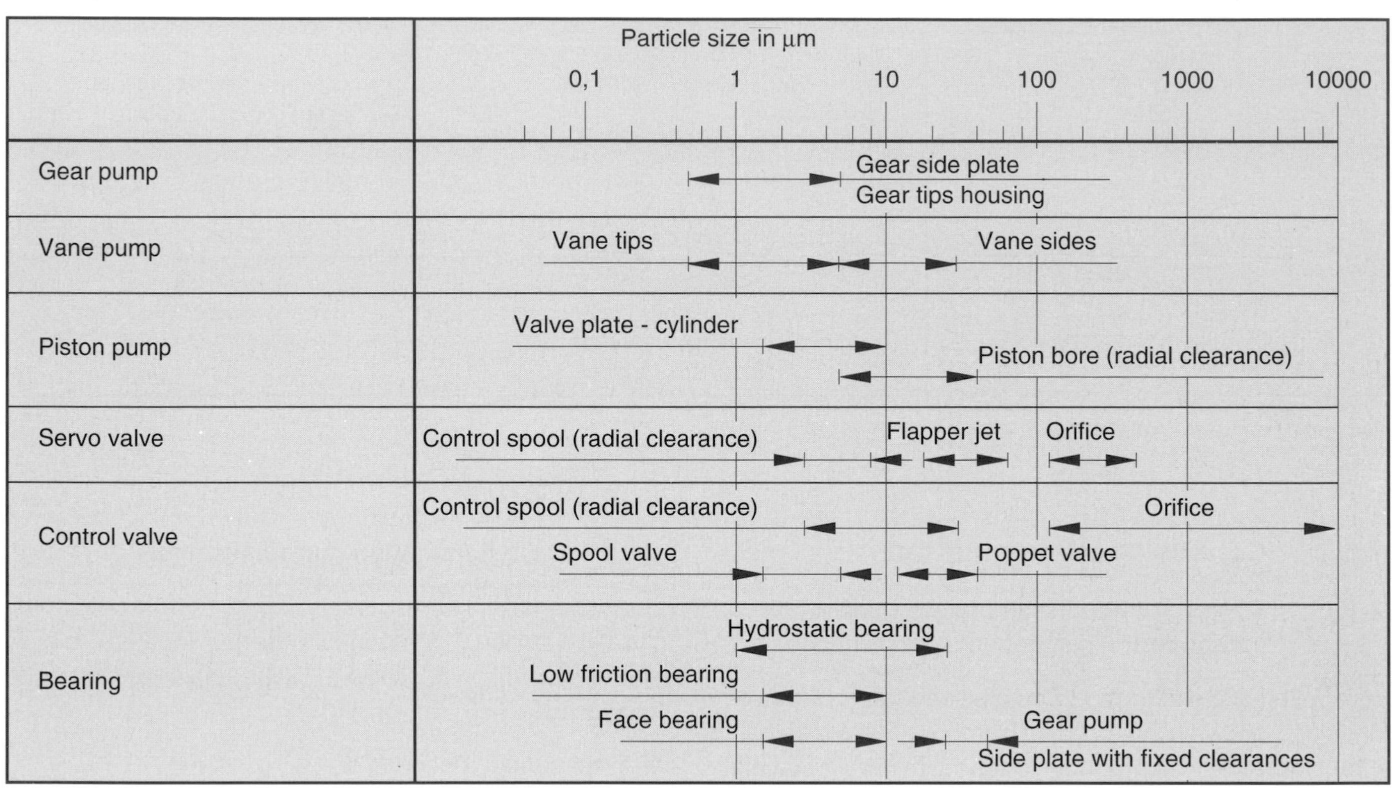

Table 5: *Clearance sizes for various hydraulic components to Cetop RP 92 H*

2.1.5 Points which are sensitive to contamination in hydraulic components

The critical tolerances (size of clearances) on parts of a gear pump, vane pump, piston pump, spool valve and servo valve are shown in *fig. 2*.

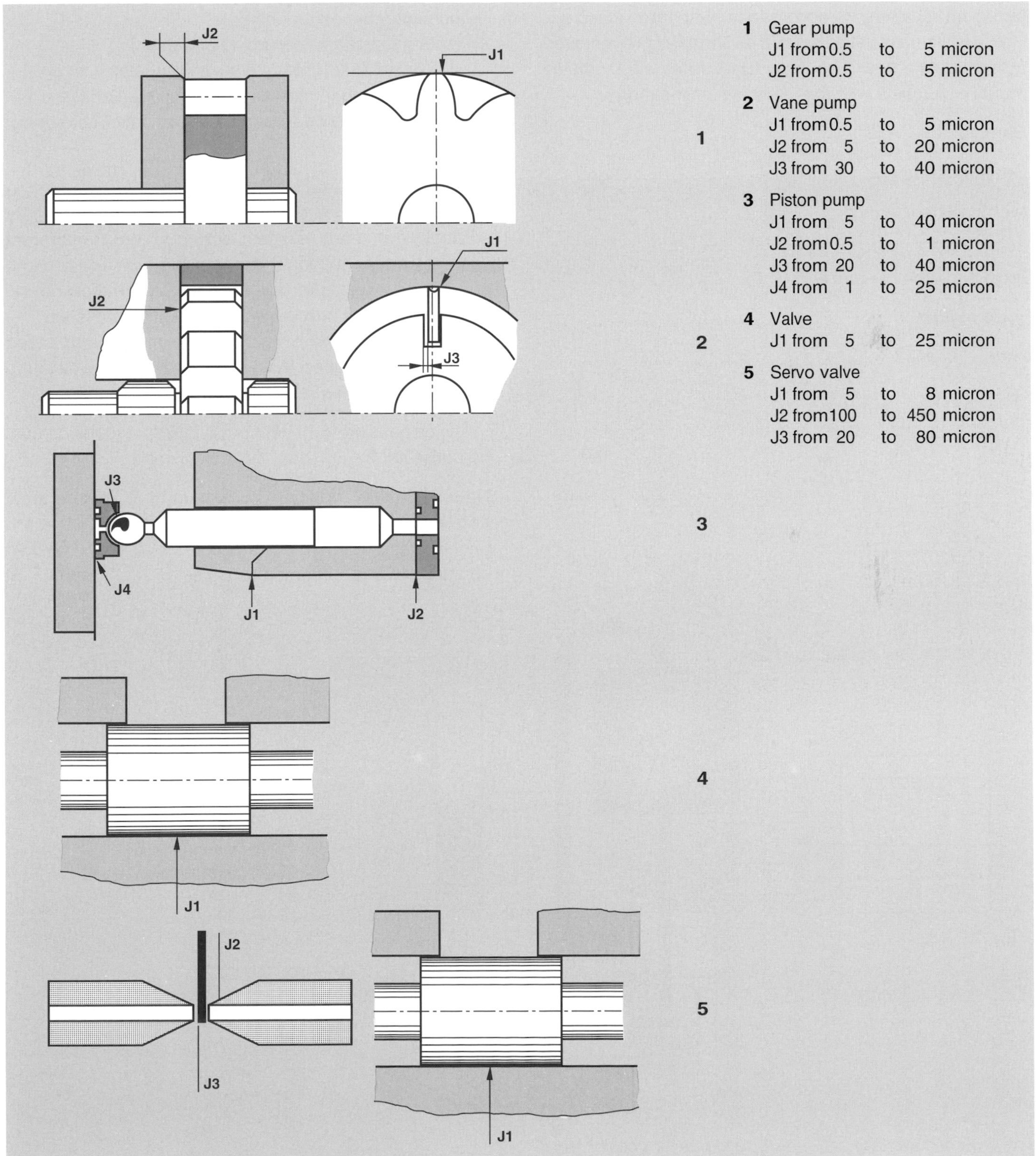

Fig. 2: *Critical tolerances in hydraulic components*

3 Analysis of solid particle contamination

In order to analyze solid particle contamination, fluid samples must be taken from the hydraulic system. The various ways of removing samples are standardised to ISO 4021, Cetop RP95H and DIN ISO 5884.

Test points should already be included in the design of a hydraulic system in accordance with the standard. However, care must be taken that samples are removed from turbulent flow. The individual bottles with samples must have labels with the following information:

Sample no.: ....

Source of sample: ....

Method of sampling: ....

....

Date and time of sampling: ....

Type of fluid: ....

Filters installed: ....

Remarks: ....

....

Particle analysis may be carried out by one of two methods:

a) Microscopic particle counting process
The fluid sample is filtered via a membrane and the residue is examined under a microscope for the size of and number of particles.
This method is standardised to ISO 4407 and 4408.
This method is very time-consuming and requires considerable experience.

b) Automatic particle counting process
It is possible to quickly analyze particles with an automatic measuring and counting device. Here the fluid sample flows through a photo-optic measuring cell.
This method is standardised to Cetop RP 94 H.

The measuring cell contains a flow channel with light sources and photo-diodes arranged on transparent windows on the sides. This process which operates on the light blocking principle provides information on the distribution of the number and size of solid particles. The particles flowing past cause the area of light being emitted to be reduced. As a result of this change in light, the size of particles may be determined.

Particles pass the light beam individually and hence may be counted (*fig. 3*).

Naturally, this optical system cannot differentiate between the types of particles and so apparent contamination such as gas bubbles and drops of fluid contaminants are counted as particles.

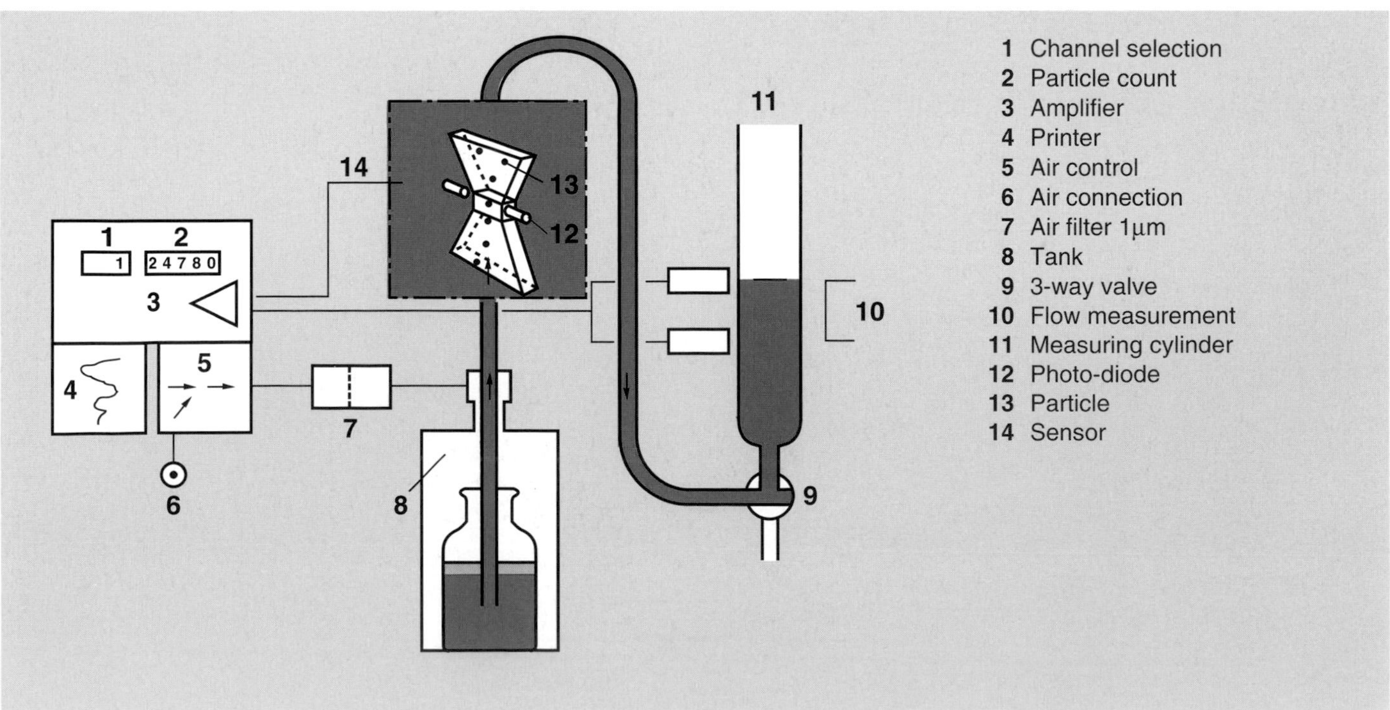

Fig. 3: *Schematic diagram — Automatic particle counter*

3.1 Classification systems for the degree of contamination in a fluid

Classification systems (standardised cleanliness classes) are used to help determine the amount of solid particles present in a fluid.

The most commonly used standards today are NAS 1638 and ISO DIS 4406.

3.1.1 Classification to NAS 1638

Fourteen cleanliness classes exist to classify fluids. In each class a specific number of particles (in 100 ml) is given for each of 5 ranges of sizes.

Table 6 shows how contamination classes are formed to NAS 1638.

Cleanliness class	Particle size in µm				
	5 – 15	15 – 25	25 – 50	50 – 100	> 100
00	125	22	4	1	0
0	250	44	8	2	0
1	500	89	16	3	1
2	1000	178	32	6	1
3	2000	356	63	11	2
4	4000	712	126	22	4
5	8000	1425	253	45	8
6	16000	2850	506	90	16
7	32000	5700	1012	180	32
8	64000	11400	2025	360	64
9	128000	22800	4050	720	128
10	256000	45600	8100	1440	256
11	512000	91200	16200	2880	512
12	1024000	182400	32400	5760	1024

Table 6: *Cleanliness classes to NAS 1638*
Maximum number of dirt particles found in 100 ml of fluid

3.1.2 Classification to ISO DIS 4406

Here the sizes larger than 5 µm and larger than 15 µm are cumulatively provided.

The cleanliness class of the fluid is determined on the basis of both particle counts.

Twenty-six ranges are available for classification. The designation of the cleanliness class comprises only two numbers. The first number indicates the range number for the particle size larger than 5 µm and the second number indicates that for the particle size larger than 15 µm.

Diagram 1 illustrates the contamination class to ISO DIS 4406.

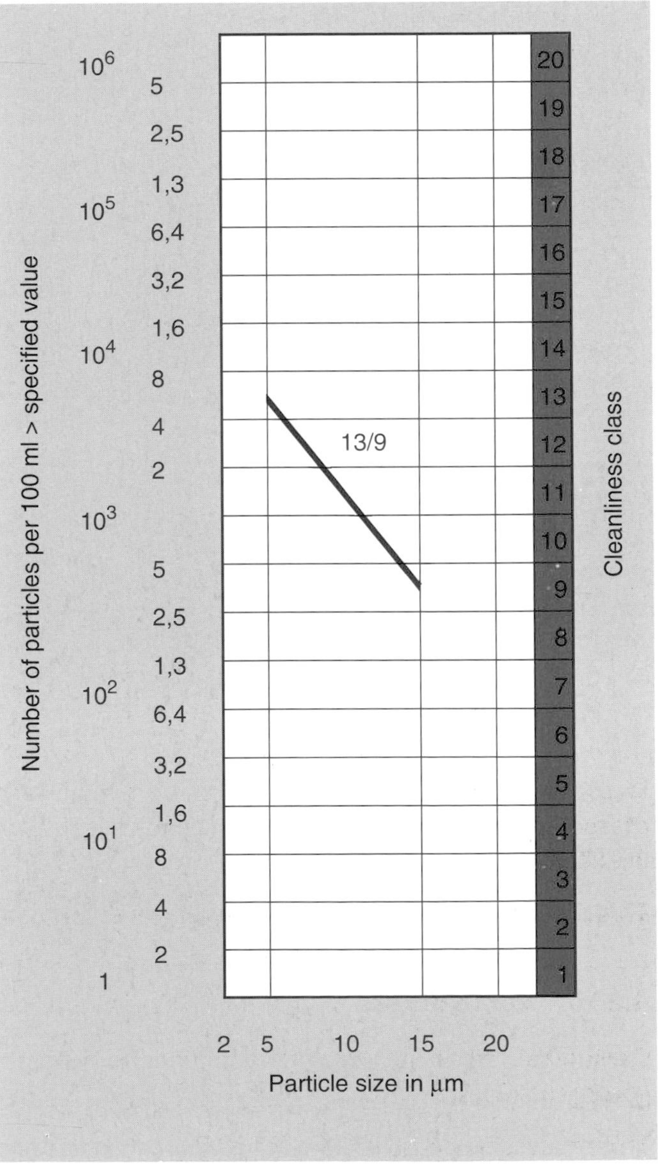

Diagram 1: *Cleanliness classes to ISO DIS 4406*

Both classification systems may be represented graphically.

It is obvious from diagram 2 that ISO DIS 4406 only deals with a small section of the complete analysis spectrum to NAS 1638 when determining contamination.

The number of particles determined by analysis cannot be matched to any one class with respect to the cleanliness classes to NAS 1638. This means that classes are usually determined for the smallest particles of 5 to 15 µm to NAS 1638.

As already mentioned, the cleanliness classes to NAS 1638 cover a larger particle spectrum than that covered by ISO DIS 4406. Hence NAS 1638 is to be used in preference to ISO DIS 4406.

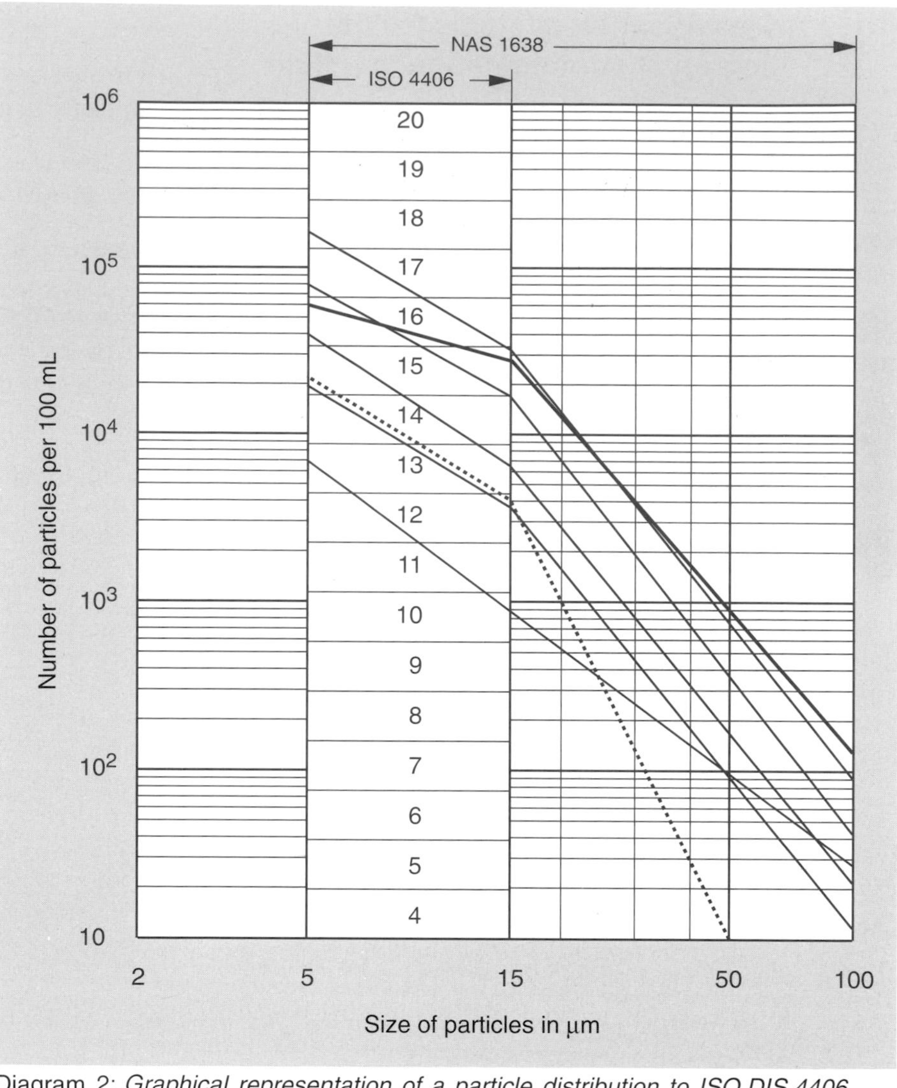

Diagram 2: *Graphical representation of a particle distribution to ISO DIS 4406 and NAS 1638*

4 Filtration processes

4.1 Gravity filters

In gravity filtration, the fluid flows through the filter as a result of its own weight.

This process is not used in hydraulics and lubrication technology. It is only used in the production of drinking water and in the preparation of operating fluids (rubble filter, paper filter).

4.2 Pressure line filter

In pressure filtration, fluid is pushed by means of a pressure drop between the dirty and clean side through the filter.

This process is used for the filtration of hydraulic fluids.

4.3 Centrifuges

Centrifugal forces are used in centrifuges to separate solids from liquids.

This process is used if a fluid is heavily contaminated and also to filter water.

4.4 Filter presses

In filter presses, fluid is pressed out of the solid particles by mechanical forces. The solid particles stay in the press and a filter cake is formed.

This process is not used in hydraulics. It is mainly the food industry which uses this process.

Each of these processes may also be used in the preparation of coolants.

5 Filter element material

In the filtration processes mentioned a variety of or combination of materials are used for the filter element.

5.2 Surface filtration
(*fig. 4*)

In surface filters, particles are removed directly on the surface of the filter element. Particles, which due to their small diameter, enter the filter element can pass through it without any further resistance. The filter resistance however increases as the surface becomes clogged. The layer of particles formed on the surface of the filter may lead to a decrease in the filtration rating.

Either a membrane filter or filters made of wire mesh, metallic edges or woven metallic twist are used for surface filtration.

5.2 Depth filters (*fig. 5*)

The fluid to be cleaned passes through the filter structure. The dirt particles become trapped in the deep layers of the filter. As the level of trapped dirt increases, the resistance to flow increases, so that the filter element needs to be changed. In these filters, the element is made of

- impregnated cellulose material (organic filter material)
- glass fibre (inorganic filter material)
- sintered metal fibre or
- porous, sintered metal.

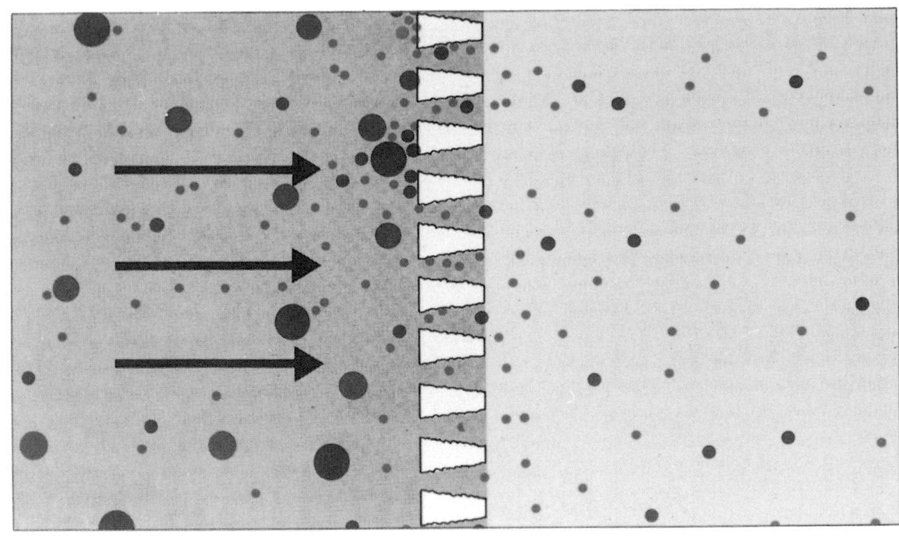

Fig. 4: *Representation of surface filter*

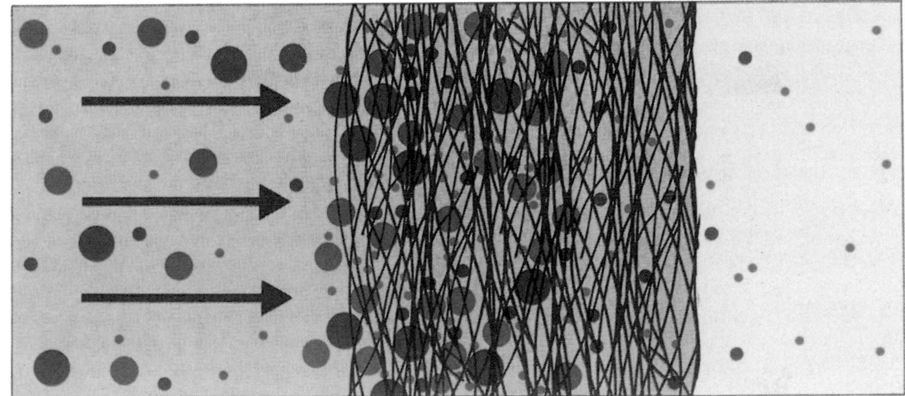

Fig. 5: *Representation of depth filter*

6 Filter element design *(Fig. 6)*

The design of filter elements varies from manufacturer to manufacturer. In simple paper elements, the filter matt is produced without a supporting wire mesh, so that at high pressure differences the filter pleats are pressed together at the filter element. Hence the possibility of drainage in the pleated matts is reduced, so that many of the layers remain unused for filtration purposes.

Higher quality elements have a multiple layer matt design. This design determines how robust the element is against pressure peaks and alternating flows.

A certain mesh width for the supporting mesh must be maintained, or else the filter dirt is pushed through the mesh and the filter becomes less effective.

The elements must be handled very carefully and according to instructions by the service engineers. If the element pleats are pushed against sharp edges when they are installed, this results in the matt construction becoming damaged and hence the filter becoming ineffective.

High quality filter elements must have the following characteristics:

- Good stability in pressure differences
- Beta stability over a wide pressure difference range
- Filtration ratings for all cleanliness classes
- Good dirt holding capacity
- Larger filtration areas and
- Long service lives.

The demands made on high quality filter elements may be determined from DIN 24550 part 2.

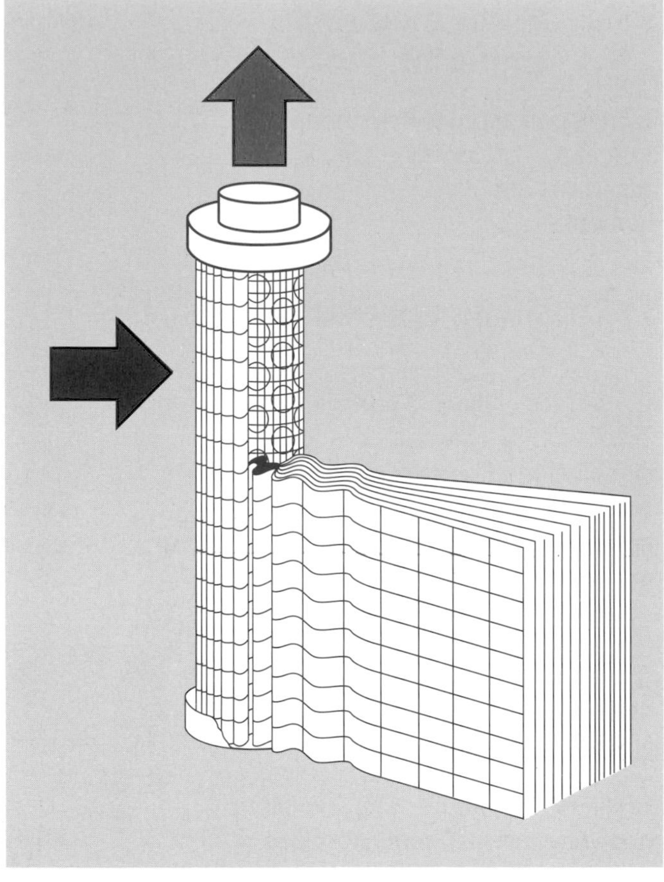

Fig. 6: *Multi-layer matt construction for Betamicron-2 elements*

7 Selection of filtration rating

The selection of a filtration rating is dependent on which main filtration group the filter is to be used in.

Table 7 describes the main filtration groups and their relevant filtrations.

In older technical documents on hydraulic components the required filtration rating is specified. However, as the safe functioning of components is dependent on the degree of cleanliness of a fluid, nearly all component manufacturers now state recommendations on the fluid cleanliness classes in their new technical documentation.

This is the correct specification in order to ensure that the components are protected, but makes the selection of a filtration rating a little harder, as the dirt load is dependent on the size of the particles as well as on the number of particles.

As a result of experiments and examinations of practical applications, filter manufacturers are able to specify the required filtration rating for a particular degree of fluid cleanliness. An example of this is shown in *table 8*.

However, the fluid cleanliness class required for a system is also dependent on the following parameters:

- Type of system
- Ambient contamination
- Excess operating pressure
- Operating period for the system
- Filter arrangement

Hence it may be very difficult to select a filtration rating for the fluid cleanliness class during the design phase. The filter size should be selected so that it is relatively simple to change the filter to a larger filter size at any time, so that during later operation of the system filter elements with a smaller filtration rating or a longer service life may be installed.

A typical cause of malfunctions in hydraulic components is the clogging of clearances and orifices. Especially sensitive to this are flow control valves, throttle valves and servo valves. If the relative movement is small, there is an increased danger of the clearances becoming blocked. Hence, considering clogging, the absolute filtration rating must be at least the same if not smaller than that of the clearances within a component.

Hydraulic components	Cleanliness class to NAS 1638	Cleanliness class to ISO DIS 4406	Recommended absolute filter pore size in μm
Gear pumps	10	19/16	20
Cylinders	10	19/16	20
Directional valves	10	19/16	20
Safety valves	10	19/16	20
Throttle valves	10	19/16	20
Piston pumps	9	18/15	10
Vane pumps	9	18/15	10
Pressure control valves	9	18/15	10
Proportional valves	9	18/15	10
Servo valves	7	16/13	5
Servo cylinders	7	16/13	5

Table 8: *Recommended absolute filter pore size for various hydraulic components (Rexroth)*

Finest contamination	**Fine contamination**	**Coarse contamination:**
Finest particles (3 to 5 μm) reduce functionality and power due to: – Effect of erosion by finest particles (often control land erosion) – Fine deposits in narrow gaps (due to gap filtration – danger of clogging) – Change in operating medium (oil ageing) as a result of chemical reaction at the particle surface.	Fine particles (5 to 20 μm) cause frictional wear especially in narrow passages. This causes: – Increase in clearance due to wear (increased internal leakages) – Periodic malfunctions (brief clogging effect at spool valves or leaks at valve pins – Total malfunction due to heavy wear	Coarse particles > 20 μm often cause a sudden total malfunction due to effects of clogging, blocking or direct disturbances. Typical effects are: – Blocking of orifices – Spool jamming or erosion – Material collapse if large forces present.
Finest filtration Effective separation of finest dispersed particles ($\beta_{3\text{ to }5} \geq 100$) High pressure difference stability, finest filters protect functionality – They minimise the creation of and development of erosion – They prevent clogging of narow gaps – They protect against oil ageing – They prevent disturbances from occuring in the system	**Fine filtration** Partial separation of fine contamination and complete separation of coarse contamination ($\beta_{5\text{ to }20} > 100$) Fine filters are used to reliably control the acceptable level of contamination in a system – They protect components to an optimum degree from contamination – They reduce frictional wear – They prevent components from suddenly malfunctioning.	**Coarse filtration** Separation of mainly coarse particles $\beta_X \geq 100$ *(see page 20)* *X*= μm particle size, which can cause a sudden mal-function of the components which are to be protected. Coarse filters protect system from coarse contamination They prevent the danger of sudden malfunctions or complete damage .

Table 7: *Effect of particles dependent on their size on components and the matching to main filtration groups*

8 Filter testing

8.1 Verification of production quality
(Bubble point test)

Using this test to ISO 29 42, it is possible to verify that production is perfect and also to verify the integrity of filter elements.

It is also used as the start of further tests (e.g. ISO 2941, ISO 2943, ISO 3723, ISO 3724, ISO 4572).

8.1.1 Test sequence (*fig. 7*)

The filter element is submerged in isopropanol and pressurised internally with pressurised air. Pressure is increased until the first bubble appears on the surface of the element. No bubbles should appear until the air pressure specified by the manufacturer has been reached. Taking into account the physical laws when the first bubble appears, the air pressure is a measure for the size of the largest pore. The creation of lots of bubbles is a measure of the average pore size.

The bubble point specified by the manufacturers is very dependent on the construction of the element. Hence it is not possible for the user to compare filter elements from various manufacturers.

In general this test may only be used to check the integrity of an element.

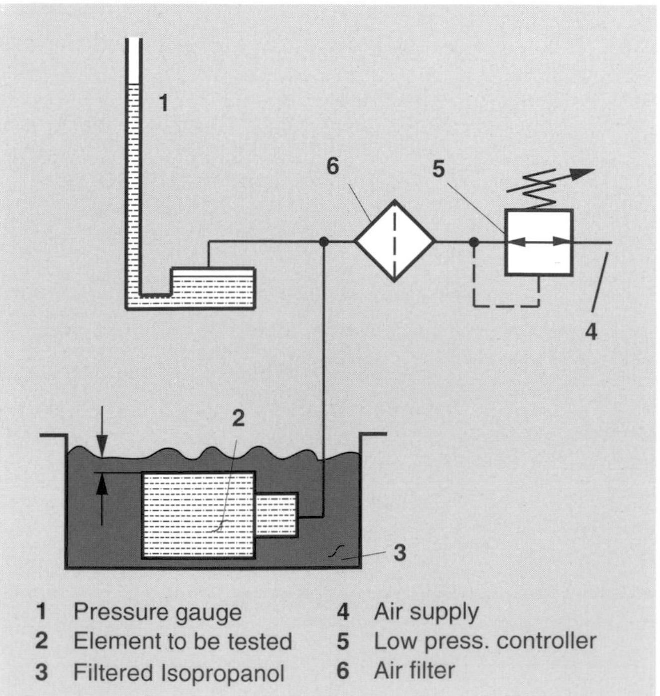

Fig. 7: *Schematic diagram of bubble point test to ISO 2942*

Fig. 8: *Bubble point test*

8.2 Collapse and burst pressure test

In the standardised test to ISO 2942, the stability of pressure differences in the filter elements are tested.

The specification "permissible collapse and burst pressure" implies the max. pressure difference which may be present for the filter element not to be damaged in a specific direction of flow.

The expression collapse pressure is used, when flow through the filter element is from outside to inside. In the opposite direction the expression burst pressure is used.

8.2.1 Test sequence (*fig. 9*)

Tests on filter elements must be carried out at the nominal flow specified by the manufacturer.

Controlled test dirt ACFTD (Air Cleaner Fine Test Dust) is fed to the filter element. Due to the contaminant which then gathers on the element, the difference between the pressure upstream and downstream of the filter element increases.

The gradient of the curve must not decrease for values below the permissible collapse or burst pressure.

In addition, once the permissible collapse or burst pressure has been reached, a bubble point test must be carried out in order to verify the integrity of the element.

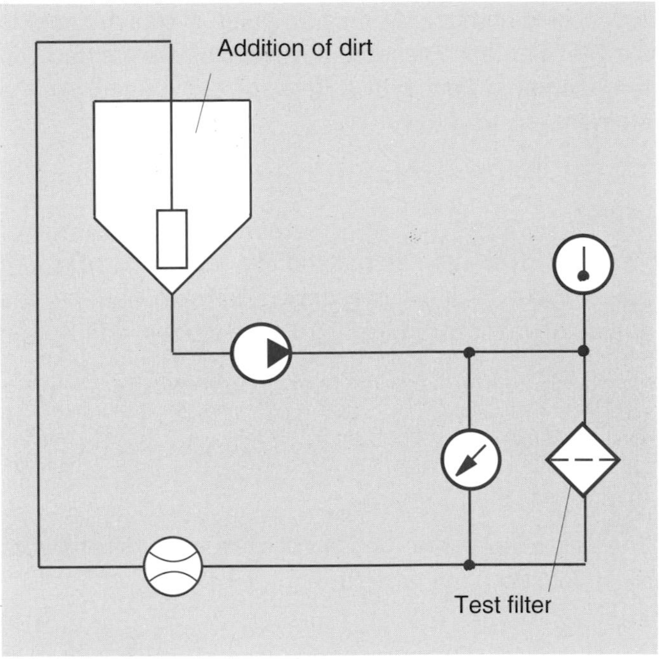

Fig. 9: *Schematic diagram of collapse and burst pressure test to ISO 2941 (δ_{test} = constant = 15 to 40 °C)*

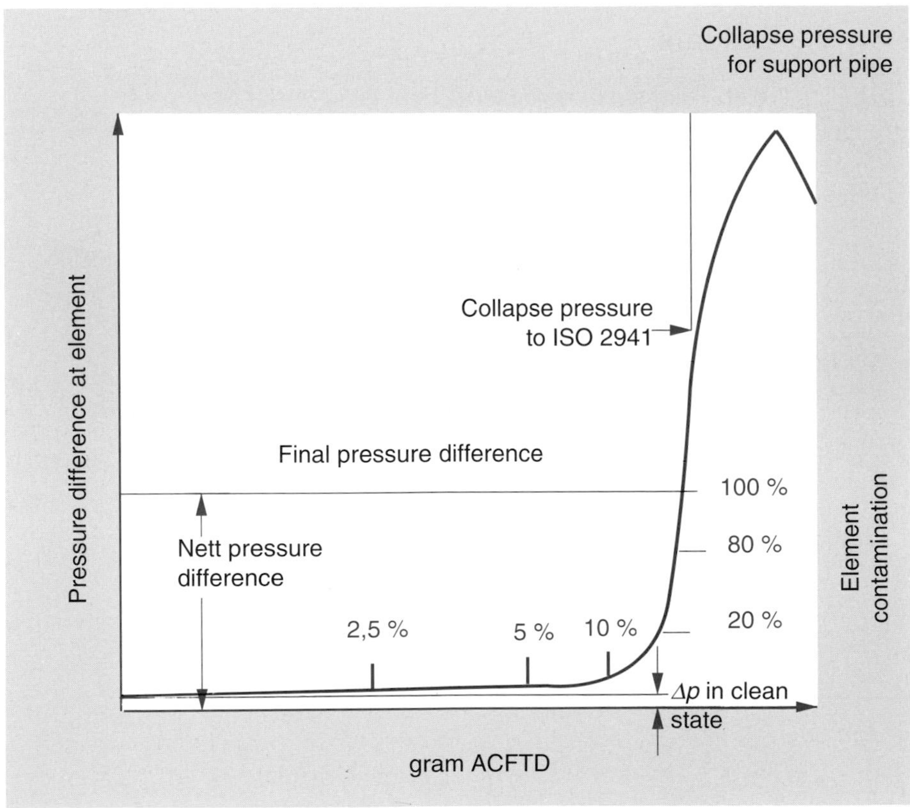

Diagram 3: *Pressure difference dependent on dirt addition*

8.3 Test of compatibility with fluid

The compatibility of the materials used in the filter element with the fluid are tested to ISO 29 43.

8.3.1 Test sequence (*fig. 10*)

The filter element is submerged in fluid for 72 hours at a test temperature of 15 °C above the max. operating temperature.

In this process the maximum safe temperature for the fluid must not be exceeded.

Once the test has been completed the filter element must not show any signs of damage or any reduction in its functionality. Afterwards a burst pressure test to ISO 2941 and a bubble point test to ISO 2942 must be carried out on the element.

The filter element has passed the test, if there are no visible signs of the element construction being damaged, no obvious decreases in functionality and if the collapse and burst pressure test is successfully passed.

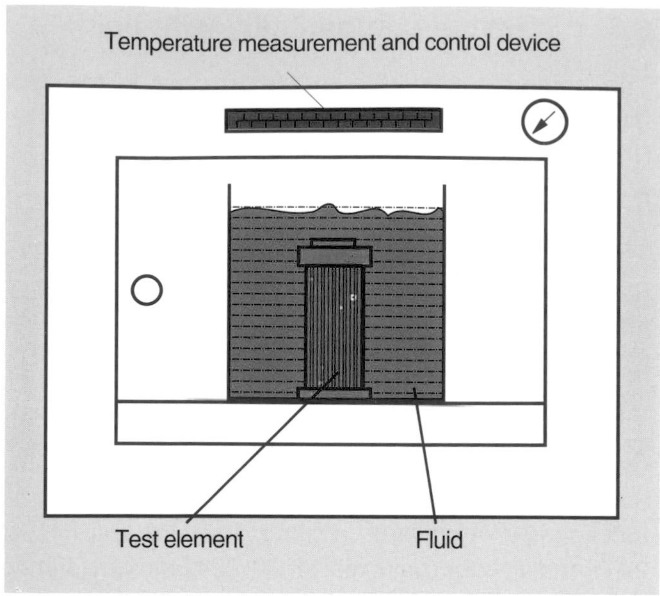

Fig. 10: *Schematic diagram of compatibility test to ISO 2943*

A specified number of pressure pulse cycles are sent to the filter element. Pressure pulse cycles are created due to changes in flow with a layer of dirt present on the element.

The pressure must be sinusoidal with a frequency of1 Hz or less.

The filter elements has passed this test, if the pressure pulse cycles (either prescribed or specified by the customer) do not produce any visible signs of damage on

- the complete element (filter construction)
- the seals or
- the filter material.

The operating curve for the collapse or burst pressure must not show any fall in the gradient.

8.4 Flow-fatigue characteristics of elements

The filter element is tested to ISO 37 24 to examine the ability of the element to resist structural damage, e.g. caused by deformation due to alternating directions of flow.

8.4.1 Test sequence (*fig. 11*)

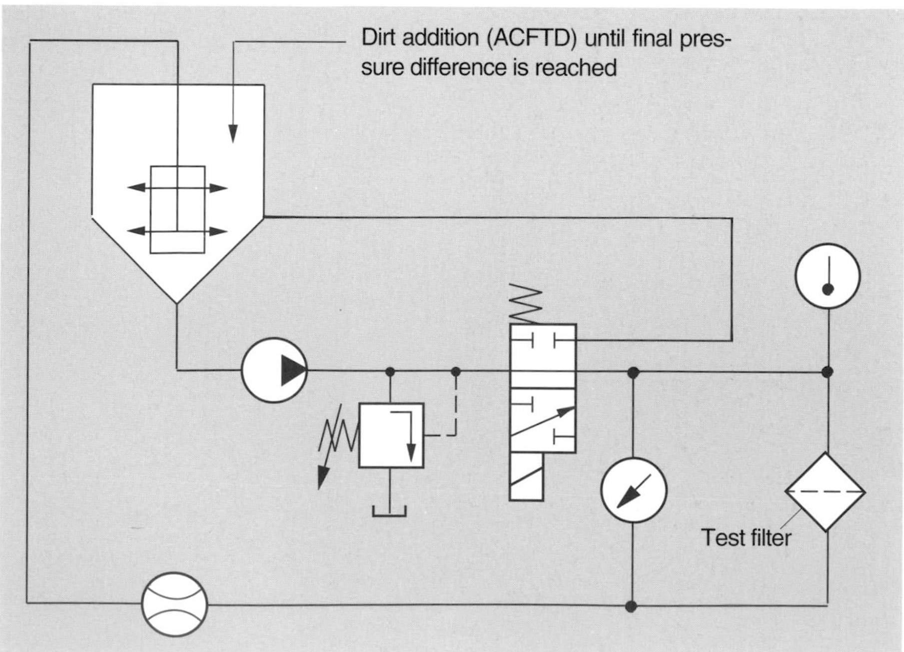

Fig. 11: *Schematic diagram of flow stability test to ISO 3742*
(δ_{test} = constant = 15 to 40 °C; $Q_{test} \leq Q_{nominal}$)

8.5 Determination of pressure losses dependent on flow

The pressure losses in the filter housing and element dependent on the flow and viscosity are determined the test to ISO 3968.

8.5.1 Test sequence (*fig. 12*)

The flow is shocklessly varied by a variable displacement pump installed in the test circuit. The test fluid used is usually a hydraulic oil from the viscosity class ISO VG 32.

The pressure losses in the housing and filter element are shown.

In this test the test points p_1 and p_2
upstream of the test filter: 5 x D_1
(D_1 = internal diameter of the pipe)
downstream of the test filter: 10 x D_1 must be arranged on a straight piece of pipe.

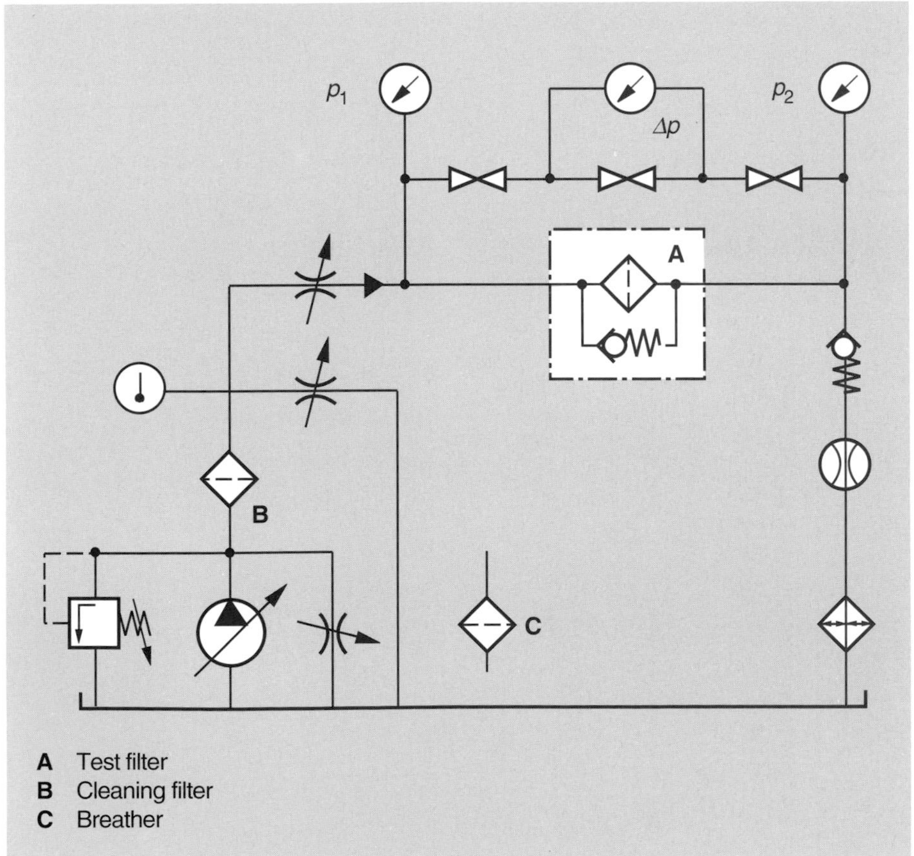

Fig. 12: *Schematic diagram for test to ISO 3968*

8.6 Multi-pass test

This test to ISO 4572 enables the filtration capacity and dirt holding capacity of filter elements to be determined.

The test is based on the principle of passing dirty fluid several times through the test filter.

This principle is justified in practice as some dirt particles which pass through the filter the first time around due to their size may be removed when they hit the filter on another pass.

8.6.1 Test sequence (*fig. 13*)

The "dirty" fluid from system 1 is injected into the circuit of system 2. Dirt is fed to the test filter by means of continuous circulation until the maximum pressure difference of the element or the test system has been reached.

During this time samples are taken from system 2 and evaluated in the automatic particle counting device. Hence it is possible to determine how the filtration power of the element changes with increasing pressure difference. The test temperature is also continually monitored.

Fig. 14: *Multi-pass test rig*

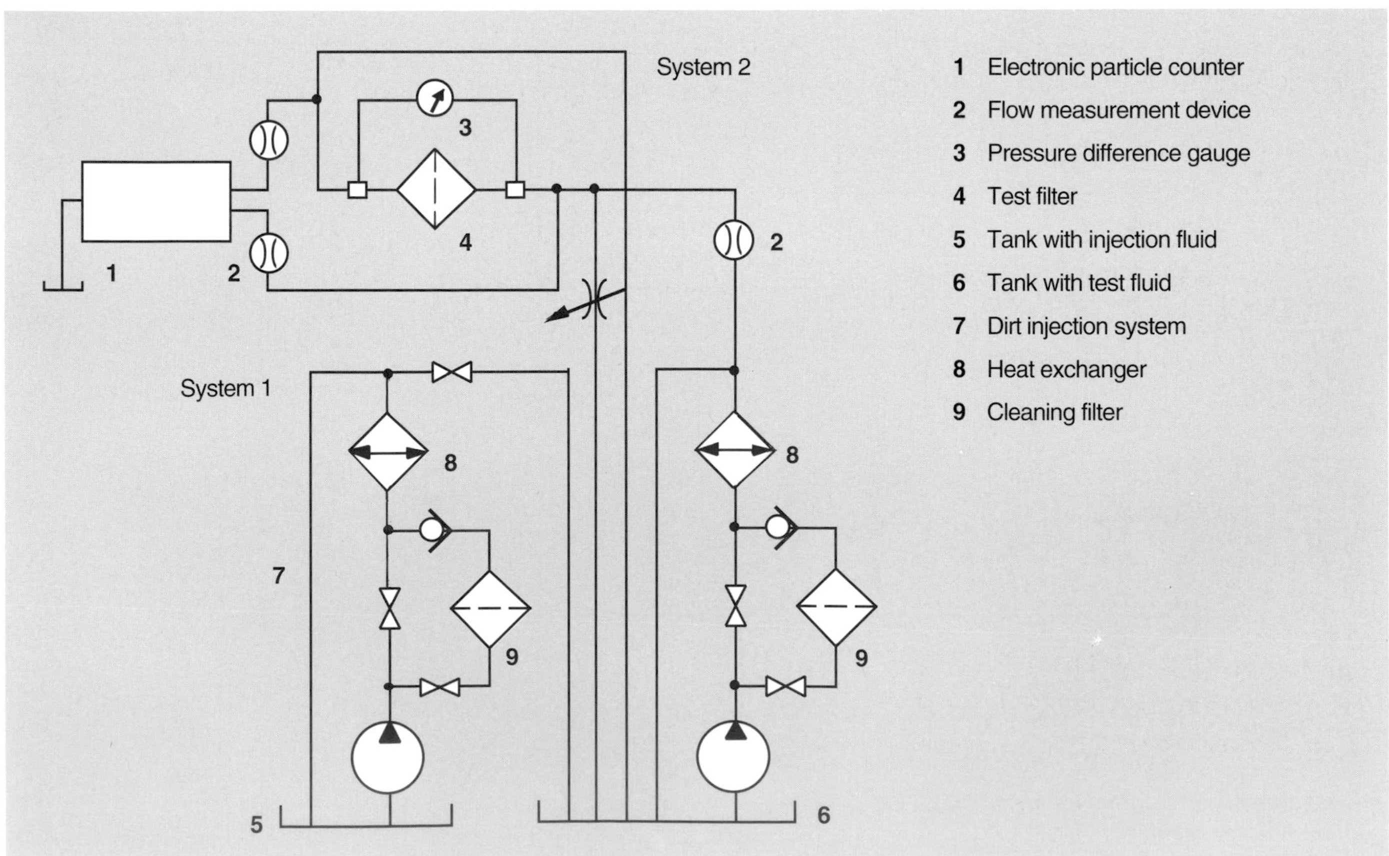

Fig. 13: *Simplified hydraulic circuit for multi-pass test rig*

The results of the test are printed out in the form of $ß_x$ values.

The filtration ratio $ß_x$ determined may also be given as a degree of separation in %.

$$\text{Degree of separation in \%} = \frac{ß_x - 1}{ß_x} \cdot 100$$

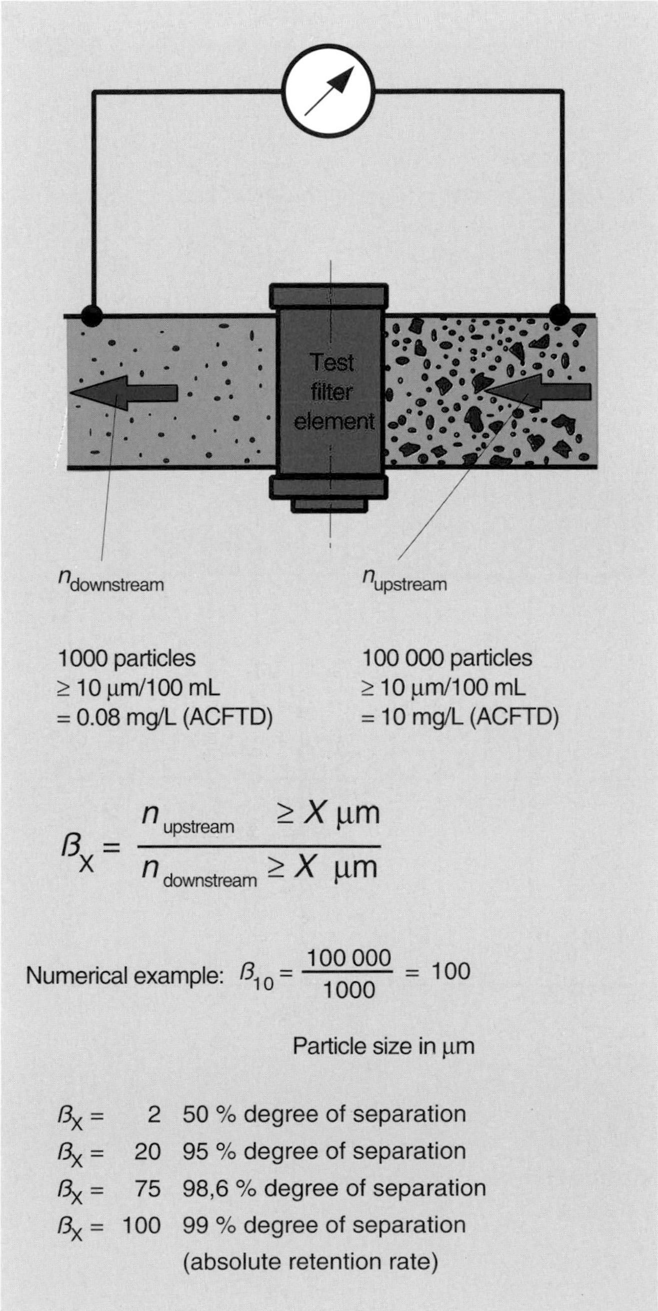

Fig. 15: *Determination of $ß_X$*

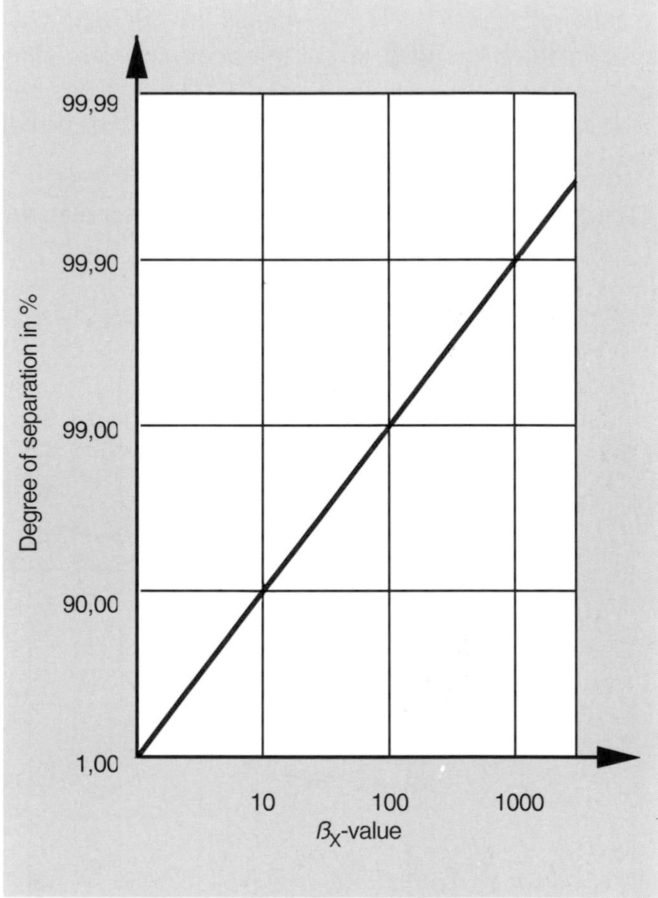

Diagram 4: *Degree of separation in % dependent on $ß_X$ value*

At $ß_x = 1$, no separation occurs. The "ß" function may have a value less than 1 if the filter produces dirt. In practice this should not happen.

The evaluation of the test results provides information on the dirt holding capacity in grammes (gram per element) and on the effectiveness of the filter material (gram per cm^2, also known as the specific dirt holding capacity).

This test which is a close approximation of practice is very accurately repeatable given the same specified test conditions. Hence it is possible to compare various makes of filter. The effectiveness of the test filter determined in this way provides the user with information on the power capability of the selected filter and ensures that the decisions on application or on the cost/power ratio are known.

Diagrams 5 and 6 show the test results for filter element 0160 D010BH/HC-2.

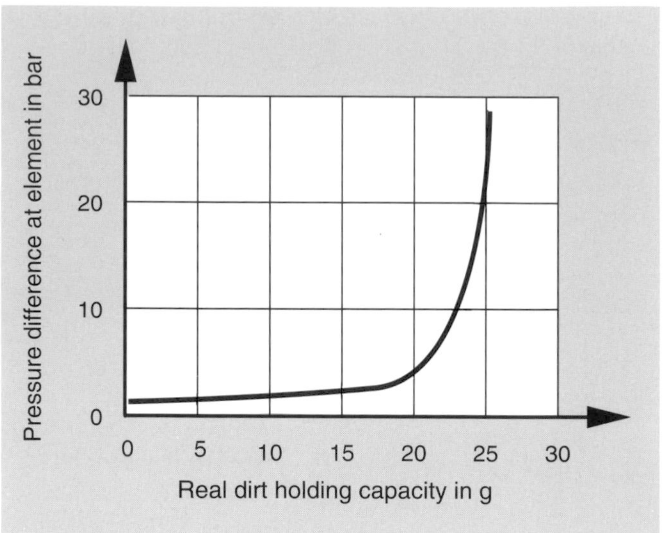

Diagram 6: *Operating curve for the dirt holding capacity of filter element*

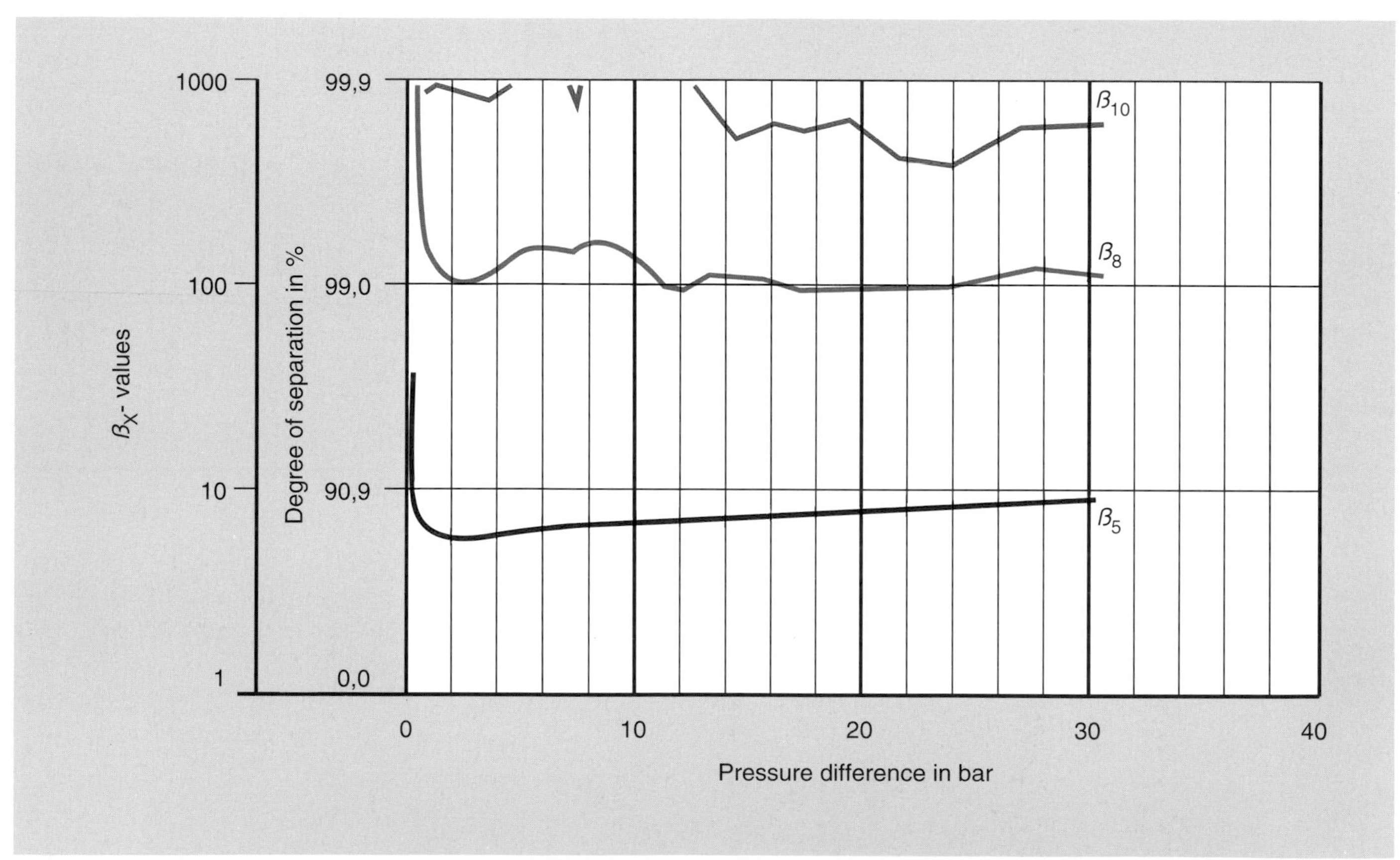

Diagram 5: $ß_x$ *values at various pressure differences at Betamicron-2 element (type ... D010BH/HC-2)*

8.7 Documentation on test results

The test parameters must be written down in a test protocol so that filter elements from various manufacturers may be compared.

This documentation must adhere to DIN 24550 and DIN 65385.

Hydraulic filters					
Line filter			Breathers		Accessories
Simple	Double	Switchable	With filling sieve	Without filling sieve	
Line	Line	Line	Tank	Tank	
	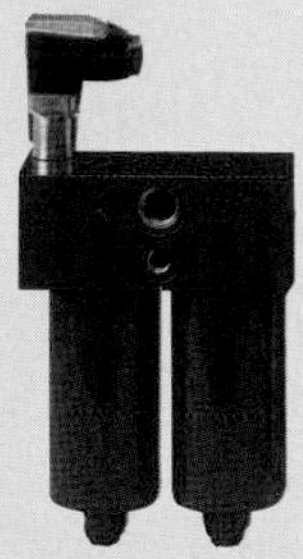				
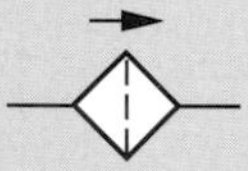	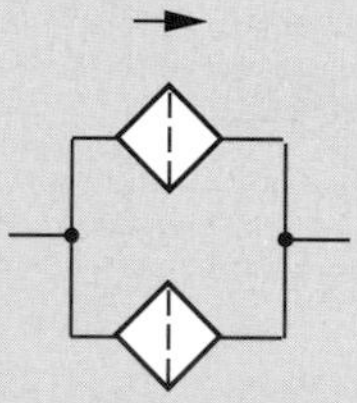	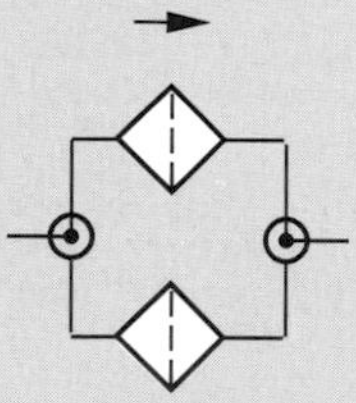	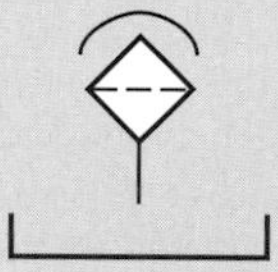	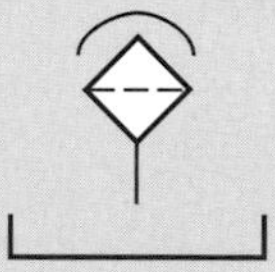	optical 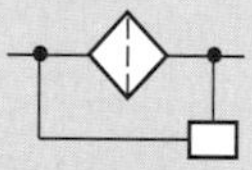 / electrical 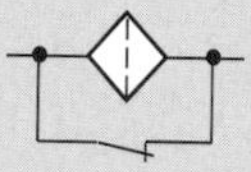
420 bar	420 bar	315 bar	1 bar	1 bar	420 bar
3 to 100 µm	3 to 100 µm	3 to 100 µm	3 to 40 µm	3 to 40 µm	—
Bypass filter, safety filter, working filter	Bypass filter, safety filter, working filter	Systems dependent on manufacture, working filters	Small Tank	Large tank; forced filling of system desired	In all filters which are used in hydraulic systems
Standard model without bypass valve.	Standard model without bypass valve.	Standard model without bypass valve.	Immense danger of very contaminated fluid entering tank	Filling of tank via filling power unit	Essential for filter servicing. Prevents elements from being damaged.

9 Types of filter housing

Various types of housing are available for the filtration of fluids.

These types are defined in DIN 24550.

Table 9 describes these types.

Type	**Suction line filter**		**Mounted return line filter**		
Model	Without housing	With housing	Simple	Double	Switchable
Place of installation	Tank, suction line	Tank, suction line	Tank	Tank	Tank
Diagram					
Symbol					
Max. operating pressure	1 bar	1 bar	25 bar	25 bar	25 bar
Filter pore size	20 to 200 μm	20 to 200 μm	3 to 100 μm	3 to 100 μm	3 to 100 μm
Typical applications	Pump protection, hydrostatic units, injection molding machines, construction machines	Pump protection, hydrostatic units, injection molding machines, construction machines	Working filter in hydraulic systems, construction machines	Working filter in hydraulic systems, construction machines	Systems dependent on manufacture
Remark	Usually only used to protect pump. Clogging indicator essential.	Usually only used to protect pump. Clogging indicator essential.	Standard model with bypass valve. With connection to fill system.	Standard model with bypass valve. With connection to fill system.	Standard model with bypass valve. With connection to fill system.

Table 9: *Summary of filter housing types*

9.1 Suction filter

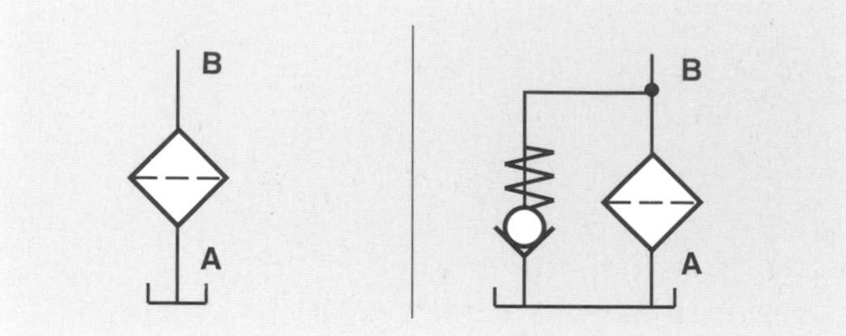

Fig. 16: *Symbol for suction line filter; (left) without and (right) with by-pass valve*

Hydraulic systems must include a suction filter, if there is likely danger of the pump being damaged due to large dirt particles.

This is especially the case when the following exists in a hydraulic circuit:

- Various hydraulic circuits operate with the same fluid supply
- Tanks cannot be cleaned due to their shape.

It is only possible to protect the functionality of the pump with a suction filter. Protection against wear must be ensured through filters which are installed in the pressure, return and bypass lines.

Due to the sensitivity of pumps to low pressure, the pressure difference at the filter must not be very large. Hence filters with large surfaces are usually installed. In addition, it is recommended that a bypass valve and a clogging indicator are installed.

In the suction region, filtration is limited to removing large particles, usually greater than 100 μm. A special model exists for the filtration in hydraulic drives. Here a suction filter is used with a filter pore size of 20 μm.

Two types of suction filter exist.

9.1.1 Suction filter without housing

Suction filters without housings are installed in the pump suction line.

Care must be taken that this suction filter is installed sufficiently below the minimum level of oil.

In order to protect the pump, a low pressure switch must be installed between the filter and pump.

Special suction filters without housings may be used as return flow distributors in the return line. They prevent foam from forming and settle the contents of the tank. Under certain conditions baffle walls may then not need to be used.

9.1.2 Suction filters with housing

These filters may also be installed below the level of fluid in the tank. So that the housing does not run empty when an element is changed, it must be fitted with a leakage barrier.

Advantages	Disadvantages
– Simple assembly – Price – It protects hydraulic components from coarse contamination	– Assembly is at the worse postion in the hydraulic system – Bypass is necessary – Bad service possiblities, as immersed in oil – Due to risk of cavitation only coarse filtration is possible – Clogging indicators may be mounted with difficulty

Table 10: *Advantages and disadvantages of suction line filters*

Fig. 17: *Suction line filter*

9.2 Pressure line filter

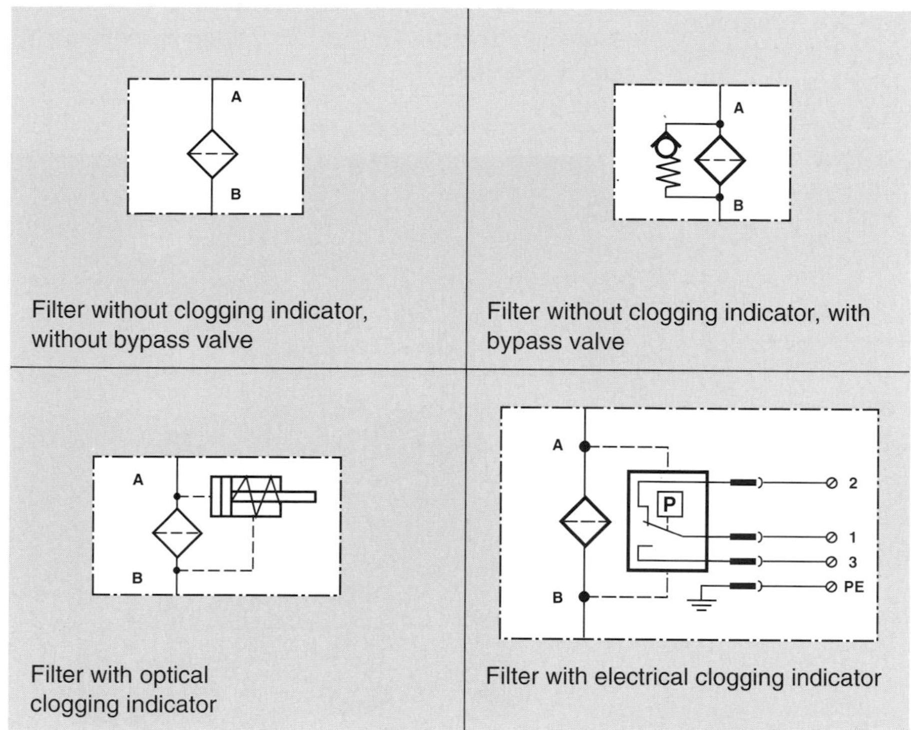

Fig. 18: *Symbols for pressure line filters*

This type of filter is used to ensure that the functionality of hydraulic components after the pump. Hence this type of filter must be fitted as close as possible to the components it is protecting.

The following points are important in deciding whether to use pressure line filters:

- Components are especially sensitive to dirt (e.g. servo valves or control valves) or are important for the functionality of the system
- Components are particularly expensive (e.g. large cylinders, servo valves, hydraulic motors) and are extremely important for the safety of the system.
- The idle time costs for the system are especially high.
- Pressure line filters may be used as safety filters and/or as working filters.

Hence these filters have the following tasks:

Working filters

- Protection against wear in components
- Maintenance of desired fluid cleanliness class.

Safety filters

- Protection of component functionality
  Safety filters are only used in combination with working filters.

pressure line filters should always be fitted with a clogging indicator. In front of especially critical components pressure line filters should only be used without bypass valves. This type of filter must comprise a filter element which can endure large pressure difference loads without sustaining any damage.

The filter housing must be able to be pressurised by the max. system pressure.

Advantages	Disadvantages
– May be mounted directly in front of sensitive components – May filter very finely – Simple servicing – May be supplied with clogging indicator – Long idle times – No pump cavitation	– Must be built robustly (weight) – Element must be designed for a high pressure difference – Depending on flow resistance power is converted into heat

Table 11: *Advantages and disadvantages of pressure line filters*

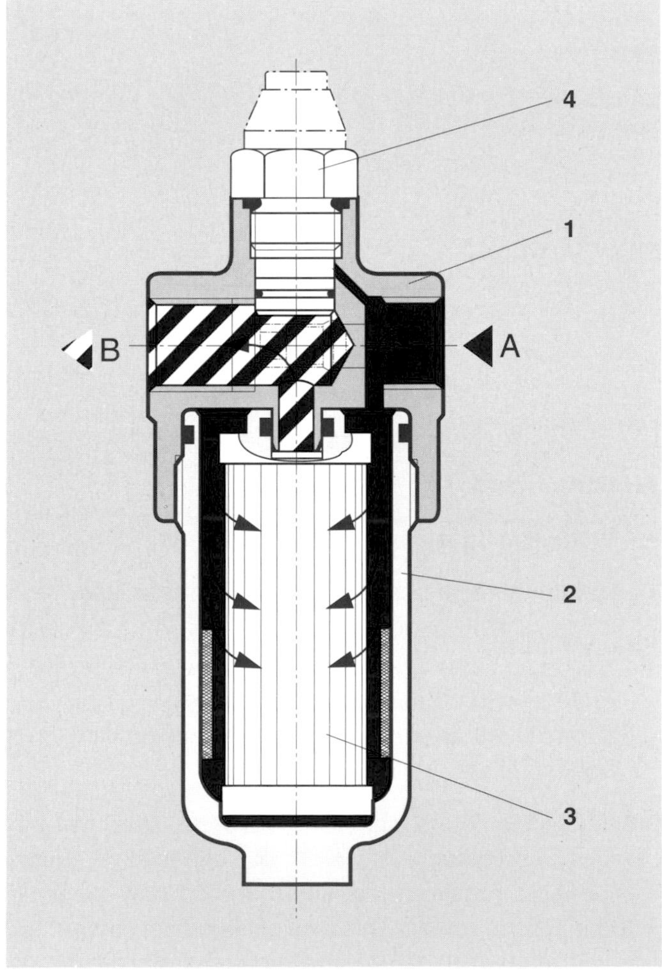

Fig. 19: *Sectional diagram of line filter*

The filter (*fig. 19*) basically comprises filter head (1) with screwed in filter housing (2) and filter element (3). The standard model is without bypass valve and without pressure bleed screw. The port for a clogging indicator (4) is usually available.

Fig. 20: *Pressure line filter*

9.3 Tank mounted return line filter

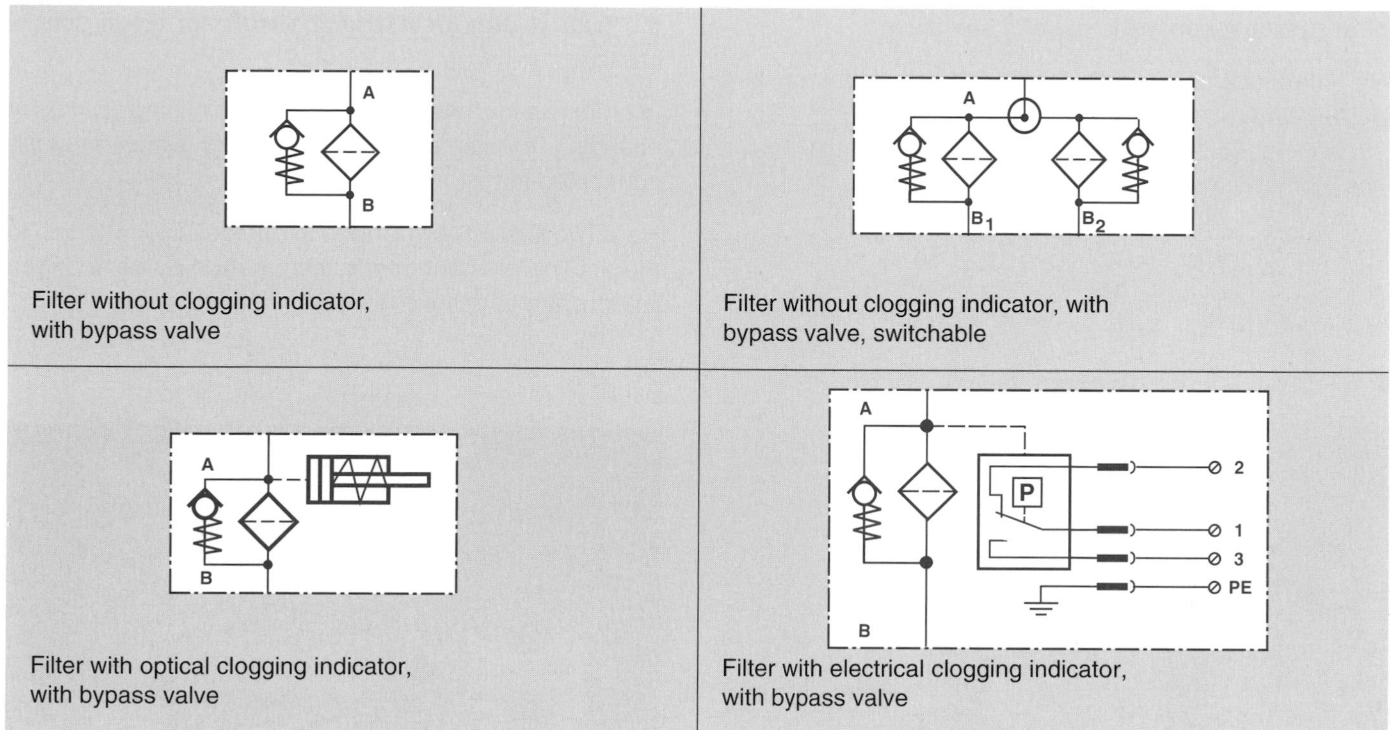

Fig. 21: *Symbols for return line filters*

These filters are situated at the end of return lines and are designed to be mounted onto tanks. This means, that the fluid returned from the system flows back into the tank filtered. Hence all the dirt particles are removed from the fluid which are in the system or produced by the system, before they manage to reach the tank.

When selecting the size of filter the maximum possible flow must be taken into account.

In order to prevent the fluid from foaming in the tank, care must be taken that fluid is returned below the level of the fluid in the tank for all operating conditions. It might be necessary to install a pipe or flow distributor in the filter return line. Care must be taken that the distance between the bottom of the tank and the end of the pipe is not less than 2 or 3 times the size of the pipe diameter.

Advantages	Disadvantages
– Low costs – Simple servicing – May be fitted with clogging indicator – Fine filtraton is possible – No pump cavitation	– Bypass valve is necessary – Allows dirt particles to pass through the open bypass valve if pressure peaks occur or if a cold start takes place

Table 12: *Advantages and disadvantages of mounted return line filters*

The filter shown in *fig. 22* is mounted using a fixing flange (1) onto the tank cover. Housing (2) and filter port protrude into the tank. An advantage of this type of filter is the ease of access and hence the ease of servicing.

By removing the cover (3) the filter element (5) may be quickly and simply removed.

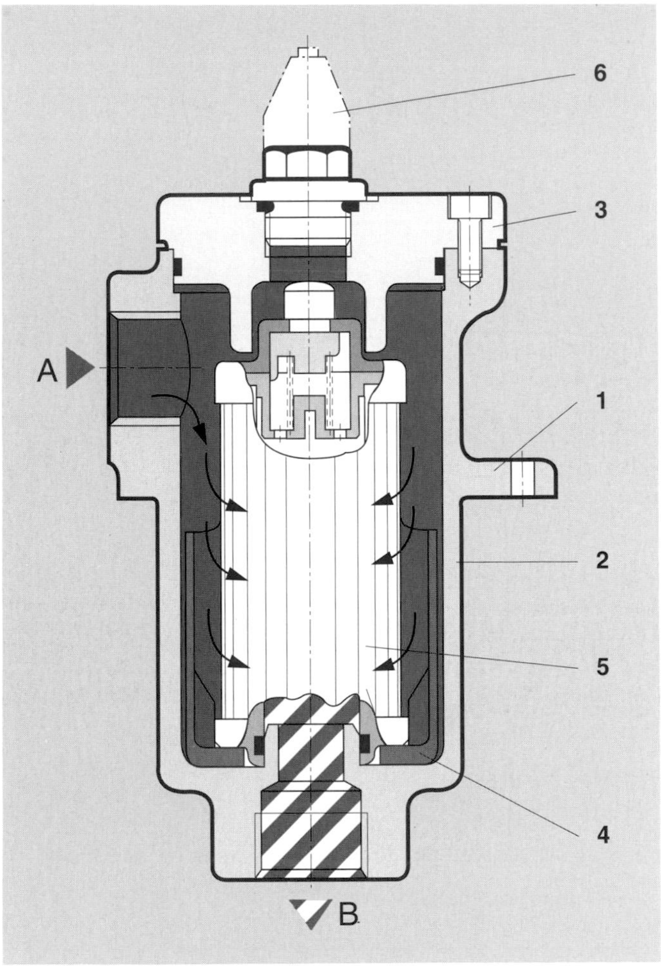

Fig. 22: *Sectional diagram of mounted return line filter for mounting in tank*

filter element (5). When the element is removed, the dirt collecting tray is also removed with it. This prevents the dirt which has been removed (collected) from flowing into the tank. A port for a clogging indicator (6) is usually present.

In order to avoid idle times due to the servicing of filters or changing of elements, double filters which may be connected in turn are used.

Here two filters are arranged in parallel. By switching to the second element, the first element may be changed without stopping the system.

Fig. 23: *Mounted return line filter for mounting in tank*

A special type of return line filter may be fitted directly into a valve stacking assembly.

By using valves within blocks there is no need to pipe the return line.

The valve stacking assembly, type VAB comprises pressure relief valves, filter element and pressure gauge port with shut-off valve. On the bottom of the stacking assembly are the ports for the pump and tank. In type H on the top is the mounting pattern for hydraulic valves of sizes 6 or 10 to DIN 24 340. In type L a longitudinal stacking system for sizes 6 or 10 may be mounted by means of flanges on top.

The standard elements (1) from the RF series are used for the filter. A clogging indicator (2) may be mounted to monitor the degree of contamination.

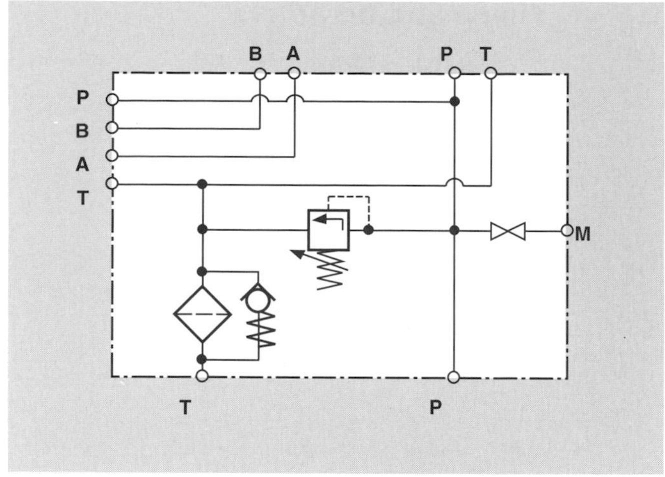

Fig. 25: *Symbol for valve connection block*

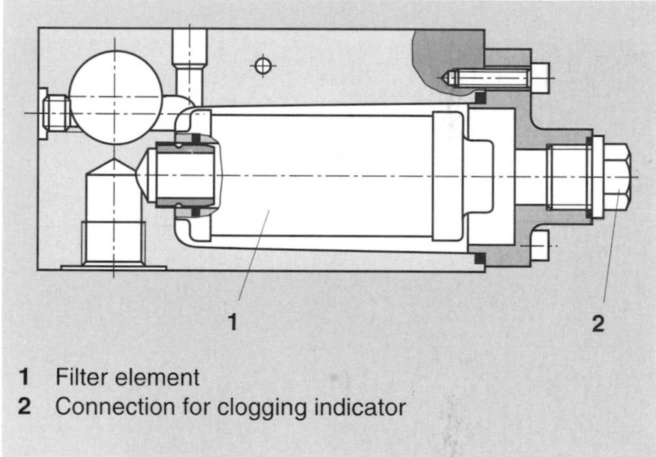

Fig. 26: *Sectional diagram for valve connection block*

Fig. 24: *Valve connection block*

9.5 Fillers and breathers

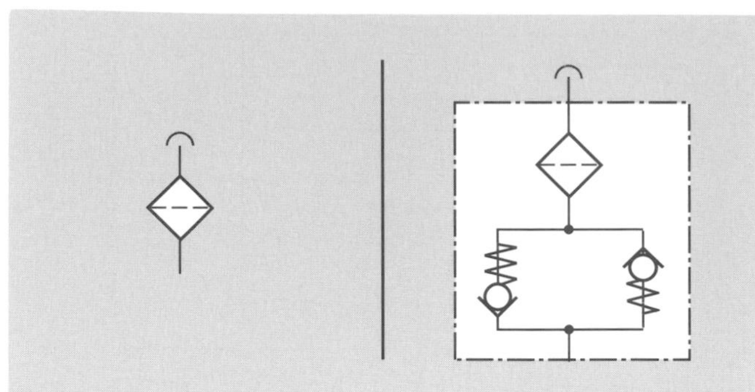

Fig. 27: *Symbol for filler and breather (left) without and (right) with bypass valve*

Fig. 28: *Filler and breather with and without filling sieve*

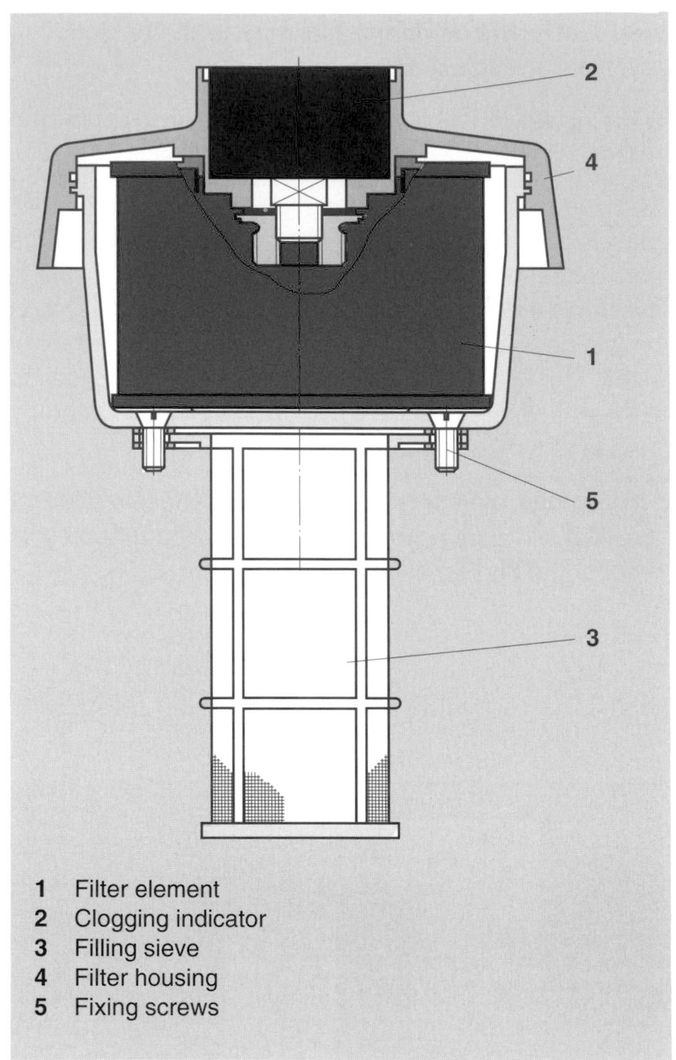

Fig. 29: *Filler and breather with filling sieve*

In the past little attention was paid to these filters in hydraulic systems. However, nowadays they are considered to be amongst the most important components for the filtration of fluid in a hydraulic system. A large amount of contamination enters hydraulic systems via unsuitable ventilation devices. Measures such as the pressurisation of oil tanks are usually uneconomic when viewed with respect to the highly effective breathers nowadays available.

Depending on the class of cleanliness required, breathers may be fitted with various interchangeable elements. These filters must be fitted with a port for a clogging indicator (2).

Fillers and breathers basically comprise an air filter (1) to filter the air flowing into the tank and a filling sieve (3) to separate any large particles when the tank is being filled. Air filters are available with various pore sizes so that the standard CETOP RP 70 may be fulfilled. This standard says that the pore sizes for system and air filters must be the same.

The requirements of this filter are laid out in DIN 24557.

9.6 Clogging indicators

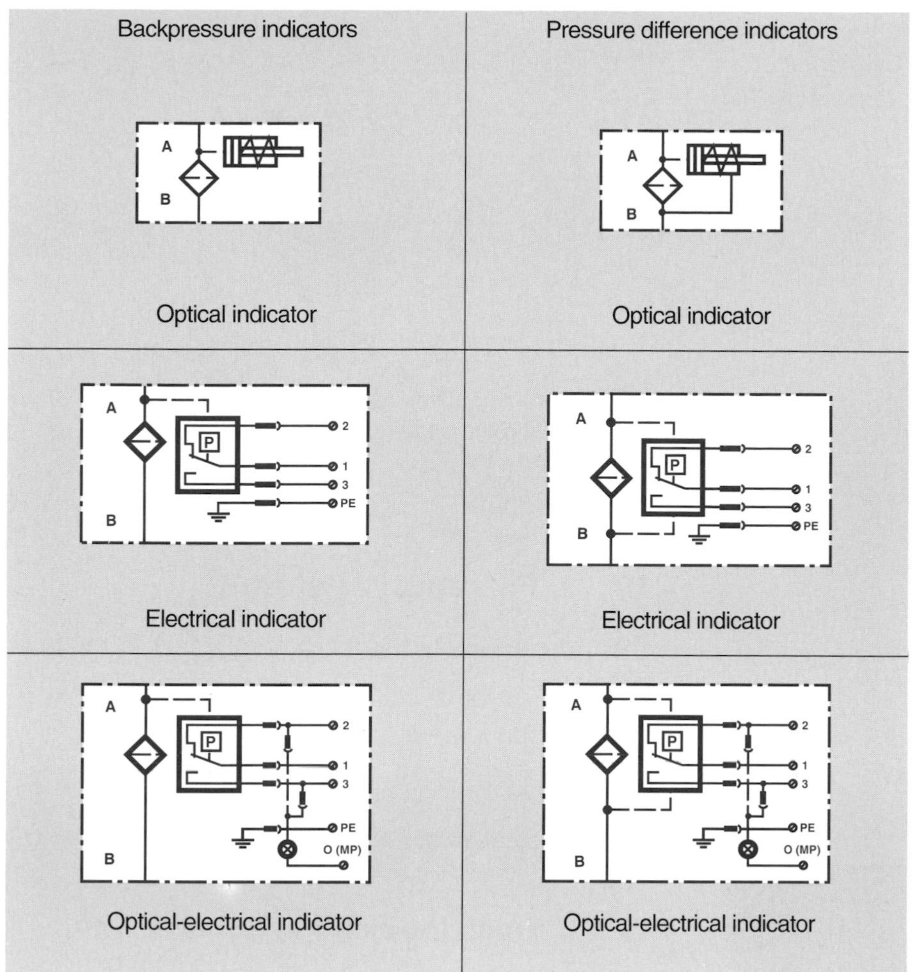

Fig. 30: *Symbols for clogging indicators*

Clogging indicators record when a pre-determined backpressure or pressure difference at the filter has been reached. Either an optical signal appears or an electrical contact is operated. The point of operation or the indicating point must be selected so that the filter element is still able to remove some more dirt. This is so that the system may continue to operate until the end of a shift.

The following types of clogging indicator are available:

- backpressure indicator
- pressure difference indicator and
- low pressure indicator

For pressure line filters the clogging indicators show the pressure drop between the filter input and output. In tank or block mounted return line filters the backpressure upstream of the element is measured. In suction filters the low pressure downstream of the filter element is measured. Clogging indicators must be able to be screwed into filters at any time as an afterthought without a lot of effort.

9.6.1 Function

In clogging indicators, each change in pressure is monitored by measuring spools or membranes as a change in stroke. Inside the clogging indicator is a spool connected to a solenoid which moves against the force of a spring. In an optical clogging indicator a solenoid with the same polarity is attached in the display head. The closer the poles come together, the greater the force with which the coils oppose each other, until the red display button jumps out.

In the electrical model a contact is closed.

Electronic clogging indicators were developed for the continuous display of element contamination. By using displays it is possible to calculate when servicing will be required.

In these completely electronic clogging indicators, the pressure difference existing in the filter as a result of element contamination is converted without movement into an analogue electrical output signal by means of a sensor. In addition a device to suppress pressure peaks and cold starts is installed.

Fig. 31: Pressure difference clogging indicators

Fig. 32: *Backpressure clogging indicators*

Fig. 33: Electronic clogging indicator

10 Filtration systems

There are basically three types of circuit in hydraulic systems:

- open loop
- closed loop
- a combination of the above

10.1 Open loop circuit *(figs. 34 and 35)*

In open loop circuits the fluid is sucked out of the tank, pushed through the hydraulic system and led back to tank. The arrangement of filters in an open loop circuit depends on the tasks which the filters are expected to perform.

10.1.1 Main flow filter

Main flow filters are used to filter fluid which is found in the actual hydraulic circuit.

Suction, line and mounted return line filters may be used as main flow filters.

10.1.2 Bypass filters

These filters are used to filter the fluid found in the tank when it is circulating. Usually complete bypass filter units, comprising pump, filter and oil cooler are used.

The advantage of bypass filters is that the filters may operated independent of the operating cycles of the hydraulic system and the fluid flowing through the filter elements remains constant and without pulses.

The ageing process of the fluid is slowed down, so that the service life of the fluid is considerably increased.

10.1.3 Breathers

These filters are used to filter the air flowing in and out of the tank.

There are two types of filter dependent on their function: working and safety filters (*fig. 35*).

10.1.4 Working filters

Tank or block mounted return line filters and pressure line filters with bypass valves as well as bypass filters may be used here.

Working filters comprise low pressure stable filter elements. Due to this type of element, they may have large filter surfaces and hence they have a high dirt holding capacity.

In order to fulfil the filter task to an optimum degree tank or block mounted return line filters and pressure line filters being used as working filters must be placed where the largest flow in the hydraulic system occurs and they must also be sufficiently large. If necessary these filters may also be installed in leakage lines.

10.1.5 Safety filters

These filters are used to protect hydraulic components from suddenly malfunctioning due to a too high a level of solid particle contamination. This means that they should only be used to filter particles, which may suddenly clog hydraulic components.

A further use of safety filters is to protect a system from contamination when a pump or motor malfunctions. By installing such a filter high repair costs for damaged components may be avoided.

These filters must have a much larger pore size than the working filters used in the hydraulic system. The size of the filter may be smaller. The filter housing must not have a bypass valve. Hence these filters must be made of components which are highly pressure stable under pressure.

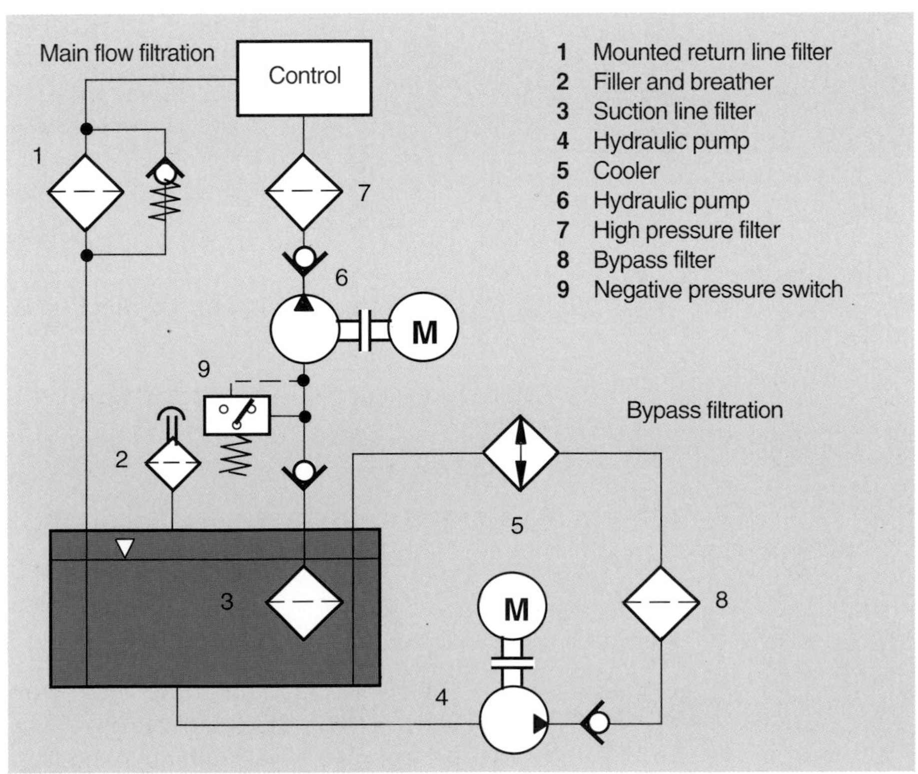

Fig. 34: *Filter arrangement in hydraulic systems*

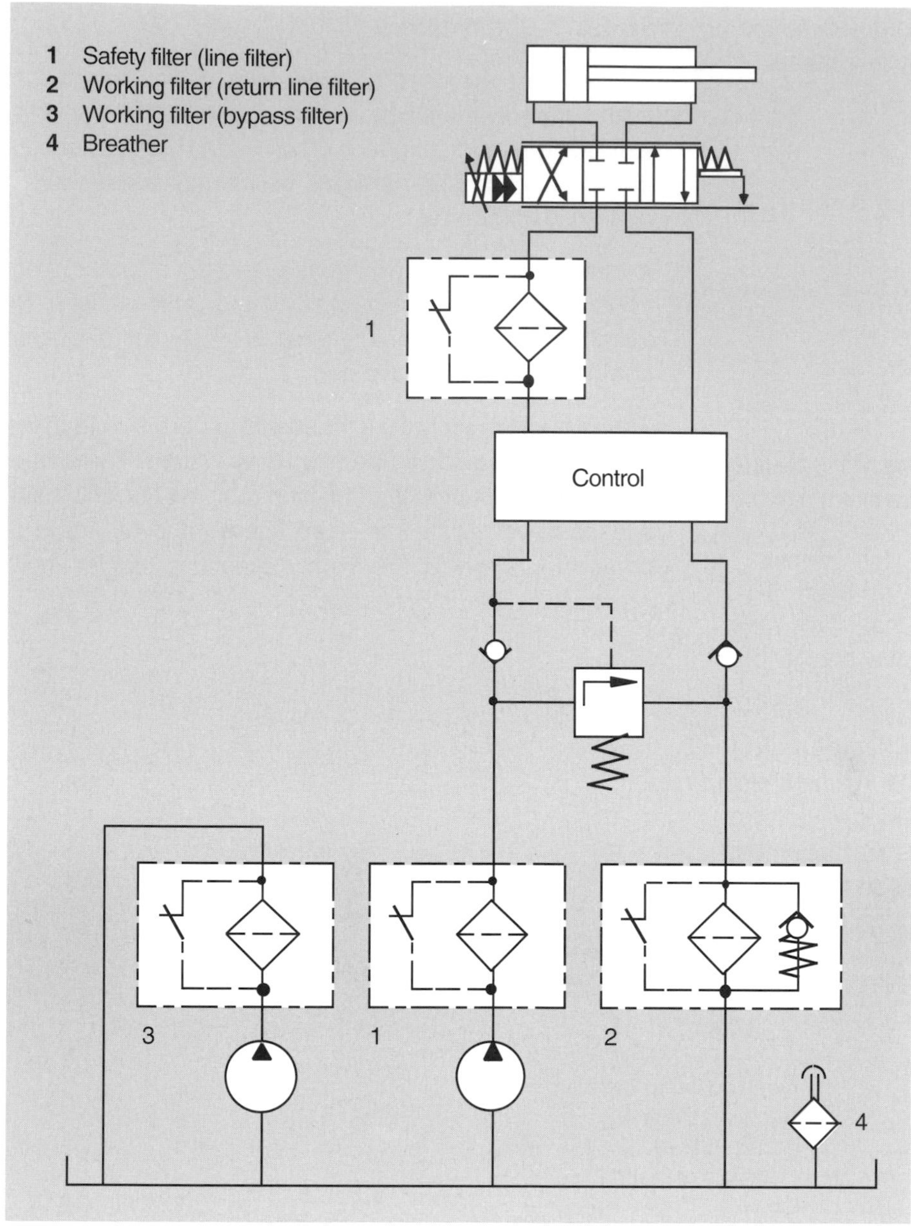

Fig. 35: *Example of open loop circuit*

10.2 Closed loop circuit

In closed loop circuits the fluid is continually pumped around the actual hydraulic circuit. Only the leakage oil flows back to the tank and is then fed back into the closed loop circuit by the boost pump.

Application: e.g. transmission hydraulics with hydraulic pump and hydraulic motor.

10.2.1 Filter model

The actual closed circuit is only filtered in the flushing stage. Once the system has been flushed the filters (4) are removed. The fluid is filtered either when the leakage oil flow is returned (1), in the suction line (2) or in the pressure line of the boost circuit (4).

By using pressure sensitive sealing systems in motors and pumps, it is only possible to filter the leakage oil flow in the return line using sieve filters with large pore sizes. These only produce a low pressure loss.

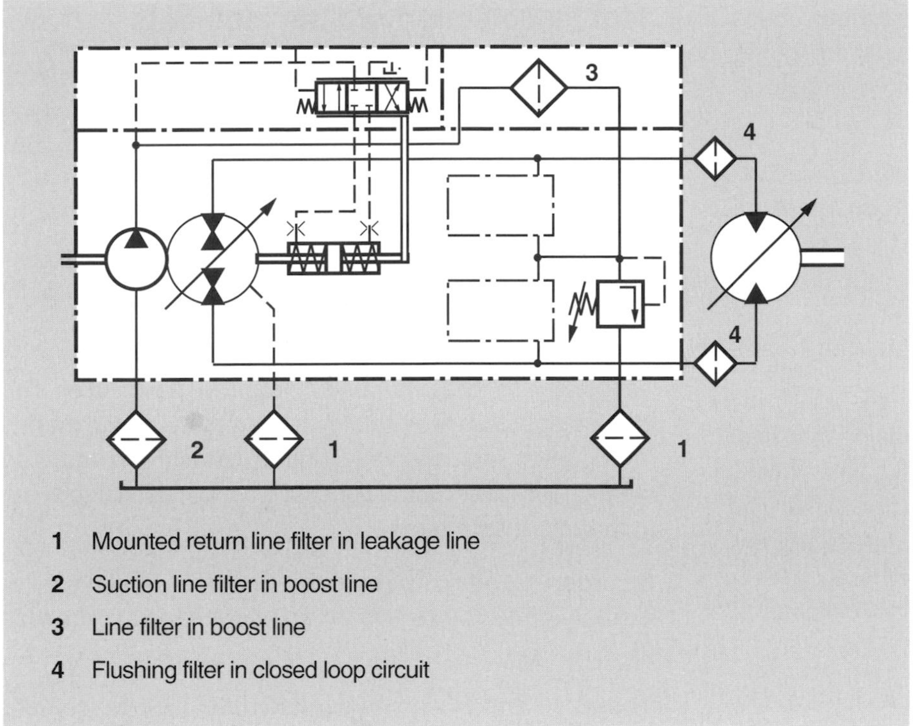

Fig. 36: *Example of closed loop circuit*

10.3 Combination of both types of circuit

Where both types of circuit are combined the open and closed loop circuits installed in the system are supplied by a common tank.

Application: For example, in mobile machines, the working hydraulics and steering is designed as an open loop system, the transmission hydraulics and rotary actuator as a closed loop system.

10.3.1 Filter model

The individual circuits may be fitted with the filter models described in *sections 10.1 and 10.2*. The filter pore sizes used in the filters should be the same for both circuits.

In order for both circuits to work to an optimum degree together, it is important that operator, component manufacturer and component supplier work together.

11 Selection of filter

11.1 Filtration design

An effective filtration in hydraulic systems prevents disturbances and at the same time increases the service life of important and expensive components.

Hence: **Filtration is not a necessary evil, but a beneficial necessity**

The effectiveness of a filter is the most important factor but not the only factor which influences the evaluation of filter design. A filter may be ineffective if it is installed in the wrong place or if it designed for the wrong task. As already mentioned, one or more filters may be used for filtration purposes.

In designing the filtration for a system the following basic rules should be taken into account:

- By using suitable seals and installing highly effective fillers and breathers, dirt must be prevented from entering the system from outside.
- Dirt should be removed as quickly as possible after it has entered the system or after it has been created.

- Hydraulic filters should always be used to help reduce wear, i.e. the filter pore sizes should be smaller than the critical clearance tolerances for the hydraulic components.
- So that the filters can clean as much fluid as possible, they should always be installed in positions where the most flow is expected.
- A specification must be written.

Following on from these basic rules the filters can then be divided into working and safety filters.

The working filters carry out the task of cleaning. The filter pore size should be chosen to comply with critical clearance tolerances of the hydraulic components. The filters may have bypass valves and be fitted with low pressure difference stable filter elements. It is recommended that a pressure difference indicator is fitted.

The required protection against clogging is achieved by fitting a safety filter, i.e. these filters only remove particles which could lead to hydraulic components becoming suddenly clogged.

Safety filters prevent long-term wear and for this reason should have a larger pore size than the working filters. Safety filters should not have bypass valves and they must comprise high pressure difference stable filter elements.

11.2 Filter design criteria

In addition to the requirement for functional safety of and long service lives for hydraulic components, the operating and system costs and the cost of disposing of the fluid are important when designing a suitable hydraulic filter system.

The following criteria should be taken into account when designing a filter system:

- Sensitivity to dirt of the hydraulic components used
- Application for the complete system
- Determination of flow
- Permissible pressure difference or backpressure
- Compatibility of fluids with the filter materials
- Operating temperature
- Viscosity of fluid
- Design temperature
- Additional devices (e.g. clogging indicator)

11.3 Selection of filter elements

The recommended pressure losses in clean elements and at operating viscosity should not exceed the following values in the complete filter (housing and element):

Line filter without bypass: $\Delta p_A = 0.2 \times \Delta p_{Indicator}$

Line filter with bypass: $\Delta p_A = 0.15 \times \Delta p_{Indicator}$

Mounted return line filter: $\Delta p_A = 0.2 \times \Delta p_{Indicator}$

Before the size of the filter can be determined it is necessary to determine the required pore size. The cleanliness class required for the complete system needs to be taken into account. This is usually the required cleanliness class for the component most sensitive to dirt in the hydraulic system.

In order to attain a specific cleanliness class filter elements must be used with an absolute filter pore size ($\beta_x \geq 100$).

Tables 13 and 14 can be used to determine which pore size to use and hence which filter element.

Hydraulic system	**Preferred absolute filter pore size ($\beta_x \geq 100$)**	**Attainable cleanliness class to NAS 1638 in particles > 5 µm**	**Attainable cleanliness class to ISO 4406**
Systems with servo valves	X = 5	7	16/13
Systems with control valves	X = 5	7 to 8	16/13
Systems with proportional valves	X = 10	9	18/15
General hydraulic systems	X = 10 to 20	9 to 10	19/16

Table 13: *Determination of recommended filter pore size in hydraulic systems using Rexroth components*

Once the required filter pore size has been determined, it is then possible to determine the size of the filter. In determining the filter size the aim is to achieve a balance between the dirt entering the system and the dirt leaving the system via the filters. An economic time between element replacement also needs to be realised.

Hence when determining the size of a filter the degree of contamination in the machine environment, the care and service of the hydraulic system and the operating temperature of the fluid need to be taken into account.

The formulae required to determine the size of a filter are shown in *table 15*.

Application	Filter pore size µm	Element designation	Pressure difference stability	Remarks
Working filter, bypass filter, mounted return line filter, line filter with bypass valve	3	.R 003 BN/HC-2	30 bar	
	3	.D 003 BN/HC-2		
	5	.R 005 BN/HC-2		
	5	.D 005 BN/HC-2		
	10	.R 010 BN/HC-2		
	10	.D 010 BN/HC-2		
	20	.R 020 BN/HC-2		
	20	.D 020 BN/HC-2		
Safety filter, line filter without bypass valve	3	.R 003 BH/HC-2	210 bar	Further filter pore sizes on enquiry
	5	.D 003 BH/HC-2		
	10	.R 005 BH/HC-2		
	20	.D 005 BH/HC-2		
	25	.D 025 W	30 bar	
	25	.D 025 T	210 bar	
	50	.D 050 W	30 bar	
	50	.D 050 T	210 bar	
	100	.D 100 W	30 bar	
	100	.D 100 T	210 bar	

Table 14: *Selection of filter elements with respect to application and corresponging required filter pore size*

Filter arrangement in hydraulic system	Filter type	Total pressure difference in filter with new filter element: By using individual diagrams for filter housing and filter element	By using design diagrams
Working filter	Mounted return line filter, line filter with bypass valve	$f_2 (\Delta p_{housing} + f_1 \times \Delta p_{element}) \leq$ 0,15 to 0,2 x $\Delta p_{indicator}$	$Q_{design} = Q_{system} \times f_1 \times f_2$
	Bypass filter, line filter; separate power units	—	—
Safety filter	Line filter without bypass valve	$f_2 (\Delta p_{housing} + f_1 \times \Delta p_{element}) \leq$ 0,2 x $\Delta p_{indicator}$	$Q_{design} = Q_{system} \times f_1 \times f_2$
	Suction filter	$f_2 (\Delta p_{housing} + f_1 \times \Delta p_{element}) \leq 0{,}01$	$Q_{design} =$ 5 to 10 x $Q_{pump} \times f_2$

Table 15: *Determination of filter size*

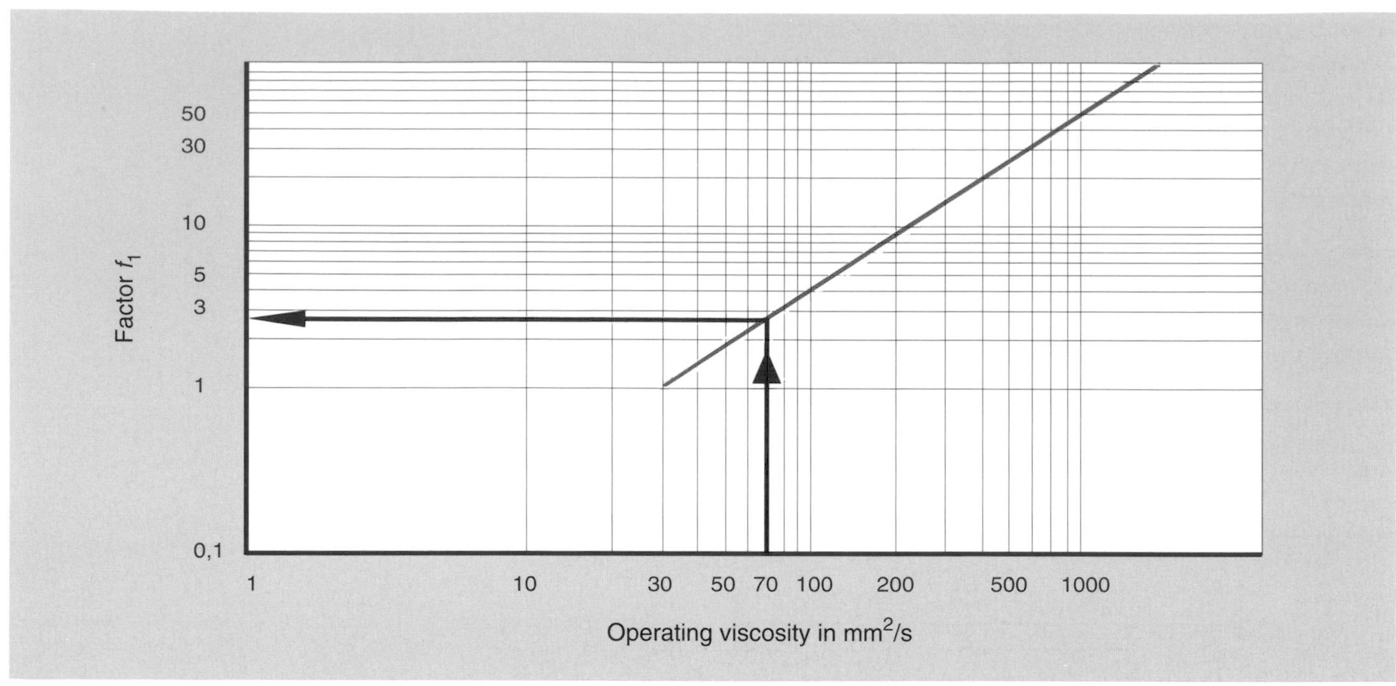

Diagram 7 : *Graphical representation of viscosity conversion factor f_1*

Servicing and care of hydraulic systems	Degree of contamination in machine environment [1] low	[2] average	[3] high
– Continuous control of filters – Immediate changing of filter element – Low dirt ingress – Good sealing of tank	1,0	1,0	1,3
– Sporadic checking of filter – Use of few cylinders	1,0	1,5	1,7
– Little or no control of filter – Many unprotected cylinders – High level of contamination entering system	1,3	2,0	2,3

Table 16: *Factor f_2 for ambient conditions*

Remarks to *table 16*

[1] low;
e.g. test machines in sealed climatised chambers

[2] average:
e.g. machine tools in heates halls

[3] high:
e.g. presses in founderies, machines for ceramic manufacture, machines in potash mines, agricultural machines and mobile devices, rolling mills, carpentry

In order to shorten and simplify the relatively complex process of determining the filter size, filter design diagrams were developed (see diagrams 8,9 and 10).

The diagrams are with respect to a viscosity of 30 mm²/s for the fluid. Higher operating viscosities and variations in ambient conditions are taken into account when determining the flow for the filter design.

The flow for the filter design using the diagrams is calculated from the following:

$$Q_A = Q_W \times f_1 \times f_2$$

Q_A = flow for filter design
Q_W = effective flow
f_1 = viscosity conversion factor
f_2 = factor for ambient conditions

The required filter size is determined from the point of intersection where the flow crosses the filter pore size.

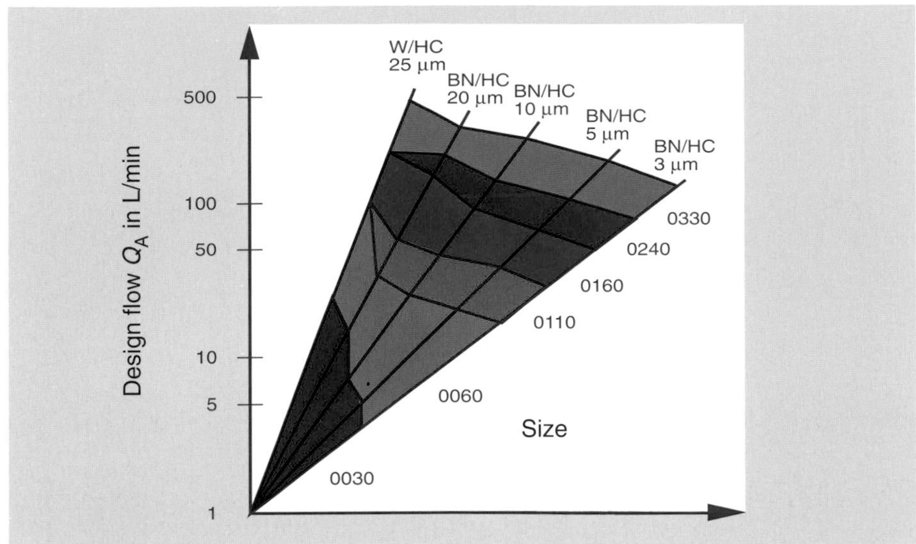

Diagram 8 :

Determination of filter size in mountec return line filters

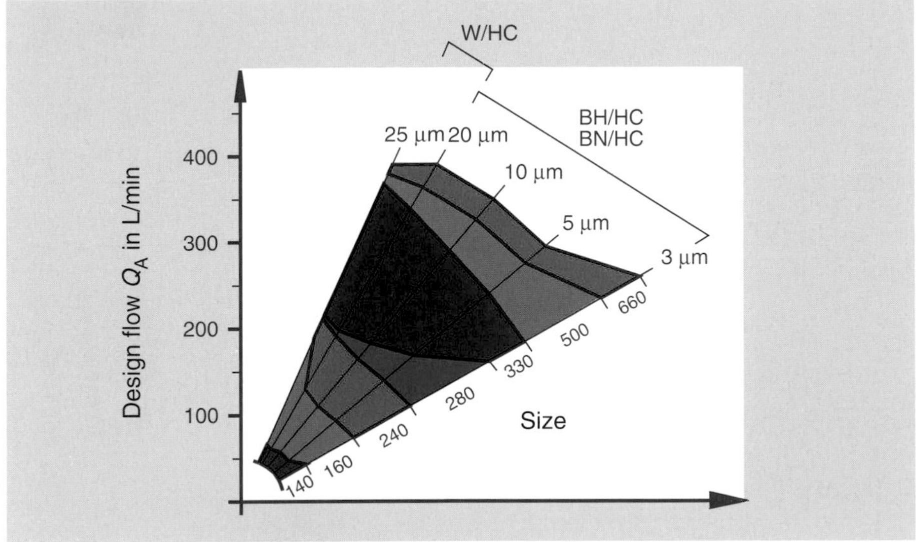

Diagram 9 :

Determination of filter size in powei filters

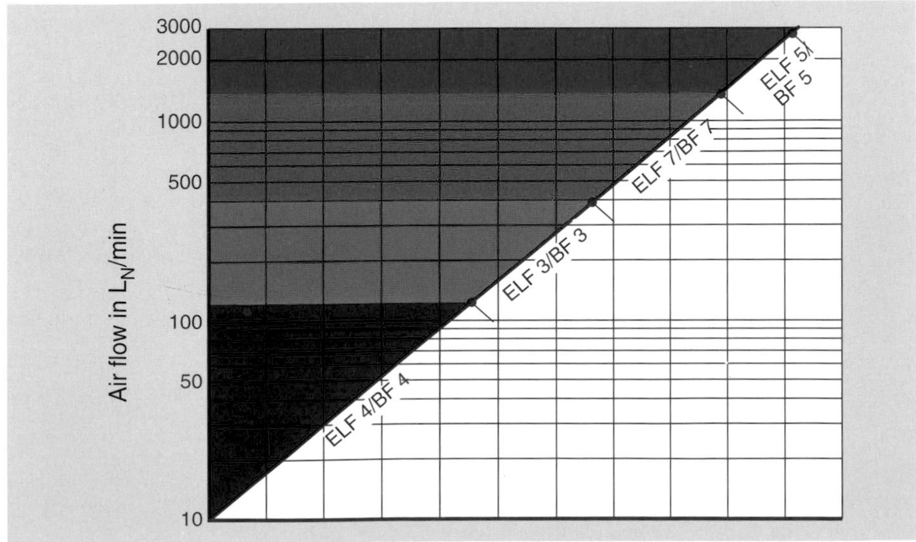

Diagram 10 :

Determination of filter size in breaters

Notes

Accessories

Chapter 15

Accessories

Martin Reik

1 Introduction

The term "accessories" actually leads to a false impression, when considering the importance of the components in this section.

Accessories are just as important for the smooth operation of hydraulic systems as the drive, control and output elements described already.

2 Components to reduce noise

2.1 General

Hydraulic systems include components which agitate fluid and air and these effects influence each other. In order to reduce noise in hydraulic power units various measures are available.

2.1.1 Decoupling of component vibrations

Due to the large surfaces and the thin metal walls used, oil tanks are very good resonators. By using materials which damp vibrations it is possible to decouple noise from the tank.

Measures which help in this are

- Placing pump on an anti vibration element
- Installing a vibration damping pump carrier
- Using pipe ducts made of rubber
- Fixing lines with noise damping fixing clamps

2.1.2 Decoupling of fluid vibrations

Vibrations occur in fluids especially when pressure pulses are present.

Measures which help in this are

- Use of accumulators which remove pressure pulses
- Creation of opposing pulses, which neutralise the pulses within the complete system

2.1.3 Decoupling of air vibrations

This is only possible by using an acoustic absorption cover over the hydraulic power unit.

2.2 Components for the decoupling of component vibrations

2.2.1 Pump carrier

The pump carrier links the pump to the drive motor.

Type	With noise damping	With noise damping and oil-air cooler	With noise damping, oil-air cooler and oil tank	Without noise damping
Desciption	Comprises several parts. Reduction of transfer of body vibration and vibrations from drive motor and hydraulic pump to the tank.	Due to the installation problems this type may only be used for the cooling of the leakage oil and for drive powers up to 22 kW. Cooling power 0.5 to 1.8 kW Reduction of vibrations.	Small power unit comprising pump carrier, oil-air cooler and tank. Drive power up to 45 kW Cooling power 1 to 7.5 kW Tank is also sutiable for closed loop drives.	Reasonable cost, single component model Transfer of vibrations to the hydraulic tank
Disadvantage	More expensive than rigid model.	Small cooling power	Small oil tank (5 to 18 litres)	Noisy power unit
Advantage	Noise level of complete hydraulic system is reduced (up to 6 dB(A).	Noise level of complete hydraulic system is reduced (up to 6 dB(A).	Compact power unit. Above all suitable for use in closed loop circuits.	Reasonable cost of pump fixing

Table 1: *Types of pump carriers*

2.2.1.1 Pump carrier with damping of vibrations

Fig. 1: *Flexible pump carrier*

The flexible pump carrier (*fig. 1*) is used to connect the hydraulic pump to the drive motor, whereby the transfer of component vibrations and oscillations is avoided to a large extent. The pump vibrations are isolated and damped by a temperature and fluid stable rubber ring which transfers all the forces. By using a rotary flexible coupling there is no metallic connection between the pump and motor. The noise level within a hydraulic system may be reduced considerably by this means.

The possible reduction in the noise level depends on many factors (type of pump, operating pressure, type of pipes, construction, etc). Hence exact values cannot be provided. In general noise levels may be reduced by up to 6 dB(A). The damping materials used in the pump carriers must be suitable for various motor-pump combinations. *Fig. 2 and diagram 1* show the measuring arrangement and typical noise reduction for an flexible pump carrier in comparison with a rigid pump carrier.

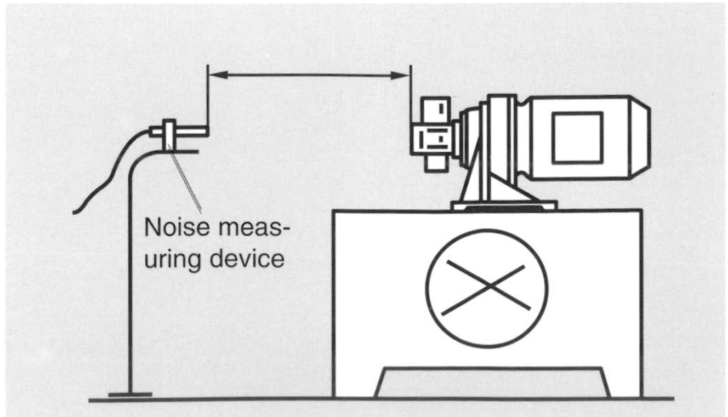

Fig. 2: *Measurement arrangement for the measurement of air noise in hydraulic power units*

Accessories

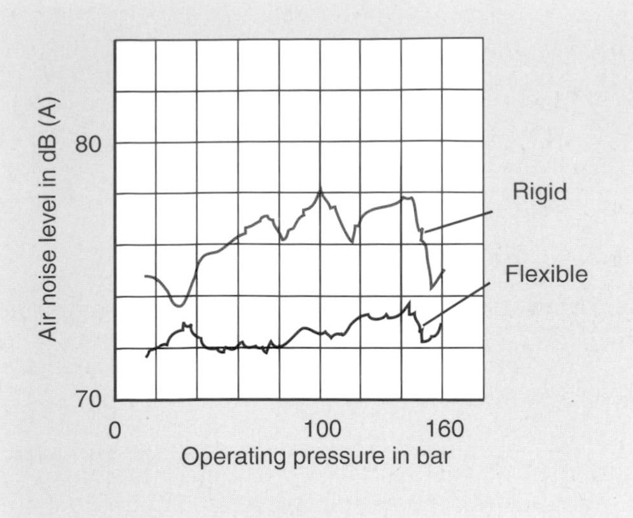

Diagram 1: *Air noise dependent on operating pressure in flexible and rigid pump carriers*

Function

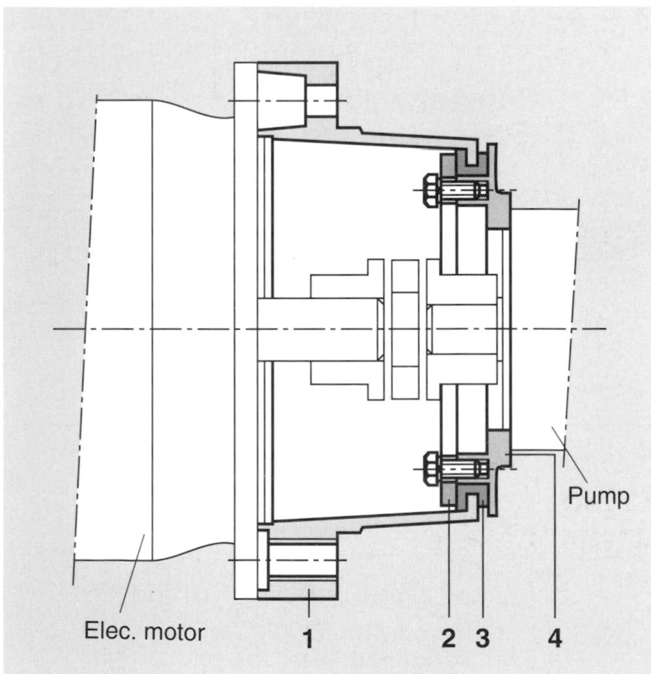

Fig. 3: C*onstruction of flexible pump carrier*

The basic body (1) together with the connecting flange for the electrical motor form a rigid unit, which is connected to the pump flange (4) by means of an rubber ring (3) and a clamping ring (2).

The Shore hardness and quality of the rubber ring are matched to the pump type, the drive power and the fluid.

2.2.1.2 Pump carrier with vibration damping and built-in oil-air cooler

Fig. 4: *Flexible pump carrier with built-in oil-air cooler*

In this model the fluid flowing from the system is cooled by means of an oil-air cooler. The air flow required for the cooling is created by a fan mounted on the motor shaft. This combination of vibration damping pump carrier and oil-air cooler (*fig. 4*) offers simplification and cost reduction in hydraulic power units. The heat exchanger is arranged around the outside of the pump carrier and hence may be easily cleaned. Air delivery is designed so that the pump carrier may be mounted horizontally as well as vertically on the tank.

Due to the shape of the device, cooling power is limited to 1.8 kW. In most cases the leakage oil in the system may be cooled by this. In addition the heat found in systems which are operated for long periods or on hot summer days may be compensated for.

The main features of the oil-air cooler used are

- Low installation costs
- Low operating costs
- No corrosion due to the coolant
- Simple servicing
- Easily available
- No damage to the hydraulics if not completely sealed
- Fan drive by means of the main drive motor.

Function

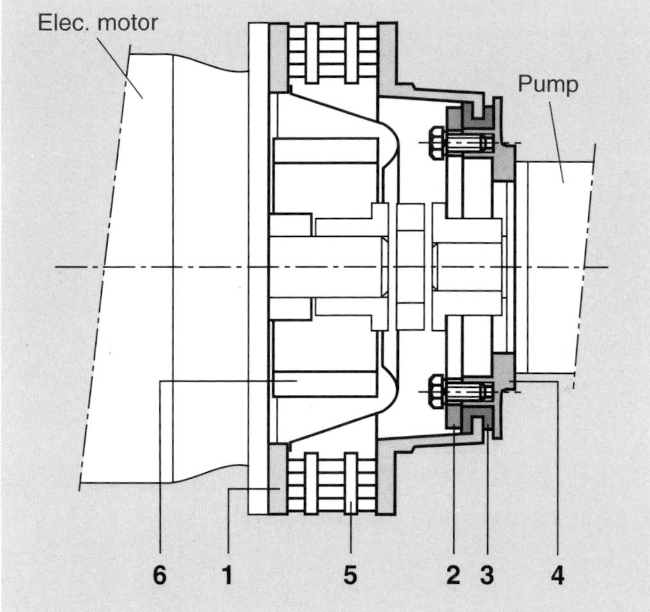

Fig. 5: *Construction of elastic pump carrier with built in oil-air cooler*

The basic body (1) together with the connecting flange for the electrical motor form a rigid unit, which is connected to the pump flange (4) by means of rubber ring (3) and a clamping ring (2).

The Shore hardness and quality of the rubber ring are matched to the pump type, the drive power and the fluid. The cooling elements (5) and the housing feeding air are mounted within the basic body and are arranged so that it is still simple to assemble the pump group. The fan (6) is mounted on the motor shaft.

2.2.1.3 Pump carrier with vibration damping, built-in oil-air cooler and tank

Fig. 6: *Tank package*

In the model shown in *fig. 6* the following three components are contained within one unit:

- vibration damping pump carrier
- oil-air cooler and
- fluid tank with return line filter

The standard model also includes

- a clogging indicator for the filter
- a visual monitor for the level of oil and
- filler and breather.

In addition it is possible to have an electrical monitoring of oil and temperature.

The main advantages for this type of unit are:

- Reduction of oil volume
- Reduction of power weight ratio by up to 80 % and volume by up to 60 % in comparison with conventional models.
- Simple mounting of electrical motor and pump
- Low noise levels
- Rotary elastic coupling

The most important technical data are:

- Drive power 0.55 to 45 kW
- Tank volume 5 to 18 litres and
- Cooling power 1 to 7.5 kW

Function

The model shown in *fig. 7* comprises pump carrier (1), tank (2) and cooler (3) which are screwed together to form one unit. As the front are the flanges for drive motor and pump. A damping ring (4) between the pump flange (5) and the pump carrier ensures that the pump vibrations are decoupled. The fan (6) which is fixed to the motor shaft via a boss supplies the air required for the integrated oil-air cooler. The cooling element may be simply hinged out of the unit to be cleaned. The motor and pump shafts are connected to each other by means of a rotary flexible coupling. The oil returning from the actuator to tank is filtered by a return line filter (8) with a suitable filter pore size.

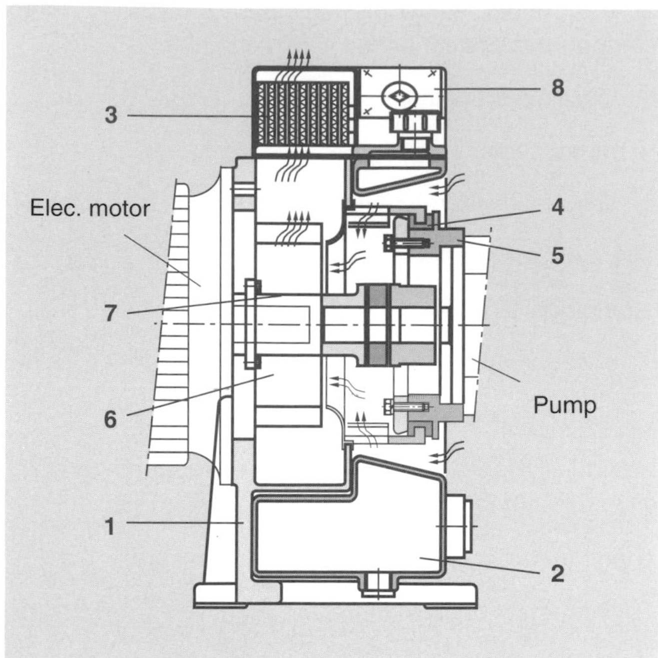

Fig. 7: *Construction of tank package*

2.2.1.4 Rigid pump carrier

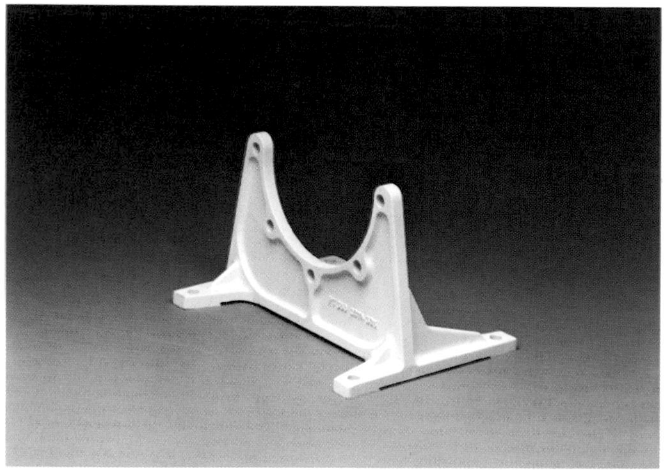

Fig. 8: *Simple pump carrier*

Rigid pump carriers are not suitable for damping vibrations

This model is a single unit which may transfer the vibrations from the drive motor and pump and the pulses from the fluid to the tank. This may even produce vibration amplification.

2.2.2 Vibration damping of pipe and hose fixing clamps

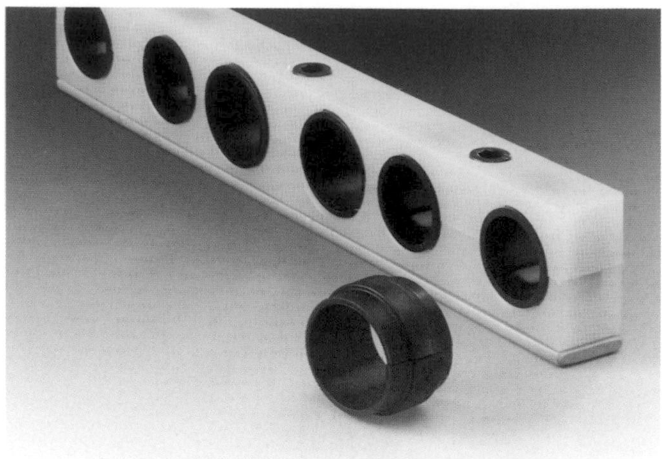

Fig. 9: *Pipe clamp wiht elastomer insert*

Shock absorbing and vibration damping fixing clamps are used for the quick, clean and clear assembly of pipe lines.

With these clamps it is possible to fix any of the following in the complete system:

- Pipes for operating fluid
- Pipes for additional media (e.g. air)
- Hose lines
- Conduits for electrical lines

The clamps must carry out the following tasks

- Secure fixing of pipes and hoses (under static and dynamic loads)
- Vibration damping
- Noise damping
- Shock absorption
- Possibility of compensating for lengths in pipes with changes in temperature.

Hoses especially must not be pressed onto sharp edges.

The lines must be fixed by clamps in such a way that chafing or bending is avoided.

The vibration and noise damping characteristics of these clamps are the most important, as transfer of component vibrations to the complete system may be avoided in this way.

The diameter of the pipes and hoses to be fixed determines the size of clamp to be used.

The internal pipe pressure as well as the dynamic loading determine the selection of clamp series (light or heavy series).

It is recommended that round steel clamps are used in pipes which are likely to expand by a large amount due to heat.

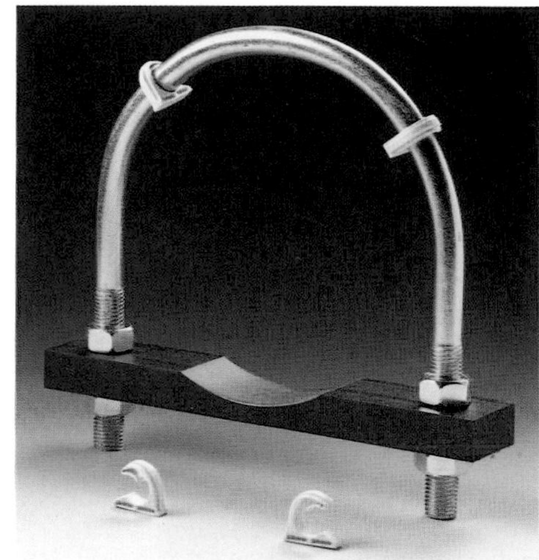

Fig. 10: *Round steel iron clamps*

2.2.3 Vibration damping pipe ducts

Fig. 11: *Pipe ducts*

Pipe ducts are rubber parts which are used to isolate component vibrations in pipes. They are mainly used in pipe ducts in tanks in hydraulic systems, the driver cabs in tractors and machine part covers. In addition they provide a seal against water spray and dust. The rubber parts are designed in such a way that a defined deflection exists between the pipe, the rubber part and the tank wall.

2.3 Components for the decoupling of vibrations in fluids

As already mentioned in *section 2.1.2* accumulators are mainly used to decouple vibrations in fluids.

The types available and which size should be used are described in the chapter "Accumulators and their Applications".

2.4 Components for the decoupling of noise travelling in air

It is only possible to decouple the noise travelling in air in hydraulic systems by using noise absorbing covers.

The material used for noise damping must be fire-resistant.

In addition, the ventilation or cooling of the hydraulic system must not be reduced.

3 Components for controlling fluid temperature

Energy is necessary for the creation of pressure and flow. This energy is partly released again by the pressure drops in lines and devices. This means that heat is given out in reduction of pressure from operating pressure to tank pressure, in pressure losses in the system, by the build up of pressure in safety elements, in throttle valves, etc.

The losses amount to about 15 to 30 % of the installed pump power.

Two ways of removing the heat exist:

- By means of the surface of the tank and
- Oil air coolers and oil/water coolers

3.1 The surface of the tank

The surface of the tank must be sufficiently large to transfer the total heat resulting from losses to the environment. However, this is often not possible due to the shortage of space for this item.

3.1.1 Sample calculation

The oil temperature in a hydraulic system stabilises at a temperature which is too high.

The temperature is kept constant by the radiation power of the tank and by the line and machine surface, i.e. the machine surface acts as a cooler.

Assumption:

Existing oil temperature T_1 = 353 K

Desired oil temperature T_2 = 323 K

Estimated surface area A = 3 m^2

$$P_K = (T_1 - T_2) \cdot \alpha \cdot A \quad (1)$$

$$P_K = (353 - 323) \cdot 0.012 \cdot 3 = 1.08 \text{ kW}$$

Legend:

P_K	= required cooling power	in kW
T_1	= existing oil temperature	in K
T_2	= desired oil temperature	in K
α	= heat transfer coefficient (in the example α = 0.012 kW/m^2K)	in kW/m^2K
A	= effective surface area	in m^2

3.2 Oil-air cooler and heat exchanger

By installing additional coolers the tank volume may be decreased (usually 2 to 4 x pump power). Heating problems, which occur due to operation over long periods and high air temperatures, may also be avoided.

The following are used for cooling:

- Oil-air coolers
- Oil-water coolers

3.2.1 Design note

The most important parameter for the design of an oil-air cooler is the power loss occurring in a hydraulic system.

3.2.1.1 Design

From experience the power losses expected are between 15 and 30 % of the installed drive power. However special operating relationships need to be taken into account.

3.2.1.2 Calculation of power loss in hydraulic systems

The increase in temperature must be measured over a set period for the calculation.

Assumption:

Increase in oil temperature over 2 hours from 20 to 70 °C

Tank contains 800 litres

$$P_V = \frac{\Delta T \cdot V \cdot \rho \cdot c}{t \cdot 3600} \quad (2)$$

$$P_V = \frac{50 \cdot 800 \cdot 0.86 \cdot 1.67}{2 \cdot 3600} = 7.98 \text{ kW}$$

Legend:

P_V	= power loss (1 kW = 1 kJ/s)	in kW
ρ	= density of oil for mineral oil ρ = 0.86 kg/dm^3	in kg/dm^3
c	= specific heat capacity for mineral oil c = 1.67 kJ/kg K	in kJ/kg K
V	= tank volume	in litres
ΔT	= temperature increase	in K
t	= operating time	in h

3.2.2 Oil-air cooler

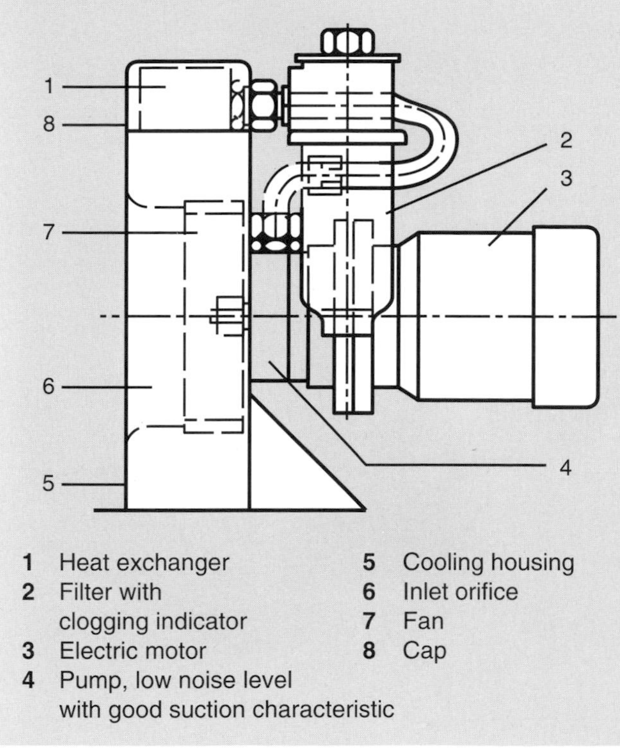

Fig. 12: *Design of oil-air cooler*

Advantages:

- Low installation costs
- Low operating costs
- No corrosion by the coolant
- Simple servicing
- Free choice of type of motor and voltage
- No damage to the hydraulics

Disadvantages:

- Twice as expensive as oil/water cooler
- Larger volume than oil/water cooler
- Prone to noise and easily strained by mechanical connectioins
- Not suitable for small rooms

The oil-air cooler (see *fig. 14*) is built into the fluid circuit of a system or machine. By having a check valve connected in parallel with a 4.5 bar pilot pressure, high backpressures in cold fluids and high flows are avoided. The cooling of the fluid is dependent on the inlet temperature difference between the fluid and the ambient air, on the flow and on the rate of air flow.

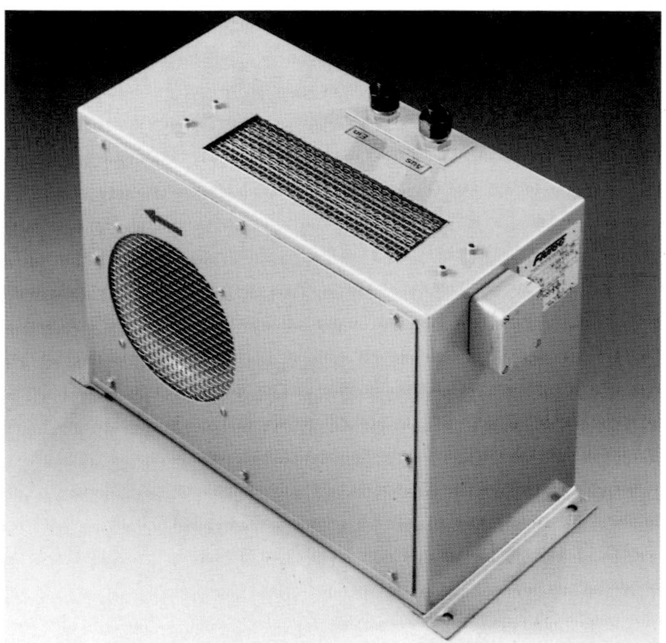

Fig. 13: *Oil-air cooler*

Fig. 14: *Oil-air cooler with mounted hydraulic filter*

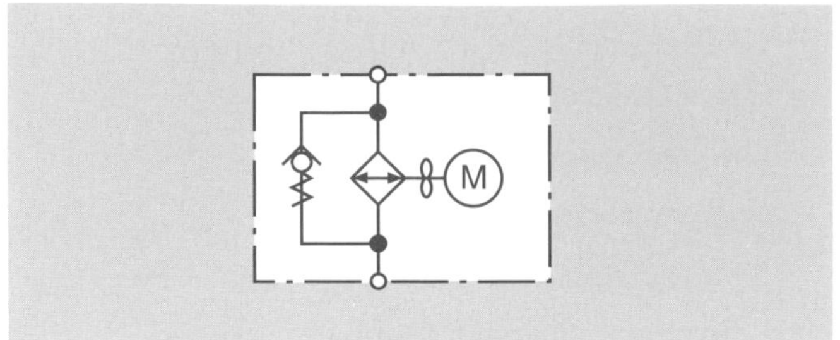

Fig. 15: *Oil-air cooler with drive motor and safety valve*

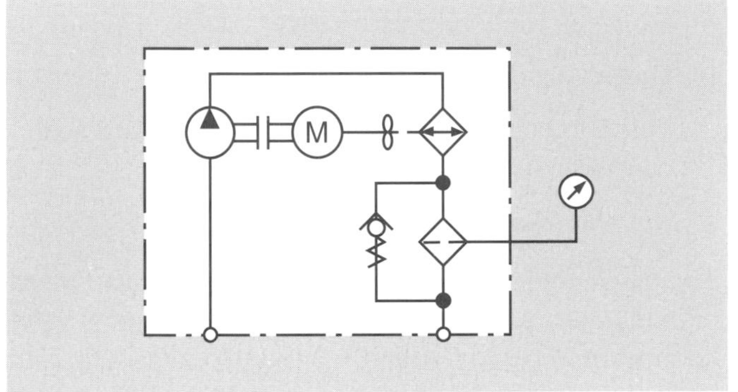

Fig. 16: *Oil-air cooler with hydraulic pump and filter*

Fig. 18: *Oil-air cooler*

In addition to the built-in damped pump, a hydraulic filter is installed into the fluid circuit in this power unit. Due to this cooling takes place to an optimum degree and the fluid is filtered at the same time. The unit is used as a bypass power unit. The power unit is independent of the rest of the system and maintains a constant cooling and filter power.

3.2.3 Heat exchangers

A high flow velocity is required in the cooling lines in order that an exchange of heat is possible.

Fig. 17: *Oil-water cooler*

4 Components to isolate flow

Isolating valves of various types are used to shut-off or reroute flows in hydraulic lines. However they are not suitable to be used as throttles, as they are usually kept either completely open or completely closed.

A notch is usually made in the operating shaft to show the position.

4.1 Ball valve

Fig. 19: *Block ball valves with pipe connection*

Ball valves may be used in a wide range of applications and are used in nearly all branches of industry. Their main features are compact design, easy operation even under high pressures, low forces required for operation, full circular passage and easily exchangeable seals. They are suitable for high pulsating pressures and leakage free sealing.

Function

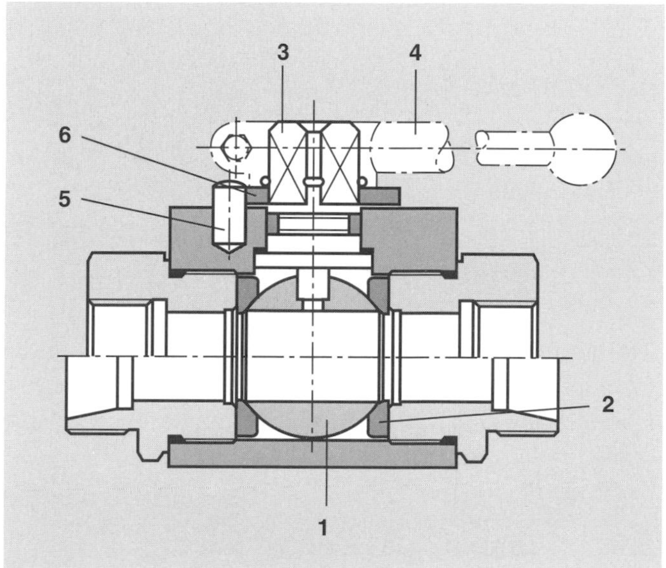

Fig. 20: *Design of single ball valve*

Ball valves are usually designed on the floating ball principle.

This means that the ball (1) slides freely between pre-tensioned seals made out of plastic (2). The ball is pushed onto the seal away from the pressure by the fluid. Hence a pressing pressure is produced which supports the permanent seal of the valve. The operating valve is operated by a hermetically sealed operating spindle (3), to the rectangular protruding end of which is fixed a operating grip (4). This may be adjusted in 45° steps. The stop-pin (5) and the stop-plate (6) are used to fix the position of the ball.

Fig. 21: *Ball valve*

	Low pressure			High pressure		
Type	Single dir.	Multi-direction		Single dir.	Multi-direction	
Model		L bore	T bore		L bore	T bore
Symbol						
Operating pressure	Up to 40 bar	Up to 40 bar	Up to 40 bar	Up to 500 bar	Up to 500 bar	Up to 500 bar
Free flow	4 to 100 mm	4 to 40 mm	4 to 40 mm	4 to 100 mm	4 to 20 mm	4 to 20 mm
Type of connection	Thread	Thread	Thread	Thread, flange	Thread	Thread

Table 2: *Types of ball valves*

4.2 Double ball valve

Function

Fig. 22: *Double ball valve with sealing segments*

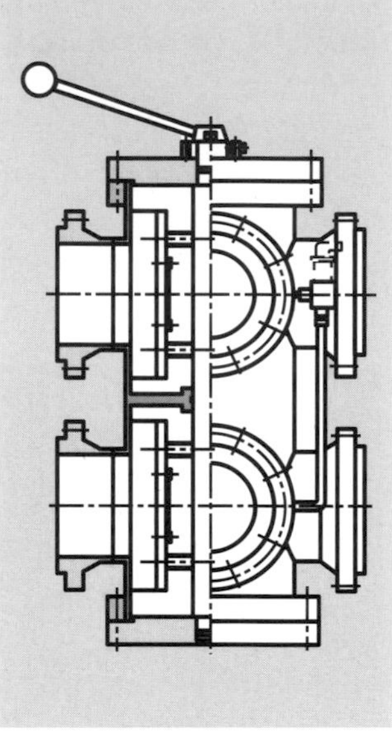

Fig. 23: *Design of double ball valve with sealing segments*

In these valves the switching element is a sealed poppet.

This poppet creates the seal. This means that a 100 % sealing is not possible. This means that where a completely leak free model is used, the valve can only be operated with great difficulty.

The seal between the shaft and the housing prevents external leaks.

In large double ball valves the sealed poppet is usually replaced by sealed segments (*figs. 22 and 23*).

The sealed segment is pushed by the fluid onto the seal edge of the housing away from the pressure. As a result a leakage free seal is produced.

Before operating the valve it is necessary to balance the pressures in the housing. Hence the pressing pressure from the fluid is neutralised and operation is enabled.

5 Components for control and display functions

5.1 General

Control and display elements are used for monitoring hydraulic systems. These display elements may be either permanently installed in the system or only installed for purposes of control when required at the installed test points for this purpose.

The following may be used for mounting display elements

- "Mini-mess" connections
- Quick release coupling
- Ball valves
- Tee pieces or
- Flange connections

The type of connection and the test point required must be included in the initial design of the system on the circuit. Connections which are added later cause unnecessary costs.

5.2 Display devices which are permanently installed

With these display elements it is possible to measure

- pressure
- temperature
- flow and
- level of fluid in tank

5.2.1 Components for pressure measurements

These components are used to monitor operation within the complete system.

The following types are used:

- Pressure gauge
- Pressure difference gauge
- Pressure gauge selection switch and
- Pressure transducer

5.2.1.1 Pressure gauge

– Pressure gauge

The operating pressure present in the system is measured with respect to atmospheric pressure by this device. Measurements are carried out by means of a bourdon tube or diaphragm. These devices are filled with damping fluid (usually glycerine) when measuring pressure at test points under high dynamic loads, which are produced with quick and frequent changes in load, pressure peaks, vibrations and pulsations. If pressure gauges are to be used to control a hydraulic system, they may be fitted with electrical contacts.

Pressure measuring device with bourdon tube

Fig. 24: *Pressure gauge with bourdon tube*

This type (*fig. 24*) is suitable for the measurement of pressure in fluid and gas mediums. It must not be used in a medium with a high viscosity or in a medium which crystalises or in a medium which attacks copper alloys.

Permissible application range:

Upper limit with still load:
3/4 of final scale value

Upper limit with changing load:
2/3 of final scale value

May be used briefly up to full scale value

Function

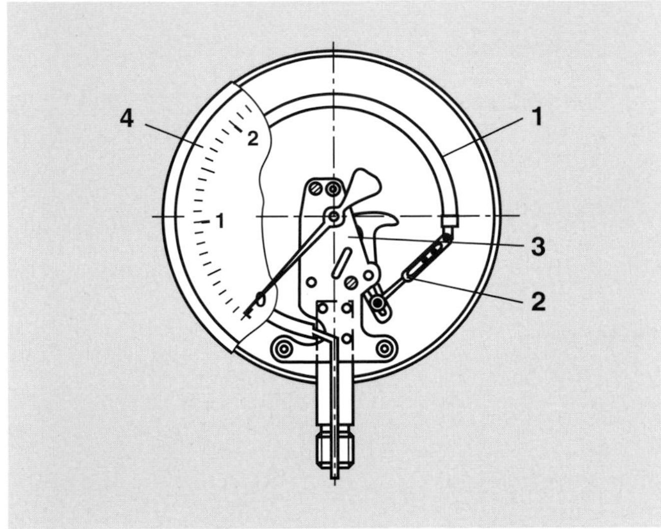

Fig. 25: *Design of pressure gauge with bourdon tube*

The pressure difference between the pressure in the pipe of the spring measuring element (1) and the atmospheric pressure causes the free end of the bourdon tube to deflect accordingly. The linear measurement is transferred via a tie rod (2) and display mechanism (3) to a hand which points to the correct position on the scale (4) in the display.

Pressure measuring device with diaphragm

Fig. 26: *Pressure gauge with diaphragm*

This pressure measuring device (*fig. 26*) is less sensitive to vibrations that the pressure measuring device with bourdon tube. In addition they are suitable for measurements of gaseous, corrosive, contaminated or highly viscous media.

Main applications:

- Concrete and cement pumps
- Coking plants
- Mud vehicles
- Mine locomotives and
- Road building machines

Function

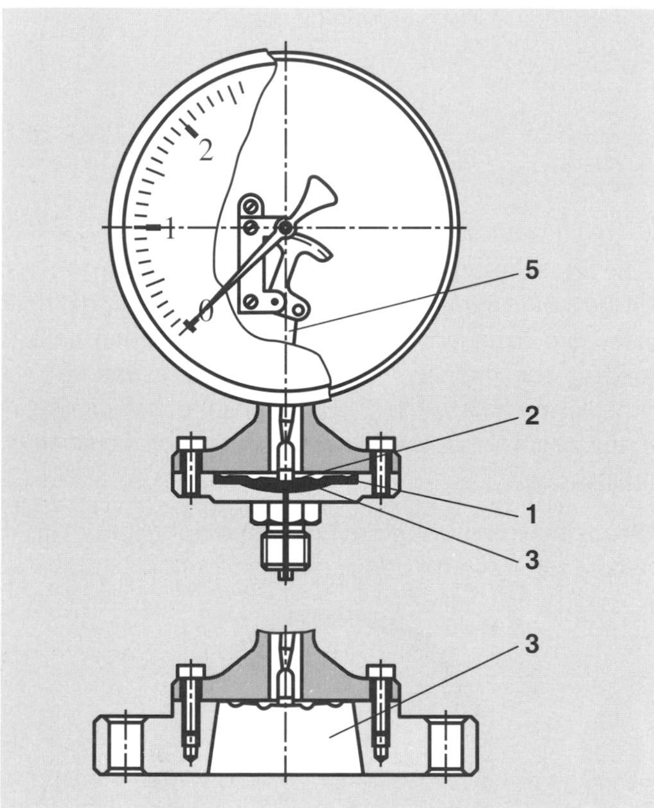

Fig. 27: *Design of pressure gauge with diaphragm*

A concentric diaphragm (1) tensioned between two flanges separates the pressure chamber into individual pressure chambers. Pressure chamber (2) is connected to the outside and hence is pressurised by atmospheric pressure. Chamber (3) is pressurised with the operating pressure at the measuring position and hence is the measurement chamber. The pressure difference between the pressure in chamber (2) and that in measuring chamber (3) causes the diaphragm to deflect accordingly. This deflection is transferred via a push rod (5) to the display mechanism and hence to an indicator pointer which points to the correct position on scale (4).

– Differential pressure gauge

The pressure difference between two operating pressures are measured using this device. Measurement is by means of either the bourdon tube or diaphragm pressure gauge. These devices may be filled with damping fluid (usually glycerine) when measuring pressures at test points under highly dynamic loads, where pulsation or vibration is present. Furthermore if these gauges are used to control a hydraulic system, they may also be fitted with electrical or pneumatic switching elements.

Differential pressure gauge with bourdon tube

This pressure gauge is used for the measurement of pressure differences in fluids and gases, as long as these do not have a high viscosity or are not crystalline.

Function

Fig. 28: *Differential pressure gauge with bourdon tube*

Two bourdon tube measuring systems operate independently of each other in this pressure measuring device. The movements of the measuring elements (resulting from pressurisation) proportional to the pressures being measured are transferred to the instrument display and shown on the display.

Differential pressure gauge with diaphragm

Fig. 29: *Differential pressure gauge with diaphragm*

These devices are suitable for measuring fluids and gases. They are mainly used for measuring pressure drops between pipe lines and filter systems.

Function

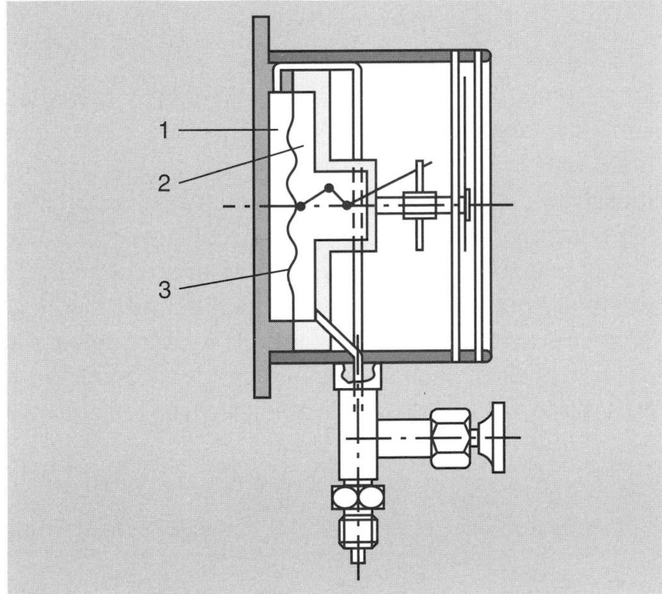

Fig. 30: *Design of pressure difference gauge with plate spring*

The pressure difference measuring device with plate spring comprises two pressure chambers (1,2) which are separated from each other by plate spring (3). When a pressure difference occurs the plate spring curves and directly shows the difference between the two pressures. The pressure difference must not exceed the display range.

– Special models

Model with fluid filled housing

In both models, the display housing must be filled with damping fluid (usually glycerine) when used at measuring points under high dynamic loading

Advantages:

- Smooth positioning of pointer, i.e. correct display of measurement is produced even with vibrations and pulsations at the measuring point.
- Low friction between the moving parts
- Low wear even for high dynamic loads and
- Long service life

Pressure measuring device which are filled with fluid are especially suitable for measurement of pressure and monitoring of pressure in pumps, compressors, presses, high pressure cleaners, hydraulic systems and in the general construction of systems.

Device with limit switches

Pressure gauges may be fitted with electrical or pneumatic limit switches for closed and open loop control functions.

5.2.1.2 Pressure gauge selection switch

Pressure gauge selection switches are used for monitoring up to 9 different pressure measuring positions in a hydraulic system.

With the help of rotary spool valves which are built into pressure gauge selection switches, a system pressure in a measurement line is fed to a pressure gauge.

This pressure gauge may be either built into the pressure gauge selection switch or mounted separately within the system.

Pressure gauge selector valve with built-in pressure gauge

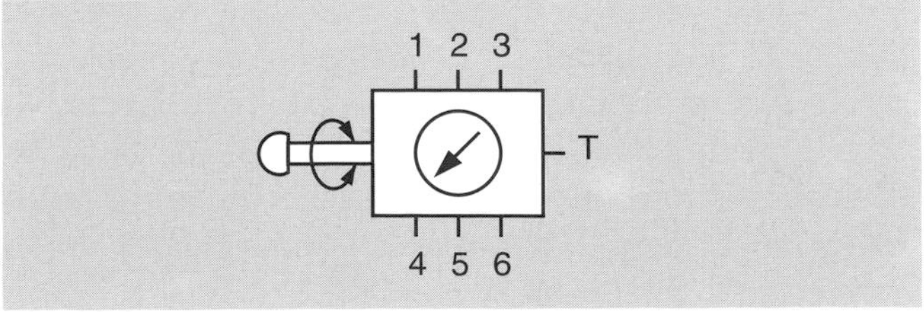

Fig. 31: *Pressure gauge selector valve with built-in pressure gauge*

Fig. 32: *Pressure gauge selector valve with built-in pressure gauge*

In this model the pressure gauge is built directly into the rotary button. Up to 6 system pressures may be monitored.

Function

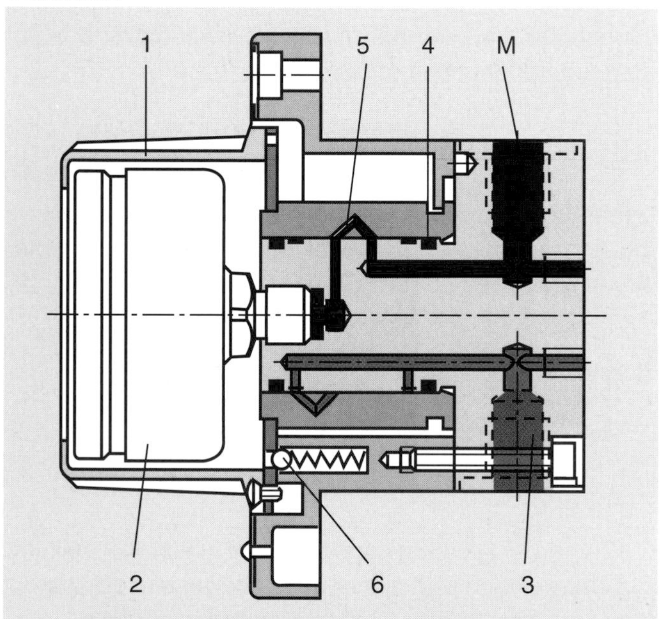

Fig. 33: *Design of pressure gauge selection switch with built-in pressure gauge*

The glycerine damped pressure gauge (2) is built into the rotary button (1). The 6 measuring ports (M) are arranged internally around the circumference of the housing (3). By rotating the rotary button and the sleeve (4) coupled to it, in turn each measuring port is connected to the pressure gauge (see *fig. 33*). In order to unload the pressure gauge zero positions exist between the measuring points. At a zero point the pressure gauge if connected via bore (5) in the sleeve with the tank (port T). The detent (6) fixes the set measuring or zero position. An arrow on the rotary knob edge shows which measuring point is connected to the pressure gauge.

In order to increase the service life of the pressure gauge, the gauge is damped by glycerine.

Pressure gauge selector valve with connection for a separate pressure gauge

Fig. 34: *Pressure gauge selector valve*

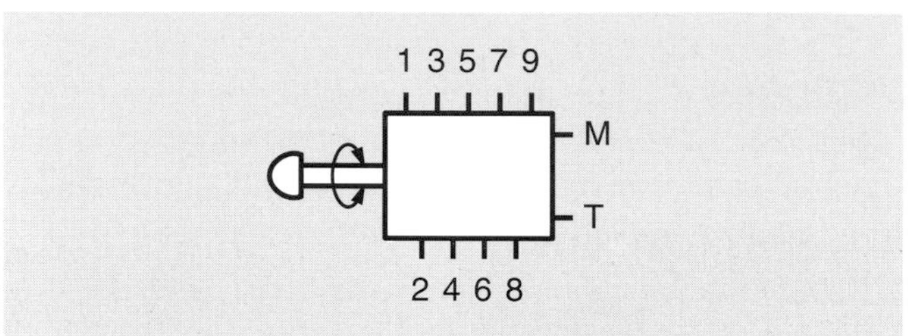

Fig. 35: *Pressure gauge valve with connection for separate pressure gauge*

In this model the pressure gauge is not directly integrated into the rotary button. Up to 9 different pressures may be measured in a hydraulic system. The pressure gauge must be mounted separately and connected to port M of the pressure gauge selection switch by a pipe or hose. The pressure display is produced by means of pressing the rotary button in an axial direction against a spring. When the rotary button is released, the button returns to its initial position and the pressure gauge is connected to the tank port. A built-in detent holds any chosen position.

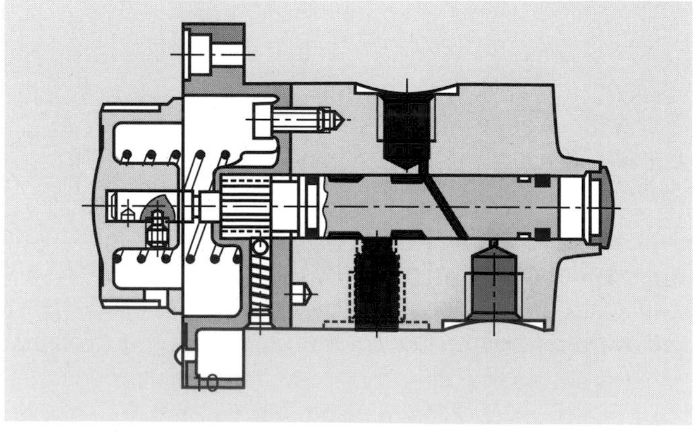

Fig. 36: *Design of pressure gauge selector valve with connection for separate pressure gauge*

5.2.1.3 Pressure switch

Pressure switches are used in hydraulic systems for closed and open loop control functions

The switching elements built into the pressure switch open or close an electrical circuit dependent on pressure.

Pressure switches may be either electronic or hydraulic-electrical.

Hydro-electrical pressure switches
are available as two types

a) Piston type pressure switch:
with or without leakage port, thread connection (p_{max} = 500 bar) subplate mounting (p_{max} = 350 bar) pressure dependent operating pressure difference

b) Bourdon tube pressure switch:
Thread connection (p_{max} = 400 bar) Constant or adjustable operating pressure difference

Fig. 37: *Piston pressure switch HED1*

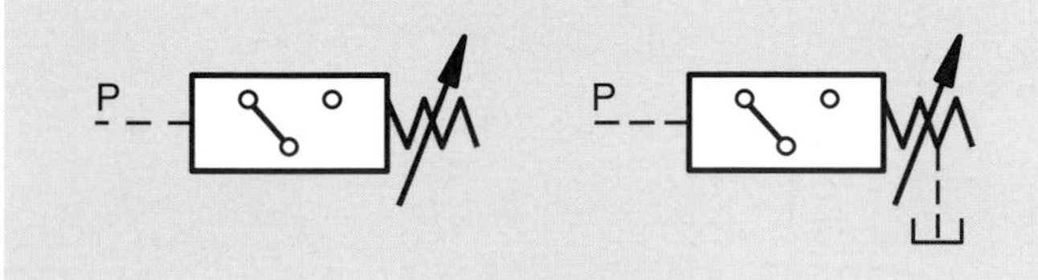

Fig. 38: *Piston pressure switch, type HED1 (left) with and (right) without drain case port*

Piston type pressure switch HED1

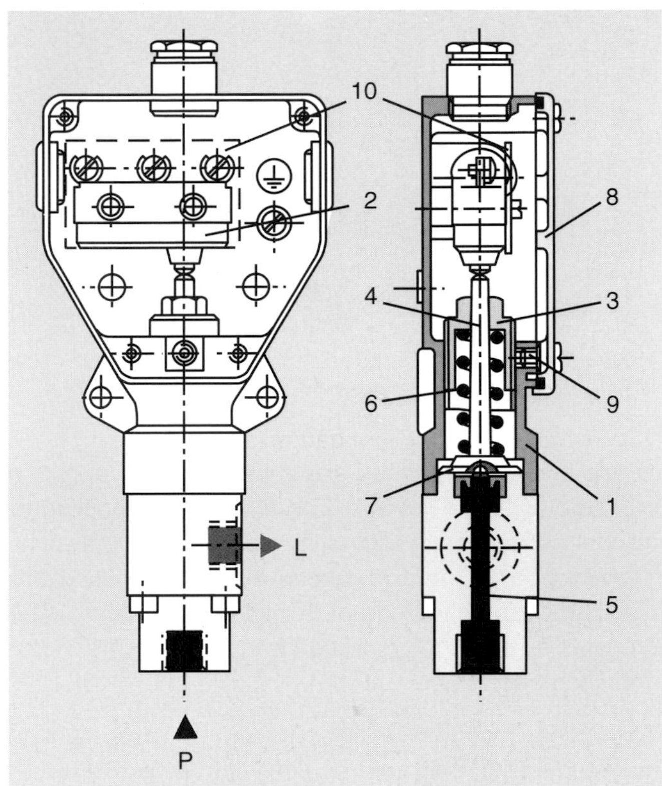

Fig. 39: *Design of piston type pressure switch, type HED1*

The piston type pressure switch HED1 basically comprises housing (1), micro switch (2), adjustment screw (3), pin (4), spool (5) and compression spring (6). The current carrying clamps are covered by isolating foil.

In order to set the switching pressure the nameplate (8) needs to be removed and the locking screw (9) loosened. By rotating the adjustment screw (3) the switching pressure is set. Then the adjustment screw (3) is fixed in position by locking screw (9) and the nameplate is remounted.

The pressure to be monitored acts on piston (5). This piston (5) is supported by pin (4) and works against the force (smoothly adjustable) of compression spring (6). Pin (4) transfers the movement of pin (5) to the micro switch (2). The electrical circuit is then connected or disconnected depending on the circuit design. A mechanical stop (7) protects the micro switch from damage if excess pressures exist.

The piston pressure switch HED1 may be optionally fitted with drain case port, control light, plug connection and protection against explosions if used in safety systems (ExFH).

Piston pressure switches HED4 and HED5

Fig. 40: *Piston pressure switch HED4 (left) & HED6 (right)*

These pressure switches are another variety of piston pressure switch. They are also used for connecting or disconnecting electrical circuits dependent on pressure. They may be mounted on subplates, in pipes or used as a stacking assembly element in hydraulic systems. The pressure switches may be fitted with control lights and/or drain case ports.

To increase their service life, pressure switches must be mounted so that they are free from vibrations. In addition suitable measures must be carried out to dampen pressure shocks.

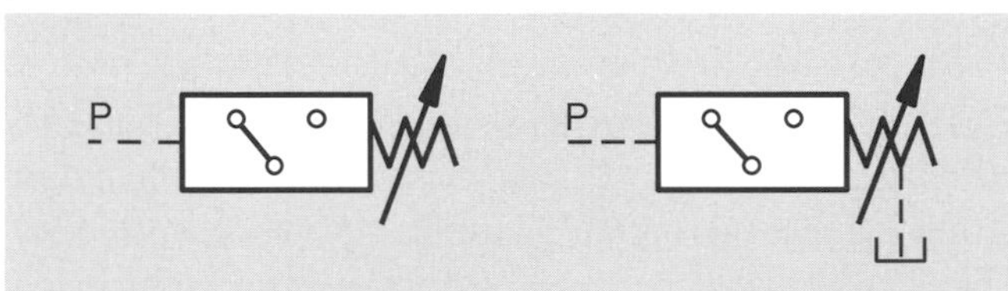

Fig. 41: *Piston pressure switch, type HED4 and HED6 left without and right with drain case port*

Piston pressure switch HED4

The hydraulic-electrical pressure switch HED4 basically comprises housing (1), cartridge unit with spool (2), compression spring (3), adjustment element (4) and micro switch (5).

The pressure to be monitored acts on piston (2). This piston (2) is supported by spring plate (6) and acts in opposition to the steplessly set force of compression spring (3). Spring plate (6) transfers the movement of spool (2) to micro switch (5). Due to this and depending on the type of circuit the electrical circuit is either connected or disconnected. Internal hexagonal screw (7) is used to set the pressure. The set pressure may be fixed by means of threaded pin (8).

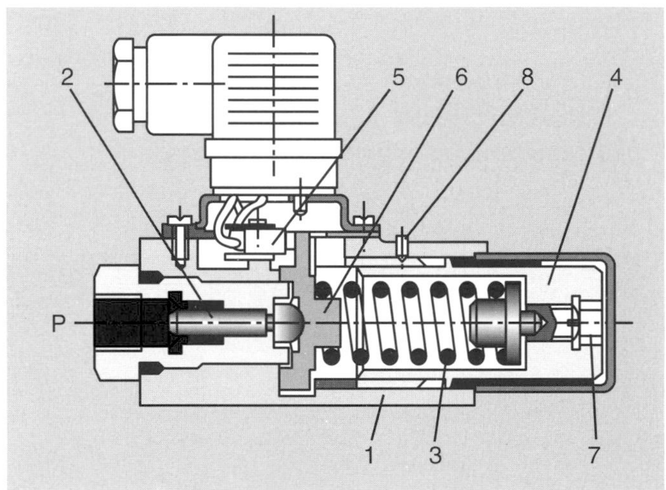

Fig. 42: *Piston pressure switch HED4*

The operating pressure differential in all piston pressure switches is dependent on pressure range. In order to attain a lower operating pressure difference, the model with drain case port is used. As the frictional forces between seal and spool are reduced, hence hysteresis is also reduced.

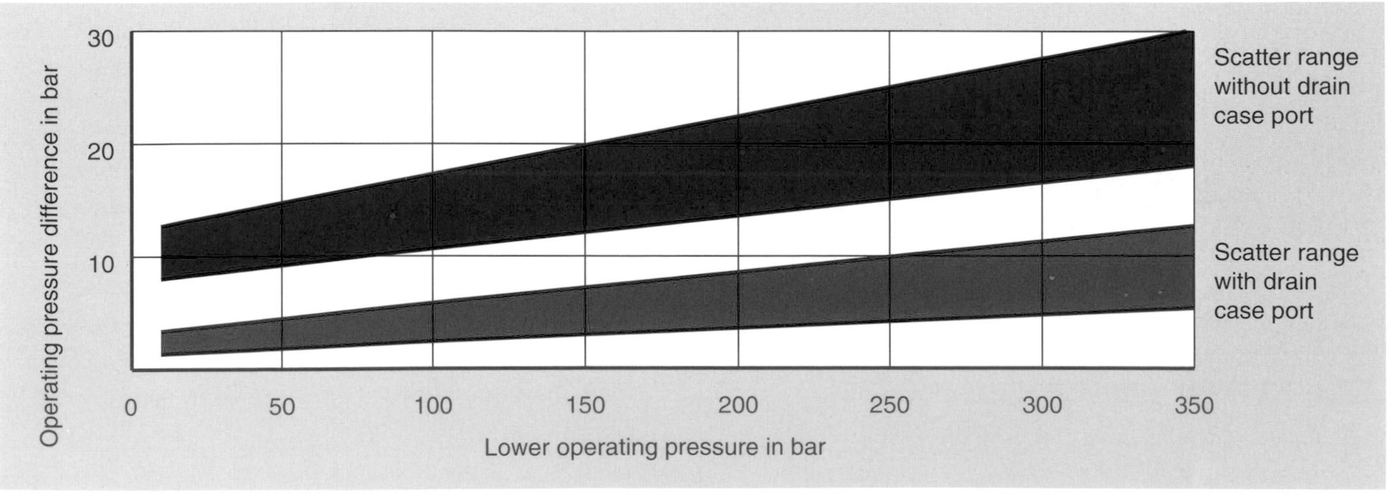

Diagram 2: *Operating pressure difference in piston pressure switch with and without drain case port, pressure rating 350 bar*

Bourdon tube switches, types HED2 and HED3

Fig. 43: *Bourbon tube pressure switches, HED 2 and HED3*

Bourbon tube pressure switches in contrast to piston pressure switches are also suitable for use with special fluids and gases.

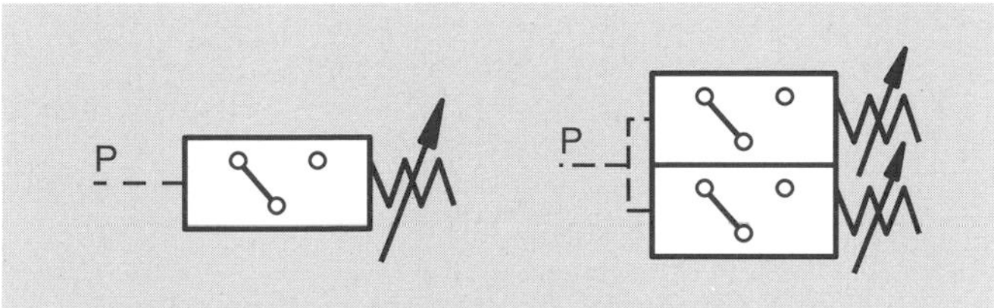

Fig. 44: *Bourbon tube pressure switches, HED2 (left) and HED3 (right)*

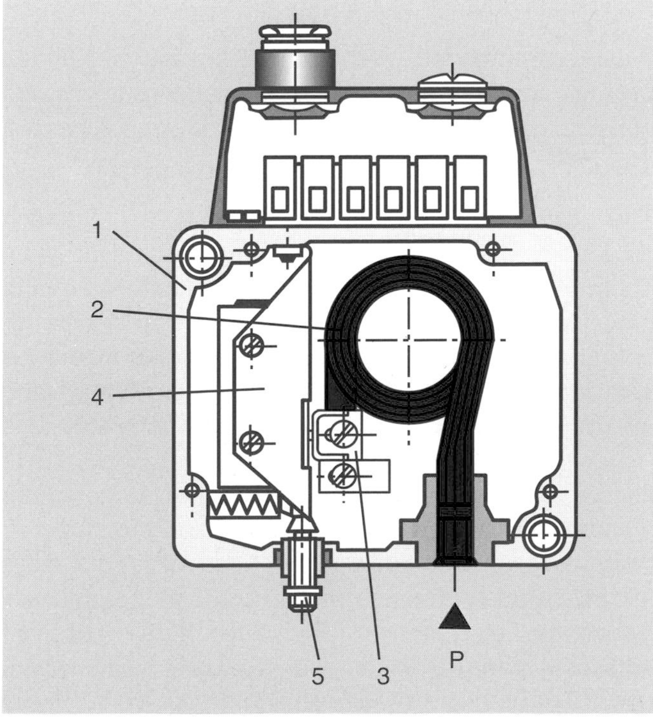

Fig. 45: *Bourbon tube pressure switch with constant operating pressure difference, type HED2*

The pressure to be monitored acts on bourdon tube (2). The tube bends on being pressurised and the operating lever (3) connected to it transfers the movement of the bourdon tube to the micro switch (4). Due to this and depending on the type of circuit the electrical circuit is either connected or disconnected. The operating pressure is determined by the distance from the micro switch (4) to the operating lever (3).

In HED2 the operating pressure is set by means of a lockable rotary knob. A constant operating pressure differential is maintained over the entire setting range.

In contrast to HED2 the movement of thebourdon tube (2) in HED3 is first transferred to one of the two micro switches (4). Due to this and depending on the type of circuit the electrical circuit is either connected or disconnected. If the pressure increases further the bourdon tube bends further and then the second micro switch is operated by the operating lever and depending on the type of circuit the electrical circuit is either connected or disconnected.

Both of the operating pressures which are determined by the settings of the micro switches are separated and are set independently of each other at two setting screws (5).

5.2.1.4 Pressure transducers

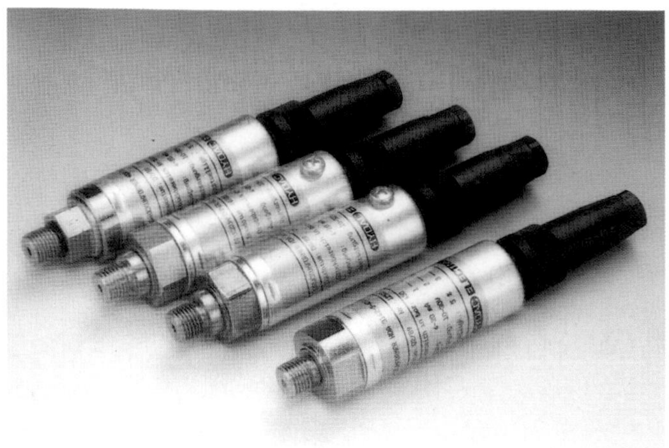

Fig. 46: *Pressure transducer*

Pressure transducers are used to connect and disconnect electrical circuits dependent on pressure. They convert a pressure linearly into an electrical signal (e.g. 0 to 10 V or 4 to 20 mA).

They are used under the roughest conditions in industry, as well as in laboratories.

Pressure transducers are

- Stable against pressure peaks
- Suitable for use with high dynamic loads and
- Stable against temperature.

Function

The pressure to be monitored stretches a measuring membrane, whose strength is suitable for the pressure range to be measured. The elastic deformation of the measuring membrane is converted into a change in resistance by means of a strain gauge. Integrated or external measuring amplifiers produce the desired electrical nominal signals.

Correct design ensures that pressure shocks are isolated from the measuring membrane. Hence pressure transducers in normal operation are resistant against quick pressure peaks as well as against air locks occurring during commissioning.

Electronic pressure switches

The electronic pressure switch is designed as a combination of pressure transducer, indicator and evaluation circuit. In contrast to the mechanical pressure switches the electronic pressure switches do not contain any moving mechanical parts, so that a much wider range of applications exists. The preferred applications for the electronic pressure switches are in pressure and limit value signalling in the field of hydraulics, process control and in the field of general measuring and control technology. Due to the pre-selectable hysteresis, the electronic pressure switch may also be used as a two point controller, e.g. in accumulator charging circuits in pumps and compressors.

Special features

- Accuracy class 0.5 for the pressure measuring and indicator part
- Semiconductor measuring element
- Integrated evaluating electronics
- Temperature compensated
- Four limit contacts independent of each other
- Adjustable back operating pressure difference
- Operating points digitally adjustable
- Voltage output 0 to 5 V

It is recommended that micro processor controlled pressure switches are used for accumulator stations with pump following circuits as well as for large hydraulic systems.

The use of a micro-computer in the pressure switch allows high flexibility in meeting the requirements of an application and, what is of even more importance for the pressure switch, is the considerable increase in operational reliability. The micro-computer monitors the semiconductor pressure sensor, power supply and internal components. The function of the computer itself is monitored independently of the computer. Errors due to sensor faults are internally detected. The computer makes sure that if a fault occurs that the programmed relay rest position is returned to. The monitoring of a cell allows the peak pressure which occurs at the pressure switch to be displayed. The user hence receives additional information on the pressure peaks which occur. The pressure switch is suitable for universal use in hydraulics and in process technology. The V24 interface allows the unit to be monitored and programmed by an external computer or connected to a printer for purposes of reports.

Electronic pressure switch with one switched output

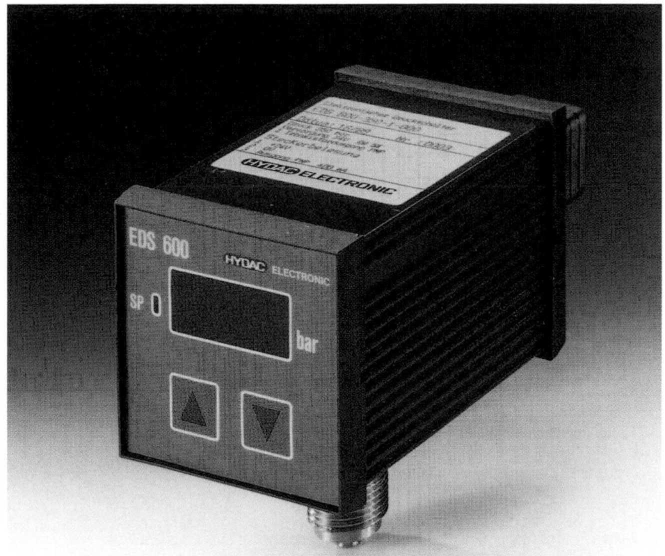

Fig. 47: *Electronic pressure switch with one switched output*

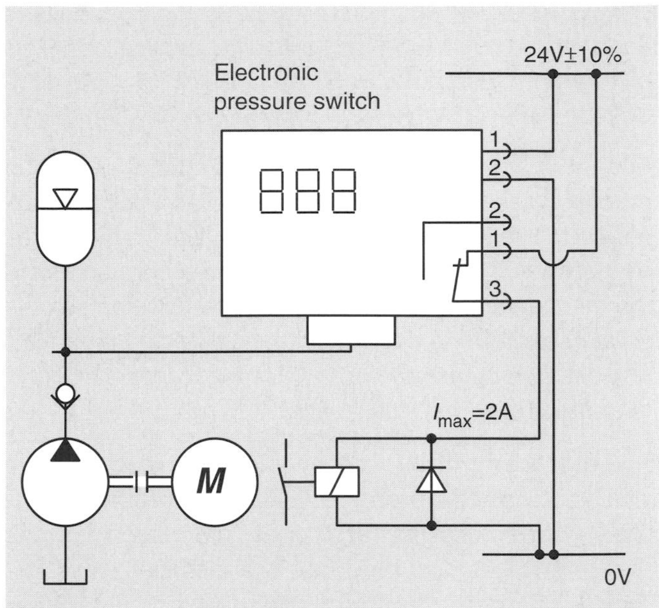

Fig. 48: *Accumulator charging circuit with electronic pressure switch with relay output*

This electronics pressure switch is an alternative to the mechanical pressure gauges with limit contacts.

Special features

- 3 digit self-lighting digital indicator (LED)
- Up and down operating points may be set separately by keys
- Indication of operational state via lights
- Adjustment of operating points without pressurising the system
- Operating output optionally PNP or relay and PNP

Construction

The electronic pressure switch is a single channel pressure switch with indicator. By means of the stainless steel adaptor fluid is fed to the measuring cell.

The evaluation of the sensor signal, the indication the current value, as well as the preparation of the operating signal is carried out by the evaluating electronics.

The electronic connection of the pressure switch is by means of a connector to DIN 43650/IEC 4400 (plug-in connector).

The start up and down operating points may be extremely easily set by two keys.

Electronic pressure switch, computer intelligent

Fig. 49: *Electronic pressure swich, computer intelligent*

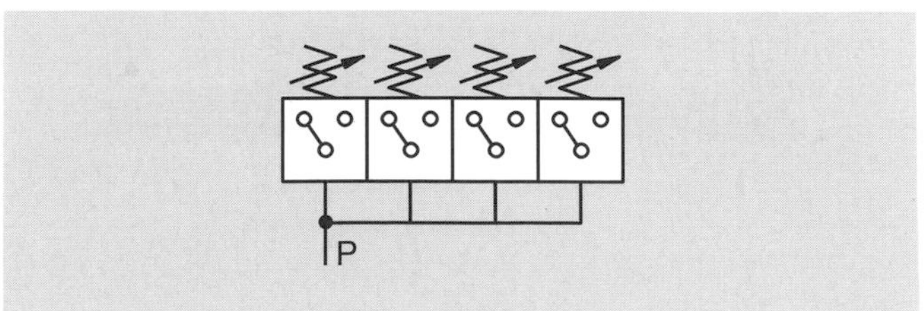

Fig. 50: *Electronic pressure switch*

Through the use of a microcomputer high flexibility is achieved in matching a particular application. This means that computer intelligent electronic pressure switches offer a high degree of operational safety.

The microcomputer monitors the semi-conductor pressure sensor, power supply and all internal components. The function of the computer itself is monitored by a so-called Watchdog circuit which is independent of the computer. Errors which occur due to defects in the sensor, e.g. due to overloading are detected internally. The computer makes sure that if an error occurs, the programmed relay rest position is taken up.

The monitoring of the cell enables the peak pressure which occurs at the pressure switch to be displayed. The user hence receives additional information on the pressure peaks occurring (as % of nominal pressure). The pressure switch is universally suitable for application in hydraulics and process engineering.

Measurement of pressure difference

Measurement of pressure differential with digital display device with 2 pressure transducers

This device combination measures the pressure at two measuring points by means of pressure transducers. The pressure difference is shown on the display device and fed externally by means of an analogue output. Four different limits may be set. A serial interface RS 232 C is available.

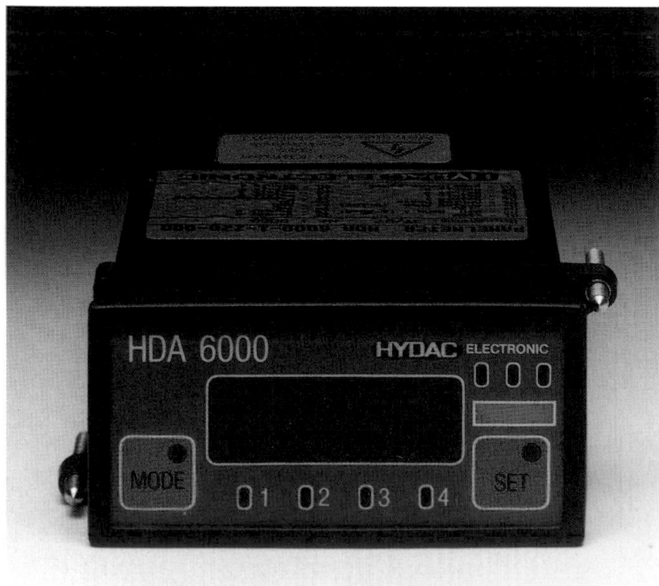

Fig. 51: *Pressure difference measurement with digital display device and two pressure conversions*

Function

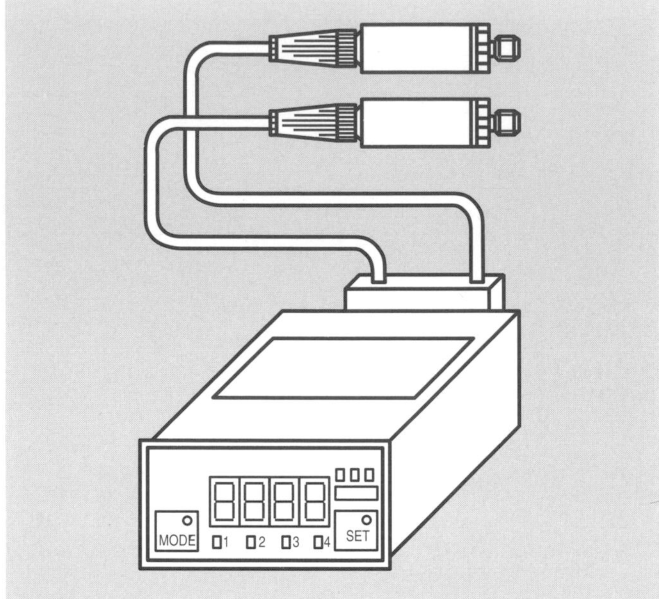

Fig. 52: *Schematic diagram of pressure transducer with display device*

The electrical signals from the pressure transducers are digitised by the display and evaluation device, subtracted, displayed and evaluated. The pressure difference may be positive or negative and may completely cover the measurement range of the sensors.

5.2.2 Components to measure temperature

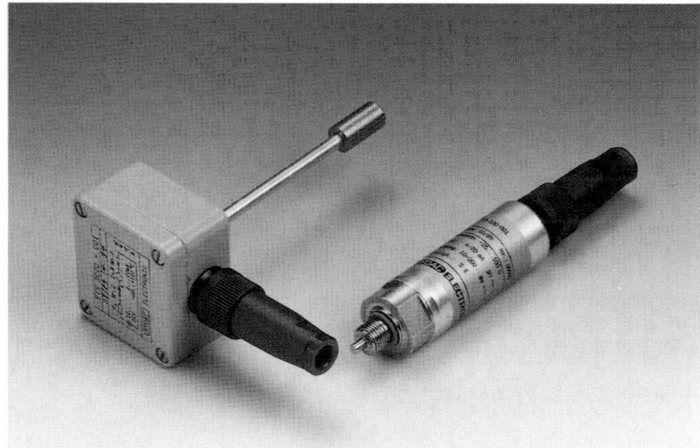

Fig. 53: *Temperature measurement transducer*

A rod type thermometer with sensor may be used to check the actual average operating temperature (may be used in connection with a cooler or heater). They are built into the fluid tank. In order to keep a desired fluid temperature constant, contact pressure gauges or thermostats are often used, which then switch the cooling or heating system as necessary.

5.2.3 Components for the measurement of flow

Various methods are available for the measurement of flow in hydraulic systems.

5.2.3.1 Direct measurement

Included here are all the measuring methods which operate to the displacement principle, such as for example:

- turbine counter
- vane counter

5.2.3.2 Indirect measurement

Included here are all the measuring methods which operate to the backpressure principle, such as for example:

- orifice
- throttle
- floating element

These display elements are particularly compact.

Fig. 54: *Flow measurement device*

Measuring methods operate ultrasonically or by laser are still relatively expensive and hence are not used in hydraulic systems.

5.2.4 Components for indicating levels in hydraulic tanks

For this measurement the following may be used:

- Float switch
- Fluid state indicators

5.2.4.1 Float switches

Fig. 55: *Float switch*

The maximum and minimum levels of fluids in tanks may be monitored by this element.

If one of the measuring points is exceeded, then the float (on passing the set operating point on a measuring scale) releases a proximity contact. This signal is either fed to a control device or it releases a function, e.g. the system may be switched off or a pump switched on if the fluid level is too low .

5.2.4.2 Fluid level indicator

Fig. 56: *Fluid level display*

Fluid state indicators may be built into hydraulic tanks with built-in thermometers or sensor thermometers. They show the height of the fluid level in tanks.

The fluid control is used for automatic monitoring of the fluid level.
If the fluid level is too low a contact is operated. This signal is fed either to a control device or it releases a function.

5.2.5 Display devices

Display devices are necessary for showing pressure, temperature, flow and changes in level measurements on the operating panels of the hydraulic system.

These devices have 3 digit indicators, an analogue output signal and an output to control relays.

Fig. 57: *Display device for pressure, temperature and flow*

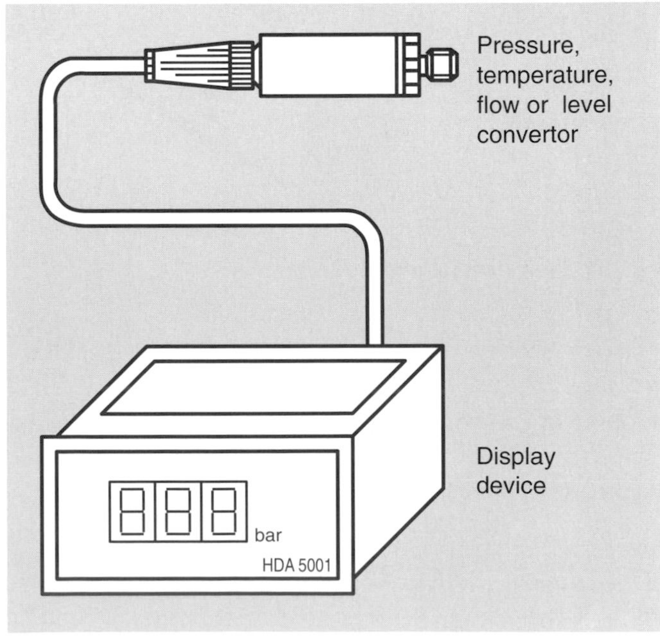

Fig. 58: *Use of display device with connected sensors*

5.3 Display devices which are not permanently installed

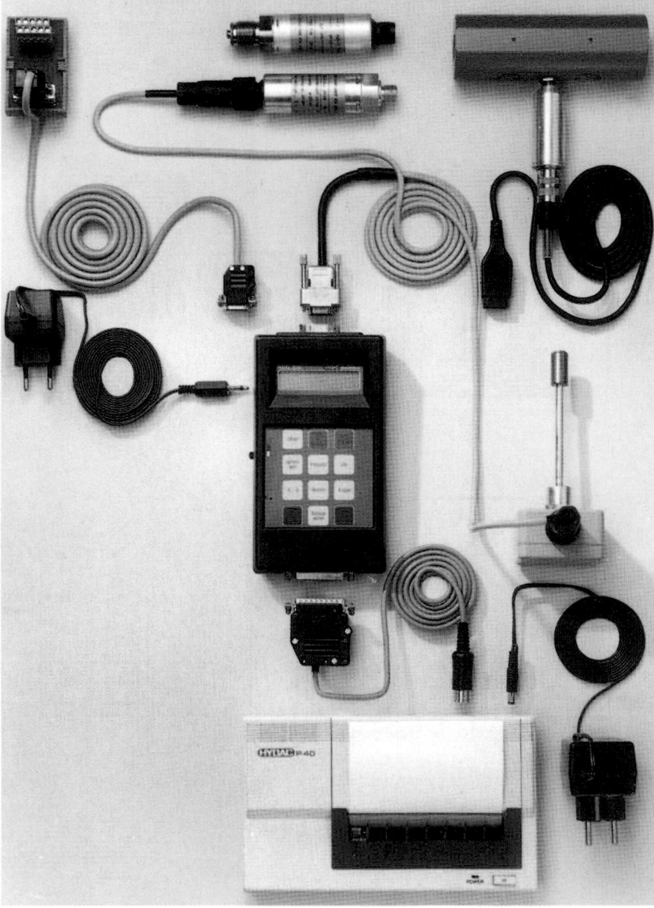

Fig. 59: *HMG 2000 with service case*

Legend to *Fig. 59*

1. Electrical adapter for checking the pressure switch
2. Power supply for the stationary operation of the HMG 2000 as well as to charge the accumulators
3. Printer for the documentation of measurements
4. Thread adaptor for the connection of pressure transducers to the available pressure ports
5. Electronic flow measurement unit (not shown)
   Measurement range 6 to 60 L/min and 40 to 600 L/min
6. Electronic pressure transducer; measurement range up to 10, 100, 200, 315 or 450 bar
7. Temperature convertor; measurement range -25 to 100 °C
8. Handheld measuring device

The display unit HMG 2000 with service case was designed as a mobile monitoring and data measuring device for servicing hydraulic systems. Due to the compact design as well as the energy supply from rechargeable accumulators it is ideally installed even at measuring points which are not easily accessible and which do not have a power supply.

In addition to the intelligent display and evaluation device, the service case includes sensors which measure

- pressure, negative pressure
- temperature
- flow
- speed

The representation of two measurements at the same time (see *diagram 3*) and the possibility of saving the measurements raise the standard of this device. Measurements and measurement curves can be saved and then output via a graphics printer. The printing of measurements shown on normal A4 paper and the use of the high resolution graphics permits a qualitive evaluation of the measurement to be carried out.

Other printers and computers may be connected via the serial interface RS 232, in order to carry out an automatic measurement analysis via a PC (for example).

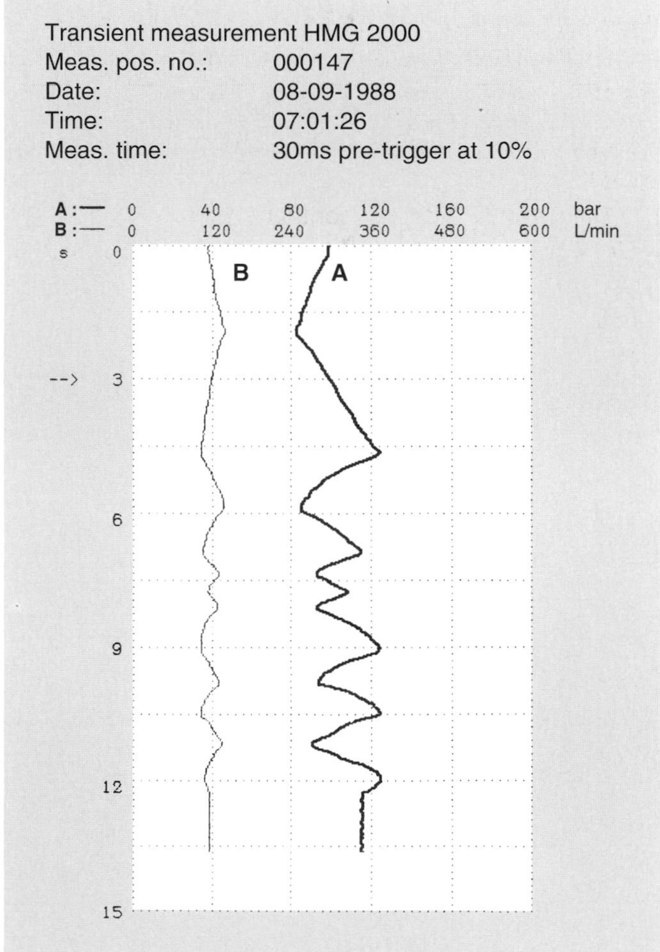

Diagram 3: *Representation of two measurements (flow and operating pressure)*

Notes

Chapter 16

Connections

Herbert Exner

1 Introduction

The hydraulic system components are connected together to form hydraulic circuits by means of suitable connections.

High demands are placed upon these connections:

- They must be good for flow, i.e. cause as few losses in pressure as possible
- They should be easy to produce, mount and service
- They must be able to withstand high pressures (and dynamic pressure peaks)
- They must be permanently leak tight
- They must be able to withstand dynamic loads (vibrations of components).

Pipe lines, hoses, fixings and flanges, etc. as connections are dealt with in their own chapter in the Hydraulic Trainer, volume 3.

In this chapter subplates, control plates, stacking assemblies, etc. will be dealt with.

2 Valves for mounting in pipe lines

Nowadays there are very few devices left in hydraulics which are mounted directly into the pipe line system.

Belonging to this group are for example the very simply designed check valves as well as simple throttle valves.

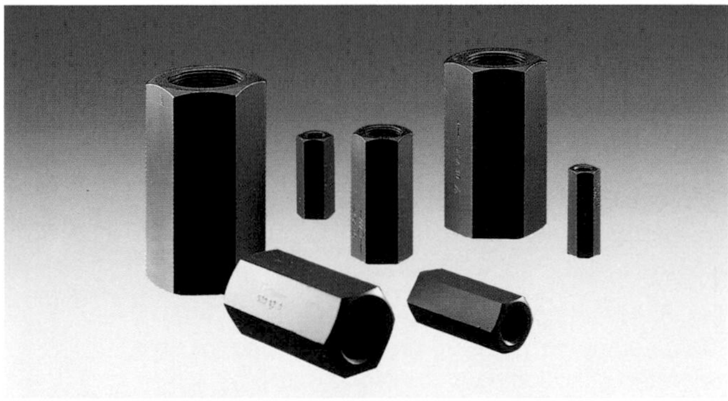

Fig. 1: *Check valve as pipe armature*

Fig. 2: *Throttle valve as pipe armature*

Such valves need only be rarely serviced, usually have two ports and hence do not require much effort when servicing or repairing them.

3 Cartridge valves with threaded cavity

Fig. 3: *Pressure reducing valve as cartridge*

Valves such as pressure relief or pressure reducing valves for example may be directly mounted into the line system. For this purpose the cartridge design has become predominant. All functional elements are collected together in a cartridge, which is completely mounted into the housing with threaded cavity. If services or repairs are carried out the complete cartridge is removed, so that the pipe line system does not need to be opened.

Valve cartridges may be used in many applications. They are also used for mounting in control and sandwich plates (see following sections).

4 Valves for subplate mounting

Fig. 4: *Directional valve mounted on subplate*

In many areas of application, but particularly in industrial systems valves for subplate mounting are preferred.

The advantages of this design are:

- The valves are easily disassembled for the purpose of servicing
- The ports lie on one plane, the fixings and sealing surface is flat
- The sealing of ports by means of elastic sealing rings is very reliable

Fig. 5: *Subplate, viewed onto valve mounting surface*

4.1 Standard mounting patterns

The mounting patterns for the subplate mounted valves are standardised to DIN 24 340. The following diagrams show typical mounting patterns.

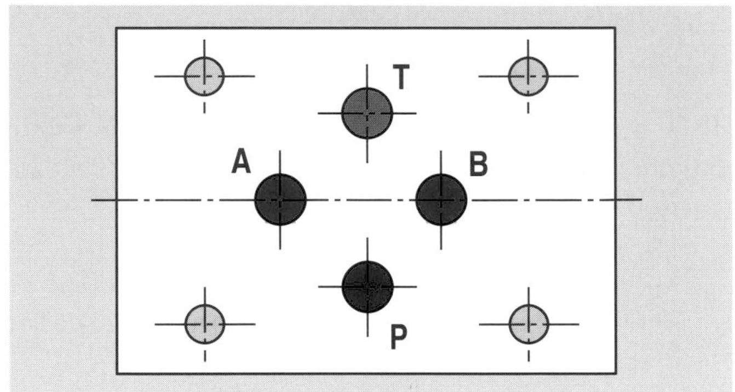

Fig. 6: *Mounting pattern, form A6 DIN 24 340*
Mounting pattern size 6 preferrably used for directional valves, but also used for pressure and flow contol valves

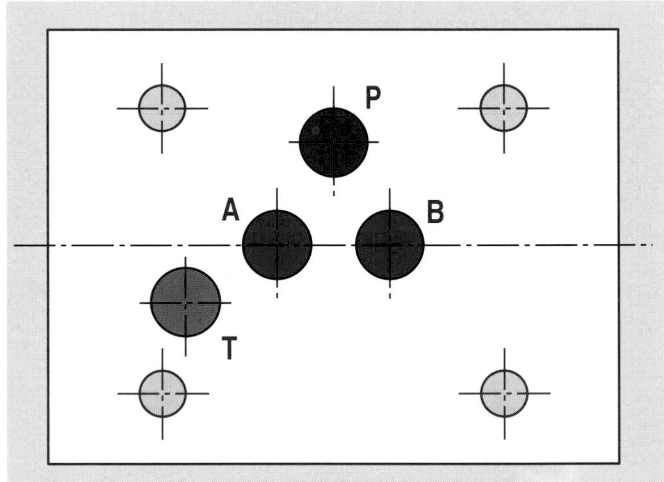

Fig. 7: *Mounting pattern, form A10 DIN 24 340*
Mounting pattern size 6 preferrably used for directional valves

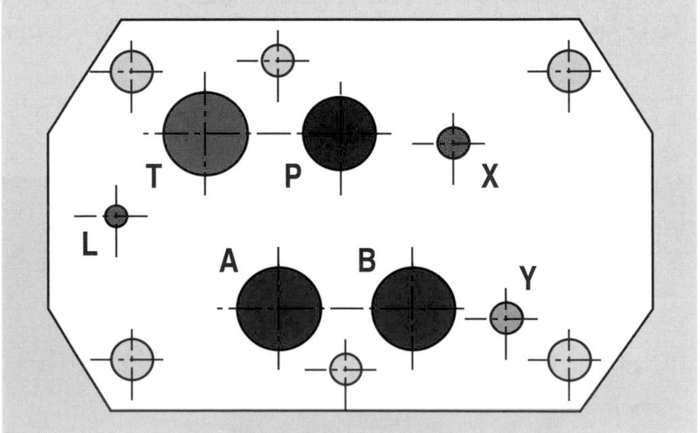

Fig. 8: *Mounting pattern, form A16 DIN 24 340*
Mounting pattern size 16 preferrably used for pilot operated directional valves of this size

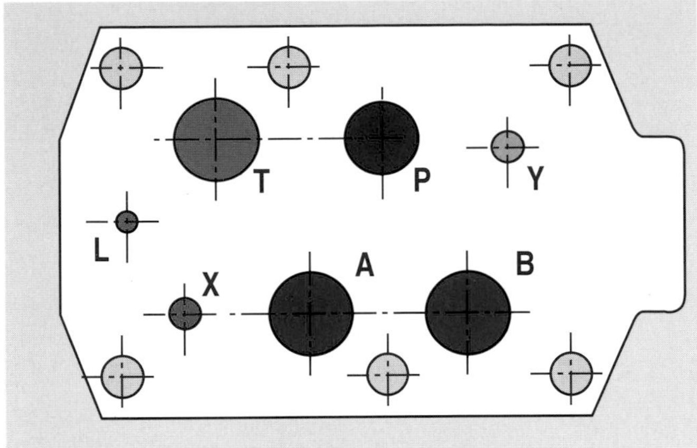

Fig. 9: *Mounting pattern, form A25 DIN 24 340 Mounting pattern size 25 preferrably used for pilot operated directional valves of this size*

The ports are designated by P, T, A, B, X and Y. These designations are used for orientation. In which direction the valves operate and which ports are to be used may be found out from the functional descriptions of the devices as well as from the circuits.

Valve fixings are normally not symmetrical. By means of locating pins or offset fixing threads, the possibility of the valve
being incorrectly mounted by mistake is avoided.

4.2 Individual subplates

the simplest form of connecting valves is by mounting valves on individual subplates and then connecting these plates together.

Fig. 10: *Subplate*

Usually the valve mounting surface is at the top and the output ports next to each other at the bottom. As a lot of space is required for the pipe fittings, the subplate is often larger than the surface mounting surface of the valves. The channels are then fed by means of diagonal and horizontal drillings to the output ports.

4.3 Standard manifold

Often several actuators are supplied with fluid from a common pump and tank line.

If the control valves are the same size or if they only vary by one stage, then it is possible to mount the valves on standard manifolds.

Fig. 11: *Standard manifold, size 6 with vertical stacking*

Standard manifolds with mounted stacking assemblies result in compact control units for several actuators. They require a minimum amount of space, do not need to be piped together and have only a few sealing points.

4.4 Control plates and control manifolds

Controls which are connected in a complex way require the use of individually designed and manufactured control plates and control manifolds.

Fig. 12: *Manifold*

For a small number of components these manifolds are made of steel blocks, in which connecting channels are drilled. The manifolds are fitted with cartridge valves, cartridges, surface mounted valves and even with complete stacking assemblies.

For larger sizes (from about size 40) the advantages of this design become especially clear. No other design allows such compact controls for the smallest possible number of sealing points as this manifold design. Prime examples of these control plates may in particular be found in large hydraulic presses.

4.5 Adaptor plates

Fig. 13: *Cylinder with mounted servo valve and adaptor plate*

Fig. 14: *Hydraulic motor with adaptor plate*

Because of reasons in control , it is advantageous if the control valves are mounted as closely as possible to the actuator. Ideally the valves should be mounted directly on the cylinders or motors by means of adaptor plates. Adaptor plates have on the one side the mounting pattern of the cylinder or motor and on the other side the mounting pattern of the control valve. The free sides are used for pipe line ports.

5 Stacking assemblies

5.1 Vertical stacking assembly

Several functions are required within the control stack for a hydraulic actuator, which may be achieved by means of various valves, e.g.:

- The function "start/stop/direction" is controlled by means of a directional valve
- The function "speed" is controlled by means of a flow control valve
- The function "force" is controlled by means of a pressure control valve
- The function "shut-off" is controlled by means of a suitable check valve
- The function "monitor pressure" is controlled by means of a pressure switch

In order to collect these continually recurring functions together in functional devices, flow control, pressure control, isolating and directional valves were developed as sandwich plates.

One or more sandwich plates below a subplate mounted valve mounted on a subplate results in a very compact functional unit.

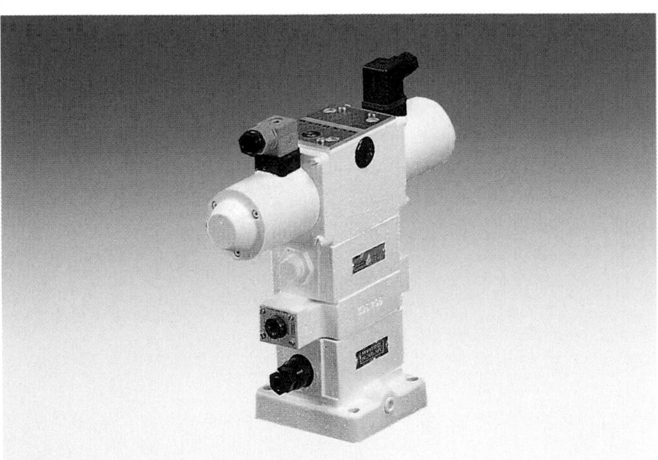

Fig. 15: *Vertical stacking assembly*

This design is generally known as a vertical stacking assembly. The top valve is usually a directional valve.

5.2 Horizontal stacking assemblies

Not every control for a hydraulic actuator may be produced without a lot of effort as a vertical stacking assembly of valves. Manifolds do not offer the numerous connection possibilities for mounting the valves for individual controls next to each other. In these cases flexible horizontal stacking systems may be used comprising a number of different port, connection and separator plates and even complex control systems.

Fig. 16: *Horizontal stacking assembly*

The flexibility of horizontal stacking assemblies does however come at a cost. Numerous different plates need to be manufactured and stored. The stacking itself comprises of many parts and has a number of sealing points.

5.3 System stacking assemblies

For control tasks which occur again and again control plates were designed, which may be put together to form a system stacking assembly.

The manifolds for a system stacking assembly are fitted with subplate mounted valves (also with sandwich plates as in vertical stacking assemblies).

Fig. 17: *System stacking assembly*

6 Mobile control valves

6.1 Single block design

Mobile machines have their own set of design parameters. Hence the control valves for mobile applications are very different from those used in industrial applications.

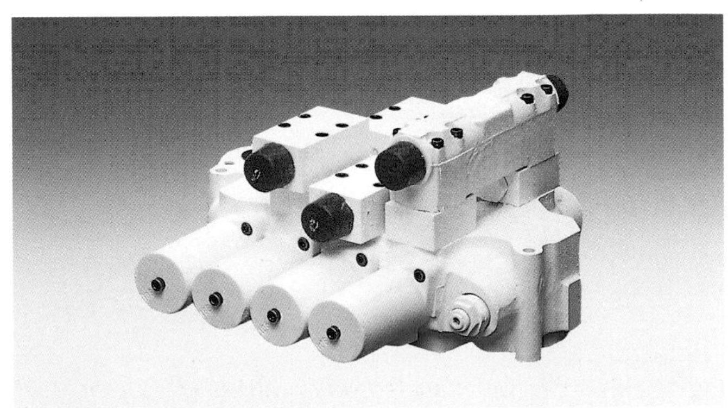

Fig. 18: *Mobile control valve (single)*

The channels are mainly cast; the spools run directly into the block; the operating mechanism for the spools are built on to the block. Cartridges complete the control functions. The cast channels are especially suitable for flow as the cast external form results in a design with complete saving of material and space required. Such a design is possible, as in mobile applications a large number of identical blocks may be used. In industrial applications blocks are often designed as one-offs and gare individually manufactured.

6.2 Sandwich design

In order to be more flexible for small numbers, mobile manifolds are also split into valve plates. Several such plates individually mounted together result in a manifold of sandwich plate design depending on the application.

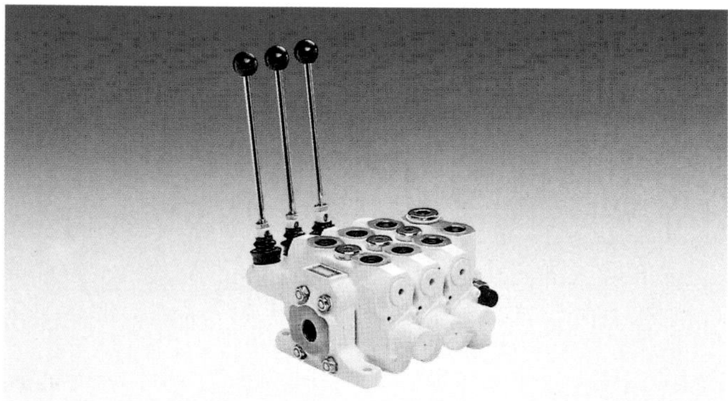

Fig. 19: *Sandwich mobile manifold*

Notes

Notes

Chapter 17

Small Hydraulic Power Units

Herbert Exner

1 Introduction

When mention is made here of hydraulics, it is really hydrostatics which is implied. Hydrostatics works with the energy of fluid pressure. On the other hand, the second field of hydraulics, hydrodynamics, works with the energy of fluid movement.

Hydraulic power units are used to create and prepare this pressure energy. Within a power unit, electrical energy from a power supply (by means of electrical motor) or chemical energy from a flammable material (by means of internal combustion engine) is converted into pressure energy. In both cases the rotation and torque of the drive motor is transformed into flow and pressure by a positive displacement pump.

In addition for the range of low powers, pneumatic-hydraulic pressure convertors exist. The proportion of these devices within the total number of power units is however relatively low.

The range of power for power units is from about 0.5 kW to over 1 MW.

Here only the small compact power units will be described which are found in large numbers in all fields of industrial applications.

2 Components of power units

Besides the motor/pump group which acts as a source of force power units comprise the following components:

- Tank for supply of fluid
- Control devices for
  - level of fluid (oil level display)
  - temperature (thermometer)
  - pressure (pressure gauge)
- Devices for the care of fluids
  - filter
  - cooler
  - heater
- Valves for protecting pressure
- Valves for control tasks
- Accumulators for supply of pressure energy (if required)

Not all of these components are always found in a power unit. In smaller power units (depending on application) heaters, coolers or thermometers for example may be omitted.

The control valves are not always mounted on the power unit. In larger systems often separate control panels or control stands are used or the control is directly mounted in the machine near to the actuator.

3 Small hydraulic power units for intermittent use

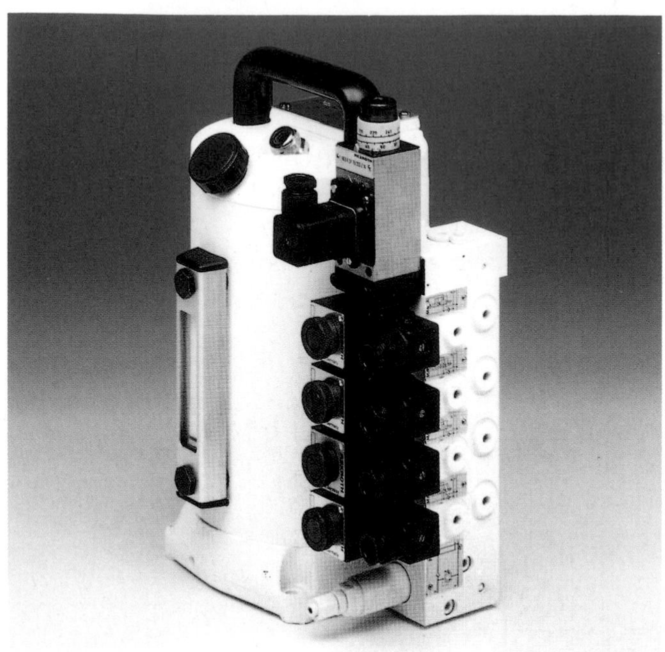

Fig. 1: *Small power unit, type UPA*

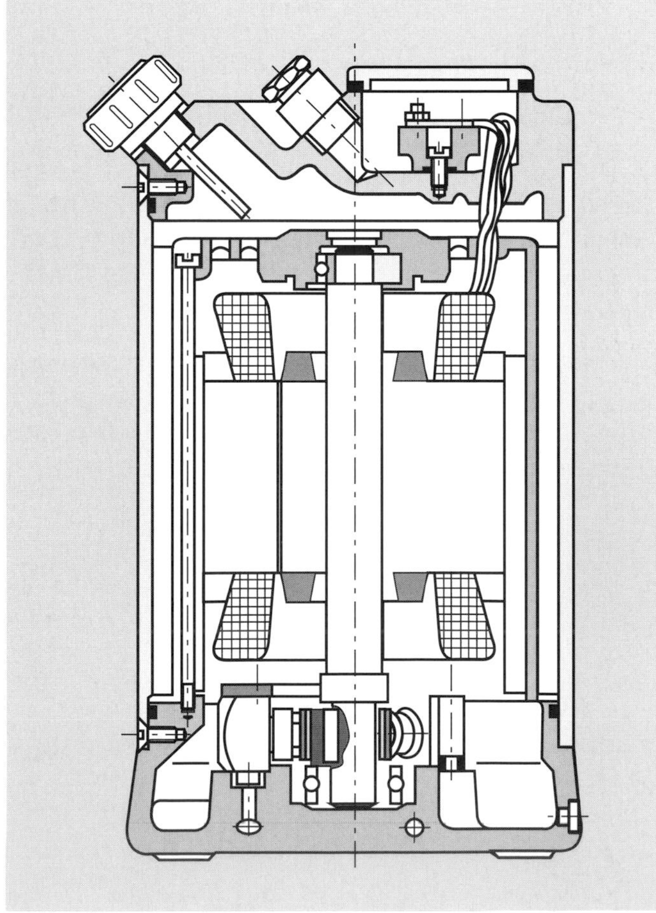

Fig. 2: *Section through small power unit*

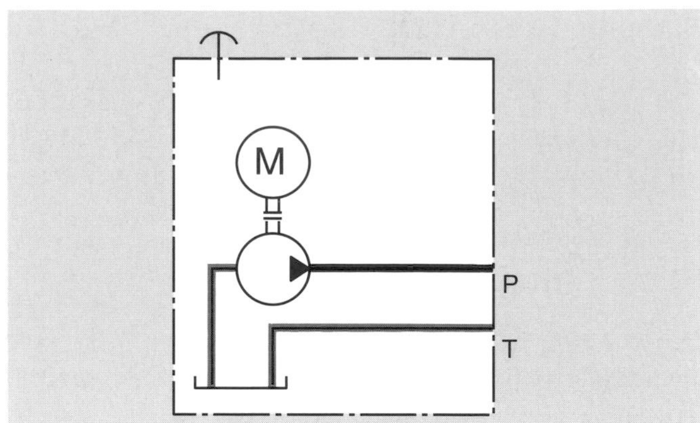

Fig. 3: *Circuit for small power unit*

In the range of low powers up to about 2 kW, very compact small power units are used for intermittent operation. These power units have a few special features.

The drive motor and pump are integrated into the tank, hence work immersed in oil. Therefore a very compact design is possible. Control valves are mounted externally as a horizontal stacking assembly. No piping is required within the power unit. Such a power unit hence has the least number of sealing points possible. Due to the very compact design however the power unit surface is very small in comparison with the drive power. In continuous operation this surface is not sufficiently large to transfer the lost power which occurs as heat to the outside. The power unit would over-heat. These power units are therefore designed for intermittent operations. Intermittent operation means, that when the operating pressure is reached the power unit is switched off. A pressure switch is required to control this intermittent operation. The duty cycle must not be too short for this. The cycle is dependent on the relationship between the actuators and the hydraulic volumes.

A hydraulic volumes may be for example an accumulator but may also be the compression volume of the fluid in a pipe line or the elasticity of a hose. Internal leakages in the control valves increase the use of pressure energy and would decrease the switching on cycle. As a result poppet valves are preferably used in these power units, which operate without internal leakages.

The intermittent operation described is especially useful in clamping functions. This means maintaining a pressure over a long period without using energy. Often such power units are hence known as clamping power units.

4 Small hydraulic power units with standard electrical motor

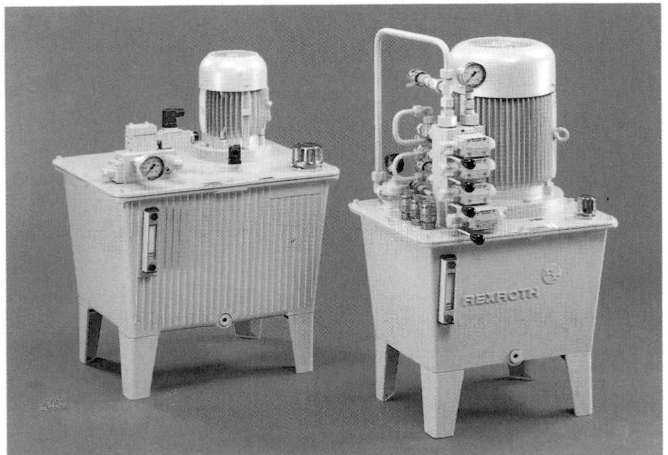

Fig. 4: *Small power unit, e.g. U1-20*

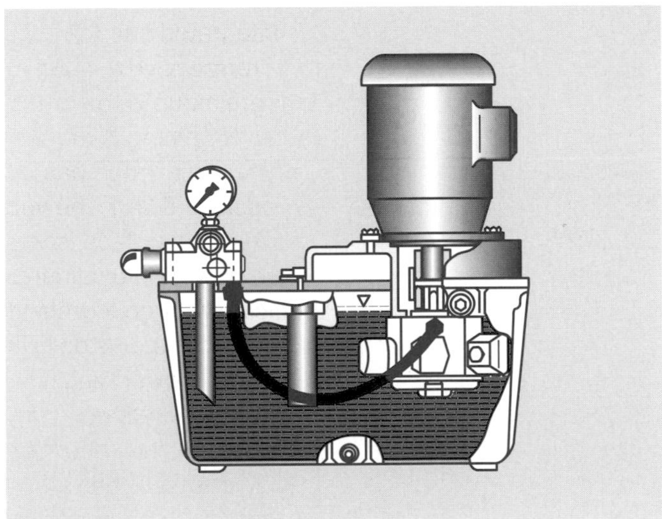

Fig. 5: *Section through small power unit*

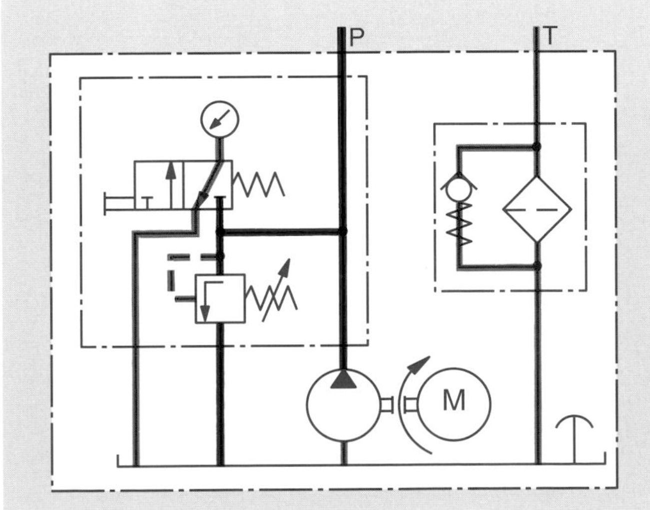

Fig. 6: *Circuit for small power unit*

Small power units with tanks containing 6, 10, 20, 40 and 60 litres (usually made of aluminium) find further use in many applications. Standard electrical motors (form V1 to DIN 42 677) are used as drive motors. In contrast to the motors immersed in oil in clamping power units these surface cooled electrical motors may run in continuous operation (100 % duty). However the heat output from the hydraulics must be taken into account here as well. The losses in power must be transferred by means of the power unit surface to the outside. This loss in power is partly deliberately introduced (e.g. flow and pressure control valves) in order to control the forces and speeds of the actuators.

On the tank covers of small power units, in addition to the pump power unit, devices such as filters, pressure gauges, pressure relief valves and even complete controls (mounted for example on a manifold) are mounted.

Further information on the design and construction of hydraulic systems may be found in the Hydraulic Trainer, Volume 3.

Notes

Summary of Symbols Used

Chapter 1

a	Acceleration
A	Area
b	Deceleration
d	Diameter
d_h	Hydraulic diameter
E	Energy
E_k	Kinetic energy
E_p	Potential energy
f	Frequency of rotation
F	Force
g	Acceleration due to gravity
J	Moment of inertia
l	Length
m	Mass
M	Torque
n	Speed
p	Pressure
p_{tot}	Total pressure
p_{st}	Static pressure
P	Power
Q	Flow
Re	Reynold's number
Re_{crit}	Value at which flow changes from laminar to turbulent flow
s	Distance
t	Time
t	Temperature (Celsius)
T	Temperature (Kelvin)
V	Volume
v	Velocity
W	Work
α	Angle
Δp	Pressure drop
ϑ	Temperature (Celsius)
Θ	Temperature (Kelvin)
ν	Kinetic viscosity
ρ	Density
φ	Angular acceleration
ω	Angular velocity

Chapter 4

A	Offset
b	Width
d	Shaft diameter
d_K	Piston diameter
D	Screw diameter
e	Eccentricity
F_A	Axial force
F_F	Spring force
F_H	Horizontal force
F_P	Force vector
F_V	Vertical force
h	Height of gears
k	Vane stroke
m	Modulus
Q	Flow
r_h	Pitch circle diameter
s	Gradient
V	Volume
z	Number
α	Swivel angle
Δp	Pressure drop
π	Circle constant

Chapter 5

F_A	Axial force
F_N	Force vector
F_T	Tangential force
α	Stroke cam angle

Chapter 6

A	Piston area
D_T	Pitch circle diameter
F_H	High pressure force
F_K	Sum of forces of 3 or 4 pistons
F_M	Resultant force on mid-point
F_N	Torque force component
F_T	Torque force component
F_Z	Force of hydrostatic pressure field of cylinder block
h	Piston stroke
I	Pilot current
H_S	Centre of gravity of hydrostatic bearing force field
M	Virtual centre of spherical face
M	Torque
n	Speed
p	Operating pressure
p_{HD}	Operating pressure
p_B	Operating pressure
p_{HD}	High pressure
p_{St}	Pilot pressure
P	Drive power
Q	Flow
r	Virtual radius of spherical face
s	Displacement
U	Pilot voltage
v	Stroke velocity
V_g	Geometric displacement
$V_{g\ max}$	Max. geometric displacement
$V_{g\ min}$	Min. geometric displacement
V_S	Positioning volume
V_S	Positioning oil flow
x	Number of spools
α	Set swivel angle
α_{max}	Max. swivel angle
α_{min}	Min. swivel angle
β	Adjustable angle
Δp	Pressure drop
$\Delta p_{max.}$	Max. pressure drop
η_{mh}	Mechanical-hydraulic efficiency
η_t	Total efficiency
η_{vol}	Volumetric efficiency

Chapter 7

a	Deceleration
A	Area
A_D	Effective cushioning area
A_K	Piston area
A_R	Annulus area
E	Modulus of elasticity
F	Force
F_B	Braking force
J	Moment of inertia for circular cross-section
K	Buckling load
l	Free buckling length
m	Moving mass
s	Cushioning length
s	Stroke
s_K	Free buckling length
S	Safety factor
p	Operating pressure
p_D	Mean cushioning pressure
$p_{bearing}$	Bearing pressure
p_{St}	Control pressure
v	Stroke velocity
v_{max}	Max. piston velocity
α	Angle of tilt
φ	Area ratio

Chapter 9

C_a	Correction factor for adiabatic change of state
C_i	Correction factor for isothermal change of state
p_m	Mean excess operating pressure
p_0	Gas pre-fill pressure
p_1	Min. operating pressure
p_2	Max. operating pressure
Q	Energy required
T_B	Operating temperature
T_1	Min. temperature
T_2	Max. temperature
V_0	Effective gas volume
$V_{0\ ideal}$	Ideal effective gas volume
$V_{0\ real}$	Real effective gas volume
V_1	Gas volume at p_1
V_2	Gas volume at p_2
ΔV	Useful volume
κ	Adiabatic exponent

Chapter 10

F	Cylinder load
F_F	Spring force with friction
A_K	Cylinder piston area
A_R	Cylinder annulus area
A_1	Area of main poppet
A_2	Area of pilot poppet
A_3	Area of control spool
A_4	Area of pilot control spool
p_{St}	Pilot pressure
p_1	Pressure at port B of valve
p_2	Pressure at port A of valve
v_{oil}	Oil velocity

Chapter 11

F_m	Mass force
F_{St}	Flow force
F_w	Resistance force
F_z	Stability force
p	Operating pressure
p_{max}	Max. operating pressure
Q	Flow
Q_{max}	Max. flow
t_A	Response delay time
t_{tot}	Spool operation time
t_1	Time for flow force to become effective
t_2	Time for solenoid force to build up
t_3	Time for control spool to cross-over
Δp	Pressure drop

Chapter 12

A	Seat area or lower area of control spool
A_H	Seat opening of main spool
A_K	Spool or poppet area
A_V	Seat opening of pilot valve
c	Spring constant
F_F	Spring force
F_H	Force of main spool spring
F_{hyd}	Hydraulic force
F_S	Flow force
p_A	Output pressure
p_E	Input pressure
p_{max}	Max. operating pressure
p_O	Opening pressure
p_S	Closing pressure
p_{St}	Pilot pressure
Q	Flow
Q_{max}	Max. flow
R	Control deviation
t	Time
t_0	Time of spool cross-over signal
t_A	Build-up period
t_E	Transient period
V_m	Max. overshoot
Δp	Pressure difference
Δp_{min}	Min. pressure difference
ΔQ	Flow difference

Chapter 13

a	Opening
A	Throttle opening
A_K	Spool area
A_1	Annulus area
A_2	Throttle area
b	Width
d	Seat diameter
d_H	Hydraulic diameter
F_F	Spring force
h	Stroke
l	Throttle range
p_1	Pump pressure
p_2	Intermediate pressure
p_3	Load pressure
Q	Flow
Q_R	Excess flow
s	Spool distance
U	Flow path
v	Flow velocity
α	Flow coefficient
α	Angle of throttle opening in longitudinal direction
β	Angle of throttle opening in radial direction
Δp	Pressure loss
π	Circle constant
ρ	Density
ν	Kinematic viscosity

Chapter 14

f_1	Viscosity conversion factor
Q_A	Flow for filter design
Q_{design}	Design flow
$Q_{nominal}$	Nominal flow
Q_{test}	Test flow
Q_{pump}	Pump flow
Q_{system}	System flow
Q_W	Effective flow
β_X	Filtration ratio
Δp_A	Pressure loss in design
$\Delta p_{indicator}$	Pressure loss in indicator
$\Delta p_{element}$	Pressure loss in filter element
$\Delta p_{housing}$	Pressure loss in housing
δ_{test}	Test temperature

Chapter 15

A	Effective surface area
c	Specific heat capacity
P_K	Required cooling power
P_V	Power loss
t	Operating time
T_1	Existing oil temperature
T_2	Desired oil temperature
V	Tank volume
α	Heat transfer coefficient
ΔT	Temperature increase
ρ	Density of oil

Notes

Notes

Glossary

Notes